The Collector's Guide
Decoys

Bob and Sharon Huxford

Collector Books
A Division of Schroeder Publishing Co., Inc.

The current values in this book should be used only as a guide. They are not intended to set prices, which vary from one section of the country to another. Auction prices as well as dealer prices vary greatly and are affected by condition as well as demand. Neither the Editors nor the Publisher assumes responsibility for any losses that might be incurred as a result of consulting this guide.

Decoy on the Cover:
Greenwinged Teal Drake by A. Elmer Crowell. Raised carved wing tips, tail feathers, and crest. Turned head, excellent feather paint. Signed. $9,000.00.

Decoy on Title Page:
Rare hollow carved Canada Goose. Of the Ward Brothers highest decorative quality. A very graceful, full-bodied carving with raised wing tips. Head tucked down into a content postition. Exceptional feather painting. $6,000.00. Inscribed on bottom:

Special Made for Purcell Jones
by Lem Ward
Wildfowl Counterfactor in Wood since 1918/1972

Isn't it strange that Princes and Kings
And Clowns that caper in Sawdust Rings
And common people like you and me
Are builders for eternity?

Each one is given a bag of tools
A shapeless mass
A book of rules
And each must make ere life is. Flown.
A stumblin block or a steppingstone!

Table of Contents

Introduction

In comparing market activity over the past four years covered by our report, it is interesting to note that decoys, as would be expected of any viable commodity in the field of antiques and collectibles, reflected a strong, steady increase in gross yearly sales, except for 1986. Record-breaking sales pushed the total for 1986 to more than $7,000,000 — a stunning sum in comparison to the previous year; and though 1987 sales finished at a strong $4,600,000, in the shadow of '86's success, even such a substantial figure might easily have been initially misinterpreted. However, market analysts attributed this approximate 35% drop in total sales to the fact that in 1986 at least seven major collections were dispersed at auction, compared to only one in 1987. The hammer bid on the top bird of 1986 was $290,000, and while many fine examples sold during '87, none made even close to the six-digit figure. (The top 1987 bird sold for $66,000.) In addition to the lack of spectacularly charismatic offerings, some of the high-dollar bidders were inactive during '87, and this also contributed to the decrease in sales. All things considered, the experts agreed that the market was sound; with 1986's activity in proper perspective, the almost 20% increase realized by 1987's market over 1985's total sales represented good investment potential over the longer haul.

1988 records indicate a steadily-increasing level of interest. New buyers entered the market in large numbers. Sales were strong. Much activity was noted in the middle to low levels, though records continued to be set and several birds exceeded the $20,000 figure: $66,000 for a hollow standing Canada Goose by Charles Schoenheider, Sr.; $38,500 for a hissing Canada Goose by George Boyd; $38,500 for a raised-wing Mallard Drake by the Caines Brothers; $35,700 for a Bufflehead and $26,400 for a Brant, both by A. Elmer Crowell; $35,000 for a hollow Black Duck and $20,900 for a Pintail, both by Shang Wheeler; $27,500 for a Wood Duck and $28,500 for a hollow-carved Pintail, both by John Blair, Sr.; a hollow stick-up Snow Goose by John Tax for $26,950; and an Albert Laing hollow-carved sleeping Redhead for $20,350. Factory decoys showed strong gains, especially those from the Mason factory. Experts express satisfaction that the very speculative buying has subsided and has been replaced by solid collector interest, much of which is from newcomers unaffected and uninfluenced by the radical fluctuations of the '86 market.

Explanation of Format

The line descriptions in this book are taken directly from auction catalogs. At the end of each line, the particular gallery and the date of each sale are indicated. 'RB' will indicate Richard Bourne; 'J/G,' Julia/Guyette; and 'RWO,' Richard Oliver. Every effort has been made to provide artist information and to describe condition, specie, and form. Provenances have also been included and will be designated by a numbered reference placed just before the auction code. These numbers correspond with the 'Provenances and Related Information' section located in the back of the book.

Values given are 'hammer prices,' that is the actual winning bid made by the buyer; they do not include a buyer's premium. Bids on high-dollar birds that fell more than 20% below the low estimate or exceeded the top of the estimated value range by more than 20% will be indicated by a percentage given in the line descriptions. For instance, 70% will indicate a bird that sold for 70% of the low estimate (30% under estimate); 135% will indicate a winning bid that exceeded the high side of the estimated value range by 35%. The term 'branded' (when not specifically signifying 'artist brand' or 'factory brand') will be used to designate collector or user markings. Unless noted 'hollow,' all decoys are solid-bodied.

Listing of Standard Abbreviations

In order to best describe the decoy in the space available to us, the following abbreviations have been used:

Attributed .... att	Heavily hit by shot .... hs	Near-mint .... NM	Repainted .... rpt
Back .... bk	Large .... lg	Nova Scotia .... NS	Repaired .... rpr
Carved .... cvd	Lightly hit by shot .... ls	Original .... orig	Replaced .... rpl
Carving.................................. cvg	Long Island LI	Paint .... pnt	Restored, restoration .... rstr
Excellent .... EX	Mint .... M	Prince Edward Island .... PEI	Small .... sm
Good .... G	Moderately hit by shot .... ms	Professional .... prof	Very good .... VG

Acknowledgments

We are deeply indebted to the following auction houses, Richard Bourne; James D. Julia — Gary Guyette, Inc.; and Richard W. Oliver, who have provided us with auction catalogs, photographs, and advice as we prepared this report covering decoy sales over the past four-year period. Background information relating to each auction house follows.

Richard A. Bourne, Co. Inc.

The Richard Bourne Company has been in business thirty-eight years, making this auction gallery one of the first in the country to be established. The originator of the decoy auction, Bourne held his first one in 1965; after that, it became an annual event.

In 1972 they acquired the prestigious collection of Bill Mackey, which contained more than 2,600 decoys. This collection was dispersed in five sessions over a two-year period. The top-dollar decoy realized $30,000, while others quadrupled their pre-auction estimate. The Stuart Gregory collection, which they sold in 1977, resulted in sales that doubled the estimated values.

The Bourne Company is also the firm that auctioned the famous Dr. George Ross Starr collection in May of 1986. The following July, they sold the collections of Dr. and Mrs. Oscar Hollander and Mr. and Mrs. Harold Corbin. Highlights of the 1985 season included the July auction of the Albert Dock collection as well as the remaining decoys from the Peter Vale and Carter Smith estates. To date they have sold more decoys and realized higher total sales than any other gallery.

4

Their mailing address is as follows: Richard A. Bourne Co., Inc.

Box 141

Hyannis Port, MA 02647

(617)775-0797

James D. Julia — Gary Guyette, Inc.

James D. Julia — Gary Guyette, Inc., is one of the foremost antique decoy auctioneering firms in the world. James D. Julia, a nationally-recognized auctioneer, has been conducting auctions for nearly eighteen years, selling not just decoys but all manner of antiques. During this period, his firm has established numerous national and world records. Gary Guyette is one of the top-recognized decoy experts in North America. A few short years ago, he and his wife Dale wrote and published a text on antique Maritime decoys titled *Decoys of Maritime Canada*, the only book to date to be published on this area of decoy collecting. Julia and Guyette travel allover the United States examining, purchasing, and taking on consignment individual decoys and decoy collections which are then offered at their nationally-advertised auctions.

In April of 1986, the firm traveled to St. Charles, Illinois, to hold a major two-day auction in conjunction with the National Antique Decoy Association Show, the largest show of this type in North America. This was the first time any professional decoy auction firm had ever conducted an auction west of New York, and it was an extremely great success.

The Julia/Guyette team offers a number of amenities to sellers and prospective buyers. Verbal appraisals may be obtained free of charge simply by sending photographs of the decoys in question. Lavishly illustrated catalogs are available for any of their upcoming or past auctions. These catalogs not only fully describe the lot, but all decoys in the sale are shown in clear, sharp photographs, some of which are in color and are full-page in size.

Decoys in the past few years have proven excellent investments and have appreciated tremendously in value. Parties interested in forming decoy collections for investment purposes or otherwise may obtain investment advice from the Julia/Guyette firm; this is also free of charge. Simply contact them at the following address: James D. Julia — Gary Guyette, Inc.

RFD #1, Box 830

Fairfield, ME 04937

(207) 453-7904

Richard W. Oliver

Richard Oliver has always been a trendsetter and has established a standard of excellence in the antique and collectibles world which is unsurpassed. He has set many world-record prices in several areas. In 1981 he sold an Alexander Pope still life for $187,000 — a price which was unheard of and which today remains a world record for that artist. For years he consistently broke records in the furniture field, and the prices realized at his auctions are still used as guidelines.

In the area of duck decoys, a uniquely American art form which was basically untouched until a few years ago, he has made great strides toward bringing this fascinating field into public awareness. In 1986 a decoy sold through his gallery for $319,000 ($290,000 plus 10% buyer's premium) setting a world record for the highest price ever realized for a decoy at auction, a record which still stands today. And at that same sale, a record price of $165,000 was set for a decorative. Mr. Oliver has been credited with initiating the current trend in fishing tackle auctions, which has become a multi-million dollar business.

In the fall of 1982, Richard Oliver had his introduction into the world of decoys. Mr. Frank Schmidt, who is now a full-time decoy consultant for Oliver, brought his expertise and lifelong love of hunting and collecting decoys to his attention. Until their first sale in March of 1983, the two men had no idea what a very lucrative and exciting field they had entered into. Ever since that first auction, their business has grown tremendously. In just a few short years, Richard Oliver and Frank Schmidt have built a multi-million dollar business and have gained a deep appreciation for the art of decoy carving as well.

The most important things that the two men have tried to accomplish is to establish a high level of integrity and to see that their sales include something for every enthusiastic collector, whether they be wealthy or not.

Richard Oliver graduated from the Ruppert School of Auctioneering and has practiced his trade in Maine since 1970. The company was incorporated in 1982 and remains a member of good standing with the State of Maine. In addition to auctioneering, Oliver maintains a real estate license and is a member of the Board of Realtors on the national, state, and local levels.

Civic pride and humanitarian undertakings have always played a major part in Mr. Oliver's life. As a member of the Maine Criminal Justice Academy, he instigated a program of identifying antiques to aid in the recovery of stolen property in the state. Richard Oliver also works closely with the local Rotarians to provide help for needy children and donates the use of the gallery for scholarship fundraising events. He is a respected member of the community and is known as one who gets things done. As a commissioner for the Arts and Humanities Council, he has helped to instill a sense of appreciation of the arts for those people who usually remain outside the realm of knowledge in this area. Because of his extensive background, Mr. Oliver has been asked to participate in the Museum of American Folk Art. After eighteen years in the auctioneering business, his integrity is without question, as is evidenced by a very loyal and enthusiastic following of both buyers and sellers.

The gallery provides free verbal appraisals. Also available is a free promotional portfolio containing information about the decoy program. Correspondence should be addressed as follows: Richard W. Oliver

P.O. Box 337

Kennebunk, ME 04043

(207) 985-3600

Photo Credits

Catalog photos courtesy of the Richard A. Bourne Co., Inc., Photographer: Alan Lieberman; James D. Julia — Gary Guyette, Inc., Photographer: David Beane; and Richard W. Oliver, Photographer: Ellen Meserve.

Artist Decoys

Ackerley, Emery; att
Brant, orig pnt worn to nice patina, EX form, RB 3/11/88, 150% 450
Adams, Burl; att
Canada Goose, hollow, cvd wing tips, rpt, average wear, chip on underside of bill, 189, RB 6/28/88 125
Adams, Frank (West Tisbury, MA)
Black Duck, rpt shows heavy flaking, 39, RB 7/08/86 600
Golden Plover, NM pnt, minor flaking to bill, EX condition, rare, RB 6/28/88 600
Goldeneye drake, pnt worn to mostly natural wood, age split at neck/bill has been chewed, 22, RB 5/02/86 300
Goldeneye hen, EX orig pnt, minor wear, 39, RB 7/08/86, 210% 3200

Adams, Frank
Merganser hen, slightly turned head, hollow, G orig pnt, minor flaking/ wear, rare, 22, RB 5/02/86, $2,500.00.

Whistler hen, old orig pnt, heavy wear, age split at neck, ms, 22, RB 5/02/86 500
Albert, Emile
Canvasback drake, old pnt, in-use flaking/wear, structurally sound, RB 7/09/85 80
Alexander, Phineas (Harpswell, ME)
Gull, top hollowed out w/wood cover, raised primaries/eyes/bill detail, initialed, EX/VG, 1840's, oversize, J/G 4/24/86 3575
Alexander, Stanley (Detroit, MI)
Canvasback drake, sleeping, balsa body, pine head/keel, orig pnt, minor wear, structurally EX, J/G 9/20/86 80
Canvasback pr, 1 rpt/1 orig, minor wear, structurally sound, RB 2/01/85 275
Alford, Oscar (Beardstown, IL)
Mallard drake, hollow, EX orig pnt covered w/a coat of varnish, EX condition, 193, RWO 7/02/88, 185% 2600
Algard, Carroll (Charlestown, MD)
Canvasback pr, each in working rpt, average wear, both structurally sound, ca 1920, RWO 7/05/85 505
Algard, Wally (Charlestown, MD)
Canvasback hen, orig pnt, structurally sound, ca 1920, RWO 11/06/85 675
Algard, Wally; att (Charlestown, MD)
Canvasback hen, pnt appears to be orig w/average wear, structurally sound, RWO 2/12/88 110
Allen, Charles (Bordentown, NJ)
Bufflehead drake, EX orig pnt, minor wear, artist stamp, no structural flaws, RWO 7/05/85 200
Bufflehead drake, hollow w/raised primaries, EX orig pnt, artist brand, rpr w/pnt touchup, very rare, J/G 9/20/86 1550
Canvasback drake, hollow, cvd raised wings, EX comb feather pnt on bk, artist brand, EX condition, RB 6/28/88 800
Canvasback drake, hollow, EX orig pnt, structurally EX, ca 1940's, RWO 11/11/87, 75% 525
Canvasback drake, hollow, old pnt, average wear, EX condition, ca 1925, RB 6/28/88 600
Canvasback drake, hollow, outstanding orig condition, 65, RWO 7/05/85 475
Mallard drake, hollow, cvd raised wing tips, orig pnt, minor wear, artist brand, EX condition, RB 6/28/88 650
Allen, Fred (Monmouth, IL)
Bluebill drake, hollow, EX orig pnt, blk in-use touchup to wht areas on sides, EX, ca 1880, rare, RWO 7/02/88, 33% 500
Bluebill drake, hollow, EX orig pnt, minor wear, G scratch pnt on bk, ca 1880, RWO 7/02/88 2800
Bluewinged Teal drake, EX orig pnt rstr in Allen's style, ca 1880, extremely rare, 42, J/G 4/23/87 550

Mallard pr, old pnt, average wear, crack in neck of hen; several reglued cracks in neck of drake, rare, J/G 4/24/86 .... **330**

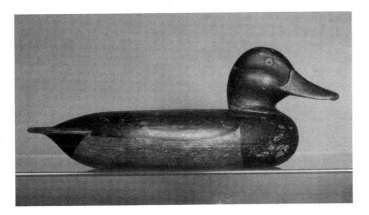

Allen, Fred
Mallard drake, slightly turned head, hollow, orig pnt, minor wear, ls, ca 1890, extremely rare, J/G 4/23/87, $6,500.00.

Allen, Fred
Mallard hen, orig pnt, minor ware, filler missing where neck joins body, ca 1890, extremely rare, J/G 4/23/87, $5,000.00.

Allen, William
   Goldeneye drake, cork body, signed/dated 1982, branded WWA, EX & orig condition, RB 8/25/88 .... **50**

Allingham, Jim
   Mallard pr, G orig pnt, average wear, both heads have been rpt, from artist's rig, 79, RB 7/09/85 .... **300**
   Wood Duck pr, fine orig pnt, minor wear, from artist's rig, 79, RB 7/09/85 .... **200**

Althoff, Charles (Princeton, IL)
   Mallard drake, G rpt, hairline crack in neck, J/G 4/23/87 .... **175**
   Mallard drake, hollow w/raised cvd wing tips, rpt as a Mallard, average flaking/wear, age splits in neck, 39, RB 7/08/86 .... **250**
   Mallard hen, orig pnt, slight wear, some old working touchup on wings/lower sides, rare, J/G 4/24/86 .... **605**
   Mallard pr, early, hollow, raised wings, EX orig pnt, both have neck cracks/chips on 1 wing tip, 193, RWO 7/02/88, 37% **1300**

Amelio, Robin; att
   Mallard drake, cvd wings, old pnt appears to be orig w/heavy wear, age split in neck, RB 2/01/85 .... **550**

Anderson, Richard (Bordentown, NJ)
   Black Duck, hollow w/raised cvd front primaries, highly detailed bill cvg, EX orig pnt, structurally EX, J/G 9/20/86 .... **650**

Andress, Ray (Ganaque, Ont)
   Bluebill hen, NM orig pnt, hairline crack part way through top of bill, ms, J/G 9/20/86 .... **400**
   Canvasback drake, orig pnt, moderate wear, rough wear on edges of tail/tight age split on 1 side, rare, J/G 9/20/86 .... **300**

Andrews, Robert (Smith's Island, VA)
   Canada Goose, hollow, rpt w/average flaking/wear, branded AJ Costin/inscribed: Pnt rstr by JR Bull/1955, RB 8/27/87 .... **275**

Anger, Cecil (Dunnville, Ont)
   Hooded Merganser pr, hollow w/raised cvd wings, artist stamp, J/G 9/20/86 .... **750**
   Mallard drake, hollow w/incised wing outline, NM orig pnt/lt varnish, hairline in bill, otherwise EX, J/G 9/19/87 .... **325**

Anger, Ken (Dunnville, Ont)
   Black Duck, content, cvd wings, wide fan-shape tail, full body, EX orig pnt, structurally EX, well preserved, RB 9/27/87 .... **2200**
   Black Duck, early, hollow, orig pnt, minor wear, tiny chip on underside of bill, ls, J/G 4/24/86 .... **385**
   Black Duck, early, wide body w/fan paddle tail, hollow, orig pnt, minor in-use flaking/wear, ca 1920, RB 8/25/88, 66% **1200**
   Black Duck, EX orig pnt, minor wear, 39, RB 7/08/86 .... **500**
   Black Duck, G orig pnt, average wear, ls, old bill repair, RB 7/09/85 .... **350**
   Black Duck, hollow, EX orig pnt, minor wear, structurally NM, RWO 7/06/86 .... **525**
   Black Duck, hollow, G orig pnt, average wear, slight wear at end of bill/ls, otherwise structurally sound, RWO 7/02/88 .... **550**
   Black Duck, hollow, orig pnt, minimal wear, structurally EX, RWO 7/05/85 .... **400**
   Black Duck, hollow, overpnt taken down to orig, some damage to neck/body, end of bill has been chewed, RWO 11/06/85 .... **140**
   Black Duck, hollow w/incised wing cvg, orig pnt, minor wear, prof rstr to most of bill, ca 1945, J/G 9/19/87 .... **275**
   Black Duck, hollow w/incised wing outline, NM orig pnt, structurally EX, J/G 4/23/87 .... **625**
   Black Duck, orig pnt w/working touchup around bill, average wear, structurally sound, RWO 2/13/87 .... **600**
   Black Duck, slightly turned head, 'Y' cvd wing division, NM orig pnt on body/minor wear on head, rare, J/G 4/23/87 .... **675**
   Bluebill drake, early, EX high-head form, old pnt w/some orig, moderate wear, replaced eye, ca 1930's, RB 8/25/88 .... **600**
   Bluebill drake, fine orig, in-use wear, well preserved, RB 2/01/85 .... **550**

Bluebill drake, incised wing cvg, orig comb pnt on bk, minor wear, no structural flaws, never had eyes, J/G 4/23/87 250
Bluebill drake, NM condition, 189, RB 6/28/88 900
Bluebill hen, early, orig pnt, heavy in-use weathering/wear, RB 7/09/85 200

Anger, Ken
Blue bill hen, EX orig pnt, minor wear, ms, othewise structurally
EX, ca 1950, RWO 7/04/87, $750.00.

Bluebill hen, fine orig pnt, minor wear, ls, 189, RB 6/28/88 525
Bluebill hen, G orig pnt, average in-use wear, RB 7/09/85 350
Bluebill hen, hollow, fine old pnt, mostly orig, moderate wear, ls, RB 8/25/88 500
Bluebill pr, drake has NM pnt; hen has orig pnt w/average wear/age split in bill, 39, RB 7/08/86 575
Bluebill pr, EX orig pnt, average wear, structurally EX, RWO 7/06/86 850
Bluebill pr, EX orig pnt, minor wear, ls, RB 3/11/88, 85% 1700
Bluebill pr, hollow, no wing cvg, orig pnt, minor wear, no structural flaws, J/G 9/19/87 400
Bluebill pr, hollow w/incised wing cvg, NM orig comb pnt, hen has 1 sm shot hole, J/G 4/23/87 1200
Bluebill pr, incised wing cvg, orig pnt, minor wear, structurally EX, from the EB Sidney rig, J/G 4/23/87 1000
Bluebill pr, NM condition, RB 7/08/86 1700
Bufflehead pr, incised wing cvg, hen has NM orig pnt; drake has minor wear, structurally EX, very rare, J/G 4/23/87 3500
Canvasback drake, hollow, NM orig pnt w/EX combing, sm chip has been reglued, structurally sound, J/G 4/23/87 900
Canvasback hen, hollow, VG orig pnt, bill may have been broken off & reglued, RWO 7/05/85 625
Canvasback pr, orig pnt, minor in-use wear, hen has minor flaking/left eye is chipped, ca 1940, rare, RB 8/25/88, 62% ... 2500
Goldeneye hen, slightly turned head, hollow, cvd wings, orig pnt, slight wear, structurally EX, very rare, J/G 4/23/87 1400
Mallard drake, hollow, M condition, RWO 7/02/88 4750
Mallard drake, hollow w/EX wing cvg, orig pnt, slight overall wear, hairline crack in bill, rare, J/B 4/23/87 1700

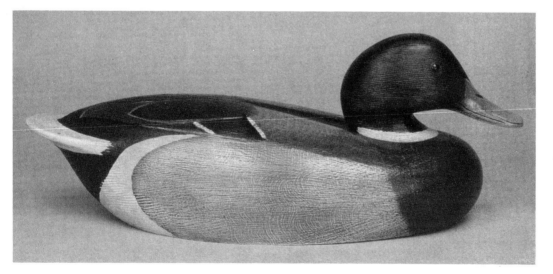

Anger, Ken
Mallard drake, hollow w/in-
cised wing cvg, minor wear
along 1 edge of wing, other-
wise M, J/G 9/19/87, 167%,
$4,200.00.

Mallard hen, hollow w/incised wing cvg, orig pnt, minor wear, sm shallow chip on edge of tail, J/G 9/19/87 1700
Mallard hen, hollow w/incised wing outline, M pnt w/G patina, rare, J/G 4/23/87, 245% 3700
Pintail drake, incised wing cvg, fine comb pnt w/2 sm rubs on lower side, extremely rare, 130, J/G 9/19/87, 165% 5700
Redhead drake, early, hollow, cvd wings, EX orig comb feather pnt, average wear, structurally sound, RB 8/27/87 900
Redhead drake, hollow, NM pnt, structurally EX, RB 7/07/87 2500
Redhead pr, hollow, fine orig pnt, average wear, both ls, RB 8/25/88 1700

Redhead pr, hollow w/incised wing cvg, orig pnt, minor wear, structurally EX, rare, J/G 4/23/87 1550
Redhead pr, orig pnt, minor wear, structurally EX, rare, J/G 9/20/86 2000

Applegate, Thomas (Tomb River, NJ)
Bluebill drake, hollow, cvd eyes, old pnt, heavy wear, bill is an old replacement, RB 7/08/86 275

Applegate Family
Brant, hollow, old pnt, heavy flaking/wear, age split in neck, rpl head, RB 3/11/88 125
Brant, hollow, old rpt, heavy flaking/wear, age split in neck, lg chip on underside of bill, RB 6/28/88 200

Applegate Family, att
Brant, hollow, old pnt worn to natural wood in many areas, age split in neck, RB 3/11/88 325
Canada Goose, hollow, old rpt, moderate flaking/wear, chip on underside of bill, age split in neck, RB 3/11/88 150
Redhead drake, hollow, old rpt, average wear, tail chip has been reglued, RB 3/11/88 180

Arness, Paul
Greenwinged Teal pr, slightly turned heads, hollow w/cvd raised wings, fine orig pnt, cvd initials, ls, RB 7/09/85 150

Avann, Cliff (Lake Simcoe, Ont)
Bluebill hen, slightly turned head, old working rpt, moderate wear, ls, J/G 9/20/86 70

Ayres, Furman
Black Duck, G orig pnt, average wear, 39, RB 7/08/86 80
Bluebill hen, orig pnt, minor wear, well preserved, RB 12/06/85 50

Ayres, Furman; att
Goldeneye drake, old rpt, average wear, age split in neck, RB 3/11/88 40

Bach, Ferdinand (Detroit, MI)
Bluebill drake, detailed wing/tail cvg, lg keel weight, M condition, ca 1930, from the Bach collection, RWO 11/11/87 5250
Bluebill drake, low-head style, relief cvd wings w/crossed tips, NM orig pnt, prof rstr to bill, rare, J/G 4/23/87 4250
Bluebill hen, early, relief cvd wings w/crossed wing tips, old working rpt, sm cracks in bill, rare, J/G 9/19/87 425

Bach, Ferdinand
Canvasback drake, hollow, cvd signature, outstanding orig condition, ca 1920's, RWO 7/05/85, 150%. $6,900.00.

Canvasback pr, detailed wing & primary cvg, hen's head has slight turn, signed, NM orig, ca 1926, RWO 7/05/86, 135% 16500

Bach, Ferdinand; att (Detroit, MI)
Bluebill drake, orig pnt, average wear, wide separation along 1 side where body halves are joined, RWO 7/06/86 400
Bluebill hen, relief cvd wings, old working rpt, hairline crack in 1 side of head, J/G 4/23/87 175

Bacon, George (Burlington, VT)
Goldeneye hen, fine orig pnt, average wear, RB 12/06/85, 175% 700
Goldeneye hen, G orig pnt, average flaking/wear, RB 12/06/85, 150% 450
Goldeneye hen, orig pnt, minor wear, bill has been slightly blunted, ls, rare, J/G 9/20/86 195
Goldeneye pr, G orig pnt, average wear, well preserved, 77, RB 12/06/85, 140% 1150

Bacon, George; att (Burlington, VT)
Goldeneye drake, orig pnt, heavy in-use weathering/wear, structurally sound, RB 7/09/85 85
Goldeneye hen, old working rpt, average wear w/area worn to bare wood on top of head, structurally sound, RWO 11/11/87 45

Goldeneye pr, G orig pnt, heavy in-use wear, structurally sound, RB 7/09/85 375

Badlum, Stephen (Dorchester, MA)

Black Duck, old pnt, average wear, branded SB, sm end-of-bill chips, ca 1850, 172, RB 6/28/88 1700

Peep, early, orig pnt, heavy flaking/wear, ls, ca 1850, rare, 172, RB 6/28/88 725

Whitewinged Scoter, old pnt, average wear, branded, roughness to edges of bill, otherwise EX, ca 1850, 172, RB 6/28/88 900

Badlum, Stephen; att (Dorchester, MA)

Old Squaw, up-tilted head, sealing wax eyes, EX orig pnt, artist brand, inset lead weight, ca 1850, 172, RB 7/07/87, 130% 10500

Whitewinged Scoter, tack eyes, old pnt shows average flaking/wear, artist brand, 2 lead weights, RB 7/07/87, 125% 1000

Bailey, Capt. Clarence (Massachusetts)

Black Duck, hollow, old pnt, crazing/wear, structurally VG, 22, RB 5/02/86 600

Bailey, Capt. Clarence
Top: Canada Goose, belligerent, EX orig pnt, average flaking/wear, rpr bill, age split in neck, 22, RB 5/02/86, $6,500.00. *Bottom:* Canada Goose, canvas-covered, fine orig pnt, average flaking/wear, 1 age crack in neck, rare, 22, RB 5/02/86, $2,500.00.

Canada Goose, canvas-covered, old pnt, average wear, age split in neck, rare, Ex-collection J Dillworth, RB 8/21/86, 60% 1200

Canada Goose, wooden, fine old orig pnt, average wear, rare, 22, RB 5/02/86 1900

Old Squaw drake, slightly raised head, hollow, fine orig pnt, minor wear, rare, 22/44, RB 5/02/86, 142% 17000

Scoter, canvas-covered, EX orig pnt, 1 eye missing, RB 7/08/86, 50% 600

Bailey, Fred (Kingston, MA)

Goose, canvas-covered slat, old pnt, average wear, structurally sound, 22, RB 5/02/86 400

Bainbridge, Ron (Royal Oaks, MI)

Bluebill hen, cvd wing tips, EX orig pnt, RB 2/01/85 175

Bluebill hen, finely cvd, artist brand, M condition, J/G 4/24/86 82

Baker, Jesse

Bluebill drake, old pnt, some of which is orig, average flaking/wear, RB 8/25/88 50

Baker, John (Edgely, PA)

Black Duck, EX orig pnt, slight wear, artist stamp, orig keel weight, structurally EX, rare, 65, J/G 9/20/86, 65% 800

Black Duck, hollow, raised wing cvg, orig pnt, average wear, some damage to pnt on breast/under tail, RWO 7/02/88 50

Black Duck pr, hollow, cvd primaries/secondaries, M condition, retains orig weight, J/G 4/23/87 350

Bluewinged Teal drake, NM orig pnt, structurally EX, rare, J/G 4/23/87 200

Bluewinged Teal pr, M condition, stamped weights, J/G 9/19/87 300

Canvasback pr, hollow w/fluted tails, orig pnt, several rubs/scrapes, otherwise EX, both retain orig weight, J/G 9/20/86 200

Greenwinged Teal pr, M condition, stamped weights, J/G 9/19/87 300

Mallard drake, hollow w/cvd raised wing tips, maker's name impressed in weight, NM condition, RB 8/25/88 110

Mallard pr, raised primaries/cvd secondaries, M condition, retains orig weight, J/G 4/23/87 300

Pintail drake, slightly turned head, hollow w/cvd primaries/secondaries, M condition, retains orig weight, J/G 4/23/87 200
Wood Duck drake, slightly turned head, hollow w/raised cvd primaries/secondaries, M condition, J/G 9/20/86 200
Wood Duck hen, raised cvd primaries/secondaries, M condition, J/G 9/20/86 70
Wood Duck pr, 2 sm rubs, otherwise M condition, stamped weights, J/G 9/19/87 275

Baker, Robert
Canvasback pr, cvd wing tips, initials cvd on bottom of drake, old pnt, minor wear, structurally sound, RB 8/25/88 170

Baldwin, Arthur (Stratford, CT)
Bluebill, early, old working rpt, minor separation at joint, crack in bill, W Baldwin/K Peck rig, ca 1890, RWO 7/04/87 225
Bluebill drake, early, old working rpt, artist brand, sm chip on edge of bill, J/G 9/19/87 200

Baldwin, John Lee (Babylon, LI, NY)
Black Duck, hollow, orig pnt, average wear, thin tight crack on bk, otherwise EX, RWO 7/02/88 300
Snipe, orig pnt w/nice scratch pnt, average wear, structurally EX, rare, 3/11, RWO 7/06/86 400
Yellowlegs, feeding, EX orig scratch pnt, minor wear, structurally EX, ca 1920, RWO 7/04/87, 65% 575

Baldwin, Willard C.
Black Duck, hollow, fine orig pnt, minor wear, artist brand, chip on underside of bill is repaired, RB 3/06/87 700
Black Duck, hollow, G orig pnt, minor flaking, artist brand, well preserved, 22/44, RB 5/02/86 700
Bluebill drake, hollow, EX orig pnt, artist brand, 22, RB 5/02/86 250
Bluebill drake, hollow, fine comb feather pnt on bk, old pnt appears to be orig w/minor wear, RB 6/28/88 575

Barber, Joel (Long Island, NY)
Black Duck, G orig pnt, average wear, head has been prof re-attached, rare, 22, RB 5/02/86 1500
Black Duck, NM orig pnt, artist brand, structurally EX, rare, J/G 9/19/87 3000
Bluebill drake, NM orig pnt, artist brand, prof rstr to one-third of bill, rare, J/G 9/19/87 2200
Bluebill hen, slightly turned head, fine orig pnt, artist brand, structurally NM, 22/44, RB 5/02/86 3000
Canvasback drake, orig pnt, minor wear, coat of varnish peeling on 1 side, otherwise EX, 193, RWO 7/02/88, 218% 3050
Mallard drake, rpt w/average wear, 22/44, RB 5/02/86 1500
Mallard hen, slightly turned head, EX orig pnt, bottom worn/hairline partway through neck, very rare, J/B 9/19/87 1700

Barkelow, Joel (Forked River, NJ)
Peep, early, rare, RWO 7/05/85 1100
Peep, EX orig pnt, average wear, structurally EX, ca 1890, RWO 7/02/88 1500
Yellowlegs, early, semi-flat, EX orig pnt, EX condition, retains orig bill, ca 1890, 193, RWO 7/02/88 1400

Barkelow, Lou (Forked River, NJ)
Bluebill drake, hollow, orig pnt, average wear, branded LB, bill has an in-use repair, ms, RB 3/11/88 235
Bluebill drake, hollow, orig pnt, moderate flaking/wear, branded, old break in bill has an in-use repair, RB 3/11/88 125
Bluebill pr, hollow, orig pnt, moderate flaking/wear, branded LB, both have age splits in necks, RB 3/11/88 175
Peep, orig pnt, average wear, artist stamp, vertical crack runs through body, RWO 7/04/87 900
Sanderling, EX orig pnt, juvenile plumage, light wear, artist brand, ls, rare, 22/44, RB 5/02/86, 125% 2750

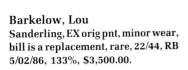

Barkelow, Lou
Sanderling, EX orig pnt, minor wear,
bill is a replacement, rare, 22/44, RB
5/02/86, 133%, $3,500.00.

Willet, orig pnt, heavy flaking/wear, rare, 20, RB 12/06/85 175
Yellowlegs, old pnt appears to be orig w/average wear, well preserved, RB 7/08/86 400

Barkelow, Lou; att (Forked River, NJ)
Brant, hollow, old pnt appears to be orig w/average wear, age split in neck/chip on underside of bill, 39, RB 7/08/86 425
Yellowlegs, cvd eyes, old pnt, average wear, branded HJ, RB 3/11/88 275

Barnard, Charles Nelson (Havre de Grace, MD)
Black Duck, hollow, old working rpt, structurally sound, very rare, RWO 11/06/85 280
Bluebill hen, G orig pnt, minor wear, hairline crack in neck, otherwise structurally EX, RWO 11/06/85 260
Canvasback drake, EX orig pnt, minor wear, structurally EX, ca 1920, from Gabler estate auction, RWO 11/06/85 500

Barnes, George Washington (Carpenter's Point, MD)
Canvasback drake, old working rpt, average wear, structurally EX, ca 1900, RWO 7/02/88 240

Barnes, Sam (Havre de Grace, MD)
Bluebill drake, old working rpt, average wear, thin crack in neck, otherwise structurally sound, RWO 11/11/87 130
Bluebill pr, early, orig pnt, average wear, thin cracks in neck, otherwise structurally sound, ca 1915, RWO 7/04/87 475
Bluebill pr, G orig pnt, average wear, drake has thin tight crack in neck/ls, ca 1915, RWO 11/06/85 400
Canvasback, pnt is stripped away, ms, otherwise sound, RWO 2/12/88 90
Canvasback drake, early, pnt worn w/only traces remaining, severe crack in neck, hs, RWO 11/11/87 270
Canvasback drake, old pnt, some orig, crack running through neck/thin age check in body, RWO 7/06/86 60
Canvasback drake, old working rpt, average wear, structurally EX, RWO 7/02/88 130
Canvasback drake, old working rpt, minor wear, hairline crack in neck, 33, J/G 9/19/87 175
Canvasback drake, orig pnt, average wear, lg chip out of tail/hs, otherwise structurally EX, RWO 7/06/86 130
Canvasback pr, EX orig pnt, hen has hairline crack in neck, otherwise structurally EX, ca 1930, RWO 11/06/85 1200
Canvasback pr, old working rpt possibly by Barnes, no structural flaws, 33, J/G 9/19/87 450
Canvasback pr, orig pnt, average wear, hen has neck crack, otherwise both structurally VG, RWO 7/05/85 425
Swan, body is constructed of 2 pcs which are pegged together, G working rpt, ca 1890, 193, RWO 7/02/88, 50% 12500

Barnes, Sam
Swan, early, old dry working rpt, flaking/worn, head loose/removable, 1 of 3 existing, ca 1890, RWO 7/04/87, $60,000.00.

Barnes, Sam; att (Havre de Grace, MD)
Bluebill drake, old working rpt, heavy flaking/wear, crack running through neck, otherwise sound, RWO 7/06/86 70
Canvasback, working rpt revealing traces of orig, structurally sound, RWO 11/11/87 130
Canvasback drake, high-head style, old working rpt, average wear, thin check in neck, otherwise sound, RWO 7/04/87 120
Canvasback drake, old rpt, average wear, several age splits in neck, RB 8/27/87 140
Canvasback drake, old working rpt, minor flaking/wear, some damage to bill, structurally sound, ca 1900, RWO 7/04/87 110
Hutchins Goose, old working rpt, in-use wear, thin tight checks in neck/thin checks at breast, rare, RWO 11/11/87 400

Barnhart, John; att (Canton, IL)
Canvasback drake, hollow, old working rpt, in-use wear, thin crack in neck, otherwise sound, ca 1900, RWO 7/04/87 110

Barrett, Jake (Northfield, NJ)
Black Duck, hollow, fine old pnt, average wear, RB 6/28/88 65

Black Duck, hollow, old pnt, average wear, re-headed, structurally sound, RB 3/11/88 75
Black Duck, hollow, orig pnt, average wear, 189, RB 6/28/88 150
Black Duck, hollow, working rpt, minor wear, structurally sound, ca 1920, RWO 7/02/88 150
Black Duck, rpt w/minor wear, RB 7/09/85 60
Canada Goose, hollow, old rpt, average wear, sm end-of-bill chip, 189, RB 6/28/88 250
Pintail, hollow, fine old pnt, average wear, age split in neck, otherwise structurally sound, RB 3/06/87 150

Barto, George (Joliet, IL)
Bluebill drake, hollow, EX orig pnt, average wear, structurally sound, RWO 7/02/88 150
Bluebill drake, hollow, orig comb pnt, average wear, structurally sound, RWO 7/06/86 225
Mallard hen, a couple of dings/dents to pnt, otherwise NM, structurally EX, ca 1940, RWO 7/06/86 300
Mallard hen, slightly turned head, strong orig pnt, minor wear, EX comb/feather pnt, ls, J/G 4/23/87 600
Mallard pr, NM pnt, end of bill on drake has been chewed, J/G 9/19/87 400
Pintail drake, fine comb pnt on bk/sides, orig pnt, minor wear, varnished, reglued neck crack, J/G 9/20/86 650
Pintail drake, hollow, G orig pnt, average wear, thin crack in neck, otherwise sound, ca 1940, RWO 7/06/86 550

Basnight, William Henry
Ruddy Duck, prof bill repair, otherwise EX, letter
B is cvd into bottom, RWO 7/05/85, 55%, $1,100.00.

Bauer, Joseph
Black Duck, hollow, EX orig pnt, minor wear, well preserved, RB 6/28/88 750
Baum, Waylon (Wanchese, NC)
Redhead hen, old working rpt, minor wear, tight check in bk/several hairlines in sides, ls, 33, J/G 9/19/87 250
Baumgardner, Frank (Houghton Lake, MI)
Bluebill pr, NM orig pnt, structurally EX, J/G 4/24/86 220
Bluebill pr, orig pnt, slight wear, structurally EX, retains orig keel, sm size, J/G 9/20/86 250
Coot, old working rpt, blunted area on bill, rare medium size, initialed RW on underside, J/G 9/20/86 50
Bawers, Ezra
Mallard drake, fine old pnt, appears to be orig, average in-use wear, RB 7/09/85 225
Bay, Frank (Astoria, OR)
Pintail drake, old working rpt, slight wear, J/G 4/24/86 154
Beardsley, William (Silverton, NJ)
Canvasback drake, balsa body, rpt, average wear, bill has an old repair, RB 7/08/86 50
Greenwinged Teal pr, balsa bodies, EX & orig, RWO 7/06/86 70
Widgeon pr, NM condition, RWO 7/06/86 90
Bearse, Horace
Turnstone, raised cvd wing tips, NM orig pnt, no structural flaws, lg, 105, J/G 4/23/87 500
Beasley, Soleman (Knott's Island, NC)
Bluebill drake, old pnt, average wear, minor tail chips, otherwise structurally sound, RWO 7/04/87 50
Behmetuik, Arthur (Lockport, IL)
Mallard drake, swimming, hollow, NM orig pnt, G patina, from artist's rig, inscribed dedication, EX, J/G 4/23/87 275
Benson, Frank; att
Goldeneye drake, old rpt, heavy flaking/wear, lg chip on underside of bill, 21, RB 2/01/85 275

Benway, Ernest (Burlington, VT)
Bluebill hen, tack eyes, orig pnt, minor wear, no structural flaws, 61, J/G 9/20/86 90
Berg, Vern; att
Bufflehead drake, EX antiqued pnt, artist brand, RB 7/09/85 75
Bergman, Charles (Astoria, OR)
Mallard hen, fine orig pnt, average wear, RB 2/01/85 1100

Bergman, Charles
Mallard pr, drake has some overpnt w/traces of orig underneath; hen is rpt w/little wear, structurally VG, RB 3/06/ 87, $550.00.

Pintail drake, white pnt is orig w/slight wear, all other is working rpt, no structural flaws, J/G 4/24/86 225
Berruet, Jean Charles (Nantucket, MA)
Merganser, standing w/open mouth, cvd primaries/secondaries, NM orig pnt, structurally EX, J/G 9/19/87 300
Berry, Bob
Whitewinged Scoter, hollow, extensive wing/feather cvg, EX condition, RB 8/25/88 130
Bertrand, Freeman; att
Pintail drake, old pnt, average wear, 21, RB 2/01/85 100
Best, James (Kitty Hawk, NC)
Redhead drake, G old pnt, moderate wear, several minor checks/nailed split, ls, ca 1890, 33, J/G 9/19/87, 145% 7250
Bianco, Tony (Bordentown, NJ)
Black Duck, hollow, raised 'V' wings, detailed head, old working rpt, slight wear, signed, EX condition, J/G 9/20/86 125
Black Duck, hollow w/raised cvd wings, EX orig pnt, no structural flaws, J/G 9/20/86 245
Bluebill, balsa body, fine old pnt, mostly orig w/moderate wear, artist brand, RB 8/25/88 50
Bluebill drake, orig pnt, minor wear, artist brand, structurally EX, J/G 9/20/86 225
Canvasback drake, hollow, rpt w/minor wear, well preserved, RB 8/27/87 150
Mallard drake, hollow, fine old pnt, average wear, artist initials, RB 7/09/85 350
Mallard drake, hollow, raised 'V' cvg at wing tips, working rpt, normal wear, structurally sound, 1940's, RWO 7/06/86 120
Pintail, head tucked, hollow w/raised cvd wing tips, rpt as a Black Duck, average wear, RB 12/06/85 275
Bibber, Oscar (Harpswell, ME)
Goldeneye drake, orig pnt, flaking/wear, w/some areas to bare wood, neck crack/head may be reglued, RWO 7/02/88 215
Goldeneye pr, early, drake has hollow body; hen has solid body, EX orig pnt, minor wear, RWO 11/11/87, 33% 500
Merganser hen, leather crest, EX orig condition, RWO 7/05/85 1900
Redbreasted Merganser drake, EX orig pnt, oversize, 48, RWO 11/06/85 500
Bicknell, Percy
Mallard drake, hollow, EX orig pnt, artist brand, 36, RB 2/01/85 125
Biddle, Bob (Media, PA)
Merganser pr, swimming, M condition, J/G 9/19/87 250
Redbreaster Merganser pr, artist signed, inscribed: From my personal rig, RB 7/07/87 350
Bieber, Bruce (Cape May, NJ)
Curlew, raised cvd primaries, orig pnt w/sm amount of shrinkage on underside, oversize, J/G 9/20/86 65
Biedenmyer, Bruce
Bluebill pr, detailed bill cvg, glass eyes, orig pnt, minor wear, slight rough area on bill, J/G 4/24/86 165
Birch, Charles (Willis Wharf, VA)
Birch Swan, hollow, orig pnt, 2 tight checks in body/crack through neck, otherwise EX, ca 1920, rare, RWO 7/04/87, 200% 50000
Black Duck, hollow, old pnt, average wear, RB 2/01/85 275
Black Duck, hollow, old pnt worn to mostly natural wood, left eye missing/several age splits, RB 7/07/87 225

Black Duck, hollow, old working rpt, average wear, structurally EX, RWO 11/11/87 875
Black Duck, hollow, old working rpt, heavy wear, several thin cracks in neck, RWO 7/02/88 120
Black Duck, hollow, old working rpt, structurally EX, 49, RWO 11/06/85 450
Black Duck, hollow, old working rpt w/traces of orig, sm bill/tail chip, crack in lower part of 1 side, RWO 7/02/88 250
Black Duck, hollow, old working rpt w/traces of orig, tight checks in head/1 side of body, otherwise sound, RWO 2/12/88 345
Black Duck, hollow, working rpt, minor wear, structurally EX, stylish, RWO 7/05/85 800
Black Duck, orig pnt, average wear, minor flaws in wood/thin crack on 1 side, RWO 7/02/88 200
Black Duck, orig pnt worn to bare wood in many areas, crack in neck/thin check in bottom, RWO 7/06/86 130
Black Duck, orig pnt worn to bare wood over the body, possible touchup to speculums, EX condition, RWO 2/12/88 700
Black Duck, 2-pc pegged body, hollow, orig pnt w/soft patina, neck crack, otherwise EX, ca 1930, RWO 2/12/88 2250
Bluebill drake, fine old pnt, average wear, age split in neck/bottom of body, RB 2/01/85 250
Bluebill drake, fine scratch feather rpt, minor in-use wear, 21, RB 2/01/85 200
Bluebill drake, old working rpt, structurally sound, ca 1910-1920, RWO 7/04/87 130
Brant, hollow, EX orig pnt, average wear, structurally EX, RWO 2/12/88 2500
Brant, hollow, EX orig pnt, neck crack/slight separation where body halves join, ca 1920, 193, RWO 7/02/88 2750
Brant, hollow, orig pnt, average wear, thin crack in neck, otherwise EX, ca 1920, RWO 7/05/85 2100
Brant, hollow, outstanding orig condition, minor pnt flaking at tail, exceptionally fine, ca 1910, RWO 11/06/85 3250

Birch, Charles
Canada Goose, fine old dry pnt, average wear, structurally sound, RWO 2/13/87, $2,950.00.

Canada Goose, hollow, entire rpt, structurally sound, from Sister Island Club, Cairo IL, RWO 2/13/87, 70% 850
Canada Goose, hollow, fine orig pnt, average wear, rare, RB 8/21/86, 170% 6000
Canada Goose, hollow, inserted hardwood bill, EX orig pnt, structurally EX, ca 1917, 193/203, RWO 7/02/88, 178% 11500
Canada Goose, hollow, old working rpt taken down to reveal traces of orig, EX condition, ca 1910, 41, RWO 11/11/87, 66% 1000
Canada Goose, hollow, pnt shows considerable wear, age split down bk, otherwise sound, RWO 7/05/85 450
Canada Goose, old working rpt, minor rstr to chips in base of neck, several hairline cracks, J/G 9/19/87 1050
Canvasback drake, hollow, old working rpt, prof bill rstr/separation where body joins near tail/neck crack, RWO 7/02/88 350
Canvasback drake, overpnt taken down to orig, ca 1920's, rare, 49, RWO 11/06/85 950
Goldeneye drake, hollow, old working rpt, average wear w/flaking around head, structurally sound, RWO 7/06/86 200
Mallard drake, hollow, rpt, minor wear, structurally sound, RWO 11/06/85 90
Swan, hollow, orig inserted bill, orig pnt, structurally EX, ca 1920, RWO 7/04/87, 200% 50000
Birch, Charles; att (Willis Wharf, VA)
Black Duck, hollow, old working rpt, heavy wear, top portion of head broken off & renailed, RWO 7/04/87 90
Bluebill drake, old working rpt by Birch, average wear, structurally sound, RWO 7/06/86 115
Bluebill drake, orig pnt, heavy wear w/some areas to bare wood, neck crack/minor tail wear, RWO 7/02/88 145
Greenwinged Teal drake, slightly turned head, hollow, old pnt, minor flaking/wear, 20, RB 12/06/85 300

Birdsall, Charles (Point Pleasant, NJ)

Black Duck, hollow, EX orig condition w/no major structural flaws, RWO 7/02/88	300
Black Duck, hollow, fine orig pnt, average wear, RB 8/21/86	300
Brant, hollow, cvd in style of Rowley Horner, orig pnt, average wear, structurally EX, RWO 7/06/86	150
Brant, hollow, pnt shows average wear, well preserved, 20/50, RB 12/06/85	175
Brant, preening, hollow, old rpt, minor wear, artist brand, ls, rare, 6, RB 7/07/87	300
Brant, preening, hollow, old rpt, minor wear, structurally sound, 9, RB 12/06/85	900
Bufflehead drake, EX orig pnt, artist brand, narrow tight check from breast along 1 side of body, RWO 11/11/87	110
Canada Goose, hollow, rpt, average wear, 9/77, RB 12/06/85	1000
Canada Goose, hollow, rpt, minor wear, well preserved, rare, 6, RB 7/07/87	450
Goldeneye drake, hollow, EX orig pnt, artist brand, RB 2/01/85	160
Goldeneye drake, hollow, old working rpt, flaking/wear, age splits in neck, otherwise sound, RB 7/07/87	275
Goldeneye pr, hollow, pnt M but smudged, artist brand, structurally M, RWO 11/06/85	170
Mallard pr, artist brand/signed, M condition, RWO 11/06/85	260
Swan, signed, EX & orig condition, RB 8/21/86	700
Wood Duck pr, drake has solid body; hen has hollow body, EX orig pnt, signed/dated 1976, RWO 11/11/87	250

Birdsall, Jess (Barnegat, NJ)

Black Duck, hollow, old pnt, average wear, heavy coat of wax applied, structurally sound, RWO 7/04/87	170
Canada Goose, hollow, old working rpt, minor crack in neck, otherwise sound, ca 1890, RWO 7/05/85	550
Canada Goose, old working rpt, rstr to neck/head, sm crack in tail/lower breast, J/G 9/20/86	100

Black, Charles (Bordentown, NJ)

Black Duck, hollow, old pnt, average flaking/wear, structurally sound, RB 6/28/88	250
Black Duck, hollow, old working rpt, average wear, 1 eye missing/head is loose, otherwise sound, ca 1913, RWO 7/06/86	200
Black Duck, hollow, orig pnt, average wear, chip at base of neck has been filled w/wood putty, ca 1930, RWO 7/04/87	200
Black Duck, hollow w/cvd wing tips, fine old pnt, average wear, RB 12/06/85	225
Bluebill drake, NM orig pnt, structurally EX, J/G 4/24/86	165
Bluebill drake, NM orig pnt, structurally EX, J/G 9/19/87	400
Canvasback drake, hollow, old pnt, average wear, structurally sound, RB 6/28/88, 40%	200
Canvasback hen, hollow, old pnt, average wear, in-use repair to bill, RB 7/09/85	550

Black, Charles; att (Bordentown, NJ)

Black Duck, low-head style, hollow, orig pnt, average wear, structurally sound, RWO 2/13/87	400

Black, Chester (Bordentown, NJ)

Black Duck, hollow w/raised cvd primaries/secondaries, EX orig pnt, slight wear, structurally EX, J/G 9/20/86	210
Mallard pr, hollow w/raised cvd wings, NM orig pnt, no structural flaws, J/G 9/20/86	450

Blackburn, Amos; att

Redbreasted Merganser drake, early, fine orig pnt, average wear, RB 7/09/85	500

Blair, John (Philadelphia, PA; Elkton, MD)

Bluebill drake, hollow, EX orig pnt, average wear, thin old coat of linseed oil, ca 1930's, RWO 7/04/87, 78%	5500
Bluewinged Teal hen, classic Blair style, orig pnt, average wear/flaking, ca 1870, RWO 7/05/85	10500
Greenwinged Teal drake, hollow, G orig pnt, average wear, end of bill is chewed/old neck repair, rare, RB 7/09/85	10750
Greenwinged Teal drake, overpnt removed & rstr to base of neck by McNair, retains initialed weight, RWO 7/05/85	2000
Mallard drake, dowelled body construction, G orig pnt, several hairlines, prof bill rstr, ls, very rare, J/G 4/23/87	7500
Mallard drake, round bottom, mostly orig pnt, minor wear, prof rstr to bill/crack in neck, very rare, J/G 9/19/87, 70%	1900
Mallard pr, high heads, lg full bodies, hollow, EX orig pnt, branded Chandler Roach, 171/50/65, RB 3/06/87, 75%	10000

Blair, John
Pintail drake, early, hollow, EX orig pnt, average wear, hairline crack in head, otherwise EX, 65, RWO 11/11/87, 140%, $28,000.00.

Pintail drake, hollow, EX orig pnt, thin wash over white, structurally EX, branded Sprickles, rare, 3, RWO 7/05/85 .... **20000**
Pintail drake, hollow, rpt in Blair style, RB 3/11/88 .... **2600**
Teal, hollow, pnt worn to natural wood, several age splits to head, RB 12/06/85 .... **2100**
Widgeon, hollow, orig pnt worn to mostly natural wood, artist brand, age split in neck, rare, RB 7/09/85 .... **2000**
Widgeon drake, in style of Mark McNair, EX condition, J/G 4/23/87 .... **1600**
Widgeon hen, hollow, orig pnt, average flaking/wear, branded WP Patton, well preserved, rare, 20/50/81, RB 12/06/85, 60% **3000**

Blair, John; att (Philadelphia, PA; Elkton, MD)
Bluewinged Teal drake, early, pnt worn to natural wood, branded CHGC, minor age split in bottom, RB 3/11/88 .... **1600**
Widgeon hen, hollow, fine orig pnt, average wear, branded WP Patton, rare, RB 3/11/88 .... **4500**

Blair, John; school of
Black Duck, hollow, graceful/folky form, fine orig pnt, average wear, 20/50, RB 12/06/85 .... **1300**
Bluebill drake, early, hollow, 3-layer body construction, EX/VG orig pnt, rpt on head, prof rstr neck crack, J/G 9/19/87 .... **650**
Bluebill drake, fine old pnt shows average wear, structurally VG, RB 7/08/86 .... **700**
Canvasback drake, hollow, tack eyes, orig pnt, average wear, sm chip on bill, see 53 for rigmate, 128, J/G 9/19/87 .... **2750**

Bliss, Roswell (Stratford, CT)
Black Duck, early, hollow, orig pnt, average wear, branded Ken Peck/1933, structurally sound, RWO 7/06/86 .... **225**
Black Duck, hollow, extremely fine feather pnt, sm amount of wear on head, artist stamp, NM condition, J/G 4/24/86 .... **660**
Bluebill drake, hollow, fine orig pnt, average wear, retains orig marked Bliss weight, RB 7/09/85 .... **500**
Bluebill drake, hollow, rpt, minor wear, well preserved, RB 12/06/85 .... **300**
Bluebill drake, hollow, rpt, moderate flaking/wear, ls, slight age check in bill, RB 7/07/87 .... **200**
Bluebill hen, hollow, G orig pnt, average wear, overall crazing, RB 12/06/85 .... **325**
Bluebill hen, orig pnt, minor wear, unused condition, RWO 2/12/88 .... **260**

Bliss, Roswell
Canada Goose, relief cvg/feather work on bk, hairline crack along 1 side of head, 95, RWO 7/04/87, $5,500.00.

Goldeneye pr, hollow, EX orig pnt, artist brand, unused, RB 3/06/87 .... **950**
Goose, swimming, NM orig pnt, no structural flaws, J/G 9/19/87 .... **900**
Old Squaw drake, hollow, EX & orig, RB 12/06/85 .... **675**
Pintail drake, hollow, EX orig pnt, minor wear, NM condition, rare, RWO 7/06/86 .... **975**
Whitewinged Scoter, made from Shang Wheeler pattern, inscribed/dated 1972, M/unused, rare, RWO 7/06/86 .... **160**

Bliss, Roswell; att (Stratford, CT)
Canada Goose, hollow, raised wing/primary cvg, orig pnt, average wear, artist brand, NM condition, RWO 7/06/86, 40% **325**

Bloom, Reg (Kingston, Ont)
Bluebill drake, cvd wing tips, VG condition, RB 2/01/85 .... **125**
Bluebill hen, cvd raised wings, M condition, ca 1960's, RWO 11/06/85 .... **230**
Bluebill hen, EX orig pnt, ca 1950's, RWO 7/04/87 .... **75**
Bluebill hen, fine orig pnt, minor wear, minor age split in neck, RB 8/25/88 .... **170**
Bluebill pr, EX orig scratch pnt, structurally EX, ca 1950's, RWO 7/06/86 .... **375**
Goldeneye drake, orig pnt, average wear, RB 3/11/88 .... **40**
Goldeneye drake, VG condition, RB 2/01/85 .... **100**
Wood Duck hen, cvd wooden crest/raised cvd wings, NM orig pnt, tail chip has been reglued, very rare, J/G 4/24/86 .... **467**

Bodette, Archie (Addison, VT)
Goldeneye drake, G old pnt, minor wear, ls, J/G 9/20/86 .... **125**

Goldeneye hen, orig pnt, minor wear, hairline crack part way through neck, J/G 4/23/87 300

Boice, Harry

Black Duck, hollow, cvd eyes, old pnt, average wear, RB 6/28/88 300

Blackbellied Plover, EX orig pnt, average wear, ls, RB 3/11 /88 350

Curlew, old pnt, average wear, bill is a replacement, age check in head/bottom of body, ms, RB 3/11/88, 160% 800

Golden Plover, fine old pnt appears to be orig, average wear, RB 3/11/88 250

Boice, Harry; att

Bluebill drake, hollow, old pnt, average wear, age split in neck & bill, RB 3/11/88 90

Ruddy Turnstone, old pnt, moderate wear, bill is a possible replacement, ls, RB 3/11/88, 133% 400

Ruddy Turnstone, old rpt, average flaking/wear, chip on left side of body, RB 3/11/88 175

Boldizar, Lou (Roebling, NJ)

Black Duck, raised cvd primaries/secondaries, orig pnt, minor wear/shrinkage, stamped, no structural flaws, J/G 9/19/87 375

Pintail drake, hollow, Delaware style, M condition, RWO 7/04/87 160

Bollman, Bernard (Boyes Hot Springs, CA)

Curlew, G orig pnt, average wear, bill may be partially rstr, RB 7/09/85 60

Greenwinged Teal pr, EX pnt, artist brand, RB 7/09/85 125

Wood Duck pr, EX orig pnt, artist brand, RB 7/09/85 75

Bonetti, Ron (Portland, ME)

Black Duck, NM orig pnt, 2 hairline cracks in 1 side, J/G 9/20/86 70

Black Duck, sleeper, EX orig pnt, branded JH Whitney, no structural flaws, rare, oversize, J/G 9/20/86 200

Goldeneye drake, turned head, NM orig pnt, structurally EX, rare, J/G 9/20/86 150

Redhead drake, NM orig pnt, no structural flaws, patented copper swiveling device for the head, J/G 9/20/86 230

Borkowski, Leon (Burlington, NJ)

Black Duck, early, NM orig pnt, J/G 9/19/87 400

Mallard hen, sleeping, EX orig pnt, minor wear, well preserved, RB 7/08/86 125

Boshart, C.F. (Logo, NY)

Bluebill drake, fine orig pnt, average wear, scratch feather pnt on bk, RB 12/06/85 90

Bounds, Samuel; att (Manahawkin, NJ)

Canada Goose, hollow, fine old pnt, average wear, well preserved, RB 7/09/85 250

Bourne, James (Pembroke, MA)

Old Squaw drake, EX orig pnt, average flaking/wear, 22, RB 5/02/86, 75% 1100

Old Squaw drake, VG orig pnt, average flaking/wear, 22, RB 5/02/86, 48% 700

Yellowlegs, fine orig pnt, V-shaped breast, 22, RB 5/02/86 300

Bowen, John (Atlantic City, NJ)

Black Duck, balsa body, orig flock pnt, average flaking/wear, structurally sound, RB 7/07/87 75

Black Duck, early, hollow, flock pnt mostly orig, average wear, structurally sound, RWO 11/11/87 200

Black Duck, hollow, early pnt, average wear, crack in neck, otherwise EX, ca 1880, RWO 2/12/88 300

Black Duck, hollow, fine orig pnt, average wear, structurally sound, RB 8/25/88 150

Black Duck, hollow, G orig pnt, average wear, oversize, RB 3/06/87 300

Black Duck, hollow, old pnt, average wear, age split in neck/roughness to edges of bill, RB 3/06/87 75

Black Duck, hollow, old pnt shows moderate wear, slightly oversized body, RB 3/11/88 125

Black Duck, hollow, rpt w/flaking/wear, RB 7/08/86 150

Black Duck, hollow w/cvd wings, EX orig scratch feather pnt, average wear, well preserved, 21, RB 2/01/85 150

Canada Goose, hollow, EX orig scratch pnt, age split running down bk, otherwise sound, ca 1880, 50, RWO 11/06/85 1400

Canada Goose, hollow, old rpt, average wear, RB 3/11/88 250

Canada Goose, swimming, hollow w/cvd wings on bk, old rpt, average flaking/wear, RB 3/11/88 375

Bowman, William (Lawrence, LI, NY)

Black Duck, hollow, fine old pnt, heavy wear, branded, old repair to neck/sm chip at end of bill, rare, RB 3/06/87 500

Blackbellied Plover, classic raised wings/shoulder cvg, orig pnt w/working rpt to breast, RWO 7/06/86 3100

Blackbellied Plover, full body w/cvd raised wings, old rpt, average wear, ms, rare, RB 7/07/87, 30% 900

Blackbellied Plover, head extended forward, raised cvd wings, old rpt, average wear, ms, RB 7/07/87, 35% 900

Bluebill drake, hollow, old pnt, average wear, slight age splits/bill has been repaired, RB 12/06/85 325

Brant, early, inlet head, rpt in Bowman style, thin crack in neck, otherwise sound, ca 1900, 3, RWO 7/04/87, 46% 700

Brant, hollow, working rpt, in-use wear, branded Edgar, crack in neck, otherwise sound, RWO 7/02/88 275

Canada Goose, hollow, rpt, average wear, 1 eye missing, RB 3/11/88 175

Canada Goose, hollow, working touchup w/some areas retaining orig pnt, prof rpr bill/sm neck crack, ca 1890, RWO 7/05/85 3000

Crow, Bowman's typical wing/thigh detail, black glass eyes, VG old pnt, reglued tail chip/split on side, RB 7/09/85 2100

Crow, 3-pc body construction, tack eyes, orig pnt, structurally EX, RWO 7/06/86, 185% 3750

Crow, 3-pc laminated body, hollow, G orig pnt, thin tail crack, few nicks/dings, rare, 193, RWO 7/02/88, 210% 2100

Dowitcher, cvd wings/wing tips, glass eyes, EX orig pnt, rosy breast, chip/age lines, ls, rare, RB 7/08/86, 63% 9500

Dowitcher, early, head slightly left, raised cvd wing tips/split tail, orig pnt, minor wear, rare, RB 3/11/88, 53% 7500

Dowitcher, molded cvd wings w/raised wing tips, EX orig pnt, prof rstr to crack in neck, rare, J/G 4/24/86 .... **6545**

Bowman, William
Dowitcher, Winter plumage, Norton stamp, outstand-
ing, deaccessioned by Stony Brook museums, 1800s,
115, RWO 7/05/85, $14,000.00.

Golden Plover, cvd wings/tips/tail feathers, muscle cvg on neck/breast, EX orig pnt, minor rstr, rare, RB 2/01/85, 190% **29000**
Golden Plover, full body, cvd wings/tips/split tail/muscle detail, EX orig pnt, minor wear, ls, rare, RB 2/10/85, 250% **50000**
Robin Snipe, extended cvd wing tips/wing outline, orig pnt, slight wear, tip of bill broken off, ls, 64, J/G 9/20/86 .... **7250**
Squaw drake, inlet head, hollow/thin, cvd eyes, rpt on white only, neck crack/tail patched, oversize, J/G 4/24/86, 137% **6875**
Yellowlegs, EX orig pnt, rpr head/wing tip, otherwise EX, commissioned by Stony Brook museums, 1800's, RWO 7/05/85 .... **6000**
Yellowlegs, pnt scorched in fire, half of bill is missing, ca 1890's, RWO 7/05/85 .... **1000**

Bowman, William
Yellowlegs, raised cvd wing tips, EX orig pnt, minor wear, head
is a DeLong replacement, ca 1800's, 148, RWO 7/06/86, $8,500.00.

Yellowlegs, raised cvd wing tips/wing outline, EX pnt w/working touchup on wing tips, prof rstr to bill, 64, J/G 9/20/86 .... **9000**
Yellowlegs, raised cvd wings w/extended tips, slight thigh cvg, orig pnt, prof rpl bill/sm chips, ms, rare, J/G 9/19/87 .... **4250**
Boyce, Harry; att
Yellowlegs, cvd eyes, old rpt, average wear, age split in head, RB 3/11/88 .... **325**
Boyd, George (Seabrook, NH)
Black Duck, overpnt taken down to orig, damage at underside of bill/head, possible rstr, oversize, RWO 7/06/86, 80% **650**
Black Duck, slightly turned head, EX orig pnt, hairline crack part way through neck, branded DA Goodwin, J/G 4/23/87 .... **1025**

Black Duck, slightly turned head, G old orig pnt, 1 eye missing/crack down side, ls, rare, oversize, J/G 9/20/86 525
Black Duck, slightly turned head, old working rpt, crack in underside of bodyblock/1 eye missing, ms, J/G 9/20/86 450
Blackbellied Plover, early, fine orig pnt, rare transitional plumage, average wear, well preserved, RB 7/08/86 2050
Blackbellied Plover, EX orig pnt, minor wear, bill has been prof replaced, RWO 7/06/86 1600
Blackbellied Plover, EX orig pnt, minor wear, RB 3/11/88 3000
Blackbellied Plover, EX orig pnt, minor wear, well preserved, RB 8/21/86, 77% 1900
Blackbellied Plover, EX orig pnt, minor wear w/sm flakes on bk, structurally superb, RWO 7/06/86 1950
Blackbellied Plover, EX orig pnt, rare, RB 7/09/85, 75% 3000
Blackbellied Plover, EX/NM condition, RWO 7/05/85 3050
Blackbellied Plover, fine orig pnt, average wear, minor flakes of wood have been tacked bk onto body, RB 6/28/88 1750
Blackbellied Plover, minor flaking on bill, otherwise EX & orig condition, RWO 7/02/88 2600
Blackbellied Plover, orig pnt, moderate wear, prof bill rpr by DeLong, RWO 7/05/85 1500
Blackbellied Plover, orig pnt, rare Winter plumage, very minor wear, structurally NM, RB 8/21/86 3500

Boyd, George
Blackbellied Plover, orig pnt, very minor wear, ms, rare, 22, RB 5/02/86, $3,750.00.

Blackbellied Plover, superb feather pnt, minor wear on bill, EX patina, bears Mackey stamp, EX condition, J/G 4/23/87 2600
Canada Goose, canvas-covered, G orig pnt, tears/holes in canvas around nail holes, otherwise sound, 193, RWO 7/02/88 6000
Canada Goose, canvas-covered, orig pnt, crazing on breast/head, structurally EX, RWO 11/11/87 3750
Canada Goose, detailed orig pnt w/shrinkage on top & head, NM/unused, sm chip on edge of tail, 143, J/G 9/19/87 7750
Canada Goose, high-head, canvas-covered, minor crazing/wear, otherwise NM, RB 6/28/88 4750
Canada Goose, old pnt, average wear, age splitting w/sm amount of dry rot in body, rare, RB 12/06/85 175
Canada Goose, slightly turned head, canvas-covered, fine orig pnt, average wear, EX patina, RB 8/21/86 4000
Goldeneye hen, fine orig pnt, minor flaking/wear, EX patina, artist brand, sm chips in tail, rare, RB 7/09/85, 310% 7750
Goldeneye pr, EX orig pnt, average wear/some blistering, drake has moderate crack in bottom, rare, RWO 7/04/87 5500
Goose, canvas-covered, old rpt, heavy crazing/wear, some sm tears in canvas, eyes are missing, RB 2/01/85 750
Merganser hen, slightly turned head, full body, orig pnt, minor wear, slight age split in neck, RB 7/07/87 6000
Redbreasted Merganser drake, early, EX orig pnt, thin check runs through bottom, 8, RWO 7/06/86, 135% 9500
Redbreasted Merganser drake, orig pnt, minor flaking/in-use wear, hairline crack on bk & side/tail chip, RWO 7/05/85 6000
Redbreasted Merganser hen, retains some orig pnt w/crazing & touchup on back, moderate chip to tail, RWO 7/06/86 3000
Yellowlegs, early, orig pnt, several rubs on 1 side, hairline crack in neck/body, 105, J/G 4/23/87 1700
Yellowlegs, EX orig pnt, average wear, neck has been prof rstr by DeLong, old bill replacement, rare, 190, RB 6/28/88 2000
Yellowlegs, EX orig pnt, minor flaking, rare, 22/44, RB 5/02/86 3500
Yellowlegs, EX orig pnt, minor wear, prof bill rpr to one-half of bill by Frank Finney, RWO 7/02/88 1900
Yellowlegs, EX orig pnt w/nice patina, minor wear, hairline crack in neck, otherwise EX, RWO 7/02/88 2300
Yellowlegs, EX pnt, structurally M, RB 8/21/86 3000

Yellowlegs, M orig pnt, EX patina, barely visible hairline crack in head, J/G 4/23/87 2900
Yellowlegs, NM condition, bill is completely original, RWO 7/04/87 3000
Yellowlegs, orig pnt, minor touchup on head & neck, structurally EX, RWO 7/05/85 2000
Yellowlegs, pnt shows no wear, very thin bill is completely intact, EX & orig, RWO 7/06/86 4250

Boyd, George; style of
Canada Goose, canvas-covered, M condition, RWO 7/04/87 240

Boyd, Taylor (Perryville, MD)
Black Duck, old working rpt, in-use wear, structurally sound, RWO 11/11/87 275
Canvasback drake, high-head style, rpt by Jim Currier, structurally EX, RWO 7/05/85 300
Canvasback drake, old working rpt worn to orig, thin crack in bk of head/around breast, otherwise sound, RWO 07/06/86 90
Canvasback drake, working rpt, average flaking/wear, thin crack running through head, otherwise sound, RWO 07/06/86 150
Canvasback drake, worn orig pnt, thin crack in neck, otherwise sound, ca 1920, RWO 11/06/85 500
Redhead drake, extremely fine form, old working rpt, slight wear, hairline cracks, dent in side, ca 1905, J/G 9/19/87 775
Redhead drake, old working rpt, average wear, thin tight checks at breast, otherwise structurally EX, rare, RWO 11/11/87 275

Boyd, Taylor; att (Perryville, MD)
Canvasback pr, old rpt, minor wear, several age splits in neck, RB 2/01/85 200

Boyle, John (Bellport, LI, NY)
Black Duck, cork body, EX orig pnt, minor wear, Rig brand on keel, minor check at bill, 188, RB 8/25/88 100
Pintail drake, cork body, NM condition, never weighted, ca 1920, 96, RWO 7/04/87 130

Boyle, John; att (Bellport, LI, NY)
Black Duck, cork body, EX pnt w/working touchup on bk, ca 1920, 96, RWO 7/04/87 90
Black Duck, hollow, old orig pnt, in-use wear, head/body may not be orig to each other, RWO 7/06/86 55
Mallard drake, cork body, M condition, ca 1920, 96, RWO 7/04/87 240
Widgeon drake, cork body, chip missing from underside of bill, otherwise EX condition, ca 1920, 96, RWO 7/04/87 100

Bracher, Vic (Ohio)
Canvasback drake, hollow, M condition, full size, RWO 2/12/88, 65% 250

Bradbeer, Robert (Spring Valley, IL)
Mallard pr, orig pnt, average crazing/wear, structurally EX, 7, J/G 4/24/86 495
Pintail drake, hollow, comb & feather pnt, minimal crazing/wear, tight split in neck, J/G 9/20/86 650

Bradshaw, Fred (Crisfield, MD)
Canvasback drake, hollow, made in the style of the Ward bros, signed/dated 1967, G orig condition, RWO 7/02/88 175

Brady, Walter (Oyster Bay, VA)

Brady, Walter
Canada Goose, cvd 'V' tail, fine old orig pnt, orig bill, rare, RB 7/09/85, $10,500.00.

Canada Goose, early, cvd tail w/orig dowelled-on beak, old working rpt, minor wear, age split in bodyblock, J/G 9/20/86 2150
Canada Goose, made from mahogany, orig pnt, moderate wear, no structural flaws, rare, ca 1900, 69/156, J/G 4/24/86, 60% 1100
Curlew, pnt worn to bare wood, structurally sound, ca 1890-1900, 28, RWO 7/05/85 625

Brady, Walter; att (Oyster Bay, VA)
Bluebill drake, early, old working rpt, average flaking/wear, age split in neck, ls, ?2, RB 8/25/88 120
Canada Goose, hollow, old pnt, heavy wear, structurally VG, ca 1890, 116/37, RWO 7/05/85, 150% 5250
Bragg, Gary (Ocracoke Island, NC)
Brant, orig pnt, structurally sound, RWO 11/06/85 50
Goose, early root-head, old working rpt, several age lines, 33/122, J/G 9/19/87 1350
Bragg, Gary; att (Ocracoke Island, NC)
Hutchins Goose, root-head, worn pnt, age split in body/side of head & neck, 122/33, J/G 9/19/87, 260% 2300
Bragg, Thomas (Portsmouth, NC)
Brant, stick-up, old working rpt, average wear, several narrow body checks, RWO 11/11/87 245
Brannick, Danny (Cambridge, MD)
Swan, pnt weathered/flaking from exposure to water, several spits in body/thin crack in neck, RWO 7/04/87 110
Bridell, Donald (Crisfield, MD)
Greenwinged Teal hen, balsa body, orig pnt, average wear, signed, structurally sound, RWO 7/06/86 90
Brittingham, Charles (Crisfield, MD)
Mallard hen, artist signed/dated, EX & orig condition, ca 1948, RWO 7/02/88 600
Mallard hen, M condition, ca 1948, RWO 11/06/85 750
Brittingham, John (Crisfield, MD)
Greenwinged Teal drake, hollow, signed/dated 1969, EX & orig, RWO 7/06/86 90
Brodson, att (Harwich, MA)
Golden Plover, NM orig pnt, 2 tiny shot holes, J/G 9/19/87 350
Brooks, Ed (Columbia, PA)
Bluebill pr, old pnt may be orig w/average wear, structurally sound, RWO 2/12/88 110
Canvasback drake, appears to be orig pnt w/average wear, EX condition, RWO 2/12/88 60
Brooks, John (Freeland, PEI)
Brant, swimming, orig pnt, minor wear, working touchup on lower sides, 2 tight checks in neck, rare, J/G 9/20/86 250
Canada Goose, hollow, tack eyes, 2 coats of pnt w/minor wear, several hairline cracks in breast, rare, J/G 9/19/87 550
Canada Goose, hollow w/cvd eyes, orig pnt, J/G 9/20/86 450
Canada Goose, old working rpt, minor wear on bottom, several tight checks on body/neck, rare, J/G 9/20/86 300
Brown, Bill (Parkertown, NJ)
Bluebill, hollow, rpt, average flaking/wear, age split in neck, RB 6/28/88 75
Bluebill pr, hollow, EX orig pnt, minor flaking/wear, several age splits in neck of hen, branded, 21, RB 2/01/85 325
Brant, hollow, old pnt, minor wear, minor chip on underside of bill, age split in neck, RB 3/11/88 100
Brown, Bill; att (Parkertown, NJ)
Bluebill pr, hollow, old pnt, appears to be orig, average wear, hen has age split in neck, otherwise sound, RB 8/25/88 150
Brown, Bob (Barnegat, NJ)
Black Duck, hollow, raised cvd wings, detailed feather pnt, artist brand, EX condition, RWO 7/02/88 150
Black Duck, hollow w/raised wings/cvd primaries, signed/#1, M condition, RWO 11/11/87 190
Black Duck, turned head, raised cvd wings, nice feather pnt, EX condition, RWO 7/02/88 220
Curlew, hollow, EX style/pnt, RWO 7/02/88 145
Curlew, long-billed, artist signed, M condition, RWO 2/12/88 120
Curlew, preening, hollow, relief cvg around wings, RJ Brown cvd in bottom, EX & orig condition, RWO 2/12/88 150
Oyster Catcher, artist signed, M condition, RWO 2/12/88 110
Willet, cypress wood, relief wing cvg, RJ Brown cvd in bottom, EX & orig condition, RWO 2/12/88 120
Yellowlegs, signed, EX condition, RB 6/28/88 125
Brown, Charlie (Wilson Point, MD)
Goldeneye pr, orig pnt, worn to bare wood in many areas on drake, structurally sound, ca 1955, RWO 11/06/85 125
Brown, Dan (Salisbury, MD)
Bufflehead drake, artist stamp, G orig condition, RWO 11/06/85 90
Brown, Fred (Point Pleasant, NJ)
Canada Goose, watch gander, slightly turned head, hollow, minor age splitting to body, otherwise EX, RB 8/21/86 325
Greenwinged Teal drake, hollow, EX comb feather pnt, EX & orig condition, RB 6/28/88 100
Mallard drake, fine orig pnt, in-use wear, RB 2/01/85 50
Merganser hen, EX orig pnt, minor wear, RB 8/27/87 120
Pintail pr, EX orig pnt, minor wear, RB 8/25/88 280
Redbreasted Merganser drake, slightly turned head, hollow, EX orig pnt, minor wear, RB 7/08/86 175
Brown, Rick (Point Pleasant, NJ)
Redhead drake, EX orig pnt, signed on bottom, RB 8/27/87 120
Bruell, Atwood (Goose Rocks Beach, ME)
Black Duck, sleeper, raised wing cvg, EX orig pnt, sm tail chip, RWO 7/04/87 80

Bruffee, Byron (Middleborough, MA)
Black Duck, preening, cvd crossed wing tips, NM orig pnt, structurally EX, cvd & pnt in the Crowell style, J/G 9/19/87 550
Bluebill drake, cvd/pnt in style of A Elmer Crowell, EX orig condition, RWO 2/13/87 140
Bufflehead drake, M pnt, artist brand, RWO 11/06/85 55
Canada Goose, artist brand, age check running down bottom, otherwise M, RWO 7/06/86 100
Canada Goose, cvd/pnt in style of Joseph Lincoln, M condition, J/G 4/23/87 300
Curlew, preening, raised primaries, glass eyes, M condition, J/G 9/20/86 150
Golden Plover, raised cvd primaries, glass eyes, M condition, J/G 9/20/86 155
Loon, orig pnt, minor flaking, thin cracks on bk, otherwise structurally sound, RWO 7/04/87 80
Merganser drake, preening, M condition, J/G 9/19/87 150
Redhead drake, cvd/pnt in style of A Elmer Crowell, EX orig condition, RWO 2/13/87 130
Swan, preening, hollow, artist brand, M condition, RWO 7/02/88 425
Bryan, Charles (Wilson Point, MD)
Black Duck, orig pnt, minor wear, thin crack in neck, otherwise structurally EX, RWO 11/06/85 70
Bluebill drake, EX orig pnt, RWO 11/06/85 70
Bluebill drake, G orig pnt, minor wear, bill has been broken off & reglued, RB 3/06/87 75
Bluebill drake, orig pnt, average wear, no structural flaws, ca 1950's, RWO 2/13/87 160
Bluebill pr, EX orig pnt, ca 1955, RWO 11/06/85 115
Canada Goose, orig pnt, hairline crack in neck, otherwise EX condition, RWO 11/06/85 140
Canvasback drake, EX orig pnt, minor wear, RB 7/08/86 110
Canvasback drake, G orig pnt, structurally fine, oversize, RWO 7/02/88 150
Canvasback drake, orig pnt, average wear, structurally EX, ca 1955, RWO 11/06/85 100
Canvasback pr, orig pnt, minor wear, structurally EX, ca 1955, RWO 11/06/85 175
Greenwinged Teal, artist signed/dated 1986, M/unused condition, RWO 7/02/88 150
Bryanton, Stacy (Kensington, PEI)
Canada Goose, body has 2 coats of pnt, head/neck orig w/minor wear, several minor age lines in body, J/G 9/19/87 450

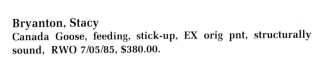

Bryanton, Stacy
Canada Goose, feeding, stick-up, EX orig pnt, structurally sound, RWO 7/05/85, $380.00.

Canada Goose, orig pnt, minor wear, age split on underside, J/G 9/19/87 600
Canada Goose, preening, EX orig pnt, artist initials, age split on underside/sm neck crack, J/G 9/19/87 750
Goose, watch gander, VG orig condition, lg, RWO 7/05/85 380
Buchanan, Charles
Black Duck, NM condition, 39, RB 7/08/86 175
Budd, Judson
Mallard, flying, signed/dated 1983, EX condition, half-size, RB 6/28/88 150
Bull, Roy (Chesapeake Bay)
Greenwinged Teal pr, fine orig pnt, RB 2/01/85 200
Bull, Russell (Northampton County, VA)
Brant, ca 1900, 49, RWO 7/05/85 270
Bundick, David (Modest Town, VA)
Redbreasted Merganser pr, hollow, hair crest, artist brand, unused, RWO 7/04/87 220

Burgess, Ned (Churches Island, NC)

Canada Goose, canvas over wire frame, old working rpt, 1 sm old patch in canvas, 33, J/G 9/19/87 200
Canada Goose, canvas over wire frame w/wooden head, orig pnt , average wear, several sm tears in canvas, J/G 4/24/86 148
Canada Goose, canvas-covered, G orig pnt, rare, RB 2/01/85 500
Canada Goose, wooden body, old working rpt, branded Ex, reglued crack in head, very rare, 33, J/G 9/19/87, 130% 1950
Canvasback drake, early, old working rpt worn to orig in areas, eyes added/hairline crack in neck, J/G 4/24/86 330
Canvasback drake, old working rpt att to artist, structurally EX, 33, J/G 9/19/87 825
Canvasback hen, orig pnt, minor wear, old repair to neck crack, 33, J/G 9/19/87 900
Coot, orig pnt, eyes have been recently added, rare, J/G 4/24/86 825
Coot, orig pnt, moderate wear, some dry rot on bill/breast/head, 33, J/G 9/19/87 350
Pintail pr, orig pnt, average wear, tight crack in necks, rare, 33, J/G 9/19/87 3250
Redhead hen, fine orig pnt, average wear, well preserved, RB 8/21/86 850
Redhead pr, old working rpt, minor wear, several hairline cracks, ls, 33/122, J/G 9/19/87, 125% 2000
Ruddy Duck, EX orig pnt, average wear, age split on underside of body, rare, 39, RB 7/08/86, 170% 5100

Burgess, Ned
Ruddy Duck, rpt w/minor wear, slight age split in bottom, rare, 39, RB 7/07/87, $1,100.00.

Widgeon drake, old rpt, average flaking/wear, slight age splitting in bottom of body, 6, RB 7/07/87 325
Widgeon drake, old rpt, average wear, well preserved, RB 12/06/85 200
Widgeon drake, orig pnt worn to bare wood, tail chips/thin crack in neck, ms, RWO 2/12/88 475
Widgeon drake, slightly turned head, orig pnt, minor wear, hairline cracks in tail, rare, 33, J/G 9/19/87, 135% 2050

Burgess, Ned; att (Churches Island, NC)

Canada Goose, canvas-covered, EX & orig, RB 7/09/85 375

Burke, Bob

Canvasback drake, hollow w/cvd wings & wing tips, fine orig pnt w/minor touchup near bottom board, rare, RB 7/09/85 250

Burke, Dr. Edgar

Brant, cork body, EX pnt, signed/dated on bottom, RB 7/08/86 75
Greenwinged Teal drake, cork body, EX & orig, RB 3/06/87 450
Greenwinged Teal hen, cork body, G orig pnt, average wear, structurally sound, 80, RB 7/09/85 380
Widgeon drake, cork body, EX orig pnt, average flaking/wear, structurally sound, 6, RB 7/07/87 200

Burke, Harold (Drumhead, NS)

Eider pr, turtleback, old working rpt, minor wear, bill chips, hen has several minor age lines/sm tail chip, J/G 9/19/87 300

Burkley, Charles

Mallard hen, hollow, cvd raised wing tips, signed/dated 1963, inscr as being rpt in 1974, EX condition, RB 6/28/88 275

Burkley, Cooper (Fieldsboro, NJ)

Mallard drake, slightly turned head, raised cvd wing tips, EX pnt, signed on bottom, RB 7/08/86 200

Burns, William (Roseberg, OR)

Mallard drake, signed/dated 1982, EX & orig condition, RB 8/25/88 100

Burr, Elisha (Hingham, MA)

Blackbellied Plover, extended neck, cvd wings, fine orig pnt, average wear, well preserved, RB 7/08/86 1250
Blackbellied Plover, feeding, cvd wings/feathers, EX orig pnt, bill is an old replacement, RB 7/07/87, 70% 1800
Blackbellied Plover, feeding, raised cvd wing tips, G orig pnt, minor wear, branded C Burr, 22/44/46, RB 5/02/86 3250
Blackbellied Plover, feeding, relief cvd wings w/detailed primary cvg, NM orig pnt, G patina, 105, J/G 4/23/87, 138% 5500
Blackbellied Plover, running, old rpt, minor wear, bill is a replacement, branded C Burr, 22, RB 5/02/86, 75% 1500
Golden Plover, beetle-head style, cvd wing tips/primary feathers, EX patina, NM condition, rare, RB 6/28/88 2250
Golden Plover, cvd split tail/primary feathers, EX pnt, minor flaking, rare, RB 7/09/85 3000
Golden Plover, EX orig pnt, minor crazing/wear, superb patina, sm chip on right wing tip, RB 7/07/87 3250
Goldeneye hen, old working rpt, 1 eye missing, sm rough area on top of head, J/G 9/20/86 145

Yellowlegs, cvd wing tips, EX orig pnt, average wear, 1 eye is a replacement, 40, RB 7/08/86, 50% **1750**
Yellowlegs, cvd wing tips, orig pnt, average wear, ls, bill is a replacement, 40, RB 7/08/86, 70% **1750**
Yellowlegs, cvd wings/primaries, EX orig pnt, average flaking/wear, ms, rare, RB 7/07/87, 35% **1000**

Burr, Elisha
Yellowlegs, running, fine orig pnt, minor wear, chip at underside of tail, branded C Burr, rare, 22/44, RB 5/02/86, $4,000.00.

Burr, Russ (Hingham, MA)
Black Duck, head tucked down, fine primary feather cvg, EX pnt, 22/44, RB 5/02/86, 185% **2800**
Bluebill hen, G orig pnt, average wear, sm chip on underside of bill, 22, RB 5/02/86 .... **450**
Bluebill hen, G orig pnt, average wear, 22, RB 5/02/86 .... **600**
Bluebill pr, cvd wings, G orig pnt, average wear, well preserved, 22/44, RB 5/02/86 .... **850**
Goldeneye pr, fine orig pnt, average flaking/wear, slight age splitting, RB 7/09/85 .... **350**
Yellowlegs, upright, EX orig pnt, 1 eye missing, 22/44, RB 5/02/86 .... **2750**
Burr Family (Hingham, MA)
Blackbellied Plover, raised cvd wings, NM condition, ca 1910, 48, RWO 7/06/86, 60% **1800**
Burrit, F.
Black Duck, early, sleeping, old rpt, flaking & wear, rpr to neck, rare, 22/44, RB 5/02/86 .... **2750**
Bush, Walter (Newark, NJ)
Black Duck, hollow, orig pnt, in-use wear, artist initials, bill has been broken & reglued, ca 1895, RWO 7/05/85 .... **1600**

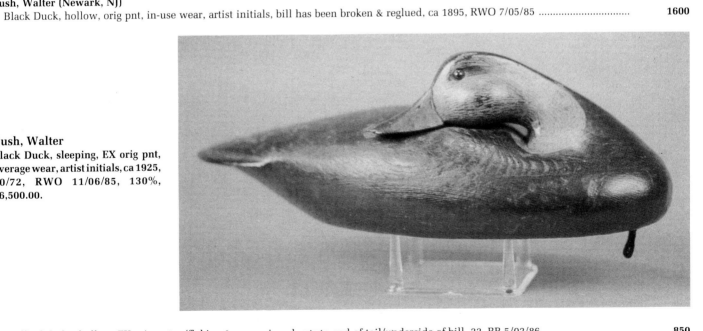

Bush, Walter
Black Duck, sleeping, EX orig pnt, average wear, artist initials, ca 1925, 50/72, RWO 11/06/85, 130%, $6,500.00.

Mallard drake, hollow, EX orig pnt w/flaking & wear, signed, rstr to end of tail/underside of bill, 22, RB 5/02/86 .... **850**
Pintail drake, hollow, G orig pnt, average wear, age split in neck, ca 1930, RB 7/09/85 .... **150**
Bush, Wilfred (Pekin, IL)
Mallard drake, orig pnt, minor wear, structurally EX, J/G 4/23/87 .... **325**

Bushnell, W.S. (Louisiana)
Pintail drake, NM pnt, break in tail has been reglued, RB 7/09/85 225
Cady, Carl (Pembroke, MA)
Canada Goose, sleeping, old pnt, average wear, slight age splits/chip on side of bill, rare, 22/44, RB 5/02/86, 180% 2700
Caen, Ray (Mystic River, CT)
Goldeneye hen, 4-pc dowelled body, EX orig pnt, structurally sound, J/G 9/19/87 175
Cain, Thomas (Clayton, NY)
Yellowlegs, feeding, EX pnt, RB 7/07/87 100
Caines Brothers (Georgetown, SC)
Black Duck, heart-shaped cvd wing pattern, flock pnt w/flaking & wear, split in neck/bill broken, 21, RB 2/01/85, 210% 4250
Black Duck, old working rpt, average wear, some damage at base of neck has been poorly repaired, ca 1900, RWO 7/06/86 180
Mallard drake, preening, fine old pnt, appears orig, 21, RB 2/01/85, 220% 15500
Mallard hen, fine old pnt, possibly orig, minor flaking/wear, age split in neck, in-use bill rpr, RB 2/01/85 3500

Caines Brothers
Mallard hen, sleeping, hollow 2-pc body, raised cvd wings, branded, structurally EX, very rare, 149, RWO 7/06/86, $16,000.00.

Cameron, Judge Glen (Chillicothe, IL)
Bluewinged Teal hen, hollow, EX orig pnt, bears initials ALA, few dings, otherwise EX, rare, 193/194, RWO 7/02/88, 56% 1700
Canvasback drake, hollow, EX orig pnt, minor flaking, well preserved, 39, RB 7/08/86 300
Canvasback hen, old working rpt, bears the initials ALA, structurally sound, 193/194, RWO 7/02/88 325
Mallard drake, early, worn working rpt, tiny chip in bk of neck, J/G 4/23/87 75
Mallard drake, G pnt, minor wear, artist brand, no structural flaws, J/G 9/20/86 350
Mallard drake, NM orig pnt w/traces of overpnt on lower sides, artist brand, structurally EX, J/G 4/24/86 935
Mallard drake, old working rpt, some orig pnt on bk, artist brand, sm crack to head, J/G 9/20/86 200
Mallard hen, early, orig pnt, minor crazing/wear, artist brand, sm chip on edge of bill, 51, J/G 9/19/87 500
Mallard hen, orig pnt, minor wear, hairline crack in neck, branded ALA, 7/51, J/G 4/23/87, 125% 2550
Ringneck drake, orig pnt, average wear, few dings to wood/ms, rare, RWO 11/11/87 325
Cameron, Judge Glen; att (Chillicothe, IL)
Canvasback hen, hollow, old working rpt, average wear, artist brand, rare, 3, RB 7/09/85, 160% 800
Campbell, Albany (La Plata, MD)
Bluebill pr, working rpt, average wear, cracks running through neck, ca 1940, RWO 2/13/87 140
Campbell, Albert (La Plata, MD)
Bluebill pr, old working rpt, thin cracks in neck, otherwise structurally sound, ca 1940, RWO 7/06/86 100
Campo, Dominique (Shell Beach, LA)
Mallard drake, full body, orig pnt w/some areas worn to bare wood around head, structurally EX, ca 1930, RWO 7/06/86 325
Canfield, Harry (Dallas City, IL)
Mallard pr, old pnt, average wear, some age splitting, RB 3/06/87 150
Mallard pr, orig pnt, minor wear, each have tight crack in neck, retain orig Canfield keel weight, EX, 89, J/G 4/24/86 715
Mallard pr, orig pnt, minor wear, tight crack in neck, both retain orig weight, J/G 9/20/86 450
Cantrelle, Adam (Louisiana)
Ringbill drake, fine old pnt appears to be orig, average wear, well preserved, RB 7/09/85 200
Carawan, Percy (Mattamuskeet, NC)
Goose, root-head, orig pnt, minor wear, several age lines, 33, J/G 9/19/87 600
Carmadelle, Alcide (Bayou Gauche, LA)
Mallard drake, gracefully cvd body, G orig pnt, average wear, rare, RB 7/08/86 2700

Carmadelle, Alcide; att (Bayou Gauche, LA)
Bluebill drake, old working rpt, heavy flaking/wear, age split in bill, 21, RB 2/01/85, 300% **600**

Carney, Armand (Tuckerton, NJ)
Black Skimmer, signed/dated 1982, EX condition, RB 3/11/88 .... **70**
Greenwinged Teal drake, signed, EX condition, RB 3/11/88 .... **50**
Greenwinged Teal pr, signed, drake's head has been reglued, otherwise both EX, RB 3/11/88 .... **125**
Hooded Merganser drake, signed/dated 1969, EX condition, RB 3/11/88 .... **100**
Hooded Merganser hen, head turned to the right, signed/dated 1975, EX condition, RB 3/11/88 .... **70**
Hooded Merganser pr, cvd primary feathers, signed/dated 1970, EX condition, RB 3/11/88 .... **175**
Hooded Merganser pr, turned heads, signed/dated 1969, both have minor crazing, otherwise EX, RB 3/11/88 .... **100**
Loon, head turned slightly to the right, artist signed, EX condition, RB 3/11/88 .... **375**
Old Squaw pr, EX pnt, signed/dated 1974 on bottom, RB 7/09/85 .... **275**
Pintail pr, turned heads, signed/dated 1975, EX condition, RB 3/11/88 .... **150**
Redhead drake, preening, signed/dated 1967, end-of-tail chip, otherwise EX, RB 3/11/88 .... **75**
Richardson Goose, artist signed, EX condition, RB 3/11/88 .... **150**
Richardson Goose, head turned left, signed/dated 1974, EX condition, RB 3/11/88 .... **150**
Ross' Goose, head slightly turned to the right, signed/dated 1972, EX condition, RB 3/11/88 .... **100**
Ross' Goose, signed/dated 1974, minor age split in bottom, otherwise EX, RB 3/11/88 .... **250**
Ruddy Duck hen, cvd crossed wing tips w/primary feathers, pnt by Lem Ward, signed/dated by Ward 1970, EX, RB 3/11/88 .... **475**
Ruddy Duck pr, turned heads, signed/dated 1970, EX condition, RB 3/11/88 .... **250**
Shoveller hen, head slightly turned to the right, signed/dated 1972, EX condition, RB 3/11/88 .... **75**
Swan, signed/dated 1982, EX condition, half-size, RB 3/11/88 .... **90**
Widgeon drake, signed/dated 1967, EX condition, RB 3/11/88 .... **75**
Wood Duck hen, head slightly turned to the right, signed/dated 1972, EX condition, RB 3/11/88 .... **75**

Carpenter, Gerald
Black Duck, preening, VG condition, RB 2/01/85 .... **150**

Carpenter, Wendall (Colchester, VT)
Black Duck, NM orig pnt, tiny chip missing from under bill, J/G 4/23/87 .... **100**
Goldeneye, NM orig pnt, no structural flaws, J/G 9/19/87 .... **50**

Carrigan, Lester (Rome, IL)
Canvasback hen, orig pnt, minor wear, 2 tight checks in neck/sm tail chip, retains orig weight, oversize, J/G 4/24/86 .... **209**

Carter, Paul
Merganser drake, NM orig pnt, structurally EX, flapping wings that raise when a string in tail is pulled, J/G 9/20/86 .... **295**
Merganser pr, inlet head w/raised cvd wings, Gus Wilson style, orig pnt, minor wear, no structural flaws, J/G 4/24/86 .... **330**

Casey, James (Newport, RI)
Dowitcher, orig pnt, minor wear, old working touchup on breast, shot hole, rare, J/G 9/19/87 .... **275**
Yellowlegs, NM orig pnt, bill is a replacement, J/G 9/19/87 .... **250**

Cassini, Frank (Galesburg, IL)
Mallard hen, hollow w/raised cvd wings, old working rpt, average flaking/wear, structurally sound, RWO 7/06/86 .... **275**

Cassius, Dr. Peacock
Coot, orig pnt, average wear, chip on end of bill/rough areas at end of tail, ls, 21, RB 2/01/85 .... **150**

Casson, Paul
Brant, preening, hollow, EX condition, RB 7/07/87 .... **50**
Loon, hollow, EX condition, RB 7/07/87 .... **40**
Redbreasted Merganser drake, hollow, EX condition, RB 7/07/87 .... **50**
Redbreasted Merganser drake, hollow, fish in mouth, EX condition, RB 7/07/87 .... **80**
Wood Duck, hollow, EX condition, RB 7/07/87 .... **30**

Catton, Hank (Ridgetown, Ont)
Canvasback drake, old working rpt, artist brand, hairline crack part way down bk, J/G 9/20/86 .... **75**

Cavaghan, John (Bristol, PA)
Pintail drake, low-head style, hollow, orig pnt, minor wear, dated 1985, structurally EX, RWO 7/04/87 ...... **250**

Cefai, George W.
Greenwinged Teal pr, branded GWC, M condition, RWO 2/12/88 .... **210**

Cerman, Stanley (Berlin, WI)
Bluebill pr, orig pnt, in-use wear, structurally sound, pre-1940, RWO 7/06/86 .... **175**

Chadwick, Keyes (Martha's Vineyard, MA)
Black Duck, EX orig condition, minor in-use wear, very thin crack down bottom, otherwise EX, RWO 7/05/85 .... **2000**
Black Duck, EX orig pnt, average wear, slight roughness to end-of-tail, 191, RB 6/28/88 .... **750**
Black Duck, G orig pnt, average wear, slight age split in bottom, 39, RB 7/08/86, 140% **1250**
Black Duck, graceful lines, EX condition, identified in Crowell's handwriting, 98, RB 2/01/85 .... **375**
Black Duck, orig pnt, minor wear, sm rough area on tip of bill/hairline crack on underside, rare, J/G 4/23/87 .... **800**

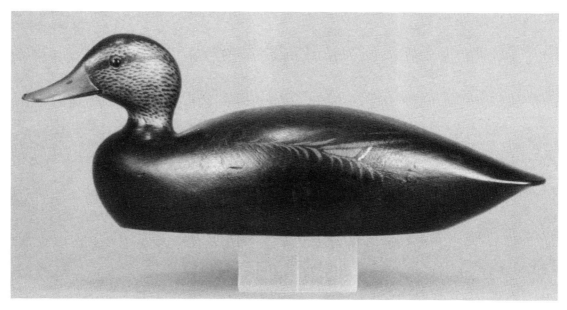

Chadwick, Keyes
Black Duck, pnt by AE Crowell, 1 of 6 sent to Crowell, it represents some of his finest work, RWO 7/05/85, $4,500.00.

Black Duck, prof rstr in Chadwick's exact style, split in bottom has been prof plugged, RWO 11/06/85	800
Black Duck, rpt, average wear, age split in bottom, RB 3/06/87	325
Black Duck, sleeping, unpnt, age split in bottom of body, 22/44, RB 5/02/86	500
Bluebill drake, early style, orig pnt, minor wear, prof rstr to chip on bill/sm crack on bk side of head, J/G 9/19/87	450
Bluebill drake, orig pnt, considerable wear, thin age check along 1 side, otherwise sound, RWO 7/05/85	280
Bluebill drake, rpt, average wear, age split in bottom of body, RB 3/06/87	400
Bluebill drake, slightly turned head, old rpt, minor wear, branded CSA, RB 2/01/85	250
Bluebill hen, slightly turned head, EX orig pnt, average wear, well preserved, RB 7/07/87	550
Bluebill pr, G orig pnt, average wear, age split in bottom of drake, from the Foote rig, RB 7/09/85, 70%	1100
Bluebill pr, orig pnt, average in-use wear, drake has filled check, otherwise both are sound, middle period, RWO 7/05/85	850
Bluebill pr, slightly turned heads, M orig pnt on hen; drake is NM orig w/few rubs, tight checks, J/G 4/23/87	1250
Brant, EX orig pnt, minor wear, age split in bottom of body, rare, RB 7/09/85	2500
Goldeneye drake, EX orig pnt, minor crazing on bk, narrow check along 1 side, otherwise EX, rare, 48, RWO 7/06/86, 50%	900
Goldeneye drake, slightly turned head, EX orig pnt, minor wear, branded CSA, well preserved, 98, RB 2/01/85	1100
Goldeneye drake, slightly turned head, EX orig pnt, minor wear, well preserved, 98, RB 2/01/85	1150
Goldeneye drake, slightly turned head, G rpt, average wear, branded CSA, 98, RB 2/01/85	500
Goldeneye drake, slightly turned head, old rpt, average wear, branded CSA, 98, RB 2/01/85	350
Goldeneye hen, low-head style, rpt, 118, RWO 7/05/85	325
Goldeneye pr, branded Foote, NM condition, RB 3/06/87	1300
Merganser drake, orig pnt, heavy flaking/wear, sm chip at end of tail/some age splitting, 23, RB 3/06/87, 120%	1800
Redbreasted Merganser drake, EX orig pnt w/sm rubs on bk, structurally EX, 14, RWO 7/06/86	3750
Redbreasted Merganser hen, EX orig pnt, minor crazing, few rubs on head/bk, structurally EX, RWO 7/06/86	3000
Redbreasted Merganser pr, slightly turned heads, NM orig pnt, slight age split in neck of drake, ca 1935, RB 3/06/87	6000

Chadwick, Keyes
Redhead drake, dings to pnt on bk/breast, sm dent on head, ms, appears on MA duck stamp, 8/48, RWO 7/06/86, 125%, $9,000.00.

Redhead drake, early style, slightly turned head, G orig pnt w/working touchup on white areas, rare, J/G 4/24/86, 140% 2255
Redhead drake, EX orig pnt, check runs from base of neck down bk, otherwise EX, middle period, RWO 7/05/85 1150
Redhead drake, few sm dents & pnt rubs, otherwise M, J/G 9/20/86 1600
Redhead drake, orig pnt, heavy wear, check running down bk/chunk of wood missing under bill, RWO 7/06/86 425
Redhead hen, fine orig pnt, minor wear, RB 12/06/85 600
Redhead hen, G orig pnt, minor flaking/wear, age check in base/tight check on 1 side, exceptional, 8/48, RWO 7/06/86 3500
Redhead hen, M condition, RWO 2/12/88, 55% 400

Chadwick, Keyes; att (Martha's Vineyard, MA)
Merganser hen, fine old pnt, average wear, bill broken off & reglued, age split in neck, 23, RB 3/06/87 500

Chambers, Thomas (Toronto, Ont)
Black Duck, low-head style, old working rpt, heavy wear, structurally sound, RWO 11/06/85 160
Bluebill drake, early, round-head style, hollow, overpnt taken down & rstr in manner of Frank Finney, RWO 7/02/88 275
Canada Goose, hollow, orig pnt, average wear, artist brand, minor bill rpr, EX condition, 1930's, 112, RWO 7/06/86 7000
Canvasback drake, hollow, branded Geo M Hendrie, EX & orig condition, RWO 7/02/88, 75% 2250
Canvasback drake, hollow, EX orig pnt, minor pnt specks, superb scratch feather pnt on bk, 2, RB 12/06/85 1250
Canvasback drake, hollow, fine comb pnt on bk/sides, tight check/2 hairlines, branded JT McMillan, oversize, J/G 9/19/87 3100
Canvasback drake, hollow, NM comb pnt, artist brand, 2 hairlines on side of head, oversize, 112, J/G 9/20/86, 135% 4150
Canvasback drake, long-body style, EX orig pnt, branded AH Buhl, structurally EX, ca 1919, 16, RWO 7/06/86 1600
Canvasback drake, long-body style, hollow, EX orig pnt, average wear, branded, ls, RB 3/06/87 3400
Canvasback drake, long-body style, orig comb pnt bold but worn, thin neck crack, stamped Geo M Hendrie, RWO 7/05/85 850
Redhead drake, early long-bill style, orig pnt, minor crazing/wear, branded Pulling, ms, very rare, J/G 9/19/87, 75% 1100
Redhead drake, early style, hollow, prof rstr to crack in bill, otherwise M, J/G 9/20/86 750
Redhead drake, EX orig pnt, average wear, branded AH Ruhl, hs, otherwise EX, ca 1900, 193, RWO 7/02/88 800
Redhead drake, EX orig pnt, slight crazing/wear, branded JT McMillan, hairline crack in neck/ls, J/G 4/24/86 495
Redhead drake, hollow, fine comb pnt, slight wear, ls, otherwise EX, J/G 9/19/87 850
Redhead drake, hollow, fine comb pnt w/minor wear, structurally EX, J/G 9/19/87 1000
Redhead drake, hollow, orig pnt, minor wear, branded BS Warren, ls, J/G 4/24/86 687
Redhead drake, racy head, EX orig pnt, average wear, initialed HMJ & WLM, about 3 dozen made in this style, RWO 7/05/85 800
Redhead pr, drake has NM orig pnt; hen has orig pnt w/minor wear, ls, 110, J/G 4/23/87 2750

Chamber, Thomas
Redhead pr, hollow, EX orig pnt, minor
flaking/wear, pnt initials: FHS, rare, RB
7/07/87, 65%, $2,000.00.

Redhead pr, orig pnt, average wear, structurally EX, ca 1930's, RWO 7/05/85 800
Chauvin, Curtis (Louisiana)
Bluewinged Teal hen, EX orig pnt, RB 8/21/86 200
Bluewinged Teal pr, EX condition, RB 6/28/88 100

Cheesman, Verne (Macombe, IL)

Bluebill drake, hollow, EX orig pnt by Edna Perdew, sm rub to bare wood on breast, EX condition, 193, RWO 7/02/88 4250

Bluebill hen, hollow, EX orig pnt by Edna Perdew, minor wear, NM condition, 193, RWO 7/02/88 5000

Canvasback drake, hollow, EX orig pnt by Edna Perdew, area rubbed to bare wood on underside, EX, 193, RWO 7/02/88 3500

Goldeneye drake, hollow, EX orig pnt by Edna Perdew, sm area of flaking on underside, EX condition, rare, RWO 7/02/88 10000

Goldeneye hen, EX orig pnt by Edna Perdew, minor wear, hairline crack in neck/bill chip, otherwise EX, 193, RWO 7/02/88 4750

Mallard drake, slightly turned head, hollow, old working rpt, no structural flaws, J/G 4/24/86 110

Mallard hen, old working rpt, minor wear, eyes are a replacement, 7, J/G 4/24/86 110

Mallard hen, swimming, orig pnt, minor wear, sm rough area on 1 side, from artist's hunting rig, J/G 4/23/87 325

Ringbill drake, old working rpt flaked to orig in many areas, several tail chips, rare, J/G 4/24/86 137

Cheramie, Tideaux (Louisiana)

Mallard drake, cvd wings, old working rpt, average wear, ls, RB 7/09/85 70

Cheslic, C. Lawrence (Peru, IL)

Bluebill drake, old working rpt, sm neck repair/tight check in bill, 7, J/G 4/24/86 132

Chesser, Grayson (Chincoteague, VA)

Black Duck, stick-up, hollow, artist brand, M condition, RWO 2/13/87 450

Bluewinged Teal pr, EX & orig, RB 7/09/85 450

Canada Goose, sleeper, hollow, few narrow checks to body, otherwise sound, RWO 2/13/87 350

Chiado, Anton (Granville, IL)

Mallard drake, hollow, orig pnt by Raymond Mason, ca 1940's, RWO 7/05/85 310

Chiado, Thomas (Spring Valley, IL)

Greenwinged Teal drake, orig pnt, minor flaking/wear, structurally EX, J/G 9/20/86 50

Wood Duck drake, EX orig pnt, slight flaking, structurally EX, ca 1944, 68, J/G 4/24/86 3850

Chief Cuffee (Long Island, NY)

Curlew, baleen bill, fine orig pnt, average flaking/wear, rare, RB 7/08/86 450

Curlew, bone bill, raised cvd wings/cvd eyes, NM orig pnt, filled-in age split, 105, J/G 4/23/87 1100

Curlew, fine orig pnt, average flaking/wear, bill is a replacement, RB 7/09/85 450

Merganser hen, cork/wood body, old weathered pnt, age split in neck, RB 7/08/85 250

Merganser hen, made of laminated cork/wood, EX orig pnt, 6, RB 7/07/87 150

Old Squaw pr, raised wings on both birds, outstanding orig condition, RWO 7/05/85 2100

Peep, EX orig pnt, minor flaking/wear, bill is a replacement, RB 7/07/87 100

Pheasant, cvd wings, EX orig condition, 6, RB 7/07/87 3200

Plover, unusual wing cvg, EX & orig in all respects, RWO 7/05/85 725

Chief Cuffee
Wood Duck drake, raised cvd wing tips, fine orig pnt, minor wear, well preserved, 6, RB 7/07/87, $1,000.00.

Yellowlegs, running, fine orig pnt, minor flaking/wear, structurally sound, RB 7/07/87 175

Chief Cuffee, att (Long Island, NY)

Curlew, pnt appears to be orig, EX condition, does not appear to be early, RWO 7/04/87 240

Chilton, Art (Toronto, Ont)

Bluebill pr, drake has slightly turned head, both have raised wing outline, artist brand, M condition, J/G 4/23/87 600

Christie Brothers (Saginaw Bay, MI)

Bufflehead pr, drake has overpnt removed from white/prof bill rpr, otherwise G orig, sm, 113, RWO 7/02/88, 55% 800

Redhead drake, old working rpt, reglued crack in bill/rough area under tail, J/G 4/23/87 125

Chrysler, Bill (Belleville, Ont)

Black Duck, EX orig pnt, structurally EX, J/G 4/24/86 385

Black Duck, hollow, NM scratch/feather pnt w/bill touchup, sm chip on edge of bill, J/G 9/19/87 1500

Black Duck, orig pnt, minor wear, sm tail chip/sm crack in base of neck has been reglued, J/G 4/23/87 325

Chrysler, C.W.; att

Bufflehead hen, old rpt, moderate flaking/wear, 6, RB 7/07/87 500

Churchill, Bill (Duxbury, MA)
Goldeneye drake, old pnt, average wear, well preserved, 22, RB 5/02/86 150
Clark, Charles (Chincoteague, VA)
Blackbellied Plover, early, lg paddle tail, EX orig pnt, tight check in 1 side of bk, J/G 4/24/86, 125% 1870
Curlew, early, orig pnt worn to natural wood, bill is a replacement, ms, rare, RB 7/09/85, 50% 400
Dowitcher, EX orig pnt, superb structural condition, rare, RWO 7/05/85 900
Plover, orig pnt, heavy flaking/wear, slight age splits, ms, rare, RB 7/09/85 800
Yellowlegs, balsa body, EX orig pnt, minor wear, age split in neck is repaired, 22/44, RB 5/02/86 675
Yellowlegs, balsa body, orig pnt, average wear, head has been broken off & reglued, 22, RWO 7/04/87 475
Yellowlegs, early, cvd eyes, EX orig pnt, average wear, bears Mackey stamp, structurally EX, RWO 7/04/87 1600

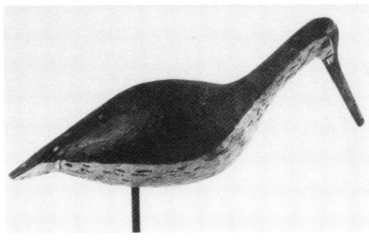

Clark, Charles
Yellowlegs, EX orig condition, bears Mackey stamp,
ca 1910, RWO 11/06/85, 65%, $1,050.00.

Yellowlegs, EX orig condition, ca 1910, 49, RWO 7/05/85 1350
Yellowlegs, exceptional orig pnt, minor wear, ls, otherwise structurally EX, ca 1920-30, RWO 7/04/87 2200
Yellowlegs, old pnt, average wear, some age splitting, 39, RB 7/08/86 350
Yellowlegs, old working rpt, no structural flaws, bears Mackey stamp, J/G 4/23/87 850
Clark, Charles; att (Chincoteague, VA)
Merganser hen, old pnt, average wear, well preserved, RB 7/09/85 60
Clark, Ed
Bufflehead drake, cvd wing tips, EX condition, RB 7/09/85 60
Canada Goose, swimming, hollow w/cvd wing tips, EX condition, RB 7/09/85 150
Coot, hollow w/cvd wing tips, EX condition, RB 7/09/85 60
Mallard drake, hollow w/cvd wing tips, EX condition, RB 7/09/85 70
Old Squaw drake, cvd wing tips, EX condition, RB 7/09/85 60
Redbreasted Merganser drake, hollow, EX & orig, RB 7/09/85 90
Ruddy Duck, hollow w/cvd wing tips, EX condition, RB 7/09/85 70
Snow Goose, hollow w/cvd wing tips, EX condition, RB 7/09/85 125
Swan, hollow w/cvd wing tips, artist brand, EX condition, RB 7/09/85 450
Wood Duck, hollow w/cvd wing tips, EX condition, RB 7/09/85 60
Clayton, Bart (Silverton, NJ)
Bluebill, hollow, old pnt, minor wear, structurally sound, 6, RB 7/07/87 250
Clayton, Keith
Scoter, canvas-covered, old orig pnt, average wear, artist brand, structurally sound, 22, RB 5/02/86 300
Clinton, Doug
Hooded Merganser drake, cvd raised wing tips/primary feathers, minor wear, otherwise EX condition, RB 6/28/88 100
Mallard hen, sleeping, raised cvd wing tips, EX orig pnt, RB 8/27/87 50
Ringbill drake, preening, hollow w/EX feather detail, orig pnt, average wear, structurally sound, RB 8/27/87 200
Clough, Orrie (Ladysmith, WI)
Mallard pr, hollow, G orig pnt, average wear, drake has some wear to primer on bk, otherwise EX, ca 1940, RWO 7/02/88 500
Cobb, Albert (Cobb Island, VA)
Brant, old pnt, heavy wear to bare wood on body, several chips/dings to body, ca 1880's, RWO 7/06/86, 25% 225
Cobb, Arthur (Cobb Island, VA)
Bluebill hen, hollow w/false inlet to head, cvd eyes, fine pnt, minor wear, artist brand, rare, 25/66, J/G 9/20/86 6700
Redbreasted Plover, early, raised cvd wings, cvd eyes, NM orig pnt, structurally sound, 105, J/G 4/23/87 2350

Cobb, Arthur; att (Cobb Island, VA)
Curlew, pnt worn mostly to natural wood, rpl bill, letter A cvd under tail, 22, RB 5/02/86 2900
Cobb, Don
Merganser hen, hollow w/extreme feather detail, elaborately cvd comb, NM orig pnt, 142, RB 7/07/87 400
Cobb, Elkenah (Cobb Island, VA)
Yellowlegs, cvd eyes, old rpt, minor wear, signed w/cvd E, bill is a replacement & is broken, ms, 6, RB 7/07/87, 125% 1900
Cobb, Nathan (Cobb Island, VA)

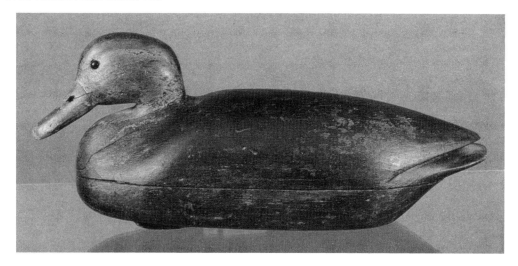

Cobb, Nathan
Black Duck, head in content position, hollow, orig pnt, black on body somewhat washed out, signed, EX, RB 3/06/87, 70%, $5,500.00.

Black Duck, hollow, old working rpt, in-use wear, 1 eye missing/several dings, otherwise sound, RWO 11/11/87 5000
Black Duck, hollow, pnt is worn/weathered, artist initial, crack in neck/1 eye missing, ca 1880, 3, RWO 7/06/86 5750
Black Duck, hollow w/cvd 'V' tail, old rpt, heavy flaking/wear, minor prof rstr, rare, RB 7/09/85 3500
Black Duck, inlet neck, hollow, cvd 'V' tail, G old scratch pnt, minor age lines in head, lg, J/G 4/23/87 7000
Black Duck, tucked head, full body, cvd 'V' tail, orig pnt worn bare in some areas, signed, minor age lines, RB 2/01/85 7000

Cobb, Nathan
Bluebill, inlet head, hollow, pnt worn bare in many areas, signed w/serified N, crack at base of neck, RWO 7/05/85, $6,500.00.

Bluebill drake, inlet head, hollow, old working rpt, crack in neck, eyes are old replacements, rare, J/G 9/20/86 3500
Brant, beligerent, head extended/twisted to right, orig w/some overpnt, average wear, unsigned, EX, RB 3/06/87, 57% 8000
Brant, full body, dowelled-on head set slightly into body, cvd eyes, EX early pnt, hairlines/age split, J/G 9/19/87 4000
Brant, full body, G old pnt, moderate wear, signed w/N, front of head is a prof rpl, J/G 9/19/87 2300
Brant, hollow, early pnt w/few areas to bare wood, serifed N in bottom, crack in bk/neck, otherwise EX, RWO 7/02/88 9500
Brant, hollow, full body, head slightly turned/cocked downward, orig w/some overpnt, ca 1860, rare, RB 3/11/88, 61% 5500
Brant, slightly turned head, hollow w/typical tail, EX orig pnt, minor overpnt, cvd signature, rare, RB 3/06/87, 60% 11000
Brant, swimming, hollow, glass eyes, several coats of pnt w/minor wear, structurally EX, J/G 4/24/86 412
Brant, swimming or hissing, hollow, old pnt, some may be orig, structurally EX, ca 1850, very rare, RWO 7/05/85 15000
Canada Goose, swimming/beligerent, hollow, cvd 'V' tail, old rpt, average wear, cvd initials, EX, RB 8/21/86, 135% 34000
Curlew, running, cvd eyes, bill is an old replacement, rstr to front/top of head, ms, rare, RB 7/09/85 3000

Cobb, Nathan
Canada Goose, swimming/belligerent, hollow, cvd 'V' tail, old rpt, average wear, cvd initials, EX, RB 8/21/86, 135%, $34,000.00.

Cobb, Nathan Jr. (Cobb Island, VA)
Bluebill hen, hollow, inlet head, orig pnt, average wear, several tight checks in body, 139, J/G 4/24/86, 180% 16500
Cobb, Nathan; att (Cobb Island, VA)
Curlew, cvd eyes/'V' tail, pnt worn to natural w/traces of orig, age split/rpl bill, cvd initial 'B,' 3/76, RB 3/06/87 12000
Plover, early, pnt worn/weathered to bare wood, gunning rpr to 1 side of head/checks in breast/hs, 45/209, RWO 7/02/88 4000
Cobb, Warren; att (Cobb Island, VA)
Black Duck, early, pnt taken down to orig w/some working rpt, age line in bk, J/G 4/23/87 500
Cobb Family (Cobb Island, VA)
Brant, early, old working rpt, in-use wear, water damage to breast area/few tight checks, RWO 11/11/87, 25% 500
Cochran, David
Brant, EX orig pnt, average wear, branded WL Suydam, crack on underside, otherwise sound, RWO 7/02/88 225
Brant, orig pnt, average wear, sm chip at end of bill, branded WL Suydam, RB 7/08/86 100
Cockey, Frank (Stevensville, MD)
Canvasback hen, orig pnt, structurally sound, ca 1946, RWO 11/06/85 85
Cocroft, Mason (Providence, RI)
Black Duck, cork body, orig pnt on head, average wear, 22/44, RB 5/02/86 250
Coffin, Charles (Nantucket, MA)
Golden Plover, mostly orig pnt w/some overpnt, ls, bill is a replacement, RB 7/08/86 350
Golden Plover, slightly turned head, NM orig pnt, structurally EX, ca 1900, rare, J/G 4/24/86 825
Golden Plover, slightly turned head, overpnt worn to reveal orig, slight age split in body, RB 7/08/86 400
Colborne, Paul
Goldeneye drake, fine orig pnt, average wear, ms, 189, RB 6/28/88 110
Coleman, Fred (Hennepin, IL)
Mallard drake, orig pnt w/fine combing on bk, average wear, no structural flaws, rare, J/G 4/24/86 275
Collins, Martin (Bridgeport, MA)
Black Duck, artist brand, EX & orig condition, RB 6/28/88 125
Black Duck, preening, detailed feather pnt, M condition, RWO 7/04/87 160
Goldeneye drake, artist brand, M condition, RWO 7/04/87 70
Collins, Sam (Essex, CT)
Black Duck, fine old pnt, average wear, right side of body has several age splits/age split at neck, RB 12/06/85 50
Black Duck, fine old pnt, minor wear, age split at neck, RB 12/06/85 150
Black Duck, old working rpt, heavy wear, slight dry rot on bottom, chip on underside of bill, RB 7/09/85 290
Black Duck, old working rpt, minor wear, crack in neck, body is joined by 4 wooden pegs, J/G 9/19/87 175
Bluebill hen, fine orig pnt, average wear, well preserved, RB 7/09/85 250
Bluebill hen, orig pnt, heavy wear, few sm chips at tail, otherwise structurally sound, ca 1895, RWO 7/06/86 180
Bluebill pr, early, G old orig pnt, minor age lines on underside, sm chip on edge of hen's bill, J/G 9/19/87 450

Bluebill pr, fine orig pnt, minor wear, several minor age splits, RB 2/01/85 500
Merganser drake, old pnt, heavy wear w/most areas to natural wood, several age splits, ls, RB 3/11/88, 140% 700
Collins Family (Essex, CT)
Bluebill drake, old pnt, some of which is orig, average wear, ls, RB 6/28/88 100
Bluebill drake, old rpt, average wear, old break at neck, RB 6/28/88 150
Mallard hen, hollow, fine orig pnt, average wear, head has been broken off & reglued a few times, 22/44, RB 5/02/86 225
Conklin, Hurley (Manahawkin, NJ)
Black Duck, cvd wing tips, artist brand, EX condition, RB 7/09/85 275
Black Duck, early, hollow, 3-pc body, appears to be working rpt w/average wear, structurally sound, RWO 7/02/88 115
Black Duck, EX pnt, artist brand, RB 7/09/85 200
Black Duck, hollow, EX orig pnt, artist brand, RWO 2/13/87 150

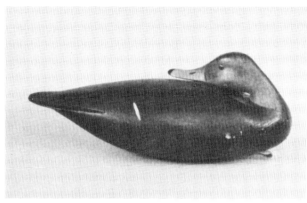

Conklin, Hurley
Black Duck, hollow w/cvd wing tips, EX pnt, artist brand, 39, RB 7/08/86, 250%, $750.00.

Black Duck, sleeping, artist brand, M condition, RWO 11/06/85 210
Black Duck, slightly turned head, hollow, NM orig pnt, artist brand, sm crack in neck, oversize, J/G 9/20/86 300
Black Duck, slightly turned head, raised cvd wing tips, M condition, J/G 4/23/87 400
Blackbellied Plover, artist brand, M condition, RWO 11/06/85 40
Bluebill drake, early, hollow, old rpt, average wear, RB 6/28/88 170
Bluebill drake, hollow, NM/unused condition, RB 7/09/85 275
Bluebill hen, EX orig pnt, minor wear, RB 7/08/86 225
Bluebill pr, artist brand, M condition, RWO 11/06/85 150

Conklin, Hurley
Bluewinged Teal pr, hollow, artist brand, RB 7/07/87, $800.00.

Brant, artist brand, EX condition, RB 7/09/85 325
Brant, early, hollow, old pnt appears to be orig, average wear, ls, RB 8/25/88 175
Brant, feeding, NM orig pnt, structurally EX, ca 1963, J/G 4/23/87 550
Brant, hissing, hollow, M condition, RWO 7/06/86 310
Brant, hollow, EX orig pnt, minor wear, break in neck has been reglued, RB 7/08/86 325
Brant, hollow, NM orig pnt, artist stamp, structurally EX, inset weight, J/G 9/20/86 375
Brant, hollow, working rpt, average wear, later signature/dated 1955, RWO 11/11/87 290

Brant, hollow w/cvd wing tips, EX pnt, artist brand, 39, RB 7/08/86	**550**
Brant, NM orig pnt, artist brand, reglued crack part way through bill, J/G 4/23/87	**375**
Brant, sleeping, hollow, EX pnt, artist brand, structurally EX, RWO 11/11/87	**325**
Brant, sleeping, NM orig pnt, artist brand, structurally EX, J/G 4/23/87	**425**
Brant, slightly turned head, hollow, EX orig pnt, RB 7/08/86	**200**
Brant, swimming, EX pnt, artist brand, 39, RB 7/08/86	**350**
Brant, swimming, 2 hairlines on bk of neck, otherwise M, J/G 9/19/87	**350**
Bufflehead pr, drake has slightly turned head; hen is preening, both w/cvd wing tips, artist brand, NM, J/G 4/23/87	**1200**
Bufflehead pr, hollow, unbranded, EX condition, 39, RB 7/08/86	**750**
Canada Goose, early, orig pnt, minor wear, branded FSM, hairline crack in bk/edge of tail, 123, J/G 9/19/87	**1050**
Canada Goose, head turned left, hollow, EX & orig condition, RB 3/11/88, 180%	**900**
Canada Goose, hollow, EX orig pnt, artist brand, slight age split in breast, RB 7/07/87	**575**
Canada Goose, hollow w/cvd wing tips, EX pnt, 39, RB 7/08/86	**1100**
Canada Goose, sleeping, hollow, EX condition, 39, RB 7/08/86	**600**
Canada Goose, swimming, hollow, EX orig pnt, fine hairline crack in neck, otherwise EX, ca 1960's, RWO 11/11/87	**950**
Canada Goose, swimming, NM orig pnt, artist brand, hairline crack part way down side, J/G 9/19/87	**1100**
Canvasback pr, orig pnt, minor wear, artist brand, reglued crack in neck of hen, J/G 4/23/87	**625**
Curlew, early, orig pnt, EX condition, RWO 11/06/85	**60**
Curlew, running, artist brand, EX & orig condition, RWO 2/12/88	**170**
Greenwinged Teal pr, slightly turned head, hollow w/raised cvd wing tips, artist brand, J/G 9/20/86	**650**
Hooded Merganser drake, cvd wing tips, artist brand, M condition, RB 7/09/85	**200**
Hooded Merganser drake, hollow, EX condition, RB 3/11/88	**325**
Hooded Merganser pr, artist brand, drake has hairline crack in lower side, otherwise M, J/G 4/23/87	**500**
Hooded Merganser pr, cvd wing tips, artist brand, EX condition, RB 7/09/85, 60%	**425**
Hooded Merganser pr, hollow, NM orig pnt, artist stamp, inset rectangular weight, rare, J/G 9/20/86	**625**
Hooded Merganser pr, unusual cvg, artist brand, M condition, RWO 11/06/85	**220**
Mallard hen, sleeping, EX orig pnt, 3, RB 3/06/87, 175%	**500**
Mallard pr, cvd wing tips, EX pnt, artist brand, 39, RB 7/08/86, 240%	**1900**
Merganser drake, American; NM orig pnt w/old touchup on most of white area, rare, J/G 4/23/87	**350**
Merganser pr, hollow w/cvd wing tips & combs, G orig pnt, some flaking/wear, artist brand, structurally sound, RB 7/8/86	**700**
Merganser pr, hollow w/raised cvd wing tips, NM orig pnt, artist brand, RB 7/07/87	**500**

Conklin, Hurley

Old Squaw pr, hen is sleeping, both have cvd wing tips, drake has wooden tail spring, artist brand, M, J/G 4/23/87, 150%, $2,100.00.

Peep, M condition, J/G 4/23/87	**90**
Redbreasted Merganser drake, early, EX orig pnt, minor wear, well preserved, RB 8/25/88	**425**
Redbreasted Merganser drake, hollow, artist brand/NJ-81; M condition, RWO 11/11/87	**450**
Redbreasted Merganser drake, hollow, EX pnt, minor wear, structurally EX, RWO 11/11/87	**275**
Redbreasted Merganser drake, hollow, M pnt, artist brand, RWO 7/04/87	**375**
Redbreasted Merganser pr, cvd combs, orig pnt, minor wear, artist brand, inset weight, J/G 9/20/86, 130%	**1050**
Redbreasted Merganser pr, cvd wings, EX pnt, artist brand, RB 7/09/85	**500**
Redbreasted Merganser pr, cvd wings, EX pnt, RB 7/09/85, 60%	**450**
Redbreasted Merganser pr, early, EX orig pnt, minor wear, structurally EX, RWO 7/06/86	**475**
Redbreasted Merganser pr, early, hollow, working rpt by Conklin, hen has bill crack, otherwise sound, RWO 2/12/88, 200%	**600**

Redbreasted Merganser pr, early, M condition, RWO 11/06/85 475
Redbreasted Merganser pr, hollow, artist brand, EX condition, RB 3/11/88 500
Redbreasted Merganser pr, hollow, artist brand, sm chip reglued on drake's tail, otherwise EX, RB 3/11/88 700
Redbreasted Merganser pr, hollow, EX orig pnt, artist brand, structurally NM, RWO 7/04/87 550
Redbreasted Merganser pr, hollow, EX pnt, artist brand on both, structurally EX, 39, RB 7/08/86, 130% 1050
Redbreasted Merganser pr, hollow w/cvd raised wing tips, M pnt, artist brand, J/G 4/23/87 750
Redhead drake, hollow w/raised cvd wing tips, NM pnt, RB 7/07/87 325
Redhead pr, few pnt dings, artist brand, M condition, RWO 11/06/85 150
Redhead pr, hollow, unbranded, EX condition, 39, RB 7/08/86 800
Ruddy Duck, artist brand, M condition, RWO 11/06/85 150
Ruddy Duck pr, hollow, drake is artist signed on underside of tail, M condition, RB 12/06/85 800
Sanderling, artist signed, M condition, RWO 11/06/85 50
Sea Gull, hollow w/raised cvd wing tips, EX pnt, 39, RB 7/08/86 375
Shoveler drake, hollow, orig pnt, minor wear, artist brand, structurally EX, RWO 7/02/88 150
Shoveler pr, slightly turned heads, cvd wings, EX pnt, artist brand, rare, 39, RB 7/08/86 1700
Snipe, branded HC, EX & orig condition, RWO 2/12/88 160
Snowy Egret, artist brand, EX condition, RB 3/11/88, 133% 400
Swan, hollow, artist brand, rare, M condition, RWO 11/11/87 1500
Wood Duck drake, worn pnt, some of which may not be orig, rare, RB 7/09/85 600
Wood Duck pr, hollow, EX & orig condition, RB 3/11/88 1400
Wood Duck pr, hollow, G orig pnt, sm chip on tail of hen, RB 2/01/85 1750
Yellowlegs, artist brand, EX condition, RB 7/09/85 100
Yellowlegs, orig pnt, minor wear, artist stamp, structurally sound, J/G 4/23/87 125

Conklin, Hurley; att (Manahawkin, NJ)
Bluebill drake, hollow, rpt, average wear, age split in neck, ls, RB 3/11/88 125
Hooded Merganser hen, fine orig pnt, artist brand, RB 7/09/85 100

Conklin, Roy (Alexandria Bay, NY)
Bluebill drake, fine orig pnt, minor wear, ls, age split in neck, RB 8/21/86 225
Canvasback drake, fine Conklin pnt, average wear, graceful neck w/old repair, RB 2/01/85 300
Canvasback hen, G orig pnt, average wear, slight age split in bottom, otherwise well preserved, RB 7/07/87 175
Mallard drake, feeding, crack in neck has been prof repaired, otherwise M, RWO 7/02/88 100
Merganser hen, American; NM orig pnt, structurally EX, oversize, J/G 9/20/86 195

Conover, Elijah; att
Yellowlegs, old rpt, average wear, bill is an old replacement, RB 3/11/88 100

Conroy, Bill (Maine)
Brant, hollow, artist brand, signed/dated 1977, M condition, RWO 7/02/88 150
Eider drake, artist brand, M condition, RWO 7/02/88 90

Cook, Harry
Canvasback drake, G orig pnt, minor wear, structurally sound, RB 8/27/87 125
Canvasback drake, old rpt, average wear, RB 8/25/88 75

Cook, Harry
Greenwinged Teal pr, cvd wing tips/ tail feathers, orig pnt, minor wear, branded, well preserved, ca 1938, RB 8/21/86, $450.00.

Coombs, Frank (Alexandria Bay, NY)
Black Duck, M unused condition, rare, 218, RWO 2/12/88, 43% 300
Bluebill drake, comb pnt area on bk, sides are orig, otherwise rpt, hairline crack in neck, J/G 4/24/86 412
Bluebill drake, fine orig pnt, average wear, slight age split in neck, well preserved, RB 3/06/87 400
Bluebill drake, old rpt, minor wear, RB 12/06/85 135
Bluebill drake, orig pnt, average wear, structurally VG, RB 7/08/86 350
Bluebill hen, EX old pnt, minor wear, 2 hairline cracks in neck area, J/G 4/23/87 625
Bluebill pr, high-head, orig pnt, hen is worn to bare wood on top of body, structurally sound, RWO 7/02/88, 75% 600
Bluebill pr, long-neck style, M unused condition, neither have ever been put in water, 218, RWO 2/12/88 1600

Bluebill pr, made for a personal friend in 1950, M condition, RWO 7/02/88 1050
Bluebill pr, rpt w/average wear, age splits in necks, drake's bill has been rstr, RB 7/08/86 175
Bluebill pr, rpt w/average wear, structurally sound, RB 2/01/85 150
Canvasback drake, orig pnt, average wear, hairline crack in neck, otherwise structurally EX, ca 1930's, RWO 11/06/85 300
Canvasback drake, rpt w/average wear, ls, RB 3/06/87 200
Goldeneye drake, early, orig pnt w/areas of working overpnt, structurally sound, RWO 11/06/85 80
Goldeneye drake, old rpt, average wear, slight age split in bk, RB 7/08/86 140
Goldeneye hen, fine old pnt, possibly orig, RB 2/01/85 450
Goldeneye hen, high-neck style, EX orig pnt, minor wear, minor specks of white pnt on bk of decoy, RB 8/27/87 850
Goldeneye hen, rpt w/average wear, ls, RB 7/08/86 110
Goldeneye pr, M unused condition, never put in water, 218, RWO 2/12/88, 52% 1050
Redhead drake, rpt, heavy wear, age split in neck/chip in tail, ls, RB 12/06/85 90

Coombs, Frank; att (Alexandria Bay, NY)
Bluebill drake, black areas are rpt, comb feather pnt all orig w/minor wear, RB 7/09/85 130
Bluebill drake, old rpt, average wear, RB 12/06/85 60
Goldeneye drake, entire rpt, thin check running down bk/crack through neck, ca 1930, RWO 7/06/86 60

Coombs, Horace
Mallard drake, fine orig pnt, average wear, slight age split in body, RB 7/09/85 110

Coombs, Lyford (Vinalhaven, ME)
Eider pr, relief cvg around bill, G orig pnt, minor wear, lg, RWO 7/04/87 200
Scoter, American; orig pnt, minor wear, structurally sound, RWO 7/04/87 70

Cooper, William (Quebec)
Goldeneye drake, detailed feather cvg on bk, orig pnt, structurally sound, RWO 7/04/87 160

Copley, Keith (Shinnecock, NY)
Sanderling, early, cvd wings, EX & orig condition, RWO 7/02/88, 37% 275
Sanderling, 3-pc laminated body, cvd wings, some pnt flaking on head, otherwise G condition, RWO 7/02/88, 35% 200

Corliss, Reuben (Manahawkin, NJ)
Black Duck, hollow, EX & orig condition, RB 8/25/88 180
Bluebill drake, hollow, orig pnt, average wear, chips of wood missing from sides, re-headed by Truex, RB 3/11/88 75
Bluebill drake, hollow, simple orig pnt, EX condition, RWO 11/11/87 70
Bluebill drake, hollow, well-detailed pnt, average wear, structurally sound, RWO 11/11/87 215
Bluebill hen, hollow, working rpt, average wear, ls, otherwise sound, RWO 7/02/88 65
Bluebill pr, hollow, working rpt, structurally poor, 28, RWO 11/11/87 85
Bluebill pr, old working rpt, no structural flaws, RB 9/20/86 95

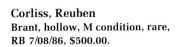

Corliss, Reuben
Brant, hollow, M condition, rare,
RB 7/08/86, $500.00.

Brant, 2 coats of pnt, top coat is NM, structurally EX, J/G 9/19/87 210
Canada Goose, hollow, EX orig pnt, RB 8/21/86 350
Redhead drake, hollow, EX orig pnt, minor wear, RB 2/01/85 225
Redhead drake, hollow, fine orig pnt, average wear, RB 8/27/87 120

Corson, Howard (New Jersey)
Black Duck, hollow, rpt, average wear, age split in body, RB 6/28/88 275

Corwin, Capt. Wilbur (Bellport, NY)
Black Duck, feeding/slightly turned head angled down, old pnt/average wear, rpl bill (?), 1875, 22/44, RB 5/02/86, 50% 2000
Blackbellied Plover, raised cvd wings, screw eyes, EX orig pnt, artist brand, prof rpl bill, rare, J/G 9/19/87, 45% 900

Corwin, Capt. Wilbur
Canada Goose, hollow, rpt by the artist, stylish, 45, RWO 7/05/85, $1,100.00.

Golden Plover, relief wing cvg, screw eyes, EX orig pnt, artist brand, prof rpl bill, rare, J/G 9/19/87, 50% 750
Greater Yellowlegs, turned head, cvd wings, screw eyes, orig pnt, branded, prof rpl bill, EX, ca 1900, rare, J/G 9/19/87 2800
Greater Yellowlegs, turned head, raised cvd wings, screw eyes, orig pnt, artist brand, EX, 1900, rare, J/G 9/19/87, 60% 1500
Hooded Merganser pr, cork body, hen has hairline crack in neck, otherwise EX & orig condition, RWO 7/02/88 550
Peep, cork body, EX & orig, 10, RB 12/06/85 150
Corwin, Capt. Wilbur; att (Bellport, NY)
Bluebill drake, old working rpt, some areas along side worn to bare wood, structurally sound, RWO 7/02/88 350
Widgeon drake, old pnt, heavy flaking/wear, structurally sound, RB 12/06/85 30
Corwin Family (Seaford, LI, NY)
Bluebill drake, early, old working rpt, age line in bk, J/G 4/23/87 175
Couch, John
Pintail drake, orig pnt, minor wear, slight age split in neck, 21, RB 2/01/85 100
Coykendell, Ralph
Goldeneye pr, NM orig pnt, hairline crack in hen's body, J/G 9/19/87 850
Mallard pr, low-head style, balsa body, orig pnt, average wear, no structural flaws, RWO 11/11/87 125
Cramer, D.K. (Drumore, PA)
Redhead drake pr, inlet heads/bills, orig pnt, minor wear, hairline cracks in breasts, 33, J/G 9/19/87 300
Crandell, Horace (Los Angeles, CA)
Mallard hen, cvd wing tips, NM pnt w/EX feather pnt, slight age split in neck, rare, RB 7/09/85 950
Pintail drake, slightly turned head w/raised wing tips, old pnt, average wear, old repair to neck & tail, RB 8/27/87 650
Crane, Dude
Black Duck, hollow, fine orig pnt, minor flaking/wear, branded JL, RB 3/11/88 250
Bluebill drake, hollow, EX orig pnt, minor wear, branded JL, RB 3/11/88 150
Bluebill drake, hollow, old pnt appears to be orig, minor wear, branded JL, RB 3/11/88 250
Canada Goose, hollow, EX orig pnt, average wear, structurally sound, RB 3/11/88 500
Canada Goose, hollow, EX orig pnt, average wear, structurally sound, RB 3/11/88, 120% 600
Crane, Dude; att
Brant, hollow, fine old pnt appears to be orig, average wear, RB 3/11/88, 240% 725
Canada Goose, fine orig pnt, average wear, branded JL, well preserved, RB 3/11/88 650
Cranmer, Bill (Beach Haven, NJ)
Black Duck, hollow, 1 eye broken, RB 2/01/85 225
Black Duck, orig pnt, average wear, structurally sound, RWO 7/04/87 250
Brant, EX orig pnt, some second coating by artist, no structural flaws, J/G 9/19/87 140
Canvasback pr, hollow, NM condition, RB 2/01/85 250
Gadwall pr, slightly turned heads, hollow, M condition, RB 2/10/85 1050
Gull, hollow, orig pnt, heavy wear, minor age splits in body, RB 3/11/88, 140% 425
Mallard pr, hollow, EX orig pnt, 21, RB 2/01/85 450
Pintail drake, EX & orig, RWO 7/06/86 275
Pintail drake, hollow, G orig pnt, average wear, 40, RB 7/08/86 300

Redbreasted Merganser pr, signed/dated 1976, inscribed: Made for Armand Carney, EX condition, RB 3/11/88, 130% 650
Redhead drake, rpt w/minor wear, RB 7/09/85 100
Widgeon pr, NM condition, RWO 7/04/87 450

Cranmer, Horace
Greenwinged Teal pr, cvd wing tips, superb & M condition, extremely rare, RB 8/25/88 3000

Cranmer, Joe Tom (Manahawkin, NJ)
Black Duck, hollow, old pnt, average wear, age split in neck, ls, 189, RB 6/28/88 125
Black Duck, hollow, old rpt, average wear, RB 6/28/88 100
Black Duck, hollow, old scratch feather pnt, average flaking/wear, age split in neck, 21, RB 2/01/85 100
Bluebill drake, hollow, old pnt w/crazing/wear, age split at neck, ls, RB 12/06/85 225
Bluebill drake, hollow, rpt, average flaking/wear, structurally sound, 9, RB 12/06/85 100
Canada Goose, hissing, hollow, orig pnt, average wear, EX condition, ca 1900, RWO 7/02/88, 45% 300
Canada Goose, hollow, working rpt, average flaking/wear, structurally sound, 21, RB 2/01/85 175
Redhead drake, hollow, old pnt, average wear, some slight age splitting, RB 12/06/85 75

Cranmer, John (Parkertown, NJ)
Blackbellied Plover, early, running, old working rpt, JC cvd in bottom, bill appears to be a replacement/hs, RWO 7/02/88 110

Crawford, W.J. (Brockville, Ont)
Goldeneye hen, EX orig pnt, minor wear, tail chip, ms, sm, RWO 7/02/88 220

Crawford, William (Smith's Falls, Ont)
Bluebill drake, hollow w/detailed wing/tail cvg, fine orig comb pnt, minor wear/varnished, artist brand, J/G 4/23/87 900

Creamer, J.M. (Provincetown, MA)
Merganser, hollow, pnt stripped to natural wood, signed/dated 1947, structurally sound, RB 2/01/85 200

Creighton, Clarence (Hooper's Island, VA)
Bufflehead hen, old pnt, average wear, chip on underside of bill, RB 8/25/88 45

Crier, Shannon (London, Ont)
Bluebill drake, orig pnt, minor wear, structurally sound, J/G 4/23/87 120

Crochet, Lester (Louisiana)
Bluewinged Teal drake, EX condition, RB 8/25/88 150
Pintail hen, cvd raised wing tips, EX condition, RB 6/28/88 50

Crooks, Floyd
Bluebill pr, bob-tail style, orig pnt, drake has few thin checks on bk, otherwise structurally EX, RWO 11/06/85 40
Canvasback drake pr, 1 has slightly turned head, G orig condition, RWO 11/06/85 80

Crowell, A. Elmer (East Harwich, MA)
Black Duck, cork body, EX orig pnt, minor wear, oval brand, EX condition, bears Winthrop brand, RWO 2/12/87, 178% 3750
Black Duck, cork body, EX orig pnt, some flaking on body, artist brand, branded F Winthrop, RWO 7/04/87 1300
Black Duck, cvd crossed wings/tail feathers, EX orig pnt, minor wear, structurally EX, 3" rstr crack, J/G 4/24/86, 63% 4400
Black Duck, early, crossed wing-tip & tail-feather cvg, orig pnt, heavy flaking/wear, 22/44, RB 5/02/86, 150% 6000
Black Duck, early, EX orig feather pnt w/blue-pnt speculum, minor flaking, otherwise NM, I Johnson stencil, RB 8/21/86 2500
Black Duck, early, orig pnt, moderate wear, old repair at base of neck/ls, oversize, J/G 4/24/86 605

Crowell, A. Elmer
Black Duck, early, sleeping, deep cvd crossed wing tips/primaries/tail feathers, rpt/head orig, 22/44/46, RB 5/02/86, $22,500.00.

Black Duck, EX detailed orig pnt, artist brand, 2 sm chips on tail, fine form, 184, J/G 9/20/86 2700
Black Duck, EX detailed pnt, oval brand, glued rpr at base of neck, 2 hairlines, ls, oversize, 87, J/G 9/19/87 2000

Black Duck, EX orig pnt, minor wear, fine feather pnt, artist brand, head has been prof reattached, RB 8/21/86 2200
Black Duck, EX orig pnt, minor wear, structurally EX, from the rig of WW Wells, RWO 7/05/85 2000
Black Duck, fine orig pnt, average wear, artist brand, roughness to edge of tail, 21, RB 2/01/85 900
Black Duck, fine orig pnt, average wear, artist brand, well preserved, Pequant Club brand, RB 7/09/85 1400
Black Duck, fine orig pnt, minor wear, artist brand, rare, RB 7/09/85 1800
Black Duck, fine orig pnt, minor wear, oval brand, rare, oversize, RB 7/07/87 2100
Black Duck, G orig pnt, some rubs to bare wood on sides, Crowell's oval brand, EX condition, 193, RWO 7/02/88, 72% 1800
Black Duck, Iver Johnson Supreme brand, NM condition, RB 3/11/88, 175% 5250
Black Duck, M orig pnt, oval brand, age split on underside extending up breast & under tail, J/G 9/19/87 3700
Black Duck, old rpt worn to areas of natural wood, ms, RB 12/06/85 400
Black Duck, old working rpt, artist brand, tight check part way down bk/prof repair to 1 side of neck, J/G 9/20/86 550
Black Duck, orig pnt, average wear, artist brand, sm cracks at base of neck/under bill, otherwise sound, RWO 7/04/87 1300
Black Duck, orig pnt, in-use touchup to bill, artist brand, head has been reattached, from RI Clark, RWO 11/11/87 2100
Black Duck, orig pnt, minor wear, artist brand, sm nail in neck, hairline cracks in body, oversize, 87, J/G 9/19/87 2250
Black Duck, orig pnt w/possible touchup, head has been shored up w/nails at base of neck, oval brand, 204, RWO 2/12/88 1400
Black Duck, outstanding orig pnt, bears 2 rectangular stamps, NM condition, RWO 11/06/85 1600
Black Duck, oval brand, NM condition, ca 1922, RB 7/08/86 6000
Black Duck, oval brand on bottom, M condition, RB 12/06/85 3100
Black Duck, rpt by George Coombs, oval brand, RB 7/07/87 500
Black Duck, slightly turned head, cork body/pine bottom board, EX orig pnt, artist brand, EX, 101, J/G 4/23/87, 75% 1900
Black Duck, slightly turned head, M orig pnt, oval brand, tight crack on underside/sm cracks in tail, J/G 9/20/86 4000
Black Duck, tail cvg, worn orig pnt w/many areas to bare wood, check runs down 1 side of bk, pre-stamp era, RWO 07/06/86 750
Black Duck, tight age check running down bk/along bottom, otherwise M, 8, RWO 07/06/86 2750

Crowell, A. Elmer
Blackbellied Plover, alert, cvd wings/layered primaries/extended wing tips, NM orig pnt/varnish, 162, J/G 4/23/87, 130%, $45,000.00.

Blackbellied Plover, feeding, raised shoulder cvg/cvd primaries, EX orig pnt, minor flaking, rare, 48, RWO 07/06/86 52500
Blackbellied Plover, full body, split tail, tack eyes, EX orig pnt, sm tail chip, otherwise NM, RB 8/21/86, 65% 3250
Blackbellied Plover, head turned, 6 cvd primaries on 1 side/5 on other, glass eyes, EX pnt, ls, 1890, RB 12/06/85, 130% 39000
Blackbellied Plover, relief cvd wings/extended tips, layered cvd primaries, NM orig pnt w/varnish, J/G 4/23/87 45000
Blackbellied Plover, tack eyes, finely executed pnt, M w/great patina, J/G 4/24/87 10450
Bluebill drake, head tucked down, cvd tail feathers, rasping to bk of head, NM condition, rare, RB 12/06/85 3250
Bluebill drake, low-head hunting model, orig pnt, minor wear, tight check on 1 side, ls, ca 1905, J/G 4/24/86 1210
Bluebill drake, low-head style, EX orig pnt w/touchup on underside, minor age lines, ls, ca 1905, J/G 4/23/87 1150
Bluebill drake, low-head style, tail cvg, M condition, pre-brand era, ca 1925, never weighted, RWO 11/06/85 3350

Bluebill drake, M orig pnt, VG patina, oval brand, minor age line on underside, J/G 9/19/87, 79% **4750**
Bluebill drake, slightly turned head, cvd crossed wing tips/primaries/tail feathers, orig pnt, heavily worn, RB 2/01/85 .... **1400**
Bluebill drake, slightly turned head, cvd tail feathers, fine orig pnt, minor flaking, artist brand, 22, RB 5/02/86 .... **5000**
Bluebill drake, slightly turned tucked head, cvd tail feathers/wing tips, artist stamp, NM, 1931, RB 8/21/86, 78% **6250**

Crowell, A. Elmer
Bluebill hen, high-head, cvd
crossed wings/cvd tail, stylized
pnt, bk of head is rasped, M
condition, RWO 11/06/85,
$5,000.00.

Bluebill hen, low-head, rpt in style of Crowell, minor age checks on bk of the head, otherwise sound, RWO 7/02/88, 42% **500**
Bluebill hen, low-head, tail cvg, EX orig pnt, minor wear, sm chip on underside of bill, otherwise M, RWO 7/02/88, 60% **3250**
Bluebill pr, low-head, cvd tail feathers, G orig pnt, minor flaking, well preserved, 22/44, RB 5/02/86 .... **5500**
Bluewinged Teal drake, cvd crossed wings/tail cvg, M pnt & structure, made for Dr JC Phillips, rare, 8/48, RWO 7/06/86 .... **35000**
Brant, tack eyes, cvd bill/nostril, minor crazing/flaking, tail chip/minor age splits, otherwise NM, RB 6/28/88 .... **8500**
Bufflehead drake, fine orig pnt, average wear w/minor flaking, hole has been filled in bk, rare, 22/44, RB 5/02/86 .... **6000**
Canada Goose, early, EX orig pnt, artist oval brand, prof repair to tail chip, structurally NM, RB 8/27/87 .... **5200**
Canada Goose, early, rpt w/average flaking/wear, age split in bottom, old neck repair, RB 7/08/86 .... **1300**
Canada Goose, EX pnt, artist brand, age split in bottom, rare, RB 7/09/85 .... **7000**
Canada Goose, full body, 1-pc head/neck, fine/worn orig pnt, artist brand, splits, rstr chips, 21, RB 2/01/85 .... **4500**
Canada Goose, orig pnt, minor wear, age check running along bottom, artist brand, EX condition, RWO 11/06/85, 142% **8500**
Canada Goose, pnt appears to be orig w/some early in-use touchup, oval brand, flaws on bk, 193/204, RWO 7/02/88, 37% **1300**
Canada Goose, prof pnt rstr, artist brand, crack in underside of bodyblock/hairline crack in bk, J/G 9/20/86 .... **600**
Canada Goose, rpt w/flaking/wear, lg age split on right side of body/end of bill is rough, 22, RB 5/02/86, 185% **950**
Canada Goose, rpt w/heavy flaking/wear, some chips to underside of bill/age splits in bottom of body, RB 7/08/86 .... **700**
Canada Goose, slat body, rpt, average wear, several age splits in head/neck area, 6, RB 7/07/87 .... **450**
Canada Goose, tack eyes, rpt, minor wear, artist brand, age split in bodyblock, otherwise EX, RB 3/06/87, 215% **3000**
Canada Goose, working rpt w/traces of orig, oval stamp, minor neck repair, otherwise sound, RWO 7/05/85 .... **950**
Canvasback, feather cvg on sides/bk, pnt stripped to natural wood, slight age splitting, 6, RB 7/07/87 .... **900**
Canvasback drake, average feather cvg on sides/bk, rpt, 21, RB 2/01/85 .... **500**
Canvasback drake, early, cvd crossed wing tips/fluted tail, pnt taken down to EX orig, signed, ls, EX, J/G 4/23/87, 55% **1600**
Canvasback drake, finely cvd head w/EX pnt pattern, cvd tail/feather-cvd crossed wing tips, oval brand, 24, J/G 9/20/86 .... **32500**
Canvasback drake, G orig pnt, average wear, head was broken off & reglued, otherwise structurally EX, RWO 2/13/87, 70% **3500**
Canvasback drake, relief cvd primaries/feathers on bk/sides, orig pnt, Mackey stamp, crack down bk, RWO 7/02/88, 40% **1400**
Canvasback drake, turned head, rasping, feather cvg on bk/sides/tail/wing tips, EX orig pnt, signed/1915, NM, RB 2/01/85 .... **12500**
Canvasback pr, detailed wing/primaries/tail cvg, detailed feather pnt, artist brand, ca 1915, rare, RWO 07/06/86 .... **50000**
Dowitcher, EX orig pnt, long bill, rare, 39, RB 7/08/86 .... **12000**
Dowitcher, EX orig pnt, minor flaking, branded PWW, ca 1890,1st Crowell Dowitcher offered to public, RB 7/09/85, 145% **26000**
Golden Plover, cvd primaries, glass eyes, orig pnt, minor wear, chip in end of wing tips, ls, rare, J/G 9/19/87, 75% **6000**
Golden Plover, cvd primary feathers, glass eyes, tiny pnt flakes missing from eye, otherwise M, oversize, J/G 4/24/86 .... **35750**
Golden Plover, early, NM condition, RB 7/08/86 .... **11500**
Golden Plover, extra rnd body, later mounted on base, NM orig pnt, rectangular brand, hairline on side, 105, J/G 4/23/87 .... **9250**
Golden Plover, NM orig pnt, transitional plumage, shrinkage exposes undercoat, sm dent on wing tip, J/G 4/23/87 .... **9000**
Golden Plover, running, glass eyes, EX orig pnt, some flaking, well preserved, PWW brand, rare, RB 7/09/85, 140% **17000**
Golden Plover, tack eyes, EX orig pnt, rare Winter plumage, minor wear, structurally NM, RB 8/21/86 .... **7000**

Golden Plover, 6 cvd primary feathers, glass eyes, EX feather pnt, ls, ca 1890, 12" long, extremely rare, RB 12/06/85 30000
Goldeneye drake, cvd tail, old working rpt, artist brand, some tight checks in bodyblock/eyes missing, J/G 4/23/87 600
Goldeneye drake, cvd tail feathers, fine orig pnt, weathered/worn, branded, RB 12/06/85 1900
Goldeneye drake, early, cvd tail feathers/crossed wing tips, fine orig pnt w/some flaking, branded JWW, 3, RB 3/06/87 4750
Goldeneye drake, hollow, cvd primaries/wing tips, EX old pnt, artist brand, made for Smiths of MA, rare, RB 8/21/86, 35% 1750
Goldeneye drake, hollow w/cvd crossed wing tips, rpt, average flaking/wear, oval brand, EX condition, 6, RB 7/07/87, 50% 1000

Crowell, A. Elmer
Goldeneye drake, preening, cvd wings w/1 wing tip raised, fine pnt, minor minor crazing/sm chip, ca 1915, RWO 7/04/87, $45,000.00.

Goldeneye drake, preening, EX feather pnt, rectangular brand, NM condition, ca 1930, RB 7/07/87, 75% 6000
Goldeneye drake, rectangular stamp, NM condition, RWO 11/06/85, 65% 2000
Goldeneye drake, sleeper, finely detailed tail cvg, M pnt w/G patina, extremely rare, 48/155, J/G 4/24/86 9900
Goldeneye drake, slightly turned head, cvd wing tips/tail/primary feathers, rpt w/average flaking/wear, 22, RB 5/02/86 1700
Goldeneye hen, cvd tail feathers, rasping to bk of head, EX orig pnt, artist brand, ls, RB 2/01/85 1800
Goldeneye hen, detailed cvd crossed wings/tail feathers, EX outstanding pnt, rectangular brand, NM, J/G 9/20/86 6500
Goldeneye hen, head slightly tucked, EX orig pnt, minor wear, artist brand, RB 7/09/85 3000
Goldeneye hen, several tiny pnt flakes missing, otherwise M, J/G 4/23/87 3300
Goldeneye hen, slightly turned head, old pnt, heavy wear, artist brand, rare, RB 8/21/86 450
Goldeneye hen, slightly turned head, rectangular brand on bottom, scratch on 1 side, otherwise M, J/G 4/24/86 1870
Goose, flying, NM orig pnt, prof rpl wing filler, very rare, one third-size, rare, J/G 9/19/87 2950
Greenwinged Teal drake, raised cvd wing tips/tail feathers/crest, trn head, EX feather pnt, signed, RB 7/07/87, 45% 9000
Greenwinged Teal drake, slightly turned head, fluted tail, detailed M pnt, artist brand, J/G 9/20/86, 72% 8000
Greenwinged Teal drake, slightly turned head, wing/tail cvg, stamped, M condition, very rare, RWO 11/06/85 13500
Greenwinged Teal hen, cvd crossed wings, EX orig pnt, minor wear, artist brand, ca 1915, 8/48/151, RWO 7/06/86, 130% 45000
Hooded Merganser drake, raised cvd wing tips/finely cvd tail feathers, M pnt w/G patina, 1 of a kind, J/G 4/24/86 24750
Mallard drake, cork body, EX orig pnt, minor flaking, artist brand, structurally EX, branded F Winthrop, RWO 7/04/87 7250
Mallard drake, cvd crossed wings/tail feathers, finely blended pnt w/several sm flakes missing, M/unused, J/G 4/24/86 9625
Mallard drake, EX orig pnt, minor wear, nail in bk of head to strengthen crack in neck/age check on bottom, RWO 11/06/85 4300
Mallard drake, slightly turned head, cvd tail feathers, NM orig pnt, artist stamp, EX condition, half-size, J/G 9/19/87 1600
Mallard drake, slightly turned head, cvd tail feathers/crossed wing tips, NM pnt, artist stamp, clean, rare, RB 8/21/86 9500
Mallard drake, slightly turned head, NM orig pnt, artist stamp, prof reglued crack, three quarter-size, J/G 9/19/87 1500
Mallard drake, slightly turned head, orig pnt, minor flaking on breast, artist stamp, EX condition, RWO 11/06/85 4250
Mallard drake, slightly turned head, raised cvd wing tips/tail feathers, EX condition, ca 1928, oversize, RB 12/06/85 5500
Mallard drake, slightly turned head, rpt w/average wear, artist brand, structurally sound, RB 8/27/87 775
Mallard drake, tail cvg, tack eyes, fine orig dry pnt, minor wear, artist brand, RWO 07/06/86 3500
Mallard drake, turned head, feather pnt, minor flaking/wear, 1920's, only known working half-size decoy, RB 3/06/87 4500
Mallard drake, turned head, M orig pnt, artist stamp, hairline crack in lower side, 58, J/G 9/20/86, 123% 8000
Mallard hen, cork body, EX orig pnt, minor wear, artist brand, structurally EX, RWO 2/13/87, 58% 3500
Mallard hen, cork body, fine orig pnt, artist brand, ca 1915, rare, 8/48/101, RWO 7/06/86, 125% 7500
Mallard hen, cork body, NM orig pnt, few dings/rubs, oval brand, structurally NM, 101, RWO 11/11/87, 40% 1250
Mallard hen, early, dry orig pnt w/EX feathering, average flaking/wear, slight age split in bottom, 22, RB 5/02/86, 150% 3750
Mallard hen, early, long narrow body style, EX orig pnt, structurally EX, RWO 2/13/87 4600

Mallard hen, EX orig pnt, average wear, oval brand, tail chip/thin neck crack, otherwise EX, rare, RWO 7/02/88, 72% 2550
Mallard hen, full body, EX orig pnt, minor wear, age check prof rstr by Kenneth DeLong, oval brand, RB 3/06/87 3000
Mallard hen, full body, EX orig pnt, minor wear, oval brand, age check rstr by Kenneth DeLong, RB 3/06/87, 145% 4300
Mallard hen, slight wing cvg on bk, cork body, orig pnt, minor wear, artist brand, structurally EX, 101, J/G 4/23/87 3000
Mallard hen, slightly turned head, EX orig pnt, minor wear, thin age check in bottom, otherwise EX, RWO 11/06/85 3750
Mallard pr, EX orig pnt, artist brand, drake has neck repair; hen has fracture in neck, otherwise sound, RWO 11/11/87 5000
Mallard pr, raised cvd primaries, EX orig pnt, minor wear, thin tight cracks in neck, RWO 2/13/87 11500
Mallard pr, turned heads w/fluted tails, cvd crossed wing tips, EX orig pnt, minor crazing, J/G 4/24/86 14850
Merganser drake, early, worn orig pnt, check in underside of bodyblock, hairline crack in head/bk, J/G 9/19/87, 28% 275

Crowell, A. Elmer
Merganser drake, slightly lifted head, fan cvd tail, NM orig pnt, structurally EX, oversize, rare, 48/154, J/G 4/24/86, $15,400.00.

Merganser hen, extremely stylized, detailed bill cvg/raised cvd wings, EX orig pnt w/varnish, J/G 9/20/86 22500
Merganser hen, head turned to right, EX feather pnt reminiscent of Lincoln's, half of bill is rpl, NM, RB 7/07/87, 60% 6000
Merganser hen, slightly turned head, NM orig feather pnt, prof rstr to end of bill, rare, J/G 4/24/86 9350
Merganser pr, early, swimming, rasping to bk of head, G orig pnt, artist brand, chip at end of drake's tail, RB 8/21/86 9500
Monomoy Brant, EX orig pnt, minor wear & flaking, slight age split on bottom, rare, 22/44, RB 5/02/86 5000
Monomoy Brant, EX orig pnt w/touchup on white area of tail, rstr age split runs full length of bk, J/G 9/19/87 850
Pintail drake, artist brand, M condition, slightly smaller than average size, J/G 4/23/87 5000
Pintail drake, cvd crossed wings/tail cvg, Crowell's finest pnt blending, oval brand, M, 217, RWO 2/12/88, 57% 28500
Pintail drake, early, rpt w/average wear, some age splitting, RB 7/07/87 400
Pintail drake, early, slightly turned head, cvd crossed wing tips/tail feathers, EX rpt, rpl bill/age split, RB 8/21/86 750
Pintail drake, fine orig pnt, minor flaking/wear, artist brand, break in neck has been reglued, 22/44, RB 5/02/86, 145% 5750
Pintail drake, preening, crossed wings, turned head, EX & orig, oval brand, ca 1915, 8/48/87, RWO 7/05/86, 200% 290000
Pintail drake, rpt w/average wear, oval brand, some slight age splitting, RB 7/07/87 800
Pintail drake, tail/crossed wing cvg, rpt in Crowell style, oval brand, old neck rpr, RWO 7/02/88 700
Pintail drake, working overpnt taken down to G orig, average wear, crack in neck, otherwise EX, oversize, RWO 07/06/86 3250
Pintail hen, early, old orig pnt, average flaking/wear, artist brand, age split in neck, ls, rare, RB 12/06/85 1700
Pintail hen, orig pnt worn to bare wood over head/body, artist brand, thin tight check in bottom, RWO 7/04/87, 65% 1000
Pintail hen, worn orig pnt w/some working touchup, artist brand, old repair to crack in neck, J/G 9/20/86, 65% 800
Pintail pr, cork body, orig pnt, minor wear, artist/F Winthrop brands, structurally EX, rare, RWO 2/13/87 15000
Pintail pr, cvd tail feathers/crossed wing tips, prof rpt by Lloyd Johnson, structurally EX, rare, RB 8/21/86, 75% 2250
Redbreasted Merganser, flying, full body, pnt worn to bare wood on head/bk, 1 glass eye missing, rare, RWO 07/06/86 20000
Redbreasted Merganser drake, early, slightly turned head, NM stippled/feather pnt, NM condition, rare, RB 7/07/87 11500
Redbreasted Merganser drake, EX orig pnt, minor wear, oval brand, structurally EX, rare, RWO 7/02/88 8000
Redbreasted Merganser hen, EX orig pnt, oval artist brand, narrow crack on underside, otherwise EX, RWO 7/04/87, 33% 1500
Redbreasted Merganser hen, pre-stamp era, orig pnt, few narrow checks/chips, pnt/eye/bill has rstr, RWO 7/04/87, 50% 700
Redhead drake, lifted/turned head, feather cvd crossed wing tips/tail, well-blended pnt, oval brand, M, 24, J/G 9/20/86 50000
Redhead drake, slightly turned head, cvd tail feathers, fine orig pnt, minor flaking, rare, 22, RB 5/02/86 12000
Redhead drake, slightly turned head, full body, fine orig pnt, average wear, artist brand, ls, rare, RB 3/06/87 6000
Redhead drake, some working overpnt taken off & touched up, some orig remains, G condition, lg, RWO 7/02/88, 70% 1400
Redhead drake, tail cvg, EX orig pnt, Crowell's best gunning decoy, ca 1910, 193, RWO 7/02/88 13000
Redhead hen, early, slightly turned head, crossed wing tips/tail cvg, NM orig pnt, bill rstr/split, lg, J/G 9/20/86, 37% 1850
Redhead hen, EX orig pnt, thin coat of shellac has been taken off, structurally EX, RWO 7/05/85 3000

Redhead hen, pre-stamp era, detailed tail feather cvg, hairline crack in neck, otherwise outstanding, J/G 4/24/86 1870
Redhead pr, early, full bodies, slightly turned heads, cvd tail/primary feathers, G orig pnt, 22/44, RB 5/02/86 19000

Crowell, A. Elmer
Sandpiper, cvd split tail, tack eyes, well-turned bill, EX
orig pnt, sm chip on underside of tail, RB 8/21/86, $7,500.00.

Sandpiper, full body, NM detailed orig pnt, sm chip missing from tail, ls, rare, 105, J/G 9/19/87 7250
Sandpiper, plump body, NM orig pnt, bill is an old replacement, ls, rare, 105, J/G 4/23/87 4750
Surf Scoter, oval brand, NM condition, branded CM, extremely rare, RB 7/07/87 10500
Whitewinged Scoter, early, orig pnt, average wear, structurally EX, rare, 193, RWO 7/02/88, 45% 450
Whitewinged Scoter, early pre-stamp era, old working overpnt prof taken down to orig, rare, RWO 07/06/86 2100
Whitewinged Scoter, tack eyes, EX orig pnt, average wear, rasped breast/bk of head, neck split/bill chewed, RB 12/06/85 2750
Widgeon, mostly stripped to natural wood showing minor age splitting, ls, 6, RB 8/21/86 375
Widgeon drake, cork body, EX orig pnt, minor flaking, artist brand, EX condition, bears F Winthrop brand, RWO 7/04/87 3750
Widgeon drake, cork body, bears Crowell's oval brand/Winthrop brand, EX & orig condition, RWO 7/02/88 3300
Widgeon drake, crossed wing tips/tail feathers/bk detail, lifted head, rasping, EX pnt, age split/ls, RB 7/07/87, 66% 9000
Widgeon drake, cvd crossed wings/tail feathers, finely detailed M pnt, G patina, identified on bottom, rare, J/G 4/24/86 13200
Widgeon drake, cvd raised wing tips/tail feathers, rpt, average wear, well preserved, RB 3/06/87 1200
Widgeon drake, prof pnt rstr, rectangular brand, rare, RWO 11/06/85, 130% 1050
Widgeon drake, slightly turned head, cvd crossed wing tips/tail feathers, artist stamp/inscription, NM, 1931, RB 8/21/86 14000
Widgeon drake, slightly turned head, cvd wing outline, cork w/pine bottom, orig pnt, artist brand, 101, J/G/4/23/87, 58% 2900
Widgeon hen, cork body, EX orig pnt, artist brand, 2 minor dings, otherwise EX, bears F Winthrop brand, RWO 7/04/87, 75% 5000
Widgeon pr, slightly turned heads, tail feather cvg, EX orig pnt, feather detail, signed, NM, 22/44/46, RB 5/02/86, 133% 40000
Willet, cvd primaries, glass eyes, tiny pnt flakes missing, NM condition, ca 1890, oversize, 12", J/G 4/24/86 17600
Willet, glass eyes, fine orig pnt, minor flaking, branded PWW, chip missing from bill, rare, RB 12/06/85 12000
Willet, glass eyes, fine orig pnt, minor wear, branded PWW, well preserved, rare, RB 12/06/85, 125% 19000
Willet, glass eyes, fine orig pnt, sm areas of flaking, bill is a prof replacement, ca 1890, extremely rare, RB 7/09/85 16000
Willet, head cvd outward, glass eyes, NM pnt, minor flaking on tail, branded PWW, ca 1890, extremely rare, RB 7/09/85 18000
Wood Duck drake, cvd crossed wings, cvd crest, feather cvg on bk, fluted tail, M orig pnt, oval brand, J/G 9/19/87 27000
Wood Duck drake, slightly turned head, cvd crossed wings/tail feather cvg, M pnt, EX patina, extremely rare, J/G 4/24/86 24750
Wood Duck drake, standing, cvd wing tips/tail, EX condition, done when Crowell was 15 yrs of age, RWO 7/05/85 8000
Yellowlegs, cvd split tail, tack eyes, fine orig pnt, ls, bill is a prof replacement, RB 8/21/86, 70% 5000
Yellowlegs, cvd split tail, tack eyes, NM pnt, ls, sm nick at end of wing tips, RB 8/21/86, 45% 3500
Yellowlegs, early, slightly turned head, cvd primary feathers, orig pnt, average wear, ms, rare, RB 7/08/86 5500
Yellowlegs, NM condition, an exceptional gunning shorebird, rare, RWO 7/06/86 7500

Yellowlegs, running, cvd split tail, tack eyes, fine pnt pattern, minor wear, bill replaced by DeLong, RB 8/21/86, 62% **5000**
Yellowlegs, running, fine orig pnt, minor flaking, bk has overall crazing, rare, 22, RB 5/02/86 .... **8000**
Yellowlegs, running, hit once by shot, otherwise M, RB 7/08/86 .... **9000**
Yellowlegs, running, NM orig pnt, ls, rare, 13" long, J/G 4/23/87 .... **18500**
Yellowlegs, running, NM pnt, 39, RB 7/08/86 .... **7000**
Yellowlegs, slightly turned head, cvd primary feathers/bill, EX orig pnt, minor flaking, 22/44/46, RB 5/02/86, 233% **35000**
Yellowlegs, tack eyes, EX orig pnt, minor wear, 22/44, RB 5/02/86, 150% **12000**
Yellowlegs, tack eyes, extra thick bold pnt, M/unused, J/G 4/24/86 .... **7700**
Yellowlegs silhouette, hairline in neck, otherwise M, rare, J/G 4/24/86 .... **2420**

Crowell, A. Elmer; att (East Harwich, MA)
Black Duck, chip-cvd body, old pnt, average wear, slight age split in bottom, RB 7/08/86 .... **300**
Black Duck, old pnt, average wear, artist brand, structurally sound, branded Hinckley, RB 7/08/86 .... **800**

Crowley, Milton (South Addison, ME)
Eider drake, fine orig pnt, average wear, age split in neck, 39, RB 7/08/86 .... **300**
Eider pr, inlet heads, G orig pnt, average wear, ms, chip at ends of both tails, RB 2/01/85 .... **400**

Crumb, Joe (Oyster Bay, VA)
Canada Goose, hollow, glass eyes, working rpt w/nice feathering, several cracks/chips in neck, rare, 49, J/G 4/24/86 .... **495**

Crumb, William (Virginia)
Yellowlegs, cvd wings/eyes, pnt shows minor wear, bill is an old replacement, RB 12/06/85 .... **150**

Culver, Reg
Black Duck, hollow, fine orig pnt, average wear, branded RI Culver, well preserved, RB 6/28/88 .... **400**
Black Duck, hollow, rpt, minor wear, shallow chip on underside of bill, otherwise well preserved, RB 3/06/87 .... **275**
Bluebill drake, hollow, EX orig pnt, minor wear, artist brand, well preserved, RB 12/06/85 .... **1300**
Bluebill drake, hollow, G orig pnt w/some areas of overpnt, minor wear, artist brand, RB 7/07/87 .... **900**
Broadbill, hollow, EX comb/feather pnt on bk, minor wear & overpnt on bill, artist brand, RB 3/06/87, 75% **800**

Cummings, Frank (Detroit, MI)
Bluebill pr, orig pnt, minor wear, EX condition, RB 8/25/88 .... **150**
Bufflehead drake, orig pnt, minor wear, slight age check in bill, RB 8/25/88 .... **110**
Widgeon drake, EX feather cvg, orig pnt, minor wear, RB 8/25/88 .... **100**

Cunningham, George (Tiskiliwa, IL)
Mallard drake, fine working rpt by Robert Weeks, hairline crack in bill/neck, 7, J/G 4/24/86 .... **247**

Currier, Jim (Havre de Grace, MD)
Black Duck, orig pnt w/some areas worn to bare wood, crack in neck, otherwise sound, ca 1955, RWO 11/06/85 .... **155**
Bluebill drake, turned head, old working rpt, bill rstr/crack in bottom, made for Holzworth's gunning rig, RWO 11/11/87 .... **180**

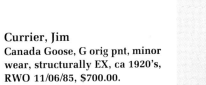

Currier, Jim
Canada Goose, G orig pnt, minor wear, structurally EX, ca 1920's, RWO 11/06/85, $700.00.

Canvasback drake, EX orig pnt, RB 2/01/85 .... **175**
Canvasback drake, old pnt, possibly orig, thin check through head, ca 1920, RWO 7/04/87 .... **275**
Canvasback drake, old rpt, average wear, age split in bk/neck, RB 7/07/87 .... **120**
Canvasback drake, old working rpt, average wear, structurally EX, ca 1940, RWO 2/12/88 .... **130**
Canvasback drake, some working rpt on body, some thin tight checks on body, otherwise structurally sound, RWO 7/04/87 .... **150**

Canvasback pr, G orig pnt, drake is ls, otherwise structurally EX, RWO 11/06/85 400
Canvasback pr, high-head, EX orig pnt, G patina, drake has neck crack/ms, otherwise EX, rare, oversize, RWO 7/02/88 2150
Canvasback pr, old working rpt, average wear, hen has hairline cracks in bk, otherwise sound, ca 1940's, RWO 2/12/88 225
Greenwinged Teal drake, EX orig pnt, thin crack along 1 side, otherwise structurally EX, ca 1930, RWO 11/06/85 325
Mallard drake, EX orig pnt, RB 2/01/85 225
Mallard pr, fine pnt, NM condition, ca 1930, RWO 11/06/85 425

Daebler, Cleve (Cape May Courthouse, NJ)
Black Duck, hollow, EX orig pnt, age split in neck, 21, RB 2/01/85 100

Daisy, Delbert (Chincoteague, VA)
Brant, cork body, orig pnt, average wear, thin cracks in body, otherwise VG condition, RWO 7/02/88 125
Brant, orig pnt, average wear w/crazing around breast/tail, artist brand, structurally sound, RWO 7/06/86 275
Curlew, sm chip on underside of bill, otherwise EX & orig condition, ca 1960's, RWO 2/12/88 130
Hooded Merganser pr, EX orig pnt, minor wear, hen has crack running from breast to top of bk, RWO 11/11/87 275
Merganser hen, branded Cigar, EX condition, RB 3/11/88 300

Dalrymple, Dale (Allenwood, NJ)
Bluewinged Teal drake, hollow, orig pnt, average wear, structurally sound, RWO 7/06/86 155

Daniels, W.E.
Bluebill drake, pnt heavily worn to reveal traces of orig, lg age split on right side of body, 21, RB 2/01/85 250

Davids, R.W. (Stratford, CT)
Black Duck, stick-up, preening, orig wooden legs, structurally sound, ca 1850, rare, RWO 7/02/88 3400

Davis, Capt. Benjamin (Monhegan Island, ME)
Old Squaw drake, early, worn orig pnt w/crazing, crack running through neck/narrow check, ca 1860's, RWO 11/11/87 445
Scoter, American; thin crack in neck, otherwise structurally EX, ca 1860's, RWO 11/11/87 200

Davis, Fairman (Alexandria Bay, NY)
Bluebill hen, G orig pnt, average wear, structurally sound, ca 1930's, RWO 11/11/87 195
Bluebill hen, old working rpt, average wear, sm chip on underside of bill, otherwise structurally sound, RWO 7/04/87 120
Bluebill hen, orig pnt, minor wear/flaking, some damage to neck area, otherwise sound, RWO 7/05/85 525
Bluebill pr, old working rpt w/orig on area around speculums of hen, prof rstr to both bills, rare, J/G 4/23/87 275
Canvasback drake, orig pnt, minor wear, pnt strengthened in black areas, rare, J/G 9/19/87 450
Goldeneye hen, VG orig condition w/some in-use wear, 1 of a dozen made in 1928, RWO 7/05/85 550

Davis, H.A. (Waquoit, MA)
Redbreasted Merganser drake, NM condition, RB 8/25/88 110

Davis, Joe (Davisville, MA)
Merganser drake, orig pnt, heavy flaking/wear, structurally sound, RWO 11/06/85 100

Davis, Muckie (Falmouth, MA)
Merganser hen, EX orig pnt, minor wear, RB 7/07/87 250
Merganser hen, thin cvd breast, EX orig pnt, minor flaking, RB 7/07/87 525

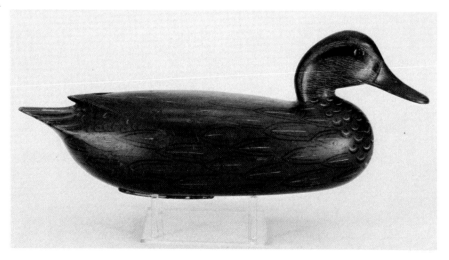

Dawson, John (Delaware River)
Pintail hen, hollow w/raised cvd wing tips, fine orig pnt, average wear, well preserved, extremely rare, 3, RB 7/07/87, $16,500.00.

Dawson, Walter (Putnam, IL)
Canvasback drake, orig pnt, minor wear, structurally EX, rare, J/G 4/23/87 1025
Mallard drake, old working rpt, several reglued cracks in neck area, J/G 4/23/87 125
Mallard drake, orig pnt, minor wear, varnished, hairline crack in neck, bears Mackey stamp, J/G 4/23/87 350

Mallard hen, orig pnt, average wear, prof rstr neck crack/sm rough area side of bill, oversize, ca 1940, J/G 9/20/86 450
Mallard pr, deep body, orig pnt, moderate flaking/wear, no structural flaws, rare, J/G 4/24/86 550
Mallard pr, deep-bottom style, EX orig pnt, formed wooden keel w/orig weights, branded CF Thompson, J/G 9/19/87 900
Mallard pr, hollow, fine orig pnt shows little wear, oversize, RB 8/21/86 1750
Pintail drake, old working rpt w/some orig showing, no structural flaws, rare, J/G 4/24/86 192

Decker, Maurice (Islesboro, ME)
Goldeneye hen pr, partial rpt primarily to white areas, structurally sound, RWO 7/06/86 140

Decker, Maurice; att (Islesboro, ME)
Black Duck, cvd w/upswung tail/cvd speculum, old orig pnt, average wear, chip in tail/age split in bk, 22/44, RB 5/02/86 750

DeCoe (Michigan)
Canvasback drake, old rpt, average flaking/wear, stamped IE Bell on bottom, ls, RB 8/25/88 70

Deiss, Capt. Eban (Oceanview, DE)
Yellowlegs, early, root-head, worn old pnt, part of bill is missing, hs, RWO 7/02/88 90

DeKam, John
Mallard pr, hollow, EX orig pnt, minor wear, RB 12/06/85 160

DeLine, George
Redbreasted Merganser pr, hollow, EX condition, RB 3/11/88 225

DeMott, Daniel; att
Black Duck, EX orig pnt, minor flaking/wear, ca 1900, rare, 2, RB 12/06/85 1700
Blackbellied Plover, old pnt shows average wear, bill is a replacement, ms, 39, RB 7/08/86 400

Denny, Sam (Clayton, NY)
Black Duck, rpt w/minor wear, well preserved, RB 3/06/87 250
Bluebill drake, old working rpt flaking away to reveal traces of orig, structurally sound, RWO 11/06/85 50
Bluebill hen, EX orig pnt, minor wear, well preserved, 39, RB 7/08/86 425
Bluebill hen, EX orig pnt shows minor wear, well preserved, 39, RB 7/08/86 425
Bluebill hen, G orig pnt, minor wear, hairline crack on 1 side, ls, J/G 4/24/86 330
Bluebill hen, old pnt, average wear, RB 7/08/86 110
Bluebill hen, orig pnt w/some working touchup, few dings, ls, otherwise structurally EX, ca 1930, RWO 7/04/87 210
Bluebill hen, rpt w/minor wear, well preserved, RB 7/08/86 50
Canvasback drake, EX orig pnt, minor wear, well preserved, RB 7/07/87 350
Goldeneye hen, old rpt, average wear, RB 12/06/85 70
Goldeneye hen, old working rpt, ls, J/G 4/23/87 125
Redhead drake, NM orig pnt, structurally EX, J/G 9/20/86 1050
Redhead drake, rpt w/average wear, end of tail has been chewed, RB 3/06/87 150

Denny, Sam; att (Clayton, NY)
Black Duck, NM orig pnt, ls, J/G 4/23/87 400
Black Duck, rpt, average flaking/wear, bill is a replacement, chip at top of tail, RB 12/06/85 60
Bluebill drake, old working rpt, glue applied to base of head, otherwise structurally sound, RWO 7/04/87 50
Goldeneye hen, old pnt, average wear, well preserved, RB 7/08/86 70

Destri, Fred (Spring Valley, IL)
Mallard pr, artist stamp, M condition, J/G 4/24/86 385

Dettman, Warren (Milwaukee, WI)
Mallard drake, relief cvg around wings/shoulders, EX orig pnt, eclipse plumage, no flaws, rare, RWO 7/02/88 2450
Pintail drake, cvd crossed wing tips/cvd primaries, orig pnt, minor wear, tail chip, J/G 4/23/87, 170% 2050

Dettman, Warren
Widgeon drake, raised cvd wings, outstanding orig pnt, M condition, ca 1935, rare, RWO 7/02/88, $2,250.00.

Dexter, Gardner (Rhode Island)
Yellowlegs, head tucked into the content position, cvd wings, orig pnt, average wear, minor roughage to tail, RB 5/23/86 1200
Dilley, John (Quogue, LI, NY)
Blackbellied Plover, EX feather pnt detail, minor flaking on front of head, ms, otherwise EX, early, RB 3/11/88 3750
Blackbellied Plover, exceptional feather pnt & form, EX dry patina, NM condition, rare, 40, RB 7/08/86 9000
Blackbellied Plover, NM extra-fine pnt, identified, from the George Thompson collection, J/G 3/24/86, 75% 11550
Blackbellied Plover, orig pnt traces remain on body, heavy wear, bill is a replacement, hs, 22, RB 5/02/86 1000
Blackbellied Plover, raised wing cvg, orig pnt, average wear w/few pnt rubs, structurally sound, RWO 7/06/86 3500
Blackbellied Plover, tack eyes, feather pnt bold but worn, minor overpnt, structurally EX, ca 1890, RWO 7/05/85 1500
Curlew, full body w/EX feather pnt, identified, prof rpl bill, otherwise NM, ms, extremely rare, RB 3/06/87, 66% 8000
Dowitcher, EX orig pnt, minor wear, rare, RB 7/09/85, 50% 2500
Dowitcher, very minor pnt flaking, late Winter plumage, ca 1880-1890, rare, RWO 11/06/85 17500
Golden Plover, early, deeply incised wing cvg, EX pnt pattern & form, EX orig pnt, minor wear, rare, 40, RB 7/08/86, 65% 6500
Golden Plover, early, deeply incised wing cvg, fine orig pnt, EX form, EX orig pnt, minor wear, RB 8/21/86, 42% 3000
Golden Plover, early, orig pnt, average wear w/much of the fine detail pnt still visible, ms, RWO 7/02/88 3400
Golden Plover, EX orig pnt, minor wear, EX dry patina, rare, 40, RB 7/08/86 7000
Golden Plover, incised wings, unusual Winter plumage, NM condition, minor prof rstr, rare, 39, RB 7/08/86, 50% 5000
Lesser Yellowlegs, orig black pnt on underside, minor flaking, otherwise NM, RB 7/07/87 8500
Plover, early, G orig pnt, average wear, bill is a replacement, bottom shaved off, 39, RB 7/08/86 800
Plover, fine cvd feather detail/cvd split tail, fine orig pnt, minor wear, well preserved, rare, RB 7/07/87 2500
Ruddy Turnstone, early, fine feather pnt, minor flaking/wear, rare, RB 7/09/85, 40% 3250
Sandpiper, early, pnt worn to reveal traces of orig, structurally sound, retains orig bill, RWO 7/04/87 300

Dilley, John
Shortbilled Dowitcher, raised cvd wings, fine feather pnt w/no wear, M condition, ca 1880-1890, RWO 7/05/85, $16,500.00.

Yellowlegs, G orig pnt, minor flaking/wear, bill is a replacement, RB 2/01/85 1300
Yellowlegs, orig pnt, average wear, prof rstr to neck, otherwise sound, RWO 7/05/85 1800
Dingman, Ed; att (Alexandria Bay, NY)
Goldeneye drake, EX orig pnt, few rubs/scrapes, 26, J/G 9/20/86 225
Disbrow, Charles (Stratford, CT)
Black Duck, cork body, fine old pnt, old break around head, age split in tail, 21, RB 2/01/85 110

Black Duck, cork body, G orig pnt, chips of cork missing out of tail, RWO 2/13/87 .... **50**
Black Duck, cork body, structurally EX, 22, RB 5/02/86 .... **175**
Black Duck, full body w/head tucked, hollow, old pnt, average wear, structurally sound, 3, RB 3/06/87, 80% **650**
Black Duck, hollow, old pnt possibly orig, average wear, RB 12/06/85 .... **150**
Black Duck, hollow, orig pnt, average wear, structurally sound, 95, RWO 7/04/87 .... **300**
Black Duck, hollow, pnt shows heavy flaking/wear, signed, 22/44, RB 5/02/86 .... **400**
Black Duck, low-head style, hollow, fine orig pnt, minor wear, RB 5/02/86 .... **700**

Disbrow, Charles
Black Duck, slightly turned head, hollow, M condition,
21, RB 2/01/85, $3,100.00.

Black Duck, slightly turned head, hollow, orig pnt, average flaking/wear, prof cleaned by K DeLong, 22, RB 5/02/86 .... **600**
Discher, Roy (Milwaukee, WI)
Black Duck, balsa body, pine head/inset tail, EX orig elaborate scratch feather pnt, few sm dents, 53/68, J/G 9/20/86 .... **275**
Widgeon drake, hollow, cvd crossed wing tips, NM intrictate scratch feather pnt, EX condition, 68/53, J/G 9/20/86, 78% **950**
Dixon, Roy
Bluebill hen, EX orig pnt, RB 12/06/85 .... **180**
Dize, Ben (Crisfield, MD)
Black Duck, few pnt rubs, signed/dated 1971, NM condition, RWO 7/06/86 .... **90**
Dobbins, Frank (Jonesport, ME)
Bufflehead drake, unused condition, RWO 7/02/88 .... **45**
Bufflehead pr, EX condition, RB 7/09/85 .... **200**
Goldeneye drake, signed, EX condition, RB 6/28/88 .... **100**
Hooded Merganser drake, signed, bill has been broken off & reglued, otherwise EX condition, RB 6/28/88 .... **100**
Redbreasted Merganser drake, EX condition, RB 7/09/85 .... **75**
Redbreasted Merganser drake, signed, EX condition, RB 6/28/88 .... **150**
Dobbins, Frank; att (Jonesport, ME)
Old Squaw drake, 2-pc bill construction, fine orig pnt, minor wear, 39, RB 7/08/86 .... **100**
Dobroski, Paul (Shrewsbury, NJ)
Black Duck, head cvd in content position, cork body, no pnt to body, 39, RB 7/08/86 .... **100**
Bluebill drake, cork body, fine orig pnt, minor wear, well preserved, from his personal rig, 39, RB 7/08/86 .... **150**
Brant, cork body, M condition, J/G 9/19/87 .... **200**
Dolbeck, Keith (Ticonderoga, NY)
Ruddy Duck hen, NM orig pnt, structurally EX, J/G 4/23/87 .... **70**
Dominick, Salvadore (Paulsboro, NJ)
Black Duck, NM flock pnt on body/regular on head, structurally EX, 'DS' molded in weight, ca 1920, J/G 4/24/86 ..... **495**
Donnelly, J.
Bufflehead drake, EX feather detail, signed, NM condition, RB 6/28/88 .... **25**
Doren, Leonard (Pekin, IL)
Mallard drake, outstanding orig pnt, EX structural condition, ca 1930, exceptional, RWO 7/05/85 .... **700**
Mallard pr, hollow, working rpt, average wear, drake has crack in bill, RWO 2/12/88 .... **275**
Owl, EX & orig w/a coat of varnish, structurally EX, ca 1940, 193, RWO 7/02/88 .... **850**
Doud, Ed
Greenwinged Teal pr, fine orig pnt, average wear, slight chipping to filler around drake's neck, 36, RB 2/01/85 .... **350**
Mallard drake, old pnt, appears to be orig w/flaking/wear, RB 2/01/85 .... **80**
Doughty, Chester
Goldeneye drake, orig pnt, average wear, several slight age splits, 22, RB 5/02/86 .... **175**
Downs, John Henry (Townsend, VA)
Black Duck, stylish form, pnt shows considerable wear, wood filler added to base of neck, ca 1870's, RWO 7/05/85 .... **1200**

Dreschel, Alfred
    Canvasback drake, fine orig pnt, minor wear, RB 2/01/85 275

Drescher, Richard (Cambridge, MD)
    Canada Goose, head in calling position, hollow, mounted on wooden base, M condition, RWO 11/11/87 350
    Canada Goose, preening, signed, M condition, RWO 11/06/85 175
    Greenwinged Teal drake, M condition, dated 1981, RWO 11/06/85 70
    Greenwinged Teal drake, swimming, hollow, M condition, RWO 7/02/88 175
    Widgeon drake, EX relief feather cvg, M condition, dated 1987, RWO 11/06/85 110

Dresser Family (Old Lyme, CT)
    Yellowlegs, cvd raised wings/wing tips, orig pnt w/some overpnt, average wear, bill is a replacement, RB 8/25/88 140

Driscoll, Gary
    Redbreasted Merganser pr, hollow w/cvd crossed wing tips, EX pnt, RB 7/08/86 350

Drury, P.O. (New Boston, IL)
    . Mallard drake, early, hollow 3-pc body, orig pnt, average wear, artist stamp, crack/pcs missing, 89, J/G 4/24/86 192

Drury, P.O.
Mallard drake, hollow w/fine combing on bk, NM orig pnt, artist stamp, 2 hairline cracks in neck, rare, J/G 4/23/87, $2,500.00.

DuCharme, Duncan
    Canvasback drake, high-head style, folky, old pnt, average wear, age split in neck, RB 8/21/86 350

Dudley, Lee (Knott's Island, NC)
    Canvasback drake, rpt/antiqued by Mark McNair, age split in neck, rare, RB 8/21/86, 75% 2250
    Mallard drake, pnt worn away, rpr head, tight checks on bill/side, pc of metal tail remains, rare, 3, RWO 11/11/87, 55% 7000
    Redhead drake, rpt shows average wear, artist signed, bill is old replacement, ls, 22/44, RB 5/02/86 5000
    Widgeon drake, pnt worn away, thin checks on bk/around breast, prof bill repair, ms, rare, 3, RWO 11/11/87, 60% 6000

Dudley, Lem and Lee (Knott's Island, NC)
    Bluebill drake, EX working rpt, artist brand, prof rstr bill/neck crack/sm chip on head, 33/124, J/G 9/19/87, 70% 4200
    Bluebill hen, worn old pnt, artist brand, several age lines, sm rough area on tail/tin neck rpr, 33/124, J/G 9/19/87 4500
    Canvasback drake, old pnt, heavy flaking/wear, prof rstr to bill, ca 1900, RWO 7/04/87 8000

Dudley, Lem and Lee
Canvasback drake, old pnt flaked away though orig patterns remain bold, crack running through neck, ca 1900, RWO 11/06/85, $25,000.00.

Canvasback drake, old working rpt, heavy wear, crack in neck, prof rstr to bill, RWO 7/04/87, 65% 2000
Canvasback drake, old working rpt flaked away to reveal orig, artist brand, prof rstr neck check, ca 1900, RWO 7/06/86 20000
Pintail drake, cypress, worn old pnt, tight check in neck, ls, rare, 3/33/125, J/G 9/19/87 3200
Pintail drake, orig pnt worn to natural wood, some age splitting/roughness to edge of tail/bill, rare, RB 2/01/85, 23% 700
Redhead drake, traces of orig pnt, most of bill is replacement, old rstr to top of head, rare, 3, RB 3/06/87, 66% 4000

Dudley, Lem and Lee; att (Knott's Island, NC)
Widgeon drake, working rpt, average wear, artist initials, minor damage around tail, RWO 7/04/87 500

Dudley, Linwood (Knott's Island, NC)
Redhead drake, old working rpt, metal straps holding head together, otherwise sound, ca 1935, very rare, RWO 11/06/85 200

Duet, William (Louisiana)
Bluewinged Teal hen, fine orig pnt, average wear, ms, RB 7/08/86 125
Mallard drake, G orig pnt, average wear, RB 7/08/86 225
Mallard pr, EX orig pnt, artist initials, sm chip on end of drake's tail, RB 7/09/85 600

Dugan, William
Bluebill hen, G orig pnt, average wear, artist brand, age split in bottom of body, 22, RB 5/02/86 350

Dunn, Roger (New Jersey)
Bluebill drake, hollow, orig pnt, minor wear, artist brand, RB 7/08/86 100
Brant, swimming, hollow, EX orig pnt, artist brand, RB 7/08/86 150
Canvasback drake, hollow, EX orig pnt, minor wear, artist brand, RB 7/08/86 75
Coot, hollow w/raised wing tips, orig pnt, average wear, artist brand, RB 3/06/87 150
Old Squaw drake, hollow, branded R Dunn, EX & orig, RB 7/08/86 225

Dunning, F.R. (Harpswell, ME)
Goldeneye hen, pnt stripped to natural wood, age splits in head, underside of bill is a replacement, 22, RB 5/02/86 175

Dutchuk, Al (Windsor, Ont)
Bluebill pr, orig pnt, average wear, structurally sound, ca 1939, RWO 11/11/87 80

Dye, Capt. Ben (Perryville, MD)
Bluewinged Teal, orig pnt, structurally sound, RWO 11/06/85 350
Canvasback drake, old working rpt, average wear, crack in neck, ca 1875, RWO 7/06/86 90
Redhead drake, old working rpt, hairline crack in neck, used in bluebill rig off Long Island, ca 1895, J/G 9/19/87 250
Ruddy Duck, rpt as a Canvasback, structurally EX, ca 1875, very rare, J/G 9/19/87, 75% 1500

Dye, Capt. Ben; att (Perryville, MD)
Bluebill drake, old pnt worn to bare wood over most of the body, age checks in body, otherwise EX, ca 1890, RWO 7/02/88 220
Canvasback drake, old orig pnt, average wear, break in neck has been reglued, RB 12/06/85 250
Canvasback drake, old working rpt, average wear, narrow check down 1 side/thin tight check, ca 1880, RWO 11/11/87 160
Canvasback drake, old working rpt, heavy flaking/wear, thin crack in neck, otherwise sound, ca 1890, RWO 7/04/87 130
Goldeneye drake, old pnt, heavy flaking/wear, some age splitting, some portions of neck have been rstr, RB 6/28/88 150
Redhead drake, rpt, minor wear, age split in neck, RB 7/08/86 100

Dye, Joe (Havre de Grace, MD)
Bluebill drake, orig pnt, in-use wear, nail driven through head, otherwise structurally sound, ca 1910, RWO 11/06/85 300

Dye, Joe; att (Havre de Grace, MD)
Canvasback drake, high-head style, old working rpt, average wear, structurally EX, RWO 7/6/86 260
Redhead drake, early, orig pnt, very worn, several thin age checks in body, ms, ca 1900, RWO 7/04/87 140

Eastland, Tim (Old Lyme, CT)
Bufflehead hen, stick-up, check running down breast, otherwise structurally sound, RWO 7/04/87 25
Knot, cvd wings, EX condition, RB 7/09/85 175
Yellowlegs, flat-body, split tail cvg, orig pnt, EX condition, RWO 11/06/85 50

Eastman, Willie (Cundy's Harbor, ME)
Loon, hollow, old orig pnt, average wear, well preserved, rare, slightly oversize, 22/47, RB 5/02/86 5000
Loon, hollow, old pnt, average wear, well preserved, rare, oversize, 22/44/46, RB 5/02/86, 200% 12000
Merganser drake, NM orig pnt, G patina, hairline crack part way through neck, ls, rare, oversize, J/G 4/24/86 2200

Eastman, Willie
Redbreasted Merganser drake, EX orig pnt, minor wear on head, hairline crack in neck, otherwise EX, RWO 7/06/86, $2,000.00.

Edrington, Jack (New Orleans, LA)
Bluewinged Teal drake, EX pnt, RB 8/21/86 75
Bluewinged Teal pr, EX condition, RB 6/28/88 100
Bluewinged Teal pr, EX orig pnt, RB 7/07/87 125
Gadwall, cypress root, EX orig pnt, structurally EX, RWO 11/11/87 50
Greenwinged Teal pr, EX pnt, RB 8/21/86 175
Widgeon drake, orig pnt, minor wear, structurally sound, RB 7/07/87 125

Edwards, Charles (Atlantic, NC)
Mallard hen, orig pnt, minor wear, minor age lines in bk/neck, 1 of 8 made in 1950, 33, J/G 9/19/87 450

Ellenberg, Fred
Redbreasted Merganser drake, EX pnt, minor wear, signed/dated 1965, RB 3/11/88 100

Elliot Brothers (Easton, MD)
Canvasback drake, orig pnt, worn/weathered, several checks in body, crack in neck, ca 1940's, RWO 7/04/87 80
Redhead pr, cork body, EX pnt, signed on bottom, RB 2/01/85 70
Wood Duck drake, orig pnt, EX condition, ca 1951, RWO 11/06/85 200

Ellis, Billy (Whitby, Ont)
Black Duck, orig pnt, minor wear, sm rough area on bk, 2 hairline cracks, ls, J/G 9/19/87 250
Bluebill drake, early, G orig pnt w/highly detailed comb pnt on bk, ls, J/G 4/24/86 220
Bluebill pr, orig pnt, minor wear w/old working touchup on white areas, J/G 9/20/86 275
Redhead hen, old working rpt, sm rough area on bk, rare, J/G 4/23/87 200
Redhead hen, old working rpt by Ellis, several tight age splits on bk, ls, rare, J/G 9/20/86 250

Elliston, Robert (Bureau, IL)
Bluebill, early, hollow, orig pnt, average wear, minor age splitting/chip on underside of bill, ls, RB 3/06/87 550
Bluebill drake, EX orig comb/feather pnt, touchup/varnished, retains orig weight, 1880's, EX, J/G 4/23/87, 80% ... 2000
Bluebill drake, fine comb/feather pnt (2 coats), minor flaking/wear, structurally EX, retains orig weight, J/G 4/24/86 ... 1430
Bluebill drake, hollow, EX scratch feather pnt, average wear, ls, sm bill chip, retains orig weight, 39, RB 7/08/86, 65% ... 950
Bluebill drake, hollow, fine orig comb pnt, minor flaking/wear, slight age split in neck, branded, rare, 21, RB 2/01/85 ... 1600
Bluebill drake, hollow, orig pnt by Catherine Elliston, hs/crack at base of neck, orig weight, 193, RWO 7/02/88, 75% ... 1100
Bluebill drake, orig pnt, minor wear, slight roughness to edge of bill, branded Gardner, retains weight, J/G 4/23/87 ... 1300
Bluebill drake, rpt w/minor wear, retains orig weight, 21, RB 2/01/85 225
Bluebill drake, taken down to mostly orig pnt, branded, no structural flaws, J/G 4/24/86 385
Bluewinged Teal, EX orig pnt, unusual light plumage/fine feathering, rstr bill/neck hairline, orig weight, J/G 4/24/86 ... 2475
Bluewinged Teal drake, rpt in Elliston style, lg chip out of 1 side of bill, otherwise M, rare, 7, J/G 4/24/86 192
Bluewinged Teal hen, hollow, EX orig pnt, minor wear, bill is worn away, retains orig weight, rare, 193, RWO 7/02/88 ... 4750
Bluewinged Teal hen, NM orig precise tail/feather pnt, prof bill rstr, retains orig weight, 1889, 68/159, J/G 4/24/86 ... 4125
Bluewinged Teal hen, rpt in Elliston style, structurally EX, retains orig Elliston weight, RWO 11/06/85 475

Elliston, Robert
Canada Goose, hollow, EX orig
pnt w/feathering on bk/sides, prof
rstr bill/face/tail chip, very rare,
68, J/G 4/24/86, $10,450.00

Canvasback drake, early, old working rpt on black areas, otherwise orig, average wear, ls/chip under bill, J/G 4/23/87 350
Canvasback drake, fine comb pnt, minor wear, hairline in neck, branded JDM, rare/highly collectible, J/G 4/24/86 5500
Canvasback drake, hollow, some overpnt taken off to reveal orig, hs, otherwise sound, ca 1880, 193, RWO 7/02/88, 40% 400
Canvasback drake, 2 coats of pnt, moderate wear, wood shrinkage/rpl eye/sm tail crack, retains weight, rare, J/G 4/23/87 400
Greenwinged Teal drake, orig pnt, heavy wear, branded Tully & KB, prof bill rpr, rare, 193, RWO 7/02/88 200
Greenwinged Teal hen, early, hollow, orig pnt, branded Trego, neck crack/ms, otherwise EX, rare, 193, RWO 7/02/88, 26% 900
Mallard drake, EX rpt in Elliston style, no structural flaws, 7, J/G 4/24/86 330
Mallard drake, fine orig pnt, slight wear, hairline crack in side of head/tail, retains orig weight, 67, J/G 9/20/86 3000
Mallard drake, hollow, EX orig pnt, sm neck crack, otherwise EX, orig weight, ca 1880, 193, RWO 7/02/88, 20% 1000
Mallard drake, hollow, fine old pnt, average flaking/wear, slight age split in neck, RB 7/07/87 450
Mallard drake, hollow, fine orig pnt, average wear, well preserved, retains orig weight, RB 8/21/86 1000
Mallard drake, hollow, orig pnt, average wear, flaking on head/breast, EX condition, orig weight, rare, RWO 7/02/88, 40% 800
Mallard drake, hollow, orig pnt, moderate wear, thin crack in neck, bill appears to have been prof rpr, RWO 7/05/85 300
Mallard drake, hollow, orig pnt worn to natural wood on sides, bill is a replacement, 21, RB 2/01/85 500
Mallard drake, hollow, orig pnt worn w/some areas to bare wood, ms, otherwise sound, orig weight, RWO 7/02/88, 53% 425
Mallard drake, hollow, pnt mostly gone w/traces of working rpt, separation where body joins/head renailed, RWO 2/12/88 150
Mallard drake, NM orig pnt w/outstanding feather & comb pnt, ls, retains orig weight, J/G 4/24/86 4125
Mallard drake, old working rpt worn bk to mostly orig, sm rough area at base of neck, retains orig weight, J/G 4/24/86 247
Mallard drake, orig pnt, average wear, varnished, tail chips, ls, J/G 4/23/87 500
Mallard drake, preening, old working rpt, chips missing from filler on edges of bill, rare, J/G 4/23/87 525
Mallard drake, sleeping, EX rpt in Elliston style, J/G 4/24/86, 235% 1650
Mallard drake, VG orig pnt, slight roughness on bill, retains orig weight, from the Carswell rig, J/G 4/23/87, 75% 1500
Mallard drake, 2 coats of pnt by Catherine Elliston, sm chip in base of neck, ca 1890, rare, J/G 4/24/86 825
Mallard hen, entire rpt in Elliston style, tight check at base of neck, retains orig weight, J/G 9/20/86 125
Mallard hen, EX orig pnt, minor flaking, tight check in tail, retains orig weight, extremely rare, J/G 4/24/86, 125% 7425
Mallard hen, hollow, orig pnt darkened under shellac, chip on bill/top of head, otherwise sound, 193, RWO 7/02/88, 50% 1250
Mallard pr, hollow, rpt w/minor wear, well preserved, retains orig weight, 39, RB 7/08/86 500
Pintail drake, EX orig comb pnt/feathering, minor wear, retains orig weight, prof rstr neck crack, rare, J/G 9/20/86 2500
Pintail drake, EX orig pnt, minor wear, few dings/ls, otherwise EX, orig weight, ca 1880, rare, 193, RWO 7/02/88, 75% 3750
Pintail drake, EX orig pnt, minor wear, structurally EX, retains orig weight, ca 1880, RWO 7/06/86, 225% 8000
Pintail drake, hollow, orig pnt, average wear, initialed, well preserved, retains orig weight, 39, RB 7/08/86 900
Pintail drake, hollow, orig pnt, in-use wear, sm neck crack/tail chip, retains orig weight, RWO 7/05/85 1000
Pintail drake, hollow, rpt, average flaking/wear, RB 7/07/87 250
Pintail drake, old working rpt w/strong comb pnt, no structural flaws, J/G 4/24/86 357
Pintail drake, overpnt taken down to EX/VG comb & feather pnt, sm rough area on tail, from the RL Week rig, J/G 4/24/86 632
Pintail drake, rpt, average wear, old break in neck has been reglued, retains orig weight, oversize, 39, RB 7/08/86 200
Pintail drake, rpt by 'Skippy' Barto, no structural flaws, 7, J/G 4/24/86 302
Redhead drake, early, hollow, orig pnt by Catherine Elliston, few nicks/dings, otherwise EX, 193, RWO 7/02/88, 30% 450
Redhead drake, early, orig pnt worn w/areas to bare wood, crack in neck/hs, bill rpr, orig weight, RWO 7/02/88, 40% 400
Redhead drake, fine orig comb/feather pnt, minor wear, coat of varnish has been removed, ls, EX condition, J/G 4/24/86 4400
Redhead drake, full body, EX orig comb/feather pnt, minor wear & touchup, ls, J/G 4/23/87, 65% 3250

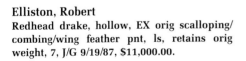

Elliston, Robert
Redhead drake, hollow, EX orig scalloping/combing/wing feather pnt, ls, retains orig weight, 7, J/G 9/19/87, $11,000.00.

Redhead drake, hollow, EX scratch feather pnt, well preserved, retains orig weight, extremely rare, 39, RB 7/08/86	2750
Redhead drake, hollow, rpt in Elliston style, sm end-of-tail chip, otherwise EX condition, RWO 7/02/88	225
Redhead drake, orig pnt, average wear, sm chip on 1 side of tail, rare, J/G 4/24/86, 55%	1045
Redhead drake, prof rpt in Elliston style, structurally EX, J/G 9/20/86	100
Redhead drake, VG orig pnt w/combing, working touchup, hairline, ls, retains orig weight, 178, J/G 9/20/86	1200
Ringbill, hollow, old rpt, average wear, structurally sound, rare, 189, RB 6/28/88	325
Ringbill drake, orig pnt, minor wear, structurally EX, retains orig weight, extremely rare, J/G 4/24/86	1430
Teal, old working rpt, moderate wear, sm old tail-chip repair, retains orig weight, J/G 4/24/86	275

Englehaupt, August (Peru, IL)

Mallard drake, slightly turned head, cvd in style of Hector Whittington, fine comb pnt, J/G 9/20/86	250
Mallard hen, signed/dated 1943 on underside, M condition, 7, J/G 4/24/86	550
Mallard hen, slightly turned head, cvd in style of Hector Whittington, orig pnt, structurally EX, J/G 9/20/86	250

Englhart, Nicholas (Manito, IL)

Snow Goose silhouette, orig pnt, average wear, identical decoy illus in 90, 3, RWO 7/05/86	2000

English, Dan (Florence, NJ)

Black Duck, hollow, EX feather cvg on bk/unusual primary feather cvg, VG orig pnt, average wear, rare, RB 7/07/87	2000
Black Duck, hollow, EX orig pnt, minor wear, branded Willis Pennington, sm chip from tail, otherwise EX, RWO 7/05/85	3000
Black Duck, low-head style, 'V' cvd primaries, old pnt flaking in several areas on bk, structurally sound, RWO 7/04/87	400
Black Duck, low-head style, hollow, old working rpt, structurally sound, ca 1905, RWO 11/11/87, 240%	290

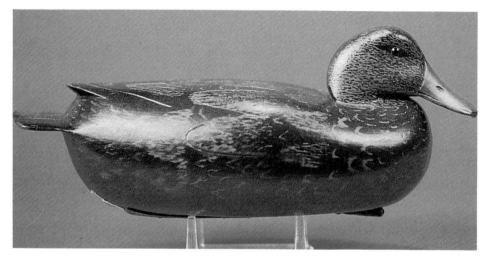

English, Dan
Black Duck, low-head style, outstanding, stamped/branded, 65/71, RWO 11/06/85, $3,750.00.

English, Dan; att (Florence, NJ)

Bluebill drake, hollow, fine orig pnt, average flaking/wear, well preserved, 81, RB 12/06/85	500

English, Jack (Florence, NJ)

Black Duck, raised cvd primaries/tail cvg, hollow, orig pnt, structurally EX, ca 1930, RWO 11/06/85, 155%	2200

English, Jack; att (Florence, NJ)

Redhead, hollow, working rpt shows average wear, structurally sound, RWO 11/11/87	120

English, John (Florence, NJ)

Black Duck, early, hollow, working rpt taken down to orig, prof repair to neck, ca 1900, RWO 7/04/87, 55%	1100
Black Duck, early, raised cvd primary feathers, old pnt, heavy flaking/wear, ls, RB 8/27/87	2200
Black Duck, raised cvd primaries/cvd tail feathers, old working rpt, moderate wear, sm crack in neck, rare, J/G 4/24/86	825
Bluebill hen, taken down to worn orig pnt, structurally sound, rare, J/G 4/23/87	150
Canvasback pr, hollow, fine orig pnt, minor wear, well preserved, rare, RB 7/07/87	3300
Mallard drake, cvd primaries/secondaries, G old pnt, minor wear, tiny chip in edge of tail, rare, J/G 4/23/87	550
Pintail drake, pnt rstr by Bob White, structurally sound, ca 1890, RWO 7/05/85	2000

English, John; att (Florence, NJ)

Black Duck, early, hollow, pnt worn/weathered w/areas to bare wood, several tail chips, ca 1930's, RWO 11/11/87	260
Bluebill drake, hollow, rpt shows minor wear, RB 7/09/85	225

English, Mark (Summers Point, NJ)

Goldeneye drake, old pnt, average flaking/wear, structurally sound, RB 3/11/88	675
Old Squaw drake, hollow, 2-pc body, working rpt, considerable wear, structurally VG, RWO 7/05/85	425
Redbreasted Merganser drake, hollow, cvd eyes, EX orig pnt, minor wear, 1, RB 12/06/85	1700
Redbreasted Merganser pr, old rpt, moderate wear, hen's orig crest has been cvd away, RB 3/11/88	800

Enright, William T. (Toledo, OH)
Pintail drake, cork body, EX orig pnt, branded JLW, structurally EX, ca 1940, RWO 7/06/86 140
Epple, Jack (Peoria, IL)
Canvasback drake, high-neck style, orig pnt, minor wear, prof bill rpr, J/G 4/24/86 385
Mallard hen, orig pnt, minimal wear, no structural flaws, J/G 4/24/86 275
Ernst, Murray (Lunenburg Count, NS)
Redbreasted Merganser drake, artist brand, M condition, RWO 7/04/87 100
Etheridge, Benjamin (Knott's Island, NC)
Canvasback drake, old working rpt, thin crack in neck, ca 1900, RWO 7/04/87 575
Evans, John (Crisfield, MD)
Pintail drake, hollow, EX orig pnt, structurally EX, RWO 7/06/86 175
Ewen, John (West Hartford, CT)
Canvasback pr, slightly turned heads, highly detailed feather/comb pnt, signed/dated 1984, M condition, J/G 9/19/87 300
Ewinger, W.O. (Burlington, IA)
Bluebill drake, old working rpt, minor wear, no structural flaws, rare, J/G 4/24/86 143
Mallard drake, hollow, pnt eyes, orig pnt, minor crazing, no structural flaws, J/G 4/24/86 154
Fabins, Samuel; att
Merganser hen, early, laminated body construction, hollow, old pnt, moderate flaking/wear, ls, RB 6/28/88 450
Fahrner, Ray (Lake St. Clair, MI)
Canvasback drake, orig pnt, average wear, some neck filler missing, otherwise structurally sound, ca 1905, RWO 7/02/88 75
Federine, Earl (Cut Off, LA)
Black Duck, M condition, inscribed on underside, J/G 9/19/87 300
Fennimore, Harry (Bordentown, NJ)
Black Duck, head tucked down, hollow w/raised cvd wing tips, orig pnt, minor wear, well preserved, RB 7/07/87 600
Black Duck, hollow, fine old pnt, minor in-use wear, well preserved, RB 7/09/85 350
Black Duck, hollow w/cvd wing tips, EX feather cvg on bk, fine orig pnt, minor wear, ls, 20, RB 12/06/85 2000
Field, Douglass (Cornwall, VT)
Mallard drake, tiny crack on top side of bill, otherwise M, J/G 9/19/87 75
Finch, William (Port Huron, MI)
Black Duck, hollow, orig pnt, average wear, structurally EX, RWO 7/06/86 150
Finkel, William (Harsen's Island, Ont)
Black Duck, thin shelled, orig pnt, in-use wear, thin neck crack, structurally VG, 113, RWO 7/05/85 600
Canvasback drake, old rpt, heavy wear, ls, RB 12/09/85 175
Finkel, William; att (Harsen's Island, Ont)
Mallard drake, hollow, fine old pnt, possibly orig w/average wear, RB 2/01/85 350
Finney, Frank (Pungo, VA; Virginia Beach, VA)
Black Duck, feeding, hollow, cvd initials, M condition, RWO 7/04/87 170
Black Duck, hollow, M condition, RWO 7/04/87 200

Finney, Frank
Black Duck, hollow body w/head in content postition, sleepy-eyed, finely detailed feather pnt w/superb tone, J/G 4/24/86, $605.00.

Black Duck, hollow w/raised wing tips, mandible is cvd partially open, artist initials, M condition, RWO 7/06/86, 75% 300
Black Duck, preening, hollow w/deep raised cvd wings, signed/numbered, structurally superb, RWO 7/06/86 450
Canada Goose, cvd in style of Walter Brady, pnt is made to look old, structurally sound, RWO 2/13/87 500
Canada Goose, hissing, hollow w/cvd wings/wing tips, EX orig pnt, lead weight on bottom, RB 8/21/86 500
Canada Goose, preening, hollow w/cvd crossed wing tips/tail feathers, M condition, J/G 9/20/86 275
Dowitcher, hollow, cvd in manner of William Bowman, EX condition, RWO 7/02/88 250

Eider pr, inlet heads, hollowed out from bottom w/applied bottom board, mouths cvd open, RWO 7/04/87	650
Golden Plover, hollow, cvd in manner of William Bowman, made to look old, EX condition, RWO 7/02/88	275
Plover, cvd in Cobb Island style, worn pnt, structurally sound, RWO 11/06/85	110
Redbreasted Merganser, thin-shelled, horsehair crest, M condition, RWO 7/02/88	450
Redbreasted Merganser drake, raised cvd wings, orig pnt, flaking around breast, horsehair crest, RWO 7/04/87	290
Swan, 2-pc hollow construction w/graceful neck, thin shelled, made to look old, RWO 7/04/87	450
Widgeon drake, nestled-head style, hollow, detailed raised cvd wing tips, M condition, J/G 9/20/86	250
Wood Duck drake, raised cvd primaries, M pnt, initialed on bottom, oversize, J/G 4/24/86	330
Wood Duck pr, flying, FF scratched into the glass eyes, outstanding orig condition, RWO 7/05/85	2100

Finney, Frank; att (Pungo, VA; Virginia Beach, VA)

Greenwinged Teal drake, antiqued, EX condition, RB 6/28/88	75

Fischer, John (Peoria, IL)

Mallard drake, hollow, EX orig pnt, narrow crack running through neck is the only flaw, RWO 2/12/88	650
Mallard hen, NM orig pnt w/EX feather pnt, structurally EX, retains orig weight, J/G 4/23/87	600

Fish, Charles

Redbreasted Merganser drake, orig pnt, minor wear, well preserved, RB 8/27/87	60

Fitchett (Smith's Island, VA)
Curlew, early, old pnt appears to be orig worn to soft patina, some dings to wood/sm tight checks, ca 1890, RWO 2/12/88, $1,050.00.

Fitzpatrick, Thomas (Delanco, NJ)

Black Duck, hollow, old pnt, minor wear, RB 3/11/88	400
Black Duck, low-head style, G old orig dry pnt, minor wear, water damage around tail, otherwise EX, RWO 11/06/85	500
Mallard hen, early/round-bottom style, raised 'V' primaries, working rpt, structurally EX, RWO 11/11/87, 70%	425
Mallard hen, hollow w/raised cvd primaries/secondaries, NM orig pnt, J/G 9/20/86	500

Fitzpatrick, Thomas; att (Delanco, NJ)

Black Duck, hollow, low-head style, working rpt, in-use wear, minor damage to end of bill, RWO 11/11/87	330
Black Duck, low-head style, hollow w/raised cvd wings, old working rpt, structurally sound, RWO 11/11/87	230

Fletcher, Columbus (Havre de Grace, MD)

Canvasback drake, old working rpt, average wear, RB 2/01/85	100

Fletcher, Columbus; att (Havre de Grace, MD)

Canvasback drake, old working rpt, average wear, chip at top of head, RB 2/01/85	50

Foch, B.L. (Louisiana)

Mallard hen, artist signed, EX condition, RB 6/28/88	25
Pintail drake, fine orig pnt, heavy wear, signed on bottom, RB 7/08/86	350

Foote, Jim (Gibralter, MI)

Black Duck, EX feather cvg on bk, EX & orig, retains 1971 US Nat'l Decoy Show label, RB 9/06/87, 165%	1000
Canvasback drake, slightly turned head, cvd primaries/secondaries, 1st place at US Nat'l, M condition, J/G 4/23/87, 250%	1500
Widgeon pr, hollow, fine feather cvg, orig pnt, minor flaking at bills, EX & orig, RB 3/06/87, 135%	1600

Forsyth, Albert (Bay Head, NJ)

Brant, early, hollow, old pnt, average wear, several age splits/old break in neck has been reglued, RB 3/06/87	225

Foster, Cliff (Hampton Beach, NY)

Merganser hen, wooden crest, orig pnt, minor wear, sm tail chip/hairline crack in neck/sm pc missing, ls, J/G 9/19/87	250

Fouts, Herman (Liverpool, IL)

Mallard hen, EX orig pnt, minor wear, 1 sm shot scar, rare, J/G 4/23/87	425

Pintail drake, orig pnt, minor wear, white pnt spattered on 1 side, no structural flaws, J/G 4/24/86 .... **440**

Fox, A.G. (Massachusetts)
Golden Plover, cvd split tail, EX/NM condition w/minor flaking, 44, RB 8/21/86, 40%, $1,200.00.

Fox, Ernie (Brockville, Ont)
Bufflehead drake, EX condition, RB 2/01/85 .... **100**
Fox, Gordon
Canvasback drake, balsa body, fine orig pnt, average wear, RB 8/25/88 .... **70**
Canvasback pr, fine orig pnt, slight age split in bill of hen, RB 2/01/85 .... **200**
Redhead drake, tucked head, fine orig pnt, average wear, RB 2/01/85 .... **130**
Fox, Pecor
Canvasback pr, worn orig pnt, structurally sound, RWO 11/06/85 .... **110**
Frady, Mike (New Orleans, LA)
Bluewinged Teal drake, preening, cypress root, cvd crossed wing tips, NM orig pnt, structurally EX, J/G 9/20/86 .... **525**
Greenwinged Teal drake, slightly turned head, cypress root, cvd wing tips, NM orig pnt, structurally EX, J/G 9/20/86 .... **175**
Mallard hen, raised cvd wings w/extended tips, sleepy eyes, tiny tail chip, otherwise M, J/G 4/23/87 .... **350**
Pintail drake, preening, cvd crossed wing tips, EX condition, RB 6/28/88 .... **350**
Pintail drake, preening, raised cvd wing tips, NM orig pnt, 2 hairline cracks in lower side, J/G 4/23/87 .... **250**
Pintail drake, tupelo wood, raised cvd primaries, highly detailed pnt, rstr to tip of tail, otherwise M, J/G 4/24/86 .... **577**
Pintail pr, cypress root, slightly turned heads, raised cvd wing tips, NM orig pnt, EX, J/G 9/20/86 .... **500**
Frakes, Eddie (Winneconne, WI)
Mallard drake, slightly turned head, orig pnt, minor wear, old coat of varnish, sm tail chip, J/G 9/19/87 .... **375**
Frazier, Nate (Tuckerton, NJ)
Robin Snipe, orig pnt, minor wear, no structural flaws, J/G 9/19/87 .... **400**
Freden, W. Ray
Curlew, EX pnt, signed on bottom, RB 7/07/87 .... **50**
Frederick, George (Phoenix, LA)
Mallard drake, preening, cvd wings, EX orig pnt, minor wear, RB 7/09/85 .... **350**
Frederick, George; att (Phoenix, LA)
Bluewinged Teal hen, G orig pnt, minor wear w/flaking around bill, 21, RB 2/01/85 .... **900**
Mallard hen, fine orig pnt, minor wear, orig bill broken off & needs reattached, 21, RB 2/01/85 ...... **500**
Mallard pr, fine orig pnt, structurally NM, 21, RB 2/01/85 .... **700**
Frederick, Jules (Phoenix, LA)
Pintail drake, EX & orig, RB 7/09/85 .... **225**
Freeman, Al (Duxbury, MA)
Goose, canvas-covered slat, old pnt, heavy flaking/wear sm tears in canvas, some dry rot to bottom, 22, RB 5/02/86 .... **150**
Goose, canvas-covered slat, old pnt w/crazing & flaking, minor age splits in neck, 22/44, RB 5/02/86 .... **350**
Old Squaw hen, fine orig pnt, average flaking/wear, some slight age splitting/chip on underside of bill, 22, RB 5/02/86 .... **200**
Old Squaw pr, G orig pnt, average wear, some slight age splitting, 22, RB 5/02/86 .... **800**
Freire, L.J. (Louisiana)
Cinnamon Teal drake, cvd wing tips, EX condition, RB 6/28/88 .... **150**
Freire, Robert (Shell Beach, LA)
Bluewinged Teal drake, cypress, orig pnt, average wear, structurally sound, RWO 2/12/88 .... **80**
Greenwinged Teal drake, head tucked in content position, EX condition, RB 6/28/88 .... **50**

Mallard hen, tupelo wood, 2-pc construction, EX & orig condition, RWO 11/11/87	55
Pintail hen, head tucked, NM condition, RWO 2/12/88	90

Fuchs, Barry (Millington, MD)

Bluebill pr, sm pnt rubs on head, signed/dated 1972, NM condition, RWO 7/06/86	100
Pintail pr, signed/dated 1972, M condition, RWO 7/06/86	70

Fulcher, Graydon (Stacy, NC)

Canvasback drake, early, sleeping, worn old pnt, age split in bk, several age lines, 33/120, J/G 9/19/87	475

Fulcher, John (Stacy, NC)

Dowitcher, orig pnt, worn/weathered, structurally sound, RWO 7/02/88	400
Yellowlegs, fine orig pnt, minor wear, 49, RB 7/08/86	600

Fulcher, Mitchell (Stacy, NC)

Bluebill hen, orig pnt w/some in-use touchup, MF cvd in bottom, tight checks in body, otherwise sound, RWO 7/02/88	950

Fulcher, Mitchell
Canvasback pr, EX orig pnt, artist initials, hen has minor age line/hairline crack, very rare, 33, J/G 9/19/87, $8,000.00.

Pintail pr, orig pnt, minor wear, several age lines on bk, drake has rough area on base, oversize, rare, 33, J/G 9/19/87	8500

Fuller, Tesse (Essex, MA)

Scoter, canvas-covered, fine orig pnt, average wear, RB 6/28/88	150

Gale, Clarence

Brant, hollow, fine old pnt, average wear, ls, well preserved, RB 3/06/87	125

Gannon, Lonnie (West Haven, CT)

Black Duck, old working rpt, slight wear, sm chip on edge of bill, J/G 9/19/87	300

Gant, Percy (Osbornville, NJ)

Black Duck, hollow, heart-shaped wings on bk, working rpt, well preserved, 21, RB 2/01/85	250
Brant, preening, incised wings, fine orig pnt, average flaking/wear, well preserved, rare, RB 3/06/87	600
Bufflehead drake, EX orig pnt, average wear, well preserved, 39, RB 7/08/86	400
Canada Goose, hollow, cvd eyes, EX orig pnt, minor wear, structurally EX, RWO 07/06/86	240
Canada Goose, hollow, rpt, moderate flaking/wear, RB 3/11/88	75

Gant, Percy; att (Osbornville, NJ)

Canvasback pr, orig pnt w/some areas of working touchup, hen has some rstr to bill, otherwise EX, ca 1910, RWO 07/06/86	330

Mallard drake, old rpt, average wear, minor age splitting, RB 8/25/88 60

Garabaldi, Emile
    Greenwinged Teal hen, slightly turned head, cvd molded wings, EX orig pnt, minor flaking, well preserved, RB 8/21/86 1000

Garatti, Frank
    Bluebill drake, cvd primary feathers, orig pnt, average wear, RB 12/06/85 75
    Bluebill hen, cvd primary feathers, fine old pnt, minor wear, RB 7/09/85 200

Gardiner, Alfred (Accord, MA)
    Curlew, pnt shows minor wear, EX condition, RB 3/11/88, 260% 650
    Yellowlegs, sleeping, EX pnt, rare, RB 2/01/85 700

Garren, Otto (Canton, IL)
    Canvasback drake, EX orig pnt, no structural flaws, rare, J/G 4/24/86 302
    Coot, hollow, fine old pnt, average wear, well preserved, RB 12/06/85 450
    Greenwinged Teal drake, hollow, old pnt, average wear, structurally sound, RB 12/06/85 200
    Hooded Merganser hen, hollow, rpt by Garren, minor wear, EX condition, ca 1945, rare, 193, RWO 7/02/88, 58% 350
    Mallard drake, early, hollow, orig pnt, average wear, crack in neck/tight check along 1 side, ca 1940's, RWO 7/04/87 140
    Mallard drake, hollow, old working rpt w/slight wear, retains orig weight, J/G 9/20/86 75
    Mallard drake, old working rpt w/some orig on bk/lower sides, structurally sound, J/G 4/23/87 175
    Mallard hen, crack in neck, otherwise M, J/G 4/24/86 467
    Mallard hen, orig pnt, flaking/wear around head/breast, structurally sound, rare, ca 1940's, RWO 7/04/87 150
    Mallard pr, EX orig pnt, minor wear, 21, RB 2/01/85 500
    Pintail drake, hollow, old working rpt, minor wear, no structural flaws, retains orig weight, J/G 9/20/86 185
    Pintail drake, hollow, old working rpt w/flaking around breast, minor dings to wood, otherwise sound, RWO 7/04/87 100
    Ringbill drake, orig pnt, minor wear, ls, rare, J/G 9/19/87 300

Garton, John B. (Smith's Falls, Ont)
    Bluewinged Teal drake, pnt as an immature, M condition, won honorable mention in 1968 Toronto show, RWO 7/05/85 325
    Bluewinged Teal hen, pnt as an immature, M condition, ca 1968, RWO 7/05/85 280
    Canvasback drake, nice comb pnt, M condition, RWO 7/06/86 190

Gaskill, Frank (North Carolina)
    Brant, root-head, old working rpt, in-use wear, several age checks in bk/head, ca 1910, RWO 11/11/87 575
    Hutchins Goose, worn orig pnt, numerous age lines, 33, J/G 9/19/87 1000

Gaskill, Tom (Barnegat, NJ)
    Bluebill hen, hollow, fine old pnt, average in-use wear, RB 7/09/85 300

Gatreau, John (Lossier Settlement, NB)
    Canada Goose, paddle tail, orig pnt, minor wear, several minor age lines in body, J/G 9/19/87 140
    Canada Goose, swimming, orig pnt, minor wear, J/G 9/20/86 100

Gavaghan, John
    Black Duck, swimming, fine orig pnt, minor wear, RB 6/28/88 75
    Pintail drake, hollow, minor wear, otherwise EX condition, RB 6/28/88 200

Gelston, Thomas (Quogue, LI, NY)
    Black Duck, hollow, old pnt, average wear, repair to neck, RB 7/09/85 175
    Black Duck, hollow w/cvd wing tips, G orig pnt, average wear, age split in neck, RB 7/07/87 250
    Black Duck pr, cork body, orig pnt, average wear, 1 has hairline crack through head, otherwise sound, RWO 2/13/87 180
    Bluebill pr, drake is preening, orig pnt, average wear, well preserved, RB 3/06/87, 65% 800
    Curlew, cork body, orig pnt, average wear, bill has been rpl, otherwise VG, lg, RWO 7/05/85 750
    Curlew, cork body, orig pnt, average wear, body broken & reglued/chip at end of tail, ms, rare, RB 3/06/87 200
    Curlew, cvd wing tips, EX orig pnt, minor wear, bill possibly orig, ms, rare, Ex-collection John Whittaker, RWO 7/04/87 ... 10500
    Curlew, wooden full body, cvd wing tips, EX orig pnt, minor wear, orig position prof rstr, extremely rare, 2, RB 12/6/85 ... 6500
    Curlew, wooden full body, cvd wings, NM orig pnt, minor wear, bill is prof rpl, extremely rare, 2, RB 12/06/85 17000
    Yellowlegs, cork body, EX orig pnt, minor wear, ls, RB 7/08/86 300
    Yellowlegs, cork body, fine old pnt, appears to be orig, age split at top of head, 3, RB 7/09/85 350
    Yellowlegs, cork body, G orig pnt, minor wear, RB 3/11/88 350
    Yellowlegs, cork body, old Gelston rpt, average wear, 9, RB 12/06/85 200
    Yellowlegs, cork body, orig pnt, average wear, minor damage to end of tail, RWO 7/05/85 375
    Yellowlegs, running, cork body, EX orig pnt, average wear, well preserved, 39, RB 7/08/86, 270% 1600
    Yellowlegs, running, cork body, orig pnt, minor wear w/working touchup on white areas, sm crack in 1 side, J/G 9/19/87 ... 300
    Yellowlegs, running, wood body, EX orig pnt, minor crazing, structurally sound, rare, ca 1890-1900, RWO 7/04/87 2100

Gelston, Thomas; att (Quogue, LI, NY)
    Heron, slightly turned head, cork body w/wooden bill, raised cvd wings, old working rpt, orig was Blue Heron, J/G 4/24/86 330

Giannetto, Vincent (Beverly, NJ)
    Black Duck, hollow, G orig pnt, minor wear, signed/dated 1965, well preserved, RB 3/11/88 100
    Canada Goose, hollow, orig pnt, EX condition, RWO 11/06/85 100

Canada Goose, hollow w/EX feather detail, signed/dated 1969, EX condition, RB 3/11/88 150
Hooded Merganser hen, preening, fine orig pnt, typical Delaware 'V' primaries, RWO 11/06/85 280
Mallard drake, raised 'V' cvd wing tips, fluted tail, NM orig pnt, signed, structurally EX, J/G 9/19/87 125
Mallard drake, slightly turned head, hollow w/detailed tail/feather cvg, NM orig pnt, structurally EX, J/G 9/20/86 150
Mallard pr, EX orig pnt, some roughness to edges of tail, RB 2/01/85 175
Pintail drake, standing, M condition, RWO 11/06/85 120
Redbreasted Merganser pr, hen has hairline crack in neck, otherwise M condition, RWO 7/04/87 170
Wood Duck drake, preening, hollow, orig pnt, NM condition, RWO 11/06/85 310

Gibbs, B.M.
Ringneck drake, hollow, EX orig pnt w/fine patina, minor rubs/discoloration on 1 side, rare, 193/208, RWO 7/02/88 1000

Giberson, Gary
Bluebill drake, hollow, fine orig pnt, age split in neck, RB 3/11/88 250

Gibian, William (Accomac, VA)
Black Duck, cvd layered primaries, M condition, J/G 4/23/87 700
Blackbellied Plover, feeding, highly detailed wing cvg, M condition, J/G 9/20/86 325
Blackbellied Plover, feeding, raised cvd wings, M condition, J/G 4/23/87 200
Blackbellied Plover, preening, cvd wings, in the style of Elmer Crowell, EX condition, RB 8/27/87 500
Bluewinged Teal drake, hollow w/fine wing cvg, detailed feather pnt, M condition, RWO 11/06/85 550
Bluewinged Teal drake, preening, EX wing cvg, EX detailed feather pnt, M condition, RWO 11/06/85, 185% 1200
Bluewinged Teal drake, preening, M condition, J/G 4/23/87 500
Bluewinged Teal drake, slightly turned head, M condition, J/G 4/23/87 300

Gibian, William
Brant, hollow, signed on the bottom, EX & orig, RB 8/21/86,
70%, $500.00.

Bufflehead drake, preening, M condition, J/G 4/23/87 275
Cinnamon Teal drake, slightly turned tucked head, M condition, rare, J/G 4/24/86 220
Cinnamon Teal hen, slightly turned head, M condition, rare, J/G 4/24/86 247
Curlew, feeding, Gibian cvd in bottom, minor flaws in pnt on underside, otherwise EX & orig condition, RWO 7/02/88 375
Curlew, slightly turned head, detailed wing cvg, fine feather pnt, 2" tight check on 1 wing, otherwise M, J/G 4/24/86 275
Dove, hollow, artist signed, M condition, RWO 7/02/88 175
Dove, raised cvd wings/primaries, cvd signature, M condition, RWO 11/11/87 425
Dowitcher, hollow, artist signed, M condition, RWO 7/02/88 180
Dowitcher, raised cvd wing tips, M condition, J/G 9/20/86 225
Dowitcher, raised cvd wings, cvd signature, M condition, RWO 11/11/87 250
Gadwall drake, hollow, superb pnt detail, artist signed, M condition, RWO 7/02/88, 155% 1100
Godwit, EX pnt, signed on bottom, RB 7/09/85 200
Golden Plover, raised cvd wings, Gibian cvd in relief, M condition, RWO 11/11/87 300
Mallard drake, M condition, J/G 4/23/87 600
Mallard drake, several pnt rubs under tail/on 1 side of breast, otherwise M, signed, J/G 9/19/87 425
Mallard drake, sleeping, cvd primaries, EX comb pnt, metal curly feathers, RWO 7/06/86 1200
Merganser drake, preening, cvd wings, horsehair crest, sm pnt rubs on 1 side of breast, otherwise M, J/G 4/24/86 302
Pintail drake, EX comb pnt, feather detail, signed, RWO 11/06/85 1100
Pintail drake, low-head style, hollow w/raised wings, comb pnt, signed, M condition, RWO 11/11/87 950
Pintail drake, preening, artist brand, M condition, RWO 7/04/87 1350
Pintail drake, preening, pnt bubbling on breast/under tail, no structural flaws, J/G 9/19/87 400
Pintail hen, hollow, signed, M condition, RWO 11/06/85 600
Redbreasted Merganser drake, racy Maine style, cvd wings/crest/eyes, artist brand, M condition, RWO 7/06/86 975
Redbreasted Merganser pr, hollow, cvd signature, M condition, RWO 7/04/87, 135% 1600
Robin Snipe, turned head, cvd signature, M condition, RWO 11/11/87 350

Ruddy Turnstone, EX pnt, signed on bottom, RB 7/09/85 250
Ruddy Turnstone, orig pnt, inscribed, EX condition, RWO 11/06/85 190
Sanderling, cvd signature, M condition, RWO 11/11/87 150
Sanderling, tucked head, raised cvd wings, cvd signature, M condition, RWO 11/11/87 375
Shoveler drake, sleeping, hollow, artist signed, M condition, RWO 2/12/88 850
Shoveler drake, sleeping, hollow, signed, M condition, RWO 2/13/87 1250
Turnstone, preening, raised cvd wings/primaries w/extended tips, M condition, J/G 4/23/87 200
Wood Duck drake, hollow, raised wings w/cvd primaries, artist signed, M condition, RWO 2/12/88 750
Wood Duck drake, preening, cvd crest/wing tips, fine comb pnt, artist brand, RWO 7/06/86, 140% 1400
Wood Duck pr, hollow, cvd signature, M condition, RWO 7/04/87 1700
Yellowlegs, Bowman style, orig pnt, inscribed, EX condition, RWO 11/06/85 175
Yellowlegs, cvd signature, slight crazing to breast, otherwise M, RWO 11/11/87 150
Yellowlegs, feeding, minnow in its mouth, signed, M condition, RWO 7/05/85 225
Yellowlegs, feeding, relief cvd wings, cvd signature, M condition, RWO 11/11/87 225
Yellowlegs, NM orig pnt, structurally EX, J/G 9/20/86 350
Yellowlegs, preening, raised wings, unusual relief cvg to neck, signed, M condition, RWO 7/05/85 400

Gibson, Paul (Havre de Grace, MD)
Black Duck, orig pnt, average wear, moderate check in neck/couple of gouges to wood on body, RWO 11/11/87 100
Bluebill drake, old working rpt w/some orig pnt showing through, structurally sound, RWO 11/06/85 95
Bluewinged Teal drake, M pnt, orig newspaper wrapping, ca 1971, J/G 4/24/86 165
Bluewinged Teal hen, M condition, orig newspaper wrapping, J/G 4/24/86 165
Bluewinged Teal pr, NM orig pnt, signed, no structural flaws, J/G 9/19/87 255
Canada Goose, EX orig pnt, average wear, crack in neck/minor damage to tip of tail, RWO 11/11/87 150
Canada Goose, orig pnt, average wear, black pnt spattered on breast/tight check near breast, otherwise EX, RWO 11/11/87 225
Canada Goose, preening, signed/dated 1975, M condition, RWO 7/06/86 225

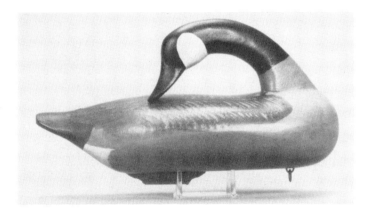

Gibson, Paul
Canada Goose, preening, signed/dated 1977, M orig condition, RWO 11/11/87, 150%, $850.00.

Canada Goose, thin hairline crack running down bk, otherwise NM, ca 1955, rare, oversize, RWO 11/06/85 350
Canvasback drake, early, sleeping, G orig pnt, average wear, ls, rare, RWO 11/11/87 600
Canvasback hen, unused, RWO 11/11/87 145
Canvasback pr, EX orig pnt, RB 8/21/86 300
Canvasback pr, sleeping, EX orig pnt, ca 1978, RWO 11/06/85 270
Coot or Mudhen, EX orig pnt w/flaking near breast, ca 1958, rare, RWO 11/11/87 240
Greenwinged Teal pr, signed/dated 1974, M condition, RWO 11/11/87 250
Mallard drake, working rpt, structurally sound, RWO 11/06/85 85
Pintail pr, drake is signed/dated 1976, M condition, RWO 11/11/87 290
Pintail pr, M/unused, ca 1950, RWO 11/11/87 320

Gibson, Paul; att (Havre de Grace, MD)
Pintail drake, NM orig pnt, G patina, sm crack on 1 edge of the face, ca 1950's, J/G 9/20/86 155
Swan, rpt taken down to orig, crack in neck/thin checks running down bk/chip in tail, RWO 7/04/87, 170% 1700

Giegl, Joseph (Fremont, WI)
Canvasback drake, cork body, unused/M, RWO 7/06/86 50

Gilbert, Gumpy (Trenton, NJ)
Canada Goose, hollow, orig pnt, average wear w/crazing on bk, structurally EX, RWO 11/11/87 330
Mallard, hollow w/raised cvd primaries, orig pnt, slight wear, structurally EX, J/G 9/20/86 70

Gilley, Wendell (Southwest Harbor, ME)
Scoter hen, hollow, G orig pnt, average wear, well preserved, 22/44, RB 5/02/86 1600
Surf Scoter drake, hollow w/cvd wing tips, G orig pnt, average flaking/wear, well preserved, 22/44, RB 5/02/86 2200
Gipe, Ralph (Craley, PA)
Canvasback drake, old working rpt, average wear, structurally sound, RWO 7/02/88 90

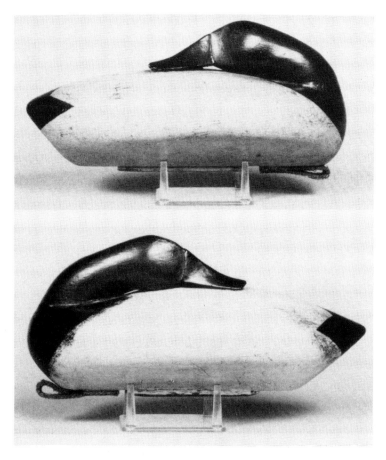

Gipe, Ralph
Canvasback pr, sleeping, old pnt, average wear, artist branded keel weights, structurally sound, RWO 11/11/87, $3,500.00.

Gisclair, Adam (Louisiana)
Bluewinged Teal drake, slightly turned head, EX & orig condition, RB 7/09/85 130
Greenwinged Teal drake, EX & orig condition, RB 7/09/85 30
Giverson, Sam (Absecon, NJ)
Ruddy Turnstone, fine orig pnt, average wear, well preserved, 20/50, RB 12/06/85 200
Glasford, Al
Black Duck, fine orig pnt, minor wear, RB 12/06/85 140
Glass, August (Florence, NJ)
Canvasback drake, early, hollow, old orig pnt, structurally sound, rare, RWO 7/06/86 220
Glenn, Capt. John (Rock Hall, MD)
Bluebill drake, orig pnt, average wear, thin crack in neck/age checks along 1 side of body, ca 1930, 41, RWO 7/04/87 130
Bluebill pr, EX orig pnt, average wear w/some areas worn to bare wood, structurally EX, ca 1940's, RWO 11/11/87 350
Canada Goose, early, preening, pnt has been worn or stripped away, some damage to bill, ca 1920's, RWO 7/06/86, 75% 750
Canada Goose, old rpt, in-use flaking/wear, several age checks in breast/crack in neck, ca 1940's, RWO 7/06/86 400
Canvasback drake, high-head style, EX orig pnt, average wear w/flaking, structurally EX, ca 1940, RWO 7/04/87 400
Canvasback drake, old working rpt w/flaking on 1 side, crack in neck/chunk of wood missing from top of head, RWO 7/04/87 200
Canvasback drake, working rpt shows some flaking/wear, structurally sound, RWO 2/12/88 120
Canvasback pr, orig pnt, average wear, hen has hairline neck crack; drake has check on side, ca 1940's, RWO 11/11/87 325
Pintail drake, EX orig pnt, average wear, structurally EX, RWO 2/12/88 475
Pintail drake, EX orig pnt, minor wear, thin crack along 1 side of head, ca 1930, 41, RWO 7/04/87 425

Pintail drake, EX orig pnt, RB 7/09/85 .... **250**
Pintail drake, orig pnt, touchup to white/top of head, sm crack at base of neck has been nailed, 1920, RWO 11/11/87, 62% **475**
Pintail pr, hen has old working rpt on head; drake has G orig pnt, hen has tail chip/drake has age check, RWO 7/02/88 .... **450**
Redhead drake, fine orig pnt, average flaking/wear, some age splitting/sm chip at end of tail, RB 8/27/87 .... **130**
Redhead drake, old rpt, average wear, chip in left side of bill, RB 3/06/87 .... **60**

Glover, John (Duxbury, MA)
Redbreasted Merganser drake, head extended, old Starr rpt, some orig horsehair remains on bk, 22/44, RB 5/02/86 .... **1400**

Goddard, Vance (Florence, NJ)
Black Duck, hollow w/raised primaries, tack eyes, orig pnt, minor wear, structurally EX, J/G 9/20/86 .... **225**

Goenne, William (King City, CA)
Greenwinged Teal drake, stick-up, artist initials, EX orig condition, RWO 7/05/85 .... **300**
Pintail drake, relief cvg around tail, orig pnt, ca 1938, RWO 11/06/85 .... **60**
Widgeon drake, orig pnt, minor wear, structurally sound, J/G 4/23/87 .... **150**

Goldthwaite, Herman (Damariscotta, ME)
Merganser hen, EX orig pnt, average wear w/some crazing, age split in neck, RB 8/21/86 .... **1000**
Merganser hen, old strengthening to pnt on head, RB 8/21/86 .... **600**

Goodrich, Joshua (North Carolina)
Coot, cork body, orig pnt, average wear, lg chunk of cork missing around breast, ca 1940, RWO 7/04/87 .... **25**
Coot, orig pnt, minor wear, structurally sound, 33, J/G 9/19/87 .... **150**

Goodspeed, David (Duxbury, MA)
Merganser drake, head extended, graceful cvg, traces of orig pnt w/heavy wear, 1 eye rpl, 22, RB 5/02/86, 200% **1400**

Goodspeed, David
Old Squaw drake, fine orig pnt, minor
wear, well preserved, tail is real feathers,
22/44, RB 5/02/88, 180%, $9,000.00.

Old Squaw pr, cork body, old pnt appears to be orig, minor wear, drake has end-of-tail chip, RB 8/25/88 .... **175**
Yellowlegs, EX orig pnt, minor wear, bill is a replacement, rare, 22, RB 5/02/86 .... **650**
Yellowlegs, feeding, rpt by George Starr, bill is a replacement, 22/44, RB 5/02/86 .... **475**
Yellowlegs, G orig pnt, average flaking, bill is a replacement, 22, RB 5/02/86 .... **450**
Yellowlegs, rpt w/flaking/wear, bill is in need of repair, 22, RB 5/02/86 .... **225**

Goodspeed, David; att (Duxbury, MA)
Old Squaw hen, cvd eyes, G old pnt, average wear, some age splitting, 22, RB 5/02/86 .... **550**

Gorsline, att (Prince Edward County, Ont)
Black Duck, hollow w/applied bottom board, G old pnt, average wear, sm tail chip, J/G 9/20/86 .... **160**

Graham, Horace (Charlestown, MD)
Canada Goose, outstanding orig pnt, structurally EX, detachable head, 1935, RWO 11/06/85 .... **750**
Mallard pr, drake has crack in neck, otherwise M condition, signed, RWO 11/11/87 .... **220**
Mallard pr, signed/dated 1968, unused condition, RWO 11/11/87 .... **525**

Graham, John (Charlestown, MD)
Canvasback drake, old working rpt, average flaking/wear, age split in head, RB 2/01/85 .... **150**
Canvasback drake, old working rpt, minor wear, slight rough area on edge of bill/base of neck, 33, J/G 9/19/87 .... **230**
Redhead drake, G old pnt, minor wear, sm chip on top of head, iron keel, ca 1870, rare, 73, J/G 9/19/87 .... **475**

Graham, John; att (Charlestown, MD)
Canvasback drake, early, rpt as a Black Duck, pnt shows flaking/wear, thin crack in neck, RWO 7/02/88 .... **425**
Canvasback drake, old rpt, average flaking/wear, some roughness to edge of bill, RB 2/01/85 .... **150**

Grant, Capt. Henry (Barnegat, NJ)
Black Duck, hollow, working rpt, average wear, thin crack in neck, otherwise structurally EX, 26, RWO 11/11/87 .... **200**

Bluebill drake, hollow, orig pnt, average wear, dings to wood, ms, otherwise structurally sound, RWO 11/11/87 220
Bluebill drake, rpt w/average wear, RB 7/09/85 200

Grant, Capt. Henry
Canada Goose, hollow, old working rpt worn away to reveal orig, thin cracks in neck/bill, ca 1930, RWO 7/04/87, $950.00.

Canada Goose, hollow, old rpt, average wear, slight age split in neck, 6, RB 7/07/87 775
Merganser hen, hollow, orig pnt, minor wear, half of bill is rstr, otherwise EX, ca 1900, RWO 7/05/85 850
Redhead drake, prof rstr pnt, artist brand, structurally EX, rare, J/G 9/20/86 1110
Grant, Capt. Henry; att (Barnegat, NJ)
Black Duck, old working rpt, average wear, slight separation where body halves join/crack in neck, ca 1900, RWO 7/04/87 275
Grant, Percy (Osbornville, NJ)
Brant, fine orig pnt, average wear, well preserved, rare, 20, RB 12/06/85 150
Canada Goose, hollow, old pnt, in-use wear, thin crack in neck strengthened w/nail, otherwise sound, RWO 7/05/85 1350
Grant, Stanley (Barnegat, NJ)
Bluebill drake, hollow, old working rpt, some flaking/wear, end of bill chewed, otherwise sound, ca 1920, RWO 7/06/86 90
Graves, Bert (Peoria, IL)
Black Duck, hollow, EX orig pnt, branded CJC, lg tail chip, otherwise EX, orig weight, rare, 193, RWO 7/02/88, 45% 900
Black Duck, several sm rubs/scrapes, otherwise M pnt, branded CJC, rpr chip, very rare/highly collectible, J/G 4/24/86 4125
Canvasback drake, diver tail, 2 coats of pnt by Graves, slight wear, oversize, J/G 4/24/86 715
Canvasback drake, EX orig detailed comb pnt, minor touchup, sm crack on side, retains orig weight, oversize, J/G 4/24/86 715
Canvasback drake, hollow, EX orig pnt, minor wear, well preserved, retains orig weight, rare, 39, RB 7/08/86 1850
Canvasback drake, hollow, G orig pnt, average wear, structurally EX, retains orig weight, RWO 2/13/87, 130% 1500
Canvasback drake, hollow, NM pnt, slight wear, orig weight on bottom, RB 12/06/85 2100
Canvasback drake, hollow, working overpnt worn down to reveal orig, chips to tail/ms, retains orig weight, RWO 7/04/87 90
Canvasback drake, 2 coats of pnt by Graves, minor wear, structurally EX, J/G 4/23/87 850
Canvasback hen, early, hollow, orig pnt, minor wear, bill crack, otherwise sound, orig Graves weight, RWO 7/02/88, 27% 175
Canvasback pr, hollow, hen has chunk missing from tail, otherwise EX, retain orig weight, oversize, 193/202, RWO 7/02/88 2500
Canvasback pr, working rpt removed to orig, both structurally fair & retain orig weight, Peacock brand, RWO 7/06/86, 50% 500
Mallard drake, early, orig pnt, minor wear, combing on sides/detailed feather pnt on bk, ls, J/G 4/24/86 660
Mallard drake, fine comb/feather pnt, hairline crack in neck, from C Caswell's rig, 3, J/G 4/23/87 1650
Mallard drake, hollow, EX orig pnt, average wear, no major structural flaws, retains orig weight, 193, RWO 7/02/88, 32% 650
Mallard drake, hollow, EX/NM condition, RB 7/09/85 1500
Mallard drake, hollow, fine orig pnt, minor wear, orig Graves weight on bottom, structurally sound, 189, RB 6/28/88 1050
Mallard drake, hollow, orig pnt, minor wear, thin check near base of neck, retains orig weight, RWO 7/04/87 1250
Mallard drake, hollow, partial rpt by Graves, flaking around breast, some bill wear/few dings, RWO 2/12/88 375
Mallard drake, hollow, working rpt, average wear, thin crack in neck, RWO 2/12/88 210
Mallard drake, NM orig pnt, EX condition, retains orig weight, 7, J/G 4/24/86 1320
Mallard drake, old working rpt in style of Graves, ls, J/G 9/20/86 300
Mallard drake, sleeping, NM orig pnt on body, head/neck are a prof replacement, retains orig weight, 7, J/G 4/24/86 330
Mallard drake, working rpt, no structural flaws, J/G 4/24/86 165
Mallard hen, early, fine feather pnt, minor flaking, tight check through neck, rare, J/G 4/24/86 1210
Mallard hen, early, orig pnt, minor wear, hairline crack in bill/neck, retains orig weight, J/G 4/23/87 1400
Mallard hen, fine orig feather pnt, minor wear/age lines in tail/breast, very rare, oversize, J/G 4/23/87 2500
Mallard hen, hollow, EX orig pnt, sm tail chunk missing/neck crack, otherwise sound, orig weight, 193, RWO 7/02/88, 50% 1000
Mallard hen, hollow, fine feather pnt, minor wear, sm chip & crack in tail, weight missing, J/G 9/19/87 1125
Mallard hen, M orig pnt, prof rstr to part of bill, hairline crack in neck, retains orig weight, 7, J/G 4/24/86 880
Mallard hen, taken down to orig pnt, modest wear, sm chip filled on 1 side of tail, J/G 4/23/87 425
Mallard pr, EX orig pnt, average wear, artist initials, thin cracks in neck, both retain orig weight, ls, RWO 7/06/86 2200

Graves, Bert
Mallard pr, early, NM orig pnt, both retain orig weight, branded CJC, exceptional pr, J/G 9/20/86, $5,750.00.

Mallard pr, hollow, drake pnt is NM; hen has EX orig pnt pattern/minor flaking, both retain orig weight, RB 7/08/86, 68% **1700**
Mallard pr, hollow, old rpt appears to be by Graves, moderate wear, minor age split in neck of drake, RB 8/25/88, 65% **650**
Mallard pr, orig pnt, minor wear, hen w/tail chip/hairline crack in tail/lower side; drake w/orig weight, J/G 4/23/87 .... **2150**
Pintail drake, EX orig pnt, area on 1 side worn to wood, tail chip, otherwise VG, orig weight, 193, RWO 7/02/88, 30% **550**
Pintail drake, fine orig comb pnt w/old touchup on white/black areas, branded, crack in neck, J/G 4/24/86 .... **1375**
Pintail drake, hollow, orig pnt, average wear, lg tail chip, otherwise sound, bears Graves weight, RWO 7/02/88, 35% **550**
Pintail drake, hollow, pnt stripped from body/head is orig w/touchup to white, neck crack, otherwise sound, RWO 2/12/88 .... **140**
Pintail drake, old working rpt, no structural flaws, J/G 4/24/86 .... **192**
Pintail drake, orig comb pnt, minor wear, detailed feathering, prof repair to crack in bill, J/G 4/23/87 .... **1150**
Pintail drake, orig pnt, minor wear w/thin wash of touchup on white area, ls, 33, J/G 9/19/87 .... **350**
Pintail hen, hollow, EX orig pnt, average wear, no structural flaws, retains orig weight, 193, RWO 7/02/88, 22% **550**
Graves, Bert; att (Peoria, IL)
Mallard drake, hollow, EX orig pnt by Catherine Elliston, structurally EX, ca 1930's, oversize, 51, RWO 7/04/87, 65% **1300**
Gray, Edson (Ocean View, DE)
Black Duck, EX pnt w/nice scratch pnt, structurally NM, ca 1930's or 1940's, oversize, RWO 7/04/87 .... **325**
Bufflehead drake, EX & orig condition, RWO 7/02/88 .... **125**
Canada Goose, working rpt, in-use wear, structurally sound, Ex-collection Edson Gray, RWO 11/11/87 .... **450**
Greenlee, Ken (Burlington, IA)
Bluebill drake, detailed bill cvg, tack eyes, old working rpt, minor wear, no structural flaws, rare, J/G 4/24/86 .... **137**
Bluebill drake, sleeping, old working rpt, structurally EX, ca 1930's, 76, RWO 7/06/86 .... **600**
Mallard drake, fine old pnt, average in-use wear, RB 7/09/85 .... **250**
Mallard drake, sleeping, hollow, working rpt, average flaking/wear, well preserved, rare, RB 2/01/85 .... **325**
Greiger, Fritz (Oshkosh, WI)
Bluebill drake, slightly turned head, hollow, highly detailed bill cvg, J/G 9/20/86 .... **145**
Griffin, Ernie (Ganaque, Ont)
Hooded Merganser hen, old working rpt by Griffin, J/G 9/20/86 .... **175**
Groenne, William
Greenwinged Teal drake, fine orig pnt, average wear, cvd initials, RB 7/09/85 .... **30**
Groff, Fred (Ontario)
Redhead drake, hollow, old pnt, may be orig, hs, otherwise structurally sound, RWO 11/11/87 .... **105**

Gunan, Lonnie (West Haven, CT)
Black Duck, hollow w/cvd raised wing tips, cvd eyes, unique EX orig pnt, ca 1930, RWO 7/04/87 225
Haber, Allen (Neenah, WI)
Mallard pr, hollow w/applied bottom board, NM detailed orig pnt, sm chip in underside of drake's bill, J/G 4/24/86 660
Haertel, Harold (Dundee, IL)
Black Duck, unpnt cork body, NM orig pnt on wood, structurally EX, made for son Tom's hunting rig, J/G 4/23/87 600
Bluewinged Teal, signed/identified/dated 1969, few sm rubs in varnish on side, otherwise M, J/G 4/23/87 300
Bufflehead pr, cork bodies, wooden heads/tails, M pnt, identified/inscribed/dated 1973, rare, J/G 4/23/87 1500
Dove, artist stamp, inscribed/dated 1972, M condition, J/G 4/23/87 1000
Gadwall drake, cork body, EX orig condition, ca 1950, 53, RWO 7/05/85 1400
Gadwall drake, cvd raised wing tips, fine orig pnt, minor wear, ls, 189, RB 6/28/88 1000
Goldeneye drake, cork body, wooden tail/head, M condition, J/G 4/23/87 200
Piping Plover, cvd layered primaries, M pnt, rare, J/G 4/23/87 800
Hall, Parker (Massachusetts)
Beetlehead, erect head, cvd split tail, G old pnt, average wear, reglued at neck, ls, 22/44, RB 5/02/86 1000
Blackbellied Plover, orig pnt, flaking to bare wood in some areas, structurally EX, RWO 7/04/87 475

Hall, Parker
Plover, orig pnt, average wear, ls, otherwise VG, RWO 2/13/87, $700.00.

Hall, Severin (Northeast, MD)
Coot, signed, M condition, ca 1947, RWO 11/06/85 550
Hall, Tom
Brant, hollow, old pnt, heavy flaking/wear, bill is a replacement, RB 7/08/86 100
Hallowell, Winslow
Old Squaw drake, orig pnt, some flaking & wear, chip at end of tail, age split at neck, 22, RB 5/02/86 175
Hamilton, John (Barnegat Bay, NJ)
Bluewinged Teal drake, sleeping, hollow, NM condition, RB 8/25/88 175
Bluewinged Teal hen, sleeping, artist brand, M condition, RWO 11/06/85 120
Brant, hollow, EX condition, RB 6/28/88 125
Brant, hollow, EX orig pnt, lead weight marked J Hamilton, RB 8/27/87 80
Bufflehead drake, EX orig pnt, RB 7/07/87 100
Bufflehead drake, M condition, RWO 11/06/85 75
Bufflehead pr, NM orig pnt, artist brand, structurally EX, J/G 9/19/87 225
Canvasback pr, signed, M condition, J/G 9/19/87 175
Goose, swimming, NM orig pnt, minor shrinkage on lower sides, artist brand, J/G 9/19/87 200
Greenwinged Teal drake, hollow, artist brand, NM condition, RWO 11/06/85 170
Greenwinged Teal pr, artist brand, M condition, J/G 9/19/87 150
Hooded Merganser drake, orig pnt, EX condition, RWO 11/06/85 80
Hooded Merganser drake, slightly turned head, hollow, M pnt, artist stamp, J/G 9/20/86 170
Hooded Merganser pr, drake has slightly turned head; hen has hairline crack in side, otherwise M, J/G 9/19/87 225
Old Squaw pr, NM orig pnt, artist brand, top tail sprig is missing on drake, J/G 9/19/87 150
Redbreasted Merganser drake, hollow, EX form, signed, M condition, RWO 11/06/85 220
Redbreasted Merganser drake, hollow, EX orig pnt, average wear, EX form, RB 7/07/87 325
Redbreasted Merganser pr, artist brand, M condition, J/G 9/19/87 225
Redbreasted Merganser pr, hollow, NM orig pnt, artist brand, structurally EX, J/G 9/20/86 175

Ruddy Duck pr, M condition, J/G 9/19/87 .... **200**
Scoter pr, signed, M condition, J/G 9/19/87 .... **150**
Surf Scoter, hollow, EX pnt, minor flaking, artist signed, RB 8/25/88 .... **225**
Widgeon drake, sleeping, fine orig pnt, average wear, artist brand, well preserved, RB 8/27/87 .... **180**
Wood Duck drake, fine orig pnt, average wear, well preserved, RB 7/07/87 .... **625**

Hammel, Bill
Merganser hen, old pnt, heavy wear, some chipping to crest, RB 3/11/88 .... **450**

Hance, Ben (Bay Head, NJ)
Brant, early, hollow, old orig pnt, average wear, crack in neck, otherwise structurally sound, RWO 07/06/86 .... **190**

Hance, Jim; att
Canvasback drake, in-use wear, several age splits in body/chips at end of tail, 21, RB 2/01/85 .... **260**

Hancock, Herb
Brant, artist signed, EX & orig condition, RB 6/28/88 .... **75**
Mallard drake, cvd crossed wing tips, artist signed/branded, EX condition, RB 6/28/88 .... **150**
Redbreasted Merganser drake, G orig pnt, slight age split on bottom, signed/dated 1979, 22, RB 5/02/86 .... **375**

Hancock, Miles (Chincoteague, VA)
Black Duck, old working rpt wearing away to reveal orig, some tail chips/sm dings in bill, RWO 7/04/87 .... **130**
Black Duck, orig pnt, heavy wear w/few places worn to bare wood, structurally sound, RWO 7/06/86 .... **820**
Bluebill drake, old pnt, average flaking/wear, slight age splits in body, RB 7/07/87 .... **110**
Bluebill drake, orig pnt by Delbert or Ira Hudson, RWO 2/12/88 .... **205**
Bluebill drake, rpt by Ira Hudson, EX condition, RB 7/09/85 .... **150**
Bluebill hen, old pnt, heavy flaking/wear, several age splits in body, RB 3/06/87 .... **125**
Bluebill pr, G orig pnt, average wear, hen has several areas of flaking, RB 2/01/85 .... **175**
Bluebill pr, orig pnt, average wear, structurally sound, RWO 7/06/86 .... **275**
Bluebill pr, orig pnt, average wear w/some areas to bare wood, bears Mackey stamp, structurally sound, RWO 7/06/86 .... **280**
Bufflehead drake, NM condition, RWO 11/11/87 .... **240**
Bufflehead drake, old working rpt, minor wear, bears Ferris Mackey stamp, sm crack in bill, J/G 9/20/86 .... **250**
Bufflehead hen, G orig pnt, average wear, chip at end of bill/tail, ls, RB 3/11/88 .... **200**
Bufflehead hen, orig pnt, average wear, circular crack in bk, otherwise structurally sound, RWO 7/06/86 .... **160**
Bufflehead pr, G orig pnt to hen; drake is rpt, both show average wear, RB 2/01/85 .... **175**
Canada Goose, floater/stick-up, old pnt, average flaking/wear, several age splits, RB 8/27/87 .... **125**
Canada Goose, old rpt, average flaking/wear, RB 2/01/85 .... **150**
Canada Goose, orig pnt, sm chip of wood missing along 1 side of head, otherwise EX, RWO 7/06/86 .... **300**
Canada Goose, signed/dated 1948, unusual, M condition, RWO 7/06/86, 275% **825**
Canvasback drake, old working rpt, average wear, splinter of wood missing from underside of bill, RWO 7/06/86 .... **140**
Canvasback drake, orig pnt, touchup to wht areas is worn to bare wood on most of body, structurally sound, RWO 2/12/88 .... **140**
Canvasback drake, working rpt worn/flaking to reveal orig, thin crack in neck/body, ls, RWO 11/11/87 .... **220**
Canvasback hen, orig pnt, average wear, thin crack in neck, otherwise structurally sound, RWO 7/06/86 .... **130**
Canvasback hen, working rpt, average wear, structurally EX, RWO 2/12/88 .... **160**
Goldeneye drake, orig pnt, average wear, structurally EX, RWO 7/06/86 .... **225**
Hooded Merganser drake, EX orig pnt, minor wear, RB 8/21/86 .... **425**
Hooded Merganser drake, orig pnt, average wear, structurally EX, rare, RWO 7/06/86 .... **825**
Hooded Merganser drake, some orig pnt w/areas of working touchup, few dings to wood, otherwise sound, RWO 7/04/87 .... **300**
Hooded Merganser hen, cottonwood body, orig pnt worn to bare wood in areas, narrow checks to head/body, RWO 11/11/87 .... **260**
Hooded Merganser pr, EX orig pnt, minor wear, hen has natural flaw in wood on 1 side, otherwise EX, 49, RWO 11/11/87 .... **1100**

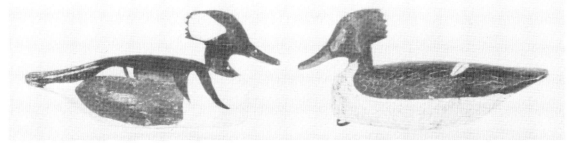

Hancock, Miles
Hooded Merganser pr, EX orig pnt, minor wear, signed on bottom, NM, RB 8/27/87, 205%, $1,450.00.

Merganser drake, orig pnt, moderate wear, tight check in breast/bill is an old replacement, J/G 9/20/86 .... **175**

Merganser hen, G orig pnt, average wear, RB 3/11/88 350
Merganser hen, NM orig pnt, scratch feathering on bk/sides, structurally EX, J/G 9/20/86 225
Merganser hen, rpt, minor wear, head appears to be an old Hancock replacement, RB 7/07/87 50
Pintail drake, few dings to pnt, otherwise unused condition, RWO 7/02/88 575
Pintail drake, old working rpt, average wear, structurally sound, RWO 11/06/85 110
Pintail drake, orig pnt, minor wear, several tight checks in head/neck, longer tail than typical, lg, J/G 4/23/87 350
Pintail drake, unused w/slight crazing of pnt on both sides of head, structurally sound, never weighted, 49, RWO 7/06/86 425
Pintail hen, G orig pnt, minor wear, RB 2/01/85 250
Pintail hen, rpt by Ward brothers, average wear, bill has been prof repaired by Kenneth DeLong, RB 12/06/85 150
Redbreasted Merganser drake, old rpt, average flaking/wear, RB 7/07/87 100
Redbreasted Merganser drake, orig pnt, average wear, old repair to neck, RB 7/07/87 275
Redbreasted Merganser hen, VG orig pnt, signed/dated 1933, several hairlines in body, 1 eye missing, 33, J/G 9/19/87 330
Redbreasted Merganser pr, old working rpt, average wear, drake has check running down bk, otherwise sound, RWO 7/06/86 200
Redbreasted Merganser pr, outstanding orig pnt, NM condition, RB 3/06/87, 140% 1400
Widgeon drake, balsa body, old pnt, appears to be orig w/flaking/wear, RB 2/01/85 80

Hancock, Miles; att (Chincoteague, VA)
Bluebill drake, old working rpt w/traces of orig around head, crack running through head, otherwise sound, RWO 7/06/86 80
Brant, old pnt, average wear, structurally sound, RWO 11/06/85 70

Hancock, Roy (Bath, IL)
Mallard drake, NM orig condition, J/G 4/24/86 385
Pintail drake, hollow, rpt w/flaking/wear, structurally sound, RB 3/06/87 80

Hancock, Russell; att (Chilmark, MA)
Black Duck, slightly turned head, slight roughness to edge of bill, RB 7/08/86 100

Hand, Jamie (Cape May, NJ)
Brant, hollow, artist brand, M condition, RWO 7/02/88 160
Eider drake, hollow, EX condition, RB 7/09/85 70
Gadwall hen, hollow, EX condition, RB 6/28/85 40
Hooded Merganser pr, hollow, artist brand, M condition, RWO 2/12/88 225
Loon, hollow, EX condition, RB 7/09/85 230
Redbreasted Merganser drake, hollow, EX & orig, RB 7/09/85 120
Swan, hollow, artist brand, M condition, RWO 11/11/87 425

Hanemann, Billy
Pintail drake, preening, G orig pnt, minor wear, RB 7/07/87 350

Hansen, Clyde (Wayne, PA)
Brant, hollow, orig pnt, average wear, structurally sound, RWO 11/11/87 75

Hardcastle, Edmund; att
Redhead drake, old pnt, heavy wear, RB 7/08/86 45

Harper, James F.; att (Hamilton, Ont)
Goldeneye hen, fine orig pnt, average wear, 189, RB 6/28/88 170

Harrington, David (Underhill Center, VT)
Goldeneye drake, fine old pnt, average flaking/wear, well preserved, RB 8/27/87 60
Goldeneye drake, orig pnt, minor wear, no structural flaws, J/G 9/19/87 100
Goldeneye hen, prof pnt rstr, structurally EX, rare, J/G 9/20/86 120

Harris, Alvin (Atlantic, NC)
Bluebill, balsa body, EX orig pnt, artist initialed, RB 7/08/86, 335% 825
Brant, 2-pc balsa body w/bottom board, EX orig condition, ca 1930, RWO 11/11/87 375
Canada Goose, cork body, NM orig pnt, several sm chips in cork, 33, J/G 9/19/87 350
Knot, old pnt, average wear, much of bill is chipped away, rare, RB 8/27/87 150
Redhead pr, balsa w/pine bottom board, hen: NM orig pnt; drake: minor wear & sm rough spot, 127/33, J/G 9/19/87, 145% 2100
Redhead pr, EX orig pnt, signed/dated 1938, hen has minor rub at end of tail, RB 3/06/87 1500

Harris, Alvin
Redhead pr, EX orig pnt, signed/dated 1938, minor splits/refitted filler, RB 7/07/87, $1,000.00.

Harris, Arthur (Nantucket, MA)
Golden Plover, eyeless, NM orig pnt, bill is a replacement, J/G 9/19/87 200
Golden Plover, NM orig pnt, hairline crack in bk, bill is a replacement, J/G 9/19/87 250
Golden Plover, NM orig pnt, sm worn area on 1 side, tip of bill missing, J/G 9/19/87 225
Golden Plover, strong NM orig pnt, ls, J/G 9/19/87 600

Harris, Ken (Woodville, NY)
Black Duck, balsa body, G orig pnt w/nice feathering, average wear, artist stamp, structurally sound, RWO 7/02/88 100
Black Duck, cork body, G orig condition, ca 1940, RWO 2/12/88 60
Black Duck, EX orig pnt, artist stamp, RB 8/21/86 275
Black Duck, EX orig pnt, artist stamp, RWO 11/06/85 90
Black Duck, fine orig pnt, minor wear, artist stamp, well preserved, 189, RB 6/28/88 175
Black Duck, hollow, G orig pnt, artist stamp, repair to bill, otherwise structurally EX, RWO 11/06/85 70
Black Duck, orig pnt, in-use wear, artist stamp/dated 1960, thin check running down bk, RWO 7/06/86 80
Black Duck, slightly turned head, cvd layered primaries/secondaries w/crossed wing tips, M condition, 103, J/G 4/23/87 625
Bluebill drake, G orig pnt, average wear, end-of-bill chip, RB 8/25/88 70
Bluebill hen, G orig pnt, average wear, stenciled w/artist name/hometown, 1 glass eye missing, otherwise EX, RWO 7/02/88 150
Bluebill hen, orig pnt, average wear, artist stamp, structurally sound, ca 1940, RWO 2/12/88 80
Bluebill hen, slightly turned head, detailed pnt pattern w/several sm rubs, otherwise M, J/G 9/20/86 275
Bluewinged Teal drake, slightly turned head, cvd crossed wing tips/fluted tail, M condition, 103, J/G 4/23/87 425
Canada Goose, balsa body, NM pnt, RB 12/06/85 225
Canvasback, full body, G orig pnt, average wear, some roughness to end of bill, RB 8/25/88 35
Canvasback drake, artist stamp, sm chip on underside of bill, otherwise EX condition, RB 8/25/88 80
Canvasback drake, EX orig condition, 39, RB 7/08/86 150
Canvasback drake, fine orig pnt, average wear, roughness to lower right side & bill, RB 8/25/88 45
Canvasback drake, G orig pnt, average wear w/minor flaking on bk, structurally EX, RWO 11/11/87 150
Canvasback drake, old working rpt, artist stamp, minor crack part way through neck, oversize, J/G 9/20/86 85
Canvasback pr, EX orig pnt, average wear, artist stamp, structurally EX, RWO 7/04/87 550
Canvasback pr, high-head style, balsa body, fine orig pnt, minor dents, slight age split in drake's head, 21, RB 2/01/85 250
Canvasback pr, NM condition, RB 7/08/86 400
Cinnamon Teal, raised wing & feather cvg on bk, M condition, RWO 7/05/85 260
Goldeneye drake, artist brand, EX & orig, RB 3/06/87 200
Goldeneye drake, EX orig condition, 39, RB 7/08/86 300
Goldeneye drake, G orig pnt, minor wear, artist stamp, both glass eyes missing/tail chip, RWO 7/02/88 80
Hooded Merganser pr, slightly turned heads, relief cvd primaries/secondaries, drake w/combed pnt, M, 103, J/G 4/23/87 850
Mallard drake, EX orig pnt, average wear, artist brand, ls, thin crack in neck, otherwise well preserved, RWO 7/04/87 325
Mallard drake, orig pnt, minor wear, artist stamp, minor age split in neck, RB 3/11/88 275
Mallard drake, outstanding orig condition, artist stamp, RWO 11/06/85 120
Mallard drake, slightly turned head, EX pnt, artist stamp, RB 8/21/86 325
Mallard hen, balsa body, G orig pnt, minor wear, 22, RB 5/02/86 300
Mallard hen, NM orig pnt w/fine comb pnt, sm rough area on edge of bill, J/G 4/23/87 225
Mallard pr, slightly turned heads, cvd primaries/secondaries w/crossed wing tips, M condition, 103, J/G 4/23/87 900
Pintail drake, EX orig comb/scratch pnt, average wear, artist stamp, structurally EX, RWO 7/04/87 400
Pintail drake, raised feather cvg on bk, EX pnt, RB 7/08/86 300
Pintail pr, slightly turned heads, cvd primaries/secondaries, EX combing on drake; G feathering on hen, 103, J/G 4/23/87 850
Redbreasted Merganser pr, turned heads, cvd wings & feathered crests, fluted tails, feather pnt, M, 103, J/G 4/23/87 900
Redhead drake, M pnt, artist stamp, RWO 11/06/85 280
Redhead drake, old working rpt, average wear w/some flaking along sides, structurally sound, RWO 7/02/88 50
Redhead drake, orig pnt w/nice scratch pnt on bk, artist stamp, sm gouge near tail, otherwise sound, RWO 7/02/88 80
Teal drake, unfinished, sm chip at end of tail, RB 7/07/87 60
Wood Duck drake, EX orig pnt, RB 2/01/85 375

Harris, Ken
Wood duck pr, slightly turned heads, cvd primaries/secondaries, extended wing tips, finely blended pnt, 103, J/G 4/23/87, $1,300.00.

Harris, Ken; att (Woodville, NY)
Black Duck, fine orig pnt, average wear, bill has been broken & reglued, RB 3/06/87 100

Hart, Archeal
Bluebill hen, detailed feather cvg on bk tail area, old pnt, some of which is orig, average wear, ls, RB 8/25/88 50

Hart, Charles (Gloucester, MA)
Black Duck, hollow, deeply cvd wings/primaries, G orig pnt, average flaking/wear, 22/44, RB 5/02/86, 295% 4400
Black Duck, hollow, detailed cvg on bk, superb form, EX orig stain/pnt w/minimal wear, 1900, RWO 7/06/86, 120% 4250
Black Duck, hollow w/detailed wing/tail cvg, EX orig pnt, minor wear, repair to bill/tail, EX, ca 1900, RWO 7/06/86 3250
Black Duck, hollow w/EX relief cvg on bk, fine feather pnt, minor wear, bottom plate is a prof replacement, J/G 4/23/87 4300
Black Duck, slightly turned head, 4-pc body, hollow, EX orig pnt, artist brand, EX condition, rare, 39, RB 7/08/86, 57% 1300
Black Duck, standing, cvd primaries/secondaries, fine form, orig stain/pnt, minor wear, sm tail/neck cracks, J/G 4/23/87 700
Black Duck, standing, cvd primaries/secondaries, orig pnt, minor wear, 2 tight checks on underside, J/G 4/23/87 450
Black Duck, swivel head, superb wing feather cvg on bk, NM pnt, RB 7/07/87, 45% 1750

Hart, Charles
Canada Goose, stick-up, hollow, G orig pnt, average wear, rare, 22/44, RB 5/02/86, $12,000.00.

Mallard drake, cvd primaries/secondaries, leather tail sprig, NM orig pnt, 106, J/G 4/23/87 4300
Mallard pr, hollow w/deeply cvd wing patterns/primary feathers, EX orig pnt, minor flaking, 22/44, RB 5/02/86, 137% 5500
Scoter, American; old working rpt, average wear, chips to tail, ms, otherwise structurally sound, RWO 7/06/86 175
Scoter, hollow, worn old pnt, hs, dings to wood, otherwise structurally sound, RWO 2/13/87 250

Harvey, George (New Jersey)
Blackbellied Plover, extremely light balsa body, G orig pnt, little wear, 9/77, RB 12/06/85 350
Bluebill drake, hollow, rpt, average wear, ca 1900, 9, RB 12/06/85 150
Canada Goose, hollow, old pnt, average wear, left eye missing, 9, RB 12/06/85 450
Goldeneye drake, fine old pnt, average wear, 1, RB 12/06/85 150
Redbreasted Merganser drake, old pnt, average flaking/wear, bk of crest is chipped away, 9/77, RB 12/06/85 900
Yellowlegs, G old pnt, bill is a prof replacement, 105, J/G 4/23/87 350

Hawkins, E.; att (Bay Head, NJ)
Redhead drake, hollow, old orig pnt, average wear, thin crack in neck, otherwise structurally sound, RWO 7/06/86 50

Hawthorne, Davey (Salisbury, MD)
Bluewinged Teal drake, slightly turned head, raised cvd wing outline, J/G 4/23/87 200
Greenwinged Teal drake, signed/dated 1972, M condition, RWO 11/11/87 225
Greenwinged Teal pr, EX orig pnt, minor wear, structurally sound, ca 1969, RWO 11/11/87 325
Gull, turned head, raised wings w/extended tips, NM orig pnt, minor discoloration, J/G 9/19/87 375
Pintail pr, EX orig pnt, signed on bottom, RB 7/09/85 425
Sea Gull, raised cvd primaries/wing tips, EX pnt, RB 7/08/86 350

Hayman, John (Churches Island, NC)
Black Duck, NM orig pnt, sm area on 1 side where pnt has bubbled from heat, 33, J/G 9/19/87 275

Canvasback drake, orig pnt, minor wear, no structural flaws, 33, J/G 9/19/87 .... **450**
Redhead drake, old working rpt worn down to orig, 2 sm tail chips, ls, 33, J/G 9/19/87 .... **225**
Haywood, Mannie (Kill Devil Hills, NC)
Canada Goose, canvas over wire frame, old working rpt, minor wear, 33, J/G 9/19/87 .... **200**
Canada Goose, canvas-covered, old working rpt, average wear, structurally sound, RWO 7/02/88 .... **25**
Greenwinged Teal pr, pnt in 1970's by Vern Berg, ca 1940's, rare, RWO 11/06/85 .... **250**
Mallard pr, orig pnt, minor wear, canvas worn through to wire in some areas, ca 1925, very rare, 33/122, J/G 9/19/87 .... **700**
Headley, Somers (Newport, DE)
Greenwinged Teal pr, EX orig pnt by Mary Lou Powell, structurally EX, from his personal hunting rig, RWO 11/11/87 .... **120**
Heard, Lew (Lacey Springs, LA)
Bluewinged Teal pr, hen is swimming, tupelo gum wood body, EX pnt, structurally NM, RWO 7/06/86 .... **130**
Heath, Ed; att
Redbreasted Merganser drake, hollow, orig pnt, average flaking/wear, structurally sound, RB 3/11/88 .... **700**
Hebert, Norman (Golden Meadow, LA)
Bufflehead pr, artist brand, EX condition, RB 6/28/88 .... **80**
Greenwinged Teal pr, EX & orig condition, RWO 2/12/88 .... **100**
Ruddy Duck pr, artist brand, EX condition, RB 6/28/88 .... **40**
Heinefield, August (Rock Hall, MD)
Canada Goose, old pnt, flaking/wear, ms, age split in bottom, RB 7/09/85 .... **450**
Redhead pr, old working rpt, minor wear, filled crack in underside of drake; hairline crack in hen's tail, J/G 9/19/87 .... **225**
Redhead pr, working rpt, average wear, thin tight checks on hen; crack in drake's neck, otherwise EX, RWO 11/11/87 .... **180**
Heinefield, August; att (Rock Hall, MD)
Redhead drake, 2-pc body construction, orig pnt mostly worn away, checks in bottom/neck, RWO 7/04/87 .... **70**
Heisler, Jess (Burlington, NJ)
Black Duck, high-head, hollow, old working rpt w/G orig around head, structurally sound, oversize, RWO 7/02/88, 40% **475**
Black Duck, hollow w/raised 'V' wing tips, tack eyes, orig pnt, minor wear, neck crack, rare, oversize, J/G 9/19/87 .... **1800**

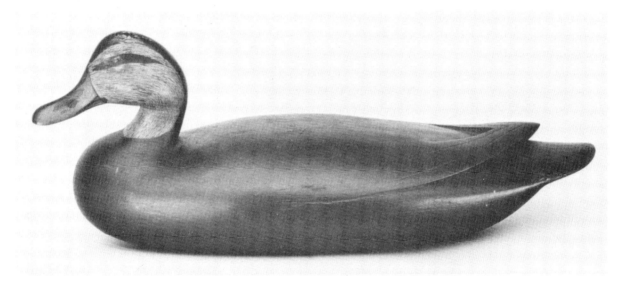

Heisler, Jess
Black Duck, raised cvd wing tips, EX orig pnt, minor wear, from his personal rig, rare, oversize, ca 1925, RB 2/01/85, $1,900.00.

Pintail drake, hollow, EX orig pnt, average wear, hairline crack in neck, otherwise EX, ca 1935, RWO 7/05/85 .... **650**
Heisler, Jess; att (Burlington, NJ)
Black Duck, low-head style, hollow, old working rpt, average wear, chip under bill, otherwise EX, RWO 7/04/87 .... **190**
Hendershot, Burl
Bluebill drake, EX orig pnt, signed on bottom, RB 2/01/85 .... **125**
Canada Goose, hollowed out from bottom, orig pnt, minor wear, RB 2/01/85 .... **75**
Hendrickson, Gene (Lower Bank, NJ)
Black Duck, hollow, M condition, RWO 7/02/88 .... **100**
Black Duck, hollow, old rpt w/flaking/wear, shallow chip at end of bill, RB 3/06/87 .... **75**
Black Duck, hollow, orig pnt w/touchup around head, structurally EX, RWO 7/06/86 .... **50**
Black Duck, swimming, hollow, M pnt, ca 1950, RWO 7/04/87 .... **170**

Brant, hollow, artist brand, M condition, RWO 7/06/86 100
Canada Goose, feeding, hollow, EX orig pnt, average flaking/wear, well preserved, RB 7/07/87 500
Canada Goose, hollow, outstanding orig pnt, artist brand/dated 1970, RWO 7/06/86 100
Canada Goose, swimming, hollow, EX & orig, RWO 7/06/86 110
Canvasback drake, hollow, artist brand/dated 1971, sm dings to pnt on head, otherwise M, RWO 7/06/86 140
Goldeneye drake, hollow, fine orig pnt, minor wear, well preserved, RB 7/07/87 175
Greenwinged Teal drake, hollow, artist brand/dated 1971, M condition, RWO 7/06/86 50
Mallard drake, hollow, EX orig pnt, branded JEH, ca 1945, RB 8/27/87 160
Mallard drake, hollow, EX pnt by Bob White, artist brand, RB 7/07/87 100
Mallard drake, hollow, orig pnt, minor wear, well preserved, RB 7/08/86 80
Mallard drake, swimming, hollow, EX orig pnt, branded JEH, ca 1945, RB 8/27/87 160
Merganser hen, American; hollow, EX orig pnt, artist's initials branded into the inletted weight, ca 1950, RWO 11/11/87 185
Merganser hen, hollow, orig pnt, minor crazing, structurally EX, inset rectangular weight, J/G 4/24/86 165
Old Squaw drake, hollow, branded JEH, M condition, RWO 7/02/88 170
Old Squaw drake, hollow, M pnt, ca 1950, RWO 7/04/87 200
Pintail drake, hollow, EX pnt, artist brand, NM condition, RWO 7/06/86 90
Redbreasted Merganser drake, hollow, artist brand/dated 1969, M condition, RWO 7/06/86 150
Hendrickson, J.E. (Lower Bank, NJ)
Black Duck, hollow, rpt, average wear, age split in neck, chip on underside of bill, RB 6/28/88 70
Black Duck, preening, hollow, pnt stripped to natural wood, some minor age splitting, RB 3//11/88, 250% 375
Bluebill pr, EX orig pnt, minor wear, 189, RB 6/28/88 325
Bluebill pr, hollow, minor flaking/wear, EX condition, RB 3/11/88 300
Bluebill pr, hollow, orig pnt, average wear, structurally sound, RB 3/11/88 300
Canada Goose, hollow, orig pnt, heavy flaking/wear, minor age splitting to body, RB 3/11/88, 62% 250
Canvasback pr, orig pnt, minor wear, no structural flaws, rare, J/G 9/19/87 150
Goldeneye drake, hollow, orig pnt, average wear, ls, RB 3/11/88 300
Merganser pr, drake has NM orig pnt; hen has orig pnt w/minor shrinkage, no structural flaws, J/G 9/19/87 300
Old Squaw drake, fine orig pnt, minor wear, RB 8/21/86 150
Old Squaw drake, hollow, orig pnt, average wear, ms, RB 3/11/88 250
Redbreasted Merganser drake, EX pnt, artist brand, RB 2/01/85 275
Redbreasted Merganser pr, hollow, both have some pnt crazing, drake has been ls, RB 3/11/88 130% 650

Hendrickson, J.E.
Redbreasted Merganser pr, hollow, minor flaking/wear, structurally EX, RB 3/11/88, $650.00.

Redbreasted Merganser pr, hollow, orig pnt, average wear, hen has age split in neck, 189, RB 6/28/88 550
Henfield, August; att (Rock Hall, MD)
Canvasback drake, old rpt, average wear, well preserved, RB 7/08/86 150
Henriegs, Pat
Brant, hollow, fine old pnt, average wear, structurally sound, RB 7/08/86 175
Henson, Brodie
Bluebill drake, hollow w/relief cvd primaries/raised wing cvg, EX orig pnt, minor wear, structurally EX, RWO 7/06/86 110
Greenwinged Teal pr, hollow, cvd raised primaries, tail cvg, M condition, RWO 11/06/85 850
Herbert, Norman (Golden Meadow, LA)
Bluewinged Teal drake, EX orig pnt, RWO 7/04/87 80
Shoveler hen, tupelo wood, M condition, RWO 11/11/87 60
Heverin, Will (Charlestown, MD)
Black Duck, high-tail style, orig pnt, average wear, check on 1 side, otherwise structurally EX, 1935, 73, RWO 11/06/85 300
Black Duck, mid-body tail style, G orig pnt, minor wear, ca 1930, 5/70, RWO 11/06/85 575
Black Duck, mid-body tail style, NM orig pnt, sm dent in lower side, rare, 5/70, J/G 9/19/87, 145% 1350
Black Duck, orig pnt, average wear, structurally EX, RWO 2/12/88 650
Bluebill drake, EX orig pnt, minimal wear, artist brand, ca 1930, 73, RWO 11/06/85 450
Bluebill drake, orig pnt, average wear, crack in neck, otherwise structurally VG, ca 1935, RWO 7/05/85 210

Bluebill drake, rpt, minor wear, well preserved, RB 7/07/87 120
Canvasback drake, fine orig pnt, average wear, well preserved, RB 3/06/87 375
Canvasback drake, head is orig pnt, body is rpt, structurally EX, RWO 7/06/86 210
Canvasback drake, high-head, some orig pnt w/touchup to head/blk areas, crack in bill, RWO 2/12/88, 230% 700
Canvasback drake, old rpt, flaking/wear, RB 2/01/85 140
Canvasback drake, old working rpt, average wear, crack running through neck, otherwise sound, ca 1900, RWO 11/11/87 220
Canvasback drake, rstr to pnt, thin crack in neck/repair to underside of bill, RWO 7/04/87 300
Canvasback hen, early, old working rpt, minor wear, crack in neck, ls, 33, J/G 9/19/87 225

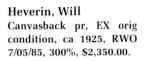

Heverin, Will
Canvasback pr, EX orig
condition, ca 1925, RWO
7/05/85, 300%, $2,350.00.

Canvasback pr, G orig pnt, hen has hairline crack in bill, otherwise structurally EX, ca 1930, RWO 11/06/85 700
Canvasback pr, old working rpt, no structural flaws, 33, J/G 9/19/87 500
Canvasback pr, old working rpt by Severin Hall, structurally EX, from the Ed Robinson rig, RWO 7/06/86 350
Canvasback pr, orig pnt, average wear, well preserved, RB 3/06/87 850
Mallard drake, cvd tail feathers/crossed wing tips, metal tail sprigs, M pnt w/G patina, ca 1950, J/G 4/23/87 650
Redhead drake, old working rpt by Severin Hall, average wear, structurally sound, from the Ed Robinson rig, RWO 7/06/86 120
Redhead drake, working rpt, minor wear, structurally sound, ca 1935, RWO 7/06/86 300
Redhead pr, orig pnt, structurally NM, never weighted, ca 1930, 5, RWO 11/06/85 2500

Hibbert, Dave (Mt. Clemens, MI)
Canvasback drake, orig pnt w/areas of working touchup, 2 thin cracks on bk, otherwise structurally sound, RWO 11/06/85 140
Canvasback pr, fine old pnt, appears to be orig w/minor wear, RB 2/01/85 275

Hickman, Calvin (Salem, NJ)
Black Duck, 3-pc body construction, rpt in Hickman style, minor wear, ls, J/G 9/19/87 200

Hildreth, Ephram (Rio Grande, NJ)
Curlew, folky lines, orig pnt, heavy wear, artist brand, replaced bill, 50, RB 12/06/85 1100
Curlew, old pnt, average flaking/wear, artist brand, replaced bill, RB 3/11/88 800
Yellowlegs, orig pnt, heavy flaking/wear, artist brand, RB 3/11/88 500

Hill, Dr. Lewis Webb (Chatham, MA)
Black Duck, head tucked down, canvas-covered, fine orig pnt, average wear, well preserved, RB 8/21/86 200
Black Duck, hollow, EX orig pnt, RB 7/09/85 150
Ruddy Turnstone, EX orig pnt, minor wear, well preserved, 22/44, RB 5/02/86 500

Hillman, Anthony
Redbreasted Merganser drake, artist signed, EX condition, RB 3/11/88 80
Sea Gull, hollow, EX pnt, artist brand, end of bill has been chewed, RB 2/01/85 120

Hills, Bob (Nantucket, MA)
Goldeneye drake, fine orig pnt, average flaking/wear, 22/44, RB 5/02/86 475

Hinckley, Charles
Yellowlegs, old working rpt taken down to reveal traces of orig, structurally sound, RWO 7/06/86, 50% 500

Hinckley, George (Massachusetts)
Yellowlegs, feeding, EX orig condition, RWO 7/05/85 1550
Yellowlegs, flat-body, EX orig pnt, RB 2/01/85 175
Yellowlegs, running, G orig pnt, minor wear, rare, RB 2/01/85, 75% 1200

Hinkley, John (Essex, CT)
Yellowlegs, orig pnt, minor wear, 2 minor age lines, bill is an old replacement, J/G 4/23/87 1200

Hitchens, Harry (Belville, Ont)
Bluebill drake, hollow, orig pnt, minor wear, artist stamp, J/G 9/20/86 175

Hoadley, Arthur (Milford, CT)
Black Duck, hollow, orig pnt, average wear, scratch pnt, slight separation at body joint, ca 1925, RWO 11/11/87 125
Holland, Mark
Curlew, EX pnt, signed on bottom, RB 7/07/87 450
Holloway, John (Florence, NJ)
Black Duck, hollow, EX orig pnt, minor wear, artist brand, some crazing to body/bk of head, RB 8/27/87 200
Black Duck, hollow w/raised cvd primaries, cvd tail feathers, artist brand, M condition, 65, J/G 9/20/86 375
Black Duck, low-head style, hollow w/raised 'V' primaries, orig pnt, minor wear, artist brand, RWO 11/11/87 160
Canada Goose, hollow, fine orig pnt, average wear, artist brand, RB 8/21/86 225
Goldeneye drake, hollow, EX orig pnt, initialed, RB 8/27/87 140
Greenwinged Teal pr, hollow, orig pnt, initials cvd in bottom, EX condition, RB 8/27/87 250
Hooded Merganser hen, artist signed, EX & orig condition, RB 3/11/88 100
Hooded Merganser hen, hollow, orig pnt is heavily flocked, RB 3/11/88 60
Mallard pr, tucked heads, hollow w/raised cvd wing tips, EX orig pnt w/minor crazing, artist brand, RB 8/27/87 400
Merganser pr, hollow, EX condition, orig pnt, average wear, initials cvd on bottom, RB 8/27/87 350
Old Squaw drake, hollow, orig pnt, average wear, slight crazing around breast, structurally sound, RWO 7/06/86 200
Old Squaw pr, hollow, fine orig pnt, average flaking/wear, RB 6/28/88 150
Redbreasted Merganser pr, hollow, artist brand, M condition, RWO 11/11/87 100
Redhead drake, hollow, EX condition, RB 6/28/88 125
Widgeon drake, low-head style, hollow, artist brand, M condition, RWO 2/13/87 245
Holloway, Tom (Monkton, VT)
Goldeneye drake, cork body, NM orig pnt, structurally EX, oversize, J/G 9/19/87 30
Holly, Capt. Ben (Havre de Grace, MD)
Canvasback drake, old rpt, heavy flaking/wear, several age splits, RB 8/25/88 140
Redhead drake, old rpt, heavy flaking/wear, well preserved, RB 2/01/85 275
Holly, James (Havre de Grace, MD)
Black Duck, early, outstanding orig pnt w/EX scratch pnt, structurally EX, rare, 69, RWO 7/02/88, 52% 1800
Black Duck, G orig pnt, average wear, crack in neck, otherwise structurally EX, ca 1922, RWO 11/06/85, 170% 1500
Black Duck, old working rpt, 2 tight checks in neck/1 in underside of body, ca 1890, rare, J/G 9/19/87 375
Bluebill drake, old working rpt, average wear, some to bare wood, thin neck crack, otherwise VG, ca 1900, RWO 7/05/85 325
Bluebill pr, orig pnt, minor wear, some neck filler missing from drake's neck; chip on hen's bill, 33, J/G 9/19/87 1700

Holly, James
Bluewinged Teal hen, orig pnt, average wear, slight age split in left side of body, otherwise sound, rare, RB 7/07/87, $4,000.00.

Bluewinged Teal hen, traces of orig pnt worn mostly to natural wood, minor age split in neck, RB 3/11/88 950
Canvasback drake, early, orig pnt, in-use wear, crack running through neck, ca 1880, 69, RWO 11/11/87 1600
Canvasback drake, G orig pnt, average wear w/some areas worn to bare wood, structurally sound, 1920's, RWO 11/06/85 450
Canvasback drake, old working rpt, thin crack in neck, otherwise structurally sound, ca 1890, RWO 7/04/87 80
Canvasback pr, EX orig pnt, drake has thin neck crack; hen has age check on bk, otherwise EX, 196, RWO 7/02/88, 64% 1900
Greenwinged Teal hen, outstanding orig condition, ca 1890, RWO 7/05/85, 157% 5500
Mallard drake, orig pnt darkened w/age, ca 1890, extremely rare, purchased in 1890 by the Boyd family, RWO 11/11/87 8000
Pintail drake, old rpt, minor wear, age split in neck, rare, RB 2/01/85 350
Pintail drake, orig pnt w/some working rpt flaking away, structurally sound, rare, ca 1890, RWO 11/11/87, 160% 2250
Pintail hen, fine orig feather pnt, in-use wear w/some wear to bare wood on 1 side, very rare, ca 1890, RWO 11/11/87 7000
Redhead drake, old rpt, heavy flaking/wear, thin checks on sides, otherwise sound, ca 1880, 3, RWO 7/06/86 140
Holly, James att; (Havre de Grace, MD)
Widgeon drake, old working rpt, average wear, no major structural flaws, ca 1890, RWO 7/02/88 180
Holly, John (Havre de Grace, MD)
Bluebill drake, old working rpt, in-use wear, crack in neck, otherwise structurally sound, ca 1890, RWO 11/06/85 200

Canvasback drake, EX orig pnt, minor wear, inletted keel weight, EX condition, ca 1880, rare, 195, RWO 7/02/88 3350
Canvasback drake, old working rpt, heavy wear, minor hairline cracks, otherwise sound, ca 1880, 73, RWO 11/06/85 300
Canvasback hen, early, old pnt, average wear, sm chip on head/neck crack, retains orig weight, 119, J/G 9/19/87 450
Redhead drake, early, EX orig pnt, average wear, thin tight check on bk, NY Hunting Club brand, RWO 11/11/87 2200
Redhead drake, old pnt appears to be orig, branded GBG/DG Elliot, inletted keel weight, ca 1880, RWO 7/02/88, 26% 900
Redhead drake, old working rpt, several age checks to body/crack at base of neck, ca 1870, 41, RWO 7/04/87 150
Redhead drake, working rpt, average wear, branded FSM & HE Jones, neck cracks, otherwise EX, ca 1870-1880, RWO 2/12/88 250

Holly, William (Havre de Grace, MD)
Canvasback drake, pnt worn away to bare wood, few thin hairline cracks in body, ca 1900, 41, RWO 7/04/87 250
Redhead hen, orig pnt, minor wear, tight check in bk, ca 1900, J/G 9/19/87, 75% 600

Holly Family (Havre de Grace, MD)
Canvasback drake, old pnt, average wear, branded, structurally sound, RB 12/06/85 350
Canvasback drake, old pnt, average wear, 2" knot missing from left side of breast, otherwise sound, RB 12/06/85 300

Holmes, Ben (Stratford, CT)
Black Duck, early, hollow, pnt appears to be orig, branded E Thorne, bill/tail rpr by Delong, EX, RWO 7/02/88, 135% 4000
Black Duck, hollow, EX orig dry pnt, pc of wood missing from bottom of bill, otherwise EX, ca 1880's, RWO 2/12/88, 75% 3000
Black Duck, hollow, old rpt, average flaking/wear, sm chips around neck/lg chip on side of bill, 2, RB 12/06/85 750
Black Duck, hollow, old working touchup worn down to orig, slight separation where body halves join, RWO 7/06/86, 33% 800
Black Duck, hollow, orig pnt, minor wear, prof bill repair, otherwise structurally EX, 74, RWO 11/11/87, 66% 4000
Black Duck, hollow w/pine bottom board, fine feather pnt, minor wear, exceptional condition, very rare, J/G 4/23/87 23500
Bluebill drake, early, old working rpt back to mostly orig, artist brand, matching print included in lot, J/G 9/20/86 2250
Bluebill drake, hollow, old pnt, heavy flaking/wear, stamped weight, ms, EX, ca 1920, rare, 22/44, RB 5/02/86, 75% 2000
Bluebill hen, early, fine old pnt, minor wear, branded FB, minor age line on tail/breast, ls, ca 1885, J/G 4/23/87, 77% 2100
Broadbill drake, hollow, EX orig pnt, structurally NM, ca 1966, rare, RB 7/09/85, 75% 1850
Broadbill hen, hollow, old rpt, heavy wear, eyes missing, head needs to be reattached to body, rare, 21, RB 2/01/85 1500

Holmes, Ben
Goldeneye drake, hollow, fine old pnt, average wear, well preserved, rare, RB 7/09/85, 150%, $3,700.00.

Goldeneye drake, hollow, old rpt, average wear, age split in bill, RB 7/09/85, 45% 550
Goldeneye hen, hollow, rpt, minor wear, poor repair to bill, 2, RB 12/06/85 700
Goldeneye hen, hollow, rpt by Wheeler, minor wear, chip to bottom of bill/shallow chips on tail, 2/77, RB 12/06/85, 200% 4000
Squaw, hollow, rpt, average flaking/wear, structurally sound, inscribed/dated 1956, rare, 173, RB 7/07/87, 75% 900

Holmes, Ben; att (Stratford, CT)
Black Duck, hollow, old pnt, heavy flaking/wear, chip at top of tail, 22, RB 5/02/86 850
Black Duck, hollow, old rpt, heavy flaking/wear, age splits on neck, bill is an old replacement, 22, RB 5/02/86 300
Bluebill drake, hollow, old working rpt, average wear, chip of wood missing from neck/chip on bill, 9, RB 12/06/85 350
Broadbill drake, hollow, rpt w/minor wear, 2 brands, 21, RB 2/01/85 1600
Goldeneye hen, hollow, old rpt by Charles Wheeler, average flaking/wear, 22/31, RB 5/02/86 800

Holmes, Ben; school of
Old Squaw drake, early, possibly made by Shang Wheeler & from his rig, 6/9/77, RB 12/06/85, 280% 2800

Holmes, Eliot (Duxbury, MA)
Crow, G orig pnt, average wear, 22, RB 5/02/86 375

Holmes, Henry (Bureau, IL)
Bluebill drake, early, old working rpt, crack in bill has been reglued, J/G 4/24/86 104
Mallard drake, early, 2 coats of pnt w/fine comb/feather pnt, moderate wear, hairline crack in neck, J/G 4/23/87 600
Mallard drake, hollow, EX orig pnt, in-use wear w/some touchup to head, crack in bill, otherwise EX, 193, RWO 7/02/88 800
Mallard drake, hollow, fine orig pnt, average wear, ls, orig weight on bottom, larger than next example, RB 12/06/85 950
Mallard drake, hollow, fine orig pnt, average wear, well preserved, RB 12/06/85 650
Mallard drake, hollow, old rpt, moderate flaking/wear, slight age split in neck, RB 7/07/87 300
Mallard hen, EX orig pnt, prof rstr to bill/neck, rare, 7, J/G 4/24/86 495

Mallard hen, hollow, G orig pnt, average wear w/some crazing, structurally EX, ca 1920's, RWO 7/06/86 600
Pintail drake, hollow, orig pnt, average wear, thin crack in neck/minor repair to tail, ca 1925, RWO 7/06/86 300
Holmes, Henry; att (Bureau, IL)
Mallard drake, hollow, old pnt, average wear, old repair to bill, RB 3/06/87 60
Holmes, Lothrop (Kingston, MA)
Blackbellied Plover, EX orig stylized pnt, structurally EX, rare, 8/48, RWO 7/06/86 34000
Blackbellied Plover, pnt eyes, superb pnt pattern, minor flaking, bill is a prof replacement, rare, 39, RB 7/08/86, 70% 7000
Goldeneye drake, EX orig pnt, weathered/worn on side, average wear on other, artist brand, 22/44, RB 5/02/86 5250

Holmes, Lothrop
Ruddy Turnstone, superb pnt pattern, M condition, extremely rare, 22/44, RB 5/02/86, $67,000.00.

Yellowlegs, feeding, highly stylized pnt, outstanding & orig w/only minor pnt flaking, rare, RWO 7/05/86 12000
Holmes, Lothrop; att (Kingston, MA)
Merganser pr, drake: high-head, raised/incised comb; hen: swimming/has old break in neck, EX orig pnt, 22/44, RB 5/02/86 45000
Old Squaw drake, rpt, average flaking/wear, branded TWD, age splits in bottom, RB 6/28/88 900
Holmes Family, att (Duxbury, MA)
Goldeneye hen, orig pnt, minor wear, 2 hairline cracks in bk, J/G 9/19/87 125
Homme, Ferde (Wisconsin)
Mallard drake, sleeping, raised wings, detailed cvg in tail, EX orig pnt, minor wear, chip in tail, EX, RWO 7/05/86 5750
Hooker, Tim (Crystal Lake, IL)
Bluewinged Teal pr, orig pnt, minor wear, cvd/pnt in style of Robert Elliston, J/G 4/23/87 400
Greenwinged Teal drake, branded, NM condition, RWO 11/06/85 75
Greenwinged Teal drake, orig pnt, minor wear, ls, J/G 9/20/86 55
Hopkins, Bruce (Smithville, NS)
Eider hen, pnt appears to be orig w/average wear, 193, RWO 7/02/88 100
Hopkins, Steve (Granby, CT)
Black Duck, sleeping, NM orig pnt, no structural flaws, J /G 9/19/87 200
Hoppe, Fred (East Peoria, IL)
Mallard drake, G orig pnt, minor wear, no structural flaws, retains orig weight, rare, 7, J/G 4/24/86 192
Horn, Daniel
Redbreasted Merganser, long slender body, old pnt appears to be orig, minor wear, age split in bottom, RB 3/11/88, 200% 1650
Horn, John
Ruddy Turnstone, orig pnt, average flaking/wear, RB 3/11/88 800
Horn, John; att
Merganser hen, old working rpt, minor flaking/wear, some minor chips to comb on bk of head, 21, RB 2/01/85 450
Horner, Nathan Rowley (Manahawkin, NJ)
Black Duck, high-head, hollow, orig pnt worn to mostly natural wood, minor neck crack, otherwise EX, RWO 7/02/88 2100
Black Duck, hollow, EX orig pnt, minor dings, otherwise EX, RWO 11/06/85 2500
Black Duck, hollow, EX orig pnt, sliver of wood missing under bill, otherwise EX, rare, ca 1930, RWO 7/04/87 6500
Black Duck, hollow, G orig pnt, average wear, branded EDT, rare, RB 7/08/86 1100
Black Duck, hollow, head is overpnt, body is EX orig, lg chip on underside of bill, branded, RB 8/21/86 350

Black Duck, hollow, head is overpnt, EX orig pnt to body, branded weight, RB 8/21/86 600
Black Duck, hollow, old pnt, average wear, orig weight removed, RB 2/01/85 950
Black Duck, hollow, outstanding orig condition, 50, RWO 7/05/85 2750

Horner, Nathan Rowley
Black Duck, hollow, outstanding orig pnt, structurally NM, ca 1930, rare, RWO 7/04/87, 133%, $8,000.00.

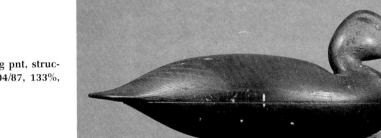

Black Duck, hollow, rpt by Chris Sprague, minor wear, RB 2/01/85 700
Bluebill drake, finely formed, some orig pnt, working touchup, prof bill repair, J/G 9/20/86 400
Bluebill drake, old working touchup to white areas/black is orig, structurally EX, ca 1930, RWO 7/04/87 1400
Bluebill hen, early, old working rpt, average wear, chips in tail/narrow crack in neck, ca 1920's, RWO 7/04/87 350
Bluebill hen, orig pnt, average wear, structurally poor, ca 1930, RWO 7/04/87 825
Bluebill pr, M condition, rare/outstanding, 50, RWO 7/05/85 5000
Brant, EX orig pnt, minor wear, no structural flaws, rare, J/G 4/24/86, 132% 4620
Brant, hollow, EX orig pnt, average wear w/some prof touchup to bk, structurally EX, RWO 7/02/88, 65% 3000
Brant, hollow, EX orig pnt, minor wear, RB 3/11/88 2700
Brant, hollow, fine orig pnt, average wear, well preserved, rare, 22/44, RB 5/02/86 2750
Brant, hollow, fine orig pnt, minor flaking/wear, NM condition, prof cleaned, extremely rare, 21, RB 2/01/85 3250
Brant, hollow, old orig pnt, average wear, shallow chip on right side of bill, RB 7/09/85, 65% 950
Brant, hollow, overpnt taken down to NM orig w/minor flaking/wear, rare, 22/44, RB 8/21/86 2500
Brant, hollow, pristine w/some rubs on bk, fine crack in neck, otherwise structurally EX, ca 1920's, RWO 11/11/87 7250
Brant, NM orig pnt, hairline part way through neck, special order made w/Black Duck body, orig weight, rare, J/G 9/19/87 2950
Brant, old working rpt taken down to mostly orig, sm tail chip/eyes are an old replacement, rare, J/G 4/23/87 600
Canada Goose, hollow, fine orig pnt has been cleaned leaving EX patina, weight branded ET Townsend, rare, RB 8/21/86 11000
Canada Goose, hollow, outstanding orig pnt, slight age split at neck, very rare, 50, RB 12/06/85 11000
Mallard hen, hollow, EX orig pnt w/soft patina, minor wear, M condition, rare, 90, RWO 7/02/88 22500
Horner, Nathan Rowley; att (Manahawkin, NJ)
Black Duck, hollow, old pnt, heavy wear, 189, RB 6/28/88 150
Brant, hollow, rpt by HW Schuyler, EX condition, RB 6/28/88 75
Hotz, Hiram (Peoria, IL)
Canvasback drake, old working touchup on white areas, otherwise EX, rare, 7, J/G 4/24/86 1320
Mallard pr, early deep 'V' body style, NM orig pnt, J/G 4/24/86 2860
Mallard pr, hollow, EX orig pnt, drake has varnish; hen has tail chip/chewed bill, otherwise EX, 193, RWO 7/02/88 3250
Hotz, Hiram; att (Peoria, IL)
Canvasback drake, hollow, old pnt, average wear, structurally sound, 39, RB 7/08/86 375
Howell, Clark
Bluebill drake, hollow, old pnt, heavy wear, ls, ca 1900, RB 7/09/85 150
Howland, Roger (Waquoit, MA)
Redbreasted Merganser drake, G orig pnt, average wear w/crazing on breast, structurally EX, RWO 7/02/88 130
Howlett, Ralph (St. John, NB)
Black Duck, NM orig pnt, 2 hairline cracks in bk, oversize, J/G 9/20/86 50
Canada Goose, sleeping, orig pnt, minor wear, structurally EX, rare, J/G 9/20/86 200
Goldeneye drake, EX orig pnt, very slight wear, no structural flaws, J/G 9/20/86 60
Goldeneye drake, NM orig pnt w/old working touchup on white cheek patches, J/G 9/20/86 60
Hudson, Delbert (Chincoteague, VA)
Canvasback drake, orig pnt, minor wear, may be some old working rpt on head, structurally sound, lg, RWO 7/02/88 900
Hudson, Ira (Chincoteague, VA)
Black Duck, early, old working rpt, lg chunk of wood out of tail/2 tight checks on bk/neck, RWO 7/06/86 80
Black Duck, EX orig pnt, average wear, old repair to bill/several age splits, RB 2/01/85 800
Black Duck, fine orig pnt, average wear, some slight age splitting, RB 2/01/85 500

Black Duck, fine orig pnt, average wear/moderate crazing, RB 3/06/87 1100
Black Duck, fluted banjo tail, EX orig scratch pnt, sm check along 1 side, broken/reglued bill, ca 1935, RWO 7/05/85 600
Black Duck, fluted tail, EX orig pnt, structurally NM, stamped ETC/44, ca 1935, RWO 7/05/85 1025
Black Duck, fluted tail, orig pnt w/several areas worn to bare wood, narrow age checks in body/head, RWO 7/04/87 450
Black Duck, full-body, tack eyes, notched tail, EX orig pnt, age split on bottom, 3 tight checks on bk, J/G 4/23/87 1000
Black Duck, hollow, old pnt w/traces of orig, heavy flaking/wear, minor age split in neck/bill chip, RB 3/11/88, 158% 475
Black Duck, hollow, orig pnt, heavy flaking on body, prof rstr/touchup to bill, RWO 7/04/87 400
Black Duck, hollow, pnt stripped to natural wood in many areas, age splitting in body/old neck repair, RB 3/11/88' 250
Black Duck, hollow 3-pc body, EX orig scratch pnt, minor flaking, sm tail chips, RWO 7/02/88, 60% 2950
Black Duck, old rpt, minor wear, structurally sound, RB 3/06/87 525
Black Duck, old working rpt, average wear, hairline crack in neck, otherwise structurally sound, RWO 7/02/88 240
Black Duck, old working rpt, average wear, minor age lines, old repair to cracks in head, 33, J/G 9/19/87 220
Black Duck, old working rpt, average wear, structurally sound, RWO 7/06/86 275
Black Duck, orig pnt, worn to bare wood in several places, structurally VG, RWO 7/05/85 650
Black Duck, round-body, orig pnt, moderate wear, prof rstr to bill, several checks in bodyblock/neck, J/G 4/24/86 825
Black Duck, rpt, average wear, some age splitting, RB 8/27/87 350
Black Duck, rpt, average wear, some slight age splitting, RB 7/08/86 300
Black Duck, slightly forward swimming position, hollow, EX scratch pnt, 1 of special order of 12, ca 1920, RWO 7/04/87 4750
Black Duck, tucked head, EX orig pnt, fine feather detail, cvd signature, age split in bk, 3, RB 3/06/87, 135% 1600
Black Duck, working rpt, minimal wear, structurally VG, ca 1920, RWO 7/05/85 310

Hudson, Ira
Bluebill, cvd/pnt as if turning to right, hollow, EX orig pnt, average wear, well preserved, 21, RB 2/10/85, 135%, $6,750.00.

Bluebill drake, cvd 'V' tail, old working rpt, minor wear, no structural flaws, J/G 9/19/87 395
Bluebill drake, early, old working rpt, bears Mackey stamp, crack in bk side of neck, 3/80/182, J/G 9/20/86, 35% 550
Bluebill drake, early, round body w/fluted tail, orig pnt, average wear, crack part way down bk, J/G 4/23/87 875
Bluebill drake, early football body w/fluted tail, rpt, average wear, thin crack in head/bottom, RWO 7/06/86 225
Bluebill drake, fine orig pnt, average wear, age split in bottom of body, RB 3/11/88, 188% 1500
Bluebill drake, fine orig pnt, average wear, 36, RB 2/01/85 700
Bluebill drake, hollow, EX orig pnt, minor wear, shallow chips on both sides of bill, rare, RB 12/06/85 2400
Bluebill drake, hollow, old rpt, average flaking/wear, minor roughness to end of tail, RB 8/25/88 500
Bluebill drake, old rpt, average flaking/wear, age split in bk/neck, RB 6/28/88 200
Bluebill drake, old rpt, average wear, several age splits in neck, RB 7/07/87 275
Bluebill drake, old working rpt, in-use wear, in-use bill rpr, RWO 7/02/88 325
Bluebill drake, old working touchup in Hudson style, thin check running down bk, otherwise structurally EX, RWO 7/06/86 375
Bluebill drake, orig pnt, average wear, some areas on body/head appear to be overpnt w/heavy flaking, RB 7/07/87 600
Bluebill drake, orig pnt w/some areas of overpnt, moderate flaking/wear, RB 6/28/88 650
Bluebill drake, rpt, average wear, age splits in neck/body, RB 3/11/88 200
Bluebill drake, rpt, heavy flaking/wear, several age splits, RB 3/11/88 325
Bluebill drake, rpt by Hudson as a hen, ms, structurally sound, RB 12/06/85 300
Bluebill drake, slightly turned head/tail, G orig pnt, heavy weathering/wear, RB 7/09/85 500
Bluebill drake, some rstr to pnt, tail wear/tight crack on bk of head, RWO 2/12/88 350
Bluebill hen, fine orig pnt, average wear, worn mostly to natural wood on sides, 39, RB 7/08/86 1250
Bluebill hen, orig pnt, heavy wear, structurally sound, RB 7/09/85 725
Bluebill pr, fine orig pnt, average wear, drake has dry rot on bottom; hen has an old bill replacement, RB 3/06/87 900
Bluebill pr, rpt, tight checks in head/body, hen is ls, J/G 9/19/87 700
Brant, crooked neck, fine orig pnt, average wear, check running along 1 side, rare, RWO 2/13/87 3200
Brant, fine orig pnt, average wear, age split in neck, RB 7/09/85 700
Brant, flat bottom, orig pnt, minor wear, structurally EX, J/G 9/20/86 1600

Brant, full-body, hollow, EX orig pnt, average wear, slight age split in neck, RB 7/09/85 500
Brant, G orig pnt, average flaking/wear, several age splits in neck, RB 12/06/85 600
Brant, hollow, EX orig pnt, some flaking around breast, slight separation where body halves join, RWO 2/13/87 1800
Brant, hollow, G orig pnt, average flaking/wear, crack at base of neck, otherwise structurally sound, RWO 7/06/86, 50% 1200
Brant, hollow, orig pnt, average wear, structurally VG, ca 1940, RWO 7/05/85 700
Brant, hollow, rpt in Hudson style, structurally EX, RWO 11/11/87 900
Brant, old working rpt, average wear, check along 1 side of body, otherwise sound, 210, RWO 2/12/88 310
Brant, orig pnt, average wear, thin crack along side of neck, otherwise structurally sound, RWO 2/13/87, 75% 900
Brant, orig pnt worn bare in many areas, thin check running down bk/front of neck, ca 1930, RWO 7/04/87 300
Brant, reaching head style, prof pnt rstr in Hudson style, structurally EX, rare, 49, RWO 11/06/85 1950
Brant, rpt w/minor wear, hairline crack in bk, J/G 4/23/87 750
Brant, VG orig pnt, flaking on bk, lg check along 1 side of body from breast to tail, otherwise sound, RWO 2/12/88, 47% 700
Bufflehead, rpt shows little wear, minor check running down bk, otherwise sound, RWO 7/05/85 160
Bufflehead drake, early, old working rpt, average wear, several tight checks in neck/bodyblock, J/G 9/19/87 400
Bufflehead drake, EX orig pnt, minor wear, age split in neck, RB 2/01/85 750
Bufflehead drake, old orig pnt, average wear, rare, RB 7/09/85 700
Bufflehead drake, old pnt, heavy flaking, structurally sound, RWO 11/06/85 400
Bufflehead drake, old pnt, heavy wear, repair to neck/ls, RB 12/06/85 275
Bufflehead drake, old working rpt, average wear, structurally EX, 3, RWO 11/11/87 1100
Bufflehead drake, orig pnt, heavy wear to bare wood in many areas, ms, otherwise structurally sound, RWO 7/06/86 775
Bufflehead drake, rpt in Hudson style by Sam Dyke, thin crack in bill, otherwise structurally sound, RWO 11/11/87 400
Bufflehead hen, EX orig pnt, average wear, well preserved, branded P, rare, 17, RB 8/21/86, 155% 1550
Bufflehead hen, orig pnt, heavy wear to bare wood in several areas, hairline checks on body, otherwise EX, RWO 11/11/87 525
Bufflehead hen, rpt in Hudson style by Sam Dyke, sm checks on base of neck/bk, RWO 11/11/87 400
Canada Goose, early, G orig pnt, average wear w/minor crazing on bk, 2 thin age checks on body, 1920's, RWO 7/06/86, 57% 1750
Canada Goose, early, high-head style, old working rpt worn to bare wood, age checks/dry rot on 1 side, RWO 11/11/87, 30% 350
Canada Goose, early, old working rpt worn to bare wood in some areas, crack in neck/breast, 33, J/G 9/19/87 400
Canada Goose, early, swimming, old pnt, average wear, several age splits, RB 2/01/85 650
Canada Goose, fine pnt by Ira Hudson, average wear, several age splits, rare, 36, RB 2/01/85 1000
Canada Goose, G orig pnt, average wear, RB 12/06/85 1100
Canada Goose, hissing, EX comb pnt on sides, flaking on head/neck, tight check on head, otherwise EX, RWO 7/06/86 9500
Canada Goose, hissing, fluted tail, orig pnt, average wear w/areas to bare wood, very sound, RWO 11/11/87, 75% 3750
Canada Goose, hissing, orig pnt, heavy wear, severe check down bk/minor check in neck, ca 1920, RWO 7/05/85 1600

Hudson, Ira
Canada Goose, hissing, outstanding orig pnt, scratch pnt on tail, information on tag: 1 of 12 made in 1948, RWO 7/05/85, $18,000.00.

Canada Goose, hollow, orig pnt w/prof rstr along sides, hairline cracks on bk/breast/neck, RWO 7/02/88, 55% 825
Canada Goose, old working rpt, age split in underside of body/2 minor age lines in neck, unusual form, J/G 4/23/87, 60% 900
Canada Goose, orig pnt w/old working touchup under tail/lower sides, rstr to neck/edge of bill, J/G 4/24/86 1100
Canada Goose, swimming, old pnt, heavy wear, beginning 2" of neck may be a replacement, RB 2/01/85 500
Canada Goose, unusual chip cvg on bk, orig pnt, some wear to bare wood, body/head checks, otherwise EX, RWO 2/12/88, 80% 2000
Canvasback drake, EX orig pnt, average wear, lg age split in right side of body, RB 7/09/85, 50% 350
Canvasback drake, minor areas of black overpnt w/G orig underneath, sm age split in bk/neck, rare, RB 8/27/87, 195% 1750
Canvasback drake, orig pnt w/working touchup to black area on breast, bears Mackey stamp, RWO 7/06/86 975
Canvasback drake, pnt worn/weathered to bare wood on body, checks on underside/crack in neck, RWO 7/02/88 275
Canvasback drake, rpt w/minor wear, some dry rot on bottom, RB 7/09/85 175
Canvasback drake, working rpt, average flaking/wear, 2 cracks running through neck, RWO 2/13/87 350
Canvasback drake, working rpt w/some taken down to orig, RWO 11/06/85 450
Goldeneye drake, fluted tail, G orig pnt, average flaking/wear, tight check along side, otherwise EX, RWO 2/13/87, 180% 1300
Goldeneye drake, fluted tail, worn orig pnt, 2 sm chips out of body, ms, RWO 2/13/87 825

Goldeneye drake, orig pnt, heavy wear/touchup to white, check running down bk, otherwise sound, ca 1925, RWO 7/05/85 800
Goldeneye drake, round full body, old working rpt, a few tight checks in body/neck, 3 sm nails added, rare, J/G 4/23/87 450
Goldeneye drake, working rpt, average wear, age split in body/chip in tail, RB 2/01/85 300
Goldeneye hen, hollow, old working rpt, structurally sound, rare, RWO 11/06/85 275
Goose, hissing, flat bottom, old working rpt, several tight checks in body & head, rare, J/G 4/23/87, 75% 1700
Greenwinged Teal drake, flying, minor prof rstr to wings/pnt, RWO 11/06/85 2200

Hudson, Ira
Greenwinged Teal drake, flying, thin coat of shellac prof removed by DeLong, structurally EX, RWO 7/05/85, $4,500.00.

Greenwinged Teal drake, rpt shows average wear, 39, RB 7/08/86, 170% 1200
Mallard drake, flying, EX scratch feather pnt, minor flaking where wings attach to body, EX condition, RB 3/11/88, 184% 4600
Mallard drake, head turned right, orig pnt worn to natural wood, age splits in body/neck chip, RB 3/11/88 600
Merganser drake, old working rpt, flaking/wear, old bill repair/crack in neck, RWO 7/02/88, 75% 950
Merganser drake, pnt worn/weathered to wood on body, age check on 1 side, prof bill rstr, rare, RWO 2/12/88 1400
Merganser hen, cvd crest, rpl bill, slight age splits, otherwise M, 78, RB 7/07/87 5000
Merganser hen, G orig pnt, average wear, chips on crest/tailhas been broken off & poorly repaired, RB 7/09/85 700
Merganser hen, sculpturesque, orig pnt, minor to moderate wear, possible bill rstr, minor roughness, J/G 4/23/87 2400
Pintail drake, banjo tail, fine orig pnt, average wear, age split in neck, old break in tail reglued, RB 7/09/85 1300
Pintail drake, banjo tail, full body, working rpt on white, otherwise orig, several minor checks, J/G 4/23/87 1800
Pintail drake, early football body style, EX orig pnt, average wear, NM condition, RWO 2/12/88 4700
Pintail drake, orig pnt, average wear w/minor flaking, poor repairs to bill/tail, narrow check down bk, RWO 2/13/87 1000
Pintail drake, orig pnt, heavy wear, part of tail missing/split on bk of head, otherwise EX, 49, RWO 11/11/87 1800
Pintail drake, pnt rstr in Hudson style, pc of tail missing/bill rstr/lg check on breast/check on bk, RWO 7/02/88 400
Pintail drake, rpt by Mark McNair, tail has been broken off & reglued, thin tight checks on bk, RWO 7/06/86 550
Pintail drake, slightly turned head, EX orig pnt, minor wear, age split at neck, otherwise NM, rare, RB 12/06/85, 165% 4100
Pintail drake, working rpt worn to bare wood in many areas, damage to neck/hairline crack on 1 side, rare, RWO 7/04/87 575
Pintail hen, flying, G orig scratch feather pnt, EX condition, RWO 11/06/85, 50% 1750
Pintail pr, flying, EX orig pnt, pnt on bottom of hen has bubbled, feet missing on drake, RWO 7/05/85 16500
Pintail pr, 2-pc balsa bodies, outstanding orig pnt, joint separations on both, hen has neck crack, 49, RWO 7/05/85 9000
Redbreasted Merganser drake, old Hudson pnt, average flaking/wear, sm bill chip, 153, RB 3/06/87, 175% 2000
Redbreasted Merganser drake, old working rpt, repair to bill, structurally fair, RWO 11/06/85 1350
Redbreasted Merganser hen, EX orig pnt, retains orig bill which has been broken off & reattached, RWO 11/06/85, 55% 1400
Redbreasted Merganser pr, cvd crests/tails/mandibles, EX orig pnt/minor wear, old chips/neck splits, ls, RB 7/09/85, 62% .. 5000
Redbreasted Merganser pr, cvd tails/crests/mandibles, EX orig pnt, crest/tail chips, neck splits, ls, RB 7/09/85, 70% 5800

Redhead drake, orig pnt, minor wear, white areas on side/bottom appear to be overpnt, RB 7/07/87 650
Redhead drake, rpt, average wear, age split in neck/body, bill is a replacement, RB 3/11/88, 233% 350
Redhead hen, orig pnt, heavy wear, thin checks in head/tail, otherwise structurally EX, rare, 49, RWO 11/11/87 750
Richardson's Goose, hollow, cvd wing line, flat bottom, working rpt w/orig on bottom, several tight checks, J/G 4/34/87 950
Widgeon drake, rpt in Hudson style, minor wear, well preserved, RB 7/08/86 450
Yellowlegs, EX orig pnt, minor wear, half of bill is a replacement, rare, 22/44, RB 5/02/86 2900
Yellowlegs, orig pnt, in-use wear, old repair to end of tail/bill is a replacement, rare, RB 7/09/85 700
Yellowlegs, orig pnt w/typical scratch pnt, minor flaking, orig bill, structurally EX, RWO 7/05/85 2200

Hudson, Ira; att (Chincoteague, VA)
Black Duck, orig pnt, heavy wear, head is rpt showing average wear, RB 7/08/86 275
Bluebill drake, fine old pnt, average wear, RB 7/09/85 200
Bufflehead drake, early, old working rpt, ls, J/G 9/20/86 100
Redbreasted Merganser drake, old pnt worn to bare wood in some areas, thin crack in neck, otherwise sound, RWO 7/04/87 290
Redhead drake, rpt by Hudson as a Bluebill drake, crack in neck/thin crack down bk, RWO 11/06/85 150
Yellowlegs, orig pnt, average wear, nice scratch pnt on bk, sm gouge to bk, otherwise sound, RWO 7/06/86 850

Hudson, Ira; school of
Mallard, flying, orig pnt, minor wear, full size, 33, J/G 9/19/87 600

Hudson Family (Chincoteague, VA)
Bluebill drake, body is by Ira/head is by Delbert, rpt by Delbert, from Wilson Byrd's rig, RWO 11/06/85 230
Canada Goose, flying, open bill, orig scratch feather pnt, minor flaking, 1 wing needs reglued, RB 3/11/88, 240% 2400

Huey, George (Friendship, ME)
Black Duck, very dry orig pnt, structurally sound, GR Huey cvd in bottom, rare, RWO 7/06/86 180
Goldeneye hen, inlet neck, cvd eyes/bill, half orig pnt/half rpt, average wear, well preserved, RB 7/09/85 375
Goldeneye hen, slightly turned inlet head, cvd eyes, EX orig pnt, average flaking/wear, artist signed, 22/44, RB 5/02/86 1100
Goldeneye hen, special cvg, fine orig pnt, average flaking/wear, signed & w/shorebird scene, 22/44, RB 5/02/86 1450
Merganser drake, cvd eyes, inlet head attached to body block, orig pnt, slight wear, inset circular weight, J/G 9/20/86 1450
Merganser drake, inlet head, leather/wooden crest, raised wings, GR Huey cvd in bottom, bill chip, RWO 2/12/88 2350
Merganser hen, all pnt except the primer is gone, hairline crack in neck, tail chip, RWO 7/02/88 275
Merganser hen, slightly turned inlet head, cvd eyes, orig pnt, slight wear, round inset weight, J/G 9/20/86 1750
Merganser hen, very stylish form, EX & orig condition, 48, RWO 7/02/88, 65% 2250
Redbreasted Merganser drake, fine orig pnt, minor wear, well preserved, RB 7/09/85, 70% 1100
Redbreasted Merganser drake, GR Huey cvd in bottom, M condition, RWO 7/06/86 5000
Redbreasted Merganser drake, hollowed out from the bottom, EX orig pnt & structure, RWO 7/05/85 2950

Huey, George
Redbreasted Merganser drake, inlet head, outstanding orig pnt, bill was broken & reglued, signed, RWO 7/05/85, $5,000.00.

Redbreasted Merganser drake, inlet neck, cvd eyes, EX orig pnt, minor wear, old break in neck reglued, 22, RB 5/02/86 4750
Redbreasted Merganser drake, inlet neck/slightly turned head, cvd wings, orig pnt, average wear, signed, RB 7/09/85, 60% 1100
Redbreasted Merganser drake, relief cvd wings, cvd crest w/leather insert, EX orig pnt, initialed, RWO 7/04/87 3250
Redbreasted Merganser drake, working overpnt taken down to orig, prof rstr to bill/minor neck crack, RWO 7/02/88, 125% 1100
Redbreasted Merganser drake, worn orig pnt, head is loose/sm chip out of bill, otherwise EX, rare, RWO 7/06/86 1125
Redbreasted Merganser hen, orig pnt, average wear, well preserved, 22, RB 5/02/86 700

Redbreasted Merganser pr, touchups to head, hairline cracks, VG orig condition, RWO 7/05/85 1200
Huff, Charles (Shrewsbury River, NJ)
    Black Duck, hollow, orig pnt w/a few dings on bk, sm crack running through neck, otherwise sound, RWO 07/06/86 325
    Black Duck, old pnt, average wear, structurally sound, ca 1930, RB 8/27/87 125
Hulse, William (Metedeconk, NJ)
    Canada Goose, hollow, old rpt, average wear, old neck repair, RB 7/09/85 125
Hunt, Bert (Massachusetts)

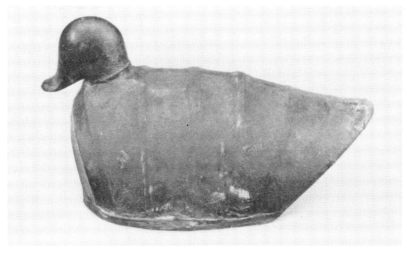

Hunt, Bert
Coot, canvas-covered slat, fine old pnt, average wear, structurally sound, oversize, 22, RB 5/02/86, $800.00.

    Scoter, G old orig dry pnt, average wear, bears Mackey stamp, structurally EX, ca 1900, RWO 7/06/86 300
Hutchins, Sam (Jones Falls, Ont)
    Goldeneye drake, stylized wing/tail feather cvg, black pnt orig/white taken down to orig, no flaws, rare, J/G 9/20/86 600
Hutchinson, Ken
    Black Duck, sleeping, cvd out of 1 pc of pine, hollowed out from rear, orig pnt, minor wear, RWO 7/04/87 70
Inman, John (Manahawkin, NJ)
    Bluebill drake, hollow, old rpt, average flaking/wear, 6, RB 8/25/88 220
    Brant, hollow, old working rpt, in-use wear, crack in neck, otherwise structurally sound, RWO 11/11/87 190
    Bufflehead drake, hollow, old pnt, average wear, RB 3/11/88 300
    Merganser drake, early, hollow, old rpt, average wear, age split in neck, well preserved, 3, RB 3/06/87 1000
Inman, John; att (Manahawkin, NJ)
    Bluebill drake, hollow, rpt, average flaking/wear, 9, RB 12/06/85 100
Ives, Francis E. (Housefield, NY)
    Bluebill drake, fine orig pnt, average wear, 39, RB 7/08/86 225
Jackson, Scott (Charlestown, MD)
    Bluewinged Teal, EX old pnt, eclipse plumage, hairline in neck/rough edge on bill, ca 1895, 69, J/G 9/19/87, 60% 1500
    Canvasback drake, old working rpt, in-use wear, structurally VG, RWO 7/05/85 210
    Canvasback drake, working rpt, minor wear, artist brand, structurally sound, RWO 11/11/87 300
    Canvasback pr, working rpt, average wear, age split in neck of hen, from the John Hanson rig, RB 2/01/85 300
Jacobsgard, Clarence (Gardner, IL)
    Mallard drake, G orig pnt, minor wear, structurally EX, J/G 4/23/87 175
Janson, Dick (California)
    Bluebill pr, cvd primary feathers along bk, cvd keels under tail, ls, otherwise well preserved, rare, RB 8/25/88, 200% 14000
    Brant, cvd primary feathers along bk, keel under tail, rpt, minor flaking/wear, extremely rare, RB 8/25/88 6500
    Canvasback hen, orig pnt, moderate wear, minor age split in left side, rare, RB 8/25/88, 125% 2200
    Mallard drake, cvd wing tips/primary feathers, EX orig pnt, minor wear, RB 12/06/85 550
    Pintail drake, cvd primary feathers, EX orig pnt, minor wear, RB 2/01/85 400
    Pintail drake, old working rpt, heavy wear, thin crack in neck, otherwise sound, RWO 7/02/88 125
    Pintail drake, slightly turned head, cvd primary feathers, orig pnt, ls, well preserved, RB 8/27/87 650
    Pintail drake, slightly turned head w/cvd primary feathers, sm age split in neck, otherwise NM, RB 8/27/87 800
    Pintail hen, cvd primary feathers, fine orig pnt on upper body, lower portions have white overpnt, RB 7/09/85 50
    Pintail hen, cvd primary feathers, NM condition, ls, RB 7/09/85 250
    Pintail pr, cvd primaries, G rpt, RB 7/09/85 150
    Pintail pr, fine orig pnt, average wear, well preserved, RB 8/21/86 1050
    Sprig drake, high-neck, cvd primary feathers, varnished orig pnt, average wear, extremely rare, RB 8/25/88 4100

Jester, Charles (Chincoteague, VA)

Bufflehead drake, hollow, fine orig pnt, average wear, tiny mar at right side of bill, rare, 21, RB 2/01/85, 230% 2700

Jester, Charles
Bufflehead pr, hollow, orig pnt, drake has sm crack in neck, otherwise EX condition, ca 1915, 49, RWO 11/06/85, $6,000.00.

Hooded Merganser drake, old pnt, average wear, RB 7/09/85 300

Jester, Doug (Chincoteague, VA)

Black Duck, fine old pnt, average wear, top of head has an old repair, otherwise well preserved, RB 3/06/87, 175% 350
Black Duck, fine scratch feather pnt, NM condition, RB 2/ 01/85 240
Black Duck, old pnt, average wear, age split in bk of body, RB 3/06/87 100
Black Duck, old working rpt, slight roughness to edge of tail, 33, J/G 9/19/87 200
Black Duck, orig pnt, in-use wear w/some areas to bare wood, minor separation where head meets body, RWO 7/02/88 170
Black Duck, worn orig pnt, hairline crack in neck/chips to tail, RWO 11/06/85 130
Bluebill drake, G old pnt, minor wear, crack in bk of neck, J/G 4/24/86 220
Bluebill drake, M orig pnt, no structural flaws, J/G 9/19/87 350
Bluebill drake, NM & orig, 21, RB 2/01/85 175
Bluebill drake, orig pnt, moderate wear, age splits in body & neck, RB 3/11/88 130
Bluebill drake, working rpt on bk shows heavy wear, structurally sound, RWO 7/04/87 90
Bufflehead, fine old pnt, average wear, structurally sound, RB 8/21/86 225
Bufflehead drake, G orig pnt, average wear, some minor age splits to body, RB 3/11/88 350
Bufflehead drake, old pnt appears to be orig, average wear, several minor age splits, RB 3/11/88 150
Bufflehead drake, old working rpt, heavy flaking/wear, short crack in bottom, otherwise structurally sound, RWO 11/11/87 130
Bufflehead drake, orig pnt, average wear, age split on underside/hairline crack in head, J/G 4/23/87 275
Bufflehead drake, orig pnt, average wear, RB 3/11/88 275
Bufflehead drake, working rpt, average wear, structurally sound, RWO 11/06/85 110
Bufflehead hen, old pnt, average wear, age split in neck/top of head, otherwise structurally sound, RB 3/06/87 225
Bufflehead pr, fine old pnt, average wear, RB 7/09/85 375
Bufflehead pr, working rpt, in-use wear, bill on drake is rough on end, both have age splits, RB 2/01/85 220
Canada Goose, G orig pnt, average wear, tight hairlines in neck, otherwise structurally EX, ca 1920's, 49, RWO 11/11/87 475
Canada Goose, orig pnt, average wear, hairline crack on 1 side of head, otherwise EX, RWO 7/06/86, 140% 650
Canada Goose, orig pnt w/some areas of working rpt, crack running down bk, 49, RWO 7/06/86 225
Canvasback drake, G orig pnt, minor wear, structurally EX, RWO 7/06/86 200
Canvasback drake, G orig pnt, moderate wear, several shallow chips on bill, ls, RB 3/11/88 200
Goldeneye drake, old working rpt, average wear, structurally sound, RWO 7/06/86 140
Hooded Merganser drake, old working rpt, repair to bill, RWO 2/13/87 275
Hooded Merganser hen, fine orig pnt, average wear, well preserved, 9/77, RB 12/06/85 750
Hooded Merganser hen, orig pnt, minor wear, prof rstr to bill, J/G 4/23/87 550
Hooded Merganser pr, prof pnt rstr, sm tail chip on hen, J/G 9/19/87 400
Merganser hen, fine old pnt, average wear, bill has been rstr, RB 8/21/86 375
Merganser hen, old pnt, heavy flaking/wear, age split in neck/body, bill is a replacement, RB 3/06/87 275
Merganser hen, old rpt, average wear, bill is a complete replacement, some slight age splitting, RB 7/07/87 100
Merganser hen, old working rpt, minor chips on edge of bill/crest, J/G 9/19/87 225
Merganser hen, old working rpt, minor wear, bill is a replacement, J/G 9/19/87 75
Merganser hen, old working rpt, old bill repair/rstr to 1 point on the comb, J/G 9/20/86 175
Merganser hen, orig pnt, heavy wear, damage to top of head/crest, check running vertically through head, RWO 11/11/87 310

Old Squaw drake, old working rpt, reglued crack in bill/hairline crack in breast, very rare, 33, J/G 9/19/87 275
Pintail drake, NM orig pnt, tight age split in neck/1 eye missing, lg, J/G 4/23/87 275
Pintail drake, orig pnt, heavy wear, age splits in neck, RB 8/21/86 300
Pintail pr, G orig pnt, drake shows more wear than hen; hen has narrow check on 1 side, otherwise EX, RWO 11/11/87 500
Redbreasted Merganser drake, fine orig pnt, average wear, some slight chips to underside of comb, RB 12/06/85 350
Redbreasted Merganser drake, old rpt, average wear, several age splits in body, old bill repair, RB 2/01/85 275
Redbreasted Merganser drake, worn orig pnt, wooden crest broken off/crack in neck, otherwise sound, RWO 7/04/87 350
Redhead, flying, EX orig pnt, 1 wing has hairline crack, otherwise structurally NM, RWO 11/11/87 375
Redhead drake, EX orig pnt, minor wear, structurally sound, RWO 7/06/86 300
Redhead drake, old working rpt, hairline crack in neck, otherwise structurally sound, RWO 11/06/85 110
Yellowlegs, raised 'V' wing cvg, orig pnt, minor wear, age split on underside, oversize, 49, J/G 4/23/87 650
Yellowlegs or Curlew, EX orig condition, ca 1930's, 49, RWO 7/05/85 600

Jester, Doug; att (Chincoteague, VA)
Bluebill drake, old working rpt, average flaking/wear, crack running through neck/cracks in body, RWO 7/02/88 95

Jobes, Capt. Harry (Havre de Grace, MD)
Black Duck, EX orig pnt, signed/dated on bottom, oversize, RB 3/06/87 75
Bluewinged Teal hen, EX & orig, RB 7/08/86 30
Bluewinged Teal pr, EX & orig condition, RWO 2/12/88 110
Bluewinged Teal pr, signed 1980, M condition, RWO 2/12/88 110
Canvasback drake, early, EX orig pnt, tight check along 1 side, lg wooden keel, RWO 11/11/87 65
Canvasback pr, high-head style, orig pnt, EX condition, RWO 11/06/85 70
Canvasback pr, M condition, RB 2/01/85 200
Greenwinged Teal drake, EX orig pnt, RB 7/08/86 60
Greenwinged Teal hen, pnt shows average wear, structurally sound, RB 3/06/87 90
Greenwinged Teal pr, EX orig pnt, RWO 2/13/87 145
Greenwinged Teal pr, M condition, RWO 2/12/88 100
Mallard pr, NM condition, RB 8/25/88 100
Mallard pr, swimming, M condition, RB 2/01/85 200
Pintail drake, EX orig pnt, minor wear, thin crack in neck, RWO 7/02/88 80
Pintail pr, orig pnt, signed/dated 1966, drake has narrow crack in neck/on bottom, RWO 2/12/88 120
Pintail pr, signed/dated 1986, M condition, RWO 11/11/87 110
Redbreasted Merganser pr, orig pnt, minor wear, drake has chip on underside of bill/age split in bk, RB 7/08/86 275
Sea Gull, G orig pnt, minor flaking/wear, artist brand, age split in body, rare, RB 2/01/85 125
Swan, barn door keel, EX & orig condition, RWO 2/12/88 250

Jobes, Capt. Harry
Swan, EX orig pnt, artist brand, thin crack along side, otherwise structurally EX, RWO 11/06/85, $225.00.

Widgeon hen, G orig pnt, minor wear, 39, RB 7/08/86 50

Joeckel, Bill (Long Island, NY)
Brant, balsa body, old orig pnt, average flaking/wear, thin age split on bottom/neck, ls, RB 7/07/87 100
Sea Gull, hollow, EX pnt, artist brand, RB 7/07/87 500

Johnson, Elroy (Bailey's Island, ME)
Loon, sleeping, old rpt, average wear, several age splits, slight dry rot to underside, 22/44, RB 5/02/86 2800

Johnson, Jesse M. (Bailey's Island, ME)
Merganser pr, sleepers, fine old orig pnt, average flaking/wear, artist initials, 22/44, RB 5/02/86 3000

Johnson, Lloyd (Bay Head, NJ)
Black Duck, hollow, EX orig pnt, minor wear, structurally EX, ca 1940's, 50, RWO 11/06/85, 160% 3250

Black Duck, sleeping, raised cvd wing tips, EX orig pnt w/nice scratch pnt on head, structurally sound, RWO 7/06/86 .... **200**
Greenwinged Teal drake, raised cvd wing tips, EX orig pnt, RB 7/07/87 .... **600**
Widgeon, early, hollow w/cvd wing tips/primary feathers, fine orig pnt, average wear, well preserved, rare, RB 7/08/86 .... **400**
Yellowlegs, cvd in manner of Harry Shourds, signed/dated 1957, M condition, RWO 7/02/88 .... **275**

Johnson, Lloyd; att (Bay Head, NJ)
Canada Goose, hollow, EX in every respect, ca 1950's, RWO 7/05/85 .... **435**

Johnson, Michael (Inman, SC)
Curlew, running, cvd primaries, M condition, RWO 7/02/88 .... **90**
Pintail drake, preening, cvd in style of Elmer Crowell, artist signed/dated 1988, M condition, RWO 7/02/88 .... **225**

Johnson, Ralph (Detroit, MI)
Bluebill drake, orig pnt, minor wear, no structural flaws, J/G 9/20/86 .... **75**
Canvasback drake, NM orig pnt, signed/dated 1955, branded DRW/HY Dahlka, no structural flaws, oversize, J/G 9/19/87 .... **250**
Canvasback drake, orig pnt, minor wear, no structural flaws, J/G 9/19/87 .... **150**
Mallard drake, artist stamp, NM condition, RB 8/25/88 .... **80**
Redhead drake, fine orig pnt, average wear, sm knot has fallen out on 1 side of neck, rare, RB 7/08/86 .... **175**

Johnson, Taylor (Point Pleasant, NJ)
Black Duck, hollow, old rpt, heavy wear, some slight age splitting, 39, RB 7/08/86 .... **200**
Bluebill drake, hollow, old rpt, average wear, structurally sound, 6, RB 7/07/87 .... **325**
Brant, hollow, working rpt shows wear, thin crack in neck, bill broken & reglued, ca 1920, 3, RWO 7/05/85 .... **230**
Mallard drake, hollow, rpt w/average wear, old age split in neck, RB 7/07/87 .... **125**
Yellowlegs, EX orig pnt, prof bill repair in Johnson style, ls, J/G 9/20/86 .... **125**

Johnson, Taylor; att (Point Pleasant, NJ)
Bluebill, hollow, old rpt, average wear, old repair to neck, RB 6/28/88 .... **100**
Canada Goose, hollow, old working rpt, prof neck rstr, J/G 9/20/86 .... **225**

Joiner, Charlie (Betterton, MD)
Black Duck, flat-bottom style, orig pnt worn to bare wood in many areas, sm crack in neck, otherwise sound, RWO 11/06/85 .... **150**
Bluebill drake, orig pnt, minor wear, structurally EX, ca 1948, RWO 11/06/85 .... **230**
Bluebill hen, orig pnt, minor wear, structurally EX, ca 1948, RWO 11/06/85 .... **220**
Canada Goose, G orig pnt, structurally sound, ca 1946, RWO 11/06/85 .... **275**
Canada Goose, NM pnt, signed/dated 1951, RWO 7/04/87, 330% **1000**
Canvasback drake, EX orig pnt, fine structural condition, RWO 7/05/85 .... **105**
Canvasback drake, old rpt, average wear, signed on bottom, ls, RB 7/07/87 .... **150**
Canvasback drake, old working rpt, minor wear, artist brand, thin crack in neck, otherwise sound, RWO 7/06/86 .... **100**
Canvasback hen, G orig pnt, average wear, signed on bottom, ls, RB 7/07/87 .... **300**
Canvasback hen, signed/dated 1960, M/unused, RWO 7/06/86 .... **145**
Canvasback pr, EX orig pnt, signed/1950, crack in drake's neck; sm crack part way through hen's neck, 33, J/G 9/19/87 .... **450**
Canvasback pr, EX pnt, both signed on bottom, RB 7/09/85 .... **250**
Redhead pr, fine orig pnt, minor wear, artist brand, 39, RB 7/08/86 .... **350**
Widgeon drake, slightly turned head, signed/dated 1963, M condition, RWO 7/06/86 .... **475**
Widgeon pr, highly stylized pnt, M condition, RWO 7/06/86 .... **300**

Jones, Bob (Demorestville, Ont)
Redhead drake, G orig pnt, average wear, well preserved, RB 7/08/86 .... **125**
Redhead drake, orig pnt, moderate flaking/wear, comb pnt on bk, ls, J/G 4/24/86 .... **440**

Jones, C.; att (Greenbackville, VA)
Merganser hen, worn orig pnt, check running down bk, otherwise VG, has old chain for keel weight, RWO 7/05/85 .... **370**

Jones, Doddie; att
Black Duck, G orig pnt, average wear, well preserved, RB 3/06/87 .... **250**

Jones, F.
Bluebill hen, hollow, old working rpt, average wear, prof bill rpr, otherwise sound, RWO 2/12/88 .... **110**

Jones, Pied; att (Crisfield, MD)
Canvasback hen, orig pnt worn to bare wood over much of body, several age checks in neck/body, lg, RWO 7/02/88 .... **375**

Jones (Alexandria Bay, NY)
Black Duck, NM condition, ca 1930-40, RWO 2/12/88 .... **165**

Kach, Rich
Loon, cvd w/fish in mouth, EX orig pnt, artist signed, oversize, RB 7/09/85 .... **500**
Old Squaw drake, fine feather/wing cvg, EX pnt, artist brand, RB 7/09/85 .... **200**
Swan, gracefully cvd, EX pnt, artist signed, RB 7/09/85 .... **350**

Kamm, Roy (Lacon, IL)
Mallard pr, orig pnt, minor wear, both have hairline cracks in neck, ca 1930, rare, 7, J/G 4/24/86 .... **1045**

Kaseman, Fred
Blackbellied Plover, cvd wings, EX pnt, RB 7/07/87 .... **70**

Kavacs, Charlie (Roebling, NJ)
Black Duck, hollow w/raised cvd primaries/secondaries, NM orig pnt, tiny chip on tip of tail, J/G 9/19/87 200
Canada Goose, hollow w/head cvd in upturned position, raised cvd wing tips, EX orig pnt, RB 7/07/87 325

Kears, Mark (Northfield, NJ)
Black Duck, hollow, old pnt, average wear, lower half of body may not be orig, RB 3/11/88 200
Black Duck, hollow, scratch feather pnt on bk/sides, EX orig pnt w/some wear near inset weight, J/G 9/20/86 225
Bluebill hen, hollow, rpt, average wear, minor chip on underside of bill, RB 6/28/88 240
Bluebill pr, gunning decoys, orig pnt, wear/flaking, drake has separation at body joint; hen has check, 3, RWO 11/11/87 700
Bufflehead drake, orig pnt, average wear, bill is an old replacement, rare, J/G 9/19/87 125

Kears, Mark; att (Northfield, NJ)
Black Duck, hollow, old rpt, average wear, RB 3/11/88 175
Black Duck, hollow, old working rpt, average flaking/wear, RB 7/09/85 180

Keefer, Jim (Woodstock, VT)
Bufflehead drake, hollow, EX pnt, signed/dated 1985 on bottom, RB 7/09/85 75
Canada Goose, hollow, EX pnt, signed/dated 1983 on bottom, RB 8/21/86 275
Canada Goose, hollow, EX pnt, signed/dated 1985 on bottom, RB 7/09/85 250
Canada Goose, neck twisted into preening position, hollow, EX pnt, signed/dated 1983 on bottom, RB 8/21/86 325
Goldeneye hen, inlet neck, hollow, EX pnt, signed/dated 1985 on bottom, RB 7/09/85 75
Redbreasted Merganser drake, EX pnt, signed/dated 1985 on bottom, RB 7/09/85 75

Keith, Clinton
Scoter, canvas-covered slat, orig pnt, average wear, artist brand, structurally VG, 22/44, RB 5/02/86 300
Whitewinged Scoter, canvas-covered, EX orig pnt, minor wear, well preserved, 39, RB 7/08/86 250

Keller, Ed (Bartonsville, IL)
Pintail drake, orig pnt w/fine feathering, minor flaking/touchup, reapplied bottom, sm crack through head, J/G 9/20/86 650

Kellie, Edward (Monroe, MI)
Bluebill pr, orig pnt, in-use wear, structurally sound, 114, RWO 7/05/85 895
Canvasback drake, pnt taken down to natural wood w/traces of orig, structurally sound, RB 2/01/85 200
Canvasback drake, rpt, minor wear, RB 7/09/85 200
Canvasback pr, G orig pnt, average wear, drake has thin check on 1 side; hen has sm tail chip, ca 1920's, RWO 7/04/87 950
Redhead drake, fine old pnt appears to be orig, average wear, minor age splitting, nailed-in bill chip, RB 8/25/88 270

Kellum, Frank (Long Island, NY)
Merganser hen, worn orig pnt, signed/dated 1895, thin crack at base of neck, otherwise sound, RWO 7/06/86 220

Kellum, Frank
Sea Gull, full-bodied stick-up, EX form, EX orig pnt, minor flaking/wear, extremely rare, 22/44, RB 5/02/86, 180%, $36,000.00.

Kellum, Frank; att (Long Island, NY)
Sea Gull, fine orig pnt, average flaking/wear, age splits in neck, rare, ca 1900, RB 7/07/87 1000

Kelson, Jim (Detroit, MI)
Bluebill pr, orig pnt, slight wear, no structural flaws, J/G 9/20/86 300
Canvasback, cast aluminum head, old working rpt to head/black areas, white is orig, structurally sound, RWO 11/11/87 85
Canvasback drake, balsa body, fine orig pnt, minor wear, RB 7/09/85 150
Canvasback drake, balsa body, relief wing cvg, old working rpt, several dents in balsa, J/G 4/23/87 175
Canvasback drake, EX pnt by Ray Trombley, RB 2/01/85 110
Canvasback drake, orig pnt, average wear, ms, otherwise structurally sound, RWO 7/02/88 150
Canvasback drake, sleeping, balsa body, cedar head, fine old pnt, minor wear, ls, J/G 4/24/86 220

Canvasback pr, balsa body, sleeping, fine old pnt, average wear, structurally sound, RB 8/25/88 300
Redhead pr, balsa bodies w/pine heads/keels, working rpt, head on hen has been broken off & reglued, J/G 9/20/86 100

Kelson, Jim; att (Detroit, MI)
Bluebill pr, sleeping, old working rpt shows flaking/wear, structurally sound, RWO 2/12/88 180

Kemble, William; att (Trenton, NJ)
Bluewinged Teal hen, hollow, orig pnt, minor wear, no structural flaws, J/G 9/19/87, 40% 400
Bufflehead drake, hollow w/layered cvd primaries, NM orig pnt, EX patina, 1 glass eye missing, 33, J/G 9/19/87, 45% 1300

Kendrick, Doughty
Black Duck, old pnt, heavy flaking/wear, several age splits, RB 5/02/86 50

Kerr, Bob (Smith's Falls, Ont)
Black Duck, hollow w/cvd raised wings, signed/dated 1967, EX condition, RB 8/25/88 300
Bluebill hen, raised cvd primaries/secondaries, M pnt w/several sm rubs, structurally EX, J/G 9/19/87 450
Bluebill hen, relief wing cvg, NM pnt, minor flaking on lower sides, several marks where keel is off, J/G 4/23/87 250
Goldeneye drake, hollow, raised wing cvg, EX orig condition, ca 1955, RWO 7/05/85 425
Greenwinged Teal hen, stamped/dated 1965, EX orig condition, RWO 7/05/85 375
Greenwinged Teal pr, detailed feather pnt, M condition, J/G 4/23/87 550
Greenwinged Teal pr, hollow, relief cvg on bk, detailed feather pnt, artist brand, RWO 7/02/88 550
Pintail drake, slightly turned head, highly detailed wing/tail cvg, fine comb pnt, oversize, 59, J/G 9/20/86 1350

Kessler, George (Pekin, IL)
Canvasback drake, body prof taken down to orig pnt, minor wear, head is working rpt, stamped 1945, EX, rare, J/G 4/23/87 250
Mallard drake, hollow, old working rpt, average wear w/flaking on the head, EX condition, RWO 2/12/88 270
Widgeon drake, orig pnt, very minor wear, very sm rough area on tail, structurally sound, J/G 9/20/86 800
Widgeon hen, orig pnt, minor wear, chip in 1 side of tail/sm dent in bk, rare, J/G 4/23/87 500
Widgeon pr, NM orig pnt, tail chip on hen; sm rough area on tail on drake, otherwise structurally EX, J/G 4/24/86 1650

Ketchum, Capt. Al (Amityville, LI, NY)
Blackbellied Plover, deeply cvd wings/wing tips, cvd eyes, fine old pnt, ls, rare, RB 7/09/85, 50% 1200

Ketchum, Capt. Al
Curlew, EX orig pnt, average wear, age split in bk/lg age split in bottom, rare, 22/44, RB 5/02/86, $2,100.00.

Peep, cvd wings/eyes, fine orig pnt, average wear, ms, rare, RB 7/09/85 1200
Ruddy Turnstone, EX orig pnt, minor flaking/wear, bill is a replacement, RWO 7/04/87, 60% 900

Ketchum, James; att
Black Duck, old pnt, average wear, hairline crack in neck/narrow check on 1 side, otherwise sound, RWO 7/06/86 50

Kidwell, Harold (California)
Greenwinged Teal drake, swimming, raised cvd wing tips, cvd K on bottom, structurally EX, RB 8/27/87 300
Mallard drake, raised crossed wing tips, HK cvd under tail, EX orig pnt, RB 8/27/87 275

Kilmon, Arthur (Pocomoke, MD)
Merganser, swimming, hollow, detailed feather pnt, J/G 4/24/86 412
Merganser pr, hollow, detailed feather pnt, J/G 4/24/86 330

Kilpatrick, Henry (Barnegat, NJ)
Bluebill drake, old working rpt w/orig on bk, J/G 9/20/86 135
Canada Goose, hollow, fine old pnt, average wear, well preserved, RB 3/06/87, 130% 2000

Kilpatrick, Will (Hudson, MA)
Wood Duck pr, made in 1985 as prototypes for Colorado Ducks Unlimited, M condition, RWO 7/06/86 150

Kimball, William; att
Redhead drake, hollow, detailed feather cvg on wings, old pnt, minor wear, eyes damaged, otherwise sound, RB 3/11/88 150

King, Joe (Manahawkin, NJ)
Black Duck, early, hollow, pnt worn to mostly bare wood, branded C Cran, cracks in head/neck/tail, RWO 7/02/88 170

Black Duck, hollow, fine old rpt, average wear, minor age split in neck, 189, RB 6/28/88 .... **150**
Black Duck, hollow, old rpt, average wear, age split in neck, sm end-of-tail chips, 189, RB 6/28/88 .... **150**
Black Duck, hollow, old working rpt, both eyes missing, structurally fair, ca 1880, RWO 11/06/85 .... **90**
Black Duck, hollow, pnt stripped to natural wood, age split in neck, chip on left side of bill, RB 6/28/88 .... **160**
Black Duck, hollow, pnt worn to mostly natural wood, age split in neck, RB 3/11/88 .... **175**
Bluebill drake, hollow, fine old pnt, average wear, age split in neck/separation where body halves join, RB 3/06/87 .... **250**
Bluebill drake, hollow, old working rpt, average wear, well preserved, RB 12/06/85 .... **75**
Bluebill pr, hollow, old rpt, average wear, structurally sound, RB 12/06/85 .... **250**
Brant, hollow, old rpt, average flaking/wear, slight age check in bill, otherwise structurally sound, 6, RB 7/07/87 .... **400**
Canada Goose, early, hollow, orig pnt, in-use wear, neck crack, bill broken & reattached, rare, RWO 7/02/88, 75% **1500**
Canada Goose, hollow, old pnt, flaking/wear, chip at end of tail, RB 7/09/85 .... **510**
Canada Goose, hollow, old pnt, heavy wear, age split in neck/old bill repair, branded Cobb, 21, RB 2/01/85 .... **675**
Canada Goose, hollow, old rpt, average flaking/wear, age split in neck, RB 7/07/87 .... **300**
Canada Goose, rpt by King, minor flaking, tight crack in neck, several short cracks under tail, J/G 9/19/87 .... **575**
Curlew, body has been rstr, head is a replacement, RB 7/07/87 .... **130**
Curlew, old orig pnt, average flaking/wear, Accomack Club brand on bottom, hs, RB 3/06/87, 200% **1400**
Curlew, orig pnt, heavy wear, much of bill has been replaced by Kenneth DeLong, RB 8/25/88, 52% **250**
Curlew, orig pnt, minor flaking, eyes missing, J/G 4/24/86 .... **1210**
Curlew, some traces of orig pnt, decoy has been rstr, patch on body, branded, hs, rare, RB 2/01/85 .... **300**
Merganser hen, hollow, old pnt worn to orig, heavy wear, RB 12/06/85 .... **400**
Plover, EX orig pnt, minor wear, RB 7/08/86 .... **425**
Plover, old working rpt, branded Accomack Club VA, rstr to side of head/bill, ls, J/G 9/19/87 .... **375**
Redhead drake, hollow, old rpt, heavy flaking/wear, age splits in neck, RB 3/11/88 .... **170**
Robin Snipe, orig pnt, average wear, bill is a replacement, ca 1880, 28, J/G 4/24/86 .... **275**

King, Joe; att (Manahawkin, NJ)
Black Duck, hollow, fine old rpt w/flaking/wear, age split in neck, 21, RB 2/01/85 .... **100**
Plover, traces of orig pnt, left side of head is a replacement, hs, RB 2/01/85 .... **200**
Redbreasted Merganser drake, hollow, rpt w/heavy flaking/wear, chips at end/underside of bill, RB 7/09/85 .... **250**

King, Oliver (Port Severn, Ontario)
Hooded Merganser pr, VG orig pnt, structurally EX, ca 1950, RWO 7/05/85 .... **425**

Kitteridge, Henry
Blackbellied Plover, head turned down, G orig pnt, minor wear, 22/44, RB 5/02/86 .... **800**

Knoeble, L.W.
Mallard hen, cvd crossed wing tips w/primary feathers, EX orig pnt, some crazing, well preserved, RB 8/27/87 .... **75**

Koehler, George; att (Peru, IL)
Mallard drake, appealing old working rpt, combing on bk appears to be orig, ms, J/G 4/24/86 .... **137**

Koehler, John (Peru, IL)
Mallard pr, M condition, ca 1950, half-size, J/G 4/23/87 .... **125**

Koehler, Leonard (Peru, IL)
Pintail drake, hollow, outstanding orig pnt, structurally superb, retains maker's weight, 89, RWO 7/05/85 .... **600**

Koehler, Leopold (Peru, IL)
Mallard drake, hollow, old working rpt, average wear, tiny chip in tail, otherwise structurally sound, RWO 7/06/86 .... **160**
Mallard drake, old working rpt, ls, from artist's rig, J/G 4/23/87 .... **150**

Koehler, Leopold; att (Peru, IL)
Mallard hen, hollow, NM orig pnt w/fine scratch pnt, ls, J/G 4/24/86 .... **220**

Kovacs, Charles (Roebling, NJ)
Gadwall hen, hollow, cvd raised wing tips, fine comb feather pnt, EX condition, RB 6/28/88 .... **125**
Hooded Merganser, swimming, hollow, EX orig pnt, RB 7/08/86 .... **175**
Mallard drake, hollow, orig pnt, moderate wear, slight age split in neck, RB 8/27/87 .... **110**
Mallard drake, hollow w/raised primaries, cvd tail feathers, orig pnt, minor wear, structurally EX, J/G 9/20/86 .... **95**
Mallard drake, low-head style, raised cvd primaries, orig pnt, minor wear, signed, RWO 7/06/86 .... **70**
Redhead drake, hollow, EX & orig condition, RB 6/28/88 .... **150**

Kraimer, Ben (New Boston, IL)
Mallard hen, cvd layered primaries, orig pnt, minor wear, 3 sm tail chips, J/G 4/23/87 .... **350**

Kraus, Jack; att
Redhead drake, hollow, fine old pnt, average wear, structurally sound, RB 2/01/85 .... **175**

Kroft, Fred
Goldeneye drake, hollow, old rpt, average flaking/wear, RB 7/07/87 .... **200**

Kruge, Otto
Brant, hollow, fine old pnt, average wear, half of bill is broken off & missing, RB 7/07/87 .... **90**

Kuhn, William (Tullytown, PA)
Black Duck, low-head style, EX orig pnt, Kuhn's name tag on bottom, RWO 7/04/87 .... **400**

LaBoeuf, Orel (St. Anicet, Que)
Black Duck, fine overall feather cvg, fine orig pnt, average wear, ls, rare, RB 3/06/87 750
Bluebill, highly detailed feather cvg on tail/bk/lower sides, old working rpt, sm tight checks in breast, J/G 9/20/86 150
Bluebill hen, EX highly detailed feather cvg, M orig pnt, G patina, hairline crack in 1 side of head, J/G 4/23/87 725
Bluebill hen, EX wing/feather cvg, orig pnt, average in-use wear, RB 7/09/85 275
Bluebill hen, feather cvg on bk, EX orig pnt, minor wear, slight age split in bk, RB 2/01/85 550
Bluebill hen, superb feather cvg, EX orig pnt, minor wear, structurally M, ca 1920-30, RWO 7/05/86, 133% 1200
Bluebill pr, extensive feather cvg, fine feather pnt, minor flaking, extremely rare, ls, 39, RB 7/08/86 1600

LaBoeuf, Orel
Bluebill hen, superb incised feather cvg, EX pnt w/very little wear, M condition, ca 1920-30, RWO 7/05/86, $1,200.00.

Bluebill pr, extremely fine detailed feather cvg on bk/sides, NM orig comb pnt w/fine patina, J/G 9/20/86 2100
Bluebill pr, feather cvd wings/tail, fine comb pnt on bks, drake is ls, otherwise M, J/G 4/23/87, 75% 1550

Lacombe, Paul Emile (St. Lawrence River area)
Goldeneye drake, cvd primary feathers, G orig pnt, average flaking/wear, RB 8/27/87 25
Goldeneye drake, EX orig pnt, RB 7/08/86 50

LaFlair, John (Ogdensburg, NY)
Canvasback hen, NM orig pnt w/comb pnt on bk, branded PATH, hairline crack near base of neck, J/G 4/23/87 225

LaFrance, Mitchell (St. Sophie, LA)
Mallard hen, minnow-chasing position, EX pnt, artist initials, RB 7/09/85 180
Mallard hen, swimming, signed, EX condition, half-size, RB 8/25/88 15
Pintail drake, cypress root, early round bottom type, raised cvd wings/fine bill cvg, orig pnt/weight, EX, J/G 9/20/86 550
Pintail drake, fine orig pnt, average wear, ls, RB 7/08/86 1200
Pintail drake, long sleek body w/raised wings, EX orig pnt, average wear, minor damage along bottom, RWO 2/12/88, 75% 1550

LaFrance, Mitchell
Pintail drake, G orig pnt, average wear, structurally EX, ca 1935, RWO 11/11/87, $900.00.

Pintail drake, orig pnt worn to bare wood in many areas, crack running through neck has been reglued, RWO 7/06/86 900
Pintail hen, cvd wings, EX orig pnt, 1" of bill has been rstr, chip smoothed, ms, ca 1940, RB 7/07/87 800
Pintail hen, orig pnt, average wear, possible repair to underside of bill, old repair to end of tail, ms, RB 6/28/88 1000

Laine, Raymond (New Orleans, LA)
Mallard drake, preening, old pnt, minor wear, well preserved, RB 3/06/87 175
Mallard drake, preening, raised cvd wings, orig pnt, minor wear, tail has been rstr, J/G 9/20/86 190
Pintail drake, preening, orig pnt, minor wear, well preserved, RB 3/06/87 275
Pintail drake, raised cvd wings, orig pnt, slight wear, tip of tail has been broken off, J/G 9/20/86 200

Laing, Albert (Stratford, CT)

Black Duck, hollow, old pnt worn to natural in many areas, rpr bill/rstr tail, rigging handle, RB 2/01/85, 175% **5250**

Black Duck, hollow, rpt by Charles Wheeler, average flaking/wear, rpl eyes/bill, branded Laing, rare, 22/44, RB 5/02/86 .... **4000**

Black Duck, hollow, rpt by Charles Wheeler, minor wear, artist brand, most of bill is a replacement, RB 12/06/85 .... **2100**

Black Duck, hollow, rpt w/average wear, artist brand, slight roughness to tail/bill has been chewed, 21, RB 2/01/85, 45% **1750**

Black Duck, hollow, traces of old pnt, artist brand, structurally sound, rare, RB 7/09/85, 12% **700**

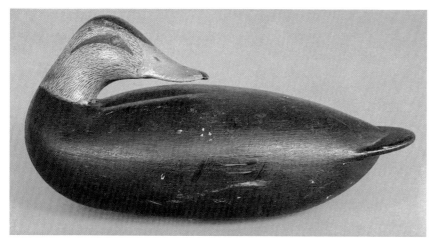

Laing, Albert
Black Duck, preening, hollow, rpt as canvasback by Chas Wheeler, minor wear, structurally EX, 1, RB 12/06/85, 220%, $33,000.00.

Black Duck, sleeping, hollow, rpt, heavy wear, artist brand, age split at top of head, eye missing, 21, RB 2/01/85, 175% **17500**

Black Duck, sleeping, orig cvd as Scoter, rpt w/average wear, sm tail chip, rare, 22/44, RB 5/02/86, 70% **5000**

Broadbill drake, preening, hollow, worn/weathered orig pnt, chip on bill, drilled rigging holes, rare, BR 2/01/85 .... **13000**

Lamdin, Charles (Elkton, MD)

Bluebill pr, EX orig pnt, RB 12/06/85 .... **60**

Landry, Ivy (Delacroix, LA)

Greenwinged Teal hen, fine orig pnt, flaking/wear, structurally sound, RB 7/08/86 .... **50**

Greenwinged Teal hen, swimming, cypress root, orig pnt, minimal wear, J/G 4/24/86 .... **121**

Mallard drake, G old pnt, minor wear, sm crack in tail, J/G 4/24/86 .... **93**

Mallard hen, cvd raised wing tips, old pnt, average wear, ls, RB 6/28/88 .... **175**

Mallard hen, cypress root, orig pnt w/some working touchup, structurally sound, ca 1930's, RWO 11/11/87 .... **60**

Mallard pr, old rpt, average wear, artist initials, from Landry's rig, RB 7/08/86 .... **300**

Mallard pr, orig pnt, possible working touchup, structurally EX, RWO 7/06/86 .... **240**

Lane, Stephen (Lacon, IL)

Bluebill drake, early, hollow, orig pnt on bk, otherwise working rpt, chips missing out of tail/bill, RWO 2/13/87 .... **225**

Bluewinged Teal hen, early, hollow, EX orig pnt, branded CS Wilcox, bill rpr, otherwise EX, rare, RWO 7/02/88, 70% **2500**

Mallard drake, early, old working rpt w/some orig, artist brand, no structural flaws, J/G 4/24/86 .... **165**

Mallard drake, G orig pnt, flaking on bk, wedge of wood at base of neck has been reglued, otherwise EX, 193, RWO 7/02/88 .... **1000**

Pintail drake, hollow, some old working overpnt, structurally sound, ca 1800's, RWO 7/05/85 .... **375**

Langan, Thomas (Long Island, NY)

Owl, EX feather cvg, EX pnt, RB 7/07/87 .... **300**

Redbreasted Merganser pr, EX orig pnt, RB 7/07/87 .... **250**

Lapham, James (Dennisport, MA)

Greenwinged Teal drake, EX pnt, branded/signed on bottom, RB 12/06/85 .... **250**

Larnard, Louis (Amityville, LI, NY)

Black Duck, fine orig pnt, minor wear, RB 7/09/85 .... **110**

Black Duck, orig pnt, average wear, structurally sound, RWO 2/13/87 .... **80**

Bluebill hen, fine orig pnt, average wear, RB 7/09/85 .... **50**

Lashbrook, Virgil (Pekin, IL)

Canvasback pr, slightly turned heads, EX comb pnt, each have pnt rub on side of head, 7, J/G 4/24/86 .... **605**

Canvasback pr, slightly turned heads, M orig pnt, artist stamp, structurally EX, J/G 9/20/86 .... **450**

Greenwinged Teal drake, early gunning style, orig pnt, minor crazing/wear, hairline through neck, J/G 4/24/86, 175% **1402**

Pintail drake, slightly turned head, comb pnt on bk, flakes missing from edge of bill, otherwise EX, 7, J/G 4/24/86 .... **357**

Pintail pr, slightly turned heads, M pnt, both retain orig weight, 7, J/G 4/24/86 .... **770**

Widgeon pr, artist brand/signed in ink/dated 1968, M condition, RWO 11/06/85 .... **300**

Widgeon pr, artist stamp/signed/dated 1969, M condition, J/G 4/24/86 .... **770**

Wood Duck pr, sm dark pnt rub on lower side of hen, otherwise M, artist stamp/signed/dated 1970, rare, 7, J/G 4/24/86 687

Lattin, William (Stratford, CT)
Bluebill drake, hollow, fine old pnt, appears to be orig w/average wear, RB 7/09/85 350

Lattin, William; att (Stratford, CT)
Bluebill drake, hollow, fine orig pnt, average wear, structurally sound, RB 7/07/87 350

Lawson, Oliver (Crisfield, MD)
Canvasback pr, M pnt, signed/dated 1980, RWO 11/06/85 325
Mallard hen, balsa body w/cedar head, worn orig pnt, minor cracking where tail joins bodyblock, J/G 9/20/86 60

Lawson, Oliver
Swan, hollow, signed/dated 1986, inscribed Whistling Swan, Hunting
Decoy, M condition, RWO 11/11/87, $700.00.

Leach, Jack
Blue Heron, VG pnt, signed/dedicated, tiny nick at end of bill has been reglued, RB 2/01/85 225
Ruddy Duck pr, M condition, 36, RB 2/01/85 350

LeCompte, Paul (Louisiana)
Bluewinged Teal pr, orig pnt, minor wear, signed on bottom, RB 7/07/87 250
Greenwinged Teal pr, signed, EX condition, RB 6/28/88 50

LeCompte, Rudy (Bourg, LA)
Mallard drake, orig pnt, minor flaking/wear, bill has been prof repaired, structurally EX, RWO 7/06/86 120
Mallard pr, orig pnt, average wear, structurally sound, J/G 4/23/87 250
Pintail drake, orig pnt, average wear, tight crack in lower side, J/G 4/23/87 200

Leeds, Daniel (Pleasantville, NJ)
Hudsonian Curlew, outstanding/orig, sm chip at end of bill, ca 1880-90, 45 (rigmates shown in 78/50), RWO 7/04/87 4500
Knot, old pnt, average wear, rpl bill, well preserved, 6, RB 7/07/87 1000
Ruddy Turnstone, outstanding orig pnt, minor wear, structurally EX, ca 1880, RWO 7/04/87 3750

Leeds, Daniel; att (Pleasantville, NJ)
Robin Snipe, cvd wings/wing tips, old orig pnt, minor wear, bill is replacement, rare, 3, RB 3/06/87 1350

Leeds Family (Sommers Point, NJ)
Curlew, relief wing cvg, orig pnt, minor wear, bill is a prof replacement, ls, ca 1890, rare, J/G 4/23/87, 75% 750

Lefever, att (Owasco, NY)
Goldeneye drake, fine orig pnt, average wear, well preserved, RB 2/01/85 125

LeGaux, Roy (Slidell, LA)
Widgeon drake, swimming, raised cvd wings, M condition, J/G 9/20/86 225

Lemack, Willie; att
Redhead drake, old working rpt, average wear, age split in bk of body/break in orig bill, 21, RB 2/01/85 150

Levins, Harold (Thomson, IL)
Greenwinged Teal pr, hollow, EX orig pnt w/nice comb pnt, both have coat of varnish, EX, ca 1920, rare, 193, RWO 7/02/88 2250

Levy, Lindsey (Little Tancook Island, NS)
Old Squaw pr, old orig pnt, slight separation where head of drake meets body, RWO 7/04/87 200

Levy, Raymond (Little Tancook Island, NS)
Whitewinged Scoter pr, VG orig condition, ca 1940, RWO 7/05/85 500

Lewis, Florence
Bluebill pr, hollow, EX orig pnt, drake is missing 1 eye, 'Lewis' cvd in bottom, 22, RB 5/02/86, 190% 950
Bluewinged Teal pr, EX orig pnt, minor wear, lower portion of drake's bill is missing, 22, RB 5/02/86 900
Greenwinged Teal pr, hollow, orig pnt, minor wear, 22/44, RB 5/02/86, 225% 1600

Lewis, Frank (Ogdensburg, NY)
Bluebill drake, hump-back model, orig pnt, worn to primer in some areas, structurally sound, RWO 7/04/87 70
Bluebill drake, NM orig pnt, structurally EX, J/G 9/20/86 125
Bluebill drake, rpt, moderate flaking/wear, age split in neck, ms, RB 8/25/88 35

Bluebill pr, hen has G orig pnt w/average wear; drake is rpt, chip at top of tail, RB 7/09/85 160
Bluebill pr, old working rpt, average wear, RB 12/06/85 50
Bluebill pr, rpt w/evidence of orig underneath, 189, RB 6/28/88 50
Goldeneye hen, old pnt, average wear, age split in neck, RB 3/06/87 110

Lewis, G. (Hamilton, Ont)
Bluebill drake, slightly turned head, hollow w/detailed bill cvg, several hairline cracks in bottom plate, J/G 9/19/87 200

Libensperger, Robert (Levittown, PA)
Black Duck, hollow w/raised cvd wings, orig pnt, minor wear, structurally EX, ca 1950's, RWO 7/06/86 85
Bluebill drake, hollow, cvd raised wings, orig pnt, average wear, EX condition, ca 1950's, RWO 7/02/88 295
Bufflehead drake, hollow, won 1st place at the 1966 IA cvg contest in the diving class, EX orig condition, RWO 7/04/87 500
Bufflehead drake, NM orig pnt, several dark rubs on lower sides, J/G 9/19/87 200

Libensperger, Robert; att (Levittown, PA)
Brant, hollow, old working rpt, average wear, structurally EX, RWO 7/06/86 60

Libensperger, Turk
Bluebill drake, hollow, pnt rub to 1 side, otherwise EX, RB 6/28/88 75
Canvasback drake, hollow, orig pnt, average wear, RB 6/28/88 75

Lincoln, Joseph (Accord, MA)
Black Duck, cvd w/shoulder groove, EX orig pnt, minor flakes, age split in bottom, 22/44/77, RB 5/02/86, 133% 12000
Black Duck, cvd w/shoulder groove, EX orig pnt, minor flaking/wear, reglued neck break, well preserved, rare, RB 8/21/86 6000
Black Duck, EX orig pnt, minor flaking/wear, slight age splitting to body, ls, rare, 48, RB 7/07/87 6500
Black Duck, fine head style, old working rpt w/some orig showing, minor wear, oversize, J/G 9/20/86 1000
Black Duck, old pnt, average wear, replaced head, age split in bottom, 22, RB 5/02/86 350
Black Duck, old rpt, average wear, age split in bottom of body, oversize, RB 7/09/85 500
Black Duck, old rpt, average wear, several chips in tail/several age splits in body, oversize, 22/44, RB 5/02/86, 125% 1500
Black Duck, prof pnt rstr, filled crack on underside of bodyblock, oversize, J/G 9/20/86 250
Black Duck, prof pnt rstr in Lincoln style, prof rstr to part of bill, oversize, J/G 4/23/87 375
Black Duck, slight shoulder grooving between wings, feather stippling, slight age split/ls, branded FB Rice, RB 3/06/87 11000
Black Duck, working overpnt worn away, showing traces of orig, prof rstr bill, branded CF Spear, RWO 7/05/85 1100
Black Duck, working touchup to body, age check running down body, otherwise sound, oversize, 48, RWO 7/06/86 2750
Blackbellied Plover, tack eyes, EX orig pnt pattern, NM on left side/flaking to right side, rare, 22, RB 5/02/86 3250

Lincoln, Joseph
Bluebill drake, G orig pnt, minor flaking to bk, EX feather pnt to bk, rare, 22/97, RB 5/02/86, 133%, $9,000.00.

Brant, detailed orig pnt, minor wear, minor split in neck/bottom, CF Spear Scituate brand, rare, 40/97, RB 7/08/86, 160% 16000
Brant, high-head style, EX stippled pnt on sides & bk, minor wear/prof rstr age split, otherwise NM, RB 3/06/87 14000
Brant, self-bailing, fine orig pnt, minor wear, well preserved, rare, 22/44/46, RB 5/02/86, 270% 13500
Brant, self-bailing, orig pnt, minor wear, head has been broken off & reglued, otherwise structurally EX, RWO 11/06/85 3750
Brant, self-bailing, rpt w/minor wear, structurally EX, J/G 9/19/87 1000
Brant, taken down to mostly orig pnt w/some minor prof touch up, sm crack in lower breast, otherwise EX, J/G 9/20/86 800
Canada Goose, canvas-covered, EX orig pnt w/old working touchup to white areas, 1 sm hole in canvas, 53, J/G 9/19/87 2500
Canada Goose, canvas-covered slat, pnt shows average wear, structurally sound, lg, RWO 7/05/85 425
Canada Goose, EX orig pnt, minor wear, age split in neck/split in bottom of body, rare, RB 7/09/85 4750
Canada Goose, fine feather pnt, minor wear, age split on bottom ending part way up breast, otherwise EX, 87, J/G 9/19/87 3500
Canada Goose, fine feather pnt, minor wear, age split on bottom, 2 hairline cracks in breast, 87, J/G 9/19/87 4750
Canada Goose, fine orig pnt, average wear, age split in bottom/neck, slight roughness to edge of bill, 22, RB 5/02/86 4500
Canada Goose, fine orig pnt, retouched by K DeLong, average wear, age split in lower right side, RB 7/07/87, 65% 1600
Canada Goose, full body, fine orig pnt, average wear, worn to fine dry patina, age split in neck/body, RB 8/21/86 5000
Canada Goose, full body, old pnt, heavy wear, 5" of neck is a replacement, RB 3/06/87 350
Canada Goose, full body, orig pnt, average wear, age check at neck rpr by DeLong, branded DD Lewis, RB 3/06/87 6000

Canada Goose, G orig pnt, average flaking/wear, some slight age splitting, rare, oversize, RB 7/08/86	6500
Canada Goose, hissing, extremely well sculpted, outstanding pnt/presence, NM condition, 48, J/G 4/24/86, 258%	90200
Canada Goose, hollowed out from bottom, fine orig pnt, average flaking/wear, RB 7/09/85	1400
Canada Goose, old rpt, heavy flaking/wear, age split in neck/chip on right side of head, ms, 21, RB 2/01/85	475
Canada Goose, old rpt, heavy flaking/wear, head is a replacement, RB 12/06/85	250
Canada Goose, old rpt w/some orig, heavy wear, several age splits/chip on underside of bill, RB 3/06/87, 50%	600
Canada Goose, old working rpt, age split on underside/several minor checks in body, J/G 9/19/87	475
Canada Goose, old working rpt, lg check running along 1 side, bill is made separately, RWO 11/06/85	125
Canada Goose, orig pnt, average flaking/wear, 2 age splits in neck/1 in bottom, rare, RB 7/08/86, 50%	1000
Canada Goose, orig pnt, average wear, thin tight age checks on bk, otherwise structurally sound, RWO 7/06/86, 53%	1300
Canada Goose, orig pnt, heavy wear, age split in neck, RB 8/21/86	1150
Canada Goose, orig pnt, moderate crazing/wear, in-use touchup, crack in bottom/under-bill chip, J/G 4/24/86	1320
Canada Goose, orig pnt, worn bare in several areas, hairline/serious check in base, neck rpr, RWO 7/05/85, 60%	1200
Canada Goose, overpnt, average wear, 2 age splits in neck, rare, oversize, RB 12/06/85	850
Canada Goose, pnt taken down to mostly orig w/average wear, age split in bottom/tight crack in neck, J/G 4/23/87, 120%	1450
Canada Goose, prof rstr to pnt, head is a replacement, lg check runs through bottom, otherwise sound, RWO 7/06/86, 33%	200
Canada Goose, rpt, moderate wear, age splits to body, 187, RB 3/11/88, 130%	650
Canada Goose, rpt in Lincoln style, average wear, age split in bottom of body, RB 7/07/87	1000
Canada Goose, rpt in Lincoln style, head/neck are a prof replacement, slight age split in bottom, RB 8/21/86, 65%	500
Canada Goose, rpt in Lincoln style, several age splits, RB 2/01/85	350
Canada Goose, rpt in Lincoln style w/minor wear, age split in bottom of body, otherwise well preserved, RB 7/07/87	500
Canada Goose, slat-body, fine old pnt, average wear, structurally sound, 22/44, RB 5/02/86, 150%	1500
Canada Goose, slat-body, old rpt, average wear, structurally sound, 21, RB 2/01/85	750
Canada Goose, swimming, superb orig pnt, break in neck has been rstr by K DeLong, 20, RB 7/08/86, 150%	2250
Canada Goose, 2 coats of pnt by Lincoln, minor flaking & wear, age split extends up breast/under tail, J/G 9/19/87	1400
Coot, old orig pnt, average flaking/wear, age split in neck/chip on lower side of bill, ms, rare, RB 7/07/87	2700
Golden Plover, EX orig pnt, structurally M, in emerging plumage, very rare, RWO 7/05/85	3950
Golden Plover, fine orig condition, nice patina, RWO 7/05/85	1800
Golden Plover, NM orig pnt, tiny chip/crack on 1 side of bill, J/G 4/24/86	825
Golden Plover, orig pnt, average wear, hs, RWO 11/06/85	475
Goldeneye drake, old working rpt flaking away to reveal orig, branded, structurally sound, RWO 7/06/86	2750
Goldeneye drake, rpt w/minor wear, CF Spear Scituate brand, 40, RB 7/08/86	1300
Goldeneye hen, EX orig pnt pattern, minor wear, underside of bill is rstr, 40, RB 7/08/86, 150%	6000
Goldeneye hen, old working rpt worn away to reveal orig, thin tight checks on bk, otherwise structurally EX, RWO 7/06/86	2000

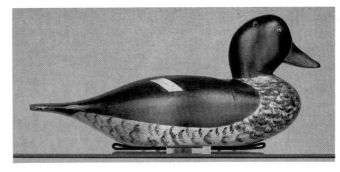

Lincoln, Joseph
**Goldeneye hen, outstanding bold orig pnt, bill is prof rpl,
J/G 9/19/87, $4,000.00.**

Goose, canvas-covered slat, G orig pnt w/some overpnt, 1 slat missing, canvas needs rstr, RB 2/01/85	250
Goose, canvas-covered slat, rpt w/heavy wear, age split in neck, canvas is in poor condition, RB 7/08/86	200
Goose, hollowed out from bottom, 2 holes to accomodate legs, 2 coats of pnt, prof rstr, NM, rare sm size, J/G 4/23/87	2700
Goose, slat-body, EX orig pnt, average wear, neck crack has been nailed, otherwise structurally EX, RWO 7/02/88, 36%	900
Goose, slat-body, old rpt, minor wear, sm age line in neck/several slats, head has been reset, J/G 9/19/87	800
Greenwinged Teal drake, rpt in the Lincoln style, crack in neck, otherwise sound, RWO 7/05/85	525
Mallard drake, rpt, average wear, branded, age split in bottom of body/neck, oversize, RB 3/06/87	1100
Merganser, rpt, branded CF Spear, 40, RB 7/08/86, 50%	700
Merganser drake, American; EX orig pnt, artist brand, age split in bottom of bodyblock, branded, ls, RB 5/02/86, 140%	28000
Merganser drake, American; full body, orig pnt, minor wear, age split in bottom, well preserved, 40/97, RB 7/08/86, 180%	45000
Merganser hen, American; EX stippled pnt, minor wear, several age splits, minor rstr, branded, rare, 21, RB 2/01/85	4500
Merganser hen, American; fine orig pnt, minor wear, age split in bk, branded, 22/44, RB 5/02/86	5000
Merganser hen, EX orig pnt, flaking around breast, crack in bk/breast, rare, RWO 7/02/88, 72%	4000
Merganser hen, G orig pnt, average wear, thin check runs down bk/breast, some prof rstr, RWO 11/06/85	4000

Merganser hen, rpt removed to reveal much orig, thin neck crack/check on bottom, otherwise sound, rare, 210, RWO 2/12/88 .... **1600**

Old Squaw drake, fine orig pnt, minor flaking, slight age split on side of head, branded, very rare, 22/44, RB 5/02/86 .... **27500**

Lincoln, Joseph
Old Squaw drake, NM exceptional pnt w/minor flaking to breast area, ls, rare, 40, RB 7/08/86, $50,000.00.

Old Squaw drake, pristine pnt w/beautiful patina, structurally EX, this is 1 of Lincoln's finest, 97, RWO 7/06/86 .... **45000**

Old Squaw hen, EX orig pnt, minor wear, branded EL Spear, several tiny mars on bk, extremely rare, RB 12/06/85 .... **13500**

Old Squaw hen, exceptional pnt pattern w/feathering on bk, minor flaking, ls, 40, RB 7/08/86, 305% **67000**

Old Squaw hen, fine orig pnt, flaking on bk/left side of head, branded, rare, 22/44/66, RB 5/02/86 .... **11000**

Old Squaw hen, orig pnt, minor wear, tight check in underside/several sm dents in bk, branded EL Spear, JG 4/23/87 .... **12500**

Old Squaw hen, outstanding orig pnt, feathering on bk, structurally EX, branded EL Spear, very rare, RWO 11/06/85 .... **19500**

Old Squaw pr, rpt showing little wear, branded HE Spear, 40, RB 7/08/86 .... **2250**

Pintail drake, old rpt, average wear, age split in bottom/neck, 22, RB 5/02/86, 270% **4000**

Pintail drake, orig highly detailed feather pnt, moderate wear, age split, shot scar, very rare, J/G 4/23/87 .... **13500**

Redbreasted Merganser drake, rpt in Lincoln style, tight check on bottom, otherwise structurally sound, RWO 7/04/87 .... **2600**

Scoter, canvas-covered slat, old orig pnt, average wear, worn areas to canvas/age check in bill, rare, RB 7/07/87 .... **500**

Scoter, self-bailing, EX orig pnt, average wear, ls, rare, RB 12/06/85, 55% **1100**

Scoter, self-bailing, EX orig pnt, slight wear, otherwise NM, RB 7/07/87 .... **2500**

Whitewinged Scoter, canvas-covered, EX orig pnt, 50% of bill is prof rstr, otherwise EX, 187, RB 3/11/88 .... **1200**

Whitewinged Scoter, canvas-covered, M condition, RWO 7/02/88, 67% **1000**

Whitewinged Scoter, canvas-covered slat, fine orig pnt, minor wear, well preserved, 22, RB 2/01/85, 375% **6800**

Whitewinged Scoter, canvas-covered slat, G orig pnt, minor flaking, rare, 22/44, RB 5/02/86, 170% **3100**

Whitewinged Scoter, EX orig pnt, light shellac, structurally EX, see 48 for rigmate, RWO 7/05/85 .... **4000**

Whitewinged Scoter, EX orig pnt, minor wear, well preserved, rare, RB 7/08/86 .... **6000**

Whitewinged Scoter, self-bailing, NM orig pnt, flaking on bk, short thin check near bottom of breast, RWO 7/04/87 .... **3700**

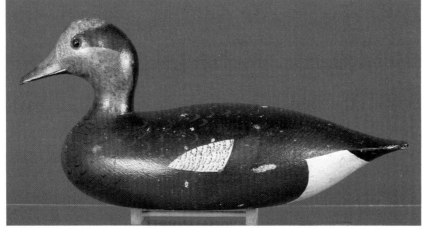

Lincoln, Joseph
Widgeon drake, EX orig pnt, prof cleaned by Kenneth DeLong, M/unused, extremely rare, 2/77, RB 12/06/85, 195%, $35,000.00.

Widgeon drake, old pnt rstr in Lincoln style, branded FB Rice, minor age split, ls, rare, 47, J/G 9/19/87, 75% **1300**

Widgeon drake, old rpt, average wear, some age splitting to body, 22, RB 5/02/86 .... **1400**

Widgeon drake, rpt, average wear, slight age split in bottom of body, structurally sound, RB 7/07/87 .... **850**

Widgeon drake, rpt, minor wear, branded FB Rice, slight age split in bottom, RB 3/06/87 1050
Widgeon drake, rpt, minor wear, slight age split in bottom, rare, 3, RB 8/21/86 750
Widgeon drake, slightly turned head, EX orig pnt, minor wear, 1 eye prof replaced, very rare, RWO 7/06/86 17500
Wood Duck, rpt, minor wear, CF Spear Scituate brand, RB 7/08/86 3000
Wood Duck drake, EX orig pnt, slight roughage to top of crest, CF Spear brand, extremely rare, 44/45, RB 5/02/86, 205% ... 205000
Yellowlegs, NM orig pnt, sm chip out of top of head, ls, J/G 4/24/86, 60% 1210
Yellowlegs, orig pnt, average wear, ls, branded '38,' structurally sound, exceptional, RWO 7/06/86 2500
Yellowlegs, smooth style, slight crazing/wear, ls, rare, J/G 4/24/86 1210
Yellowlegs, wire bill, tack eyes, unused condition, RWO 7/05/86 5000

Lincoln, Joseph; att (Accord, MA)
Eider drake, early, hollow, old working rpt, sm hairline cracks, rot to baseboard, made w/sq nails, ls, J/G 9/19/87 550
Golden Plover, EX orig pnt, minor wear, structurally EX, RWO 7/06/86 1750
Knot, old.rpt taken down to orig, bill is a prof replacement, well preserved, rare, RB 7/09/85 3000
Plover, EX orig pnt, minor wear, well preserved, rare, 78, RB 7/09/85 1100
Plover, fine orig pnt, average wear, well preserved, rare, RB 2/01/85 1300
Plover, outstanding orig feather pnt, sm end-of-tail chips, otherwise EX, RWO 7/02/88, 152% 3800
Yellowlegs, EX orig pnt, minor wear, retains Mackey stamp, ls, rare, 3, RB 2/01/85 3000
Yellowlegs, fine orig pnt, average wear, well preserved, rare, RB 7/09/85 1300
Yellowlegs, orig pnt, heavy wear w/lg area on 1 side worn to bare wood, branded '38,' hs, RWO 7/06/86, 37% 450
Yellowlegs, overpnt taken down to worn orig, old neck repair, RB 7/09/85 550

Lindsey, Levy (Little Tancook Island, NS)
Surf Scoter, orig pnt, minor wear, lg check running down bottom/narrow split down bk of head, RWO 7/04/87 30
Whitewinged Scoter, preening, orig pnt, minor wear, RWO 7/04/87 40

Linton, Andrew
Pintail drake, fine old pnt, possibly orig w/average wear, age split in neck/bill, rare, RB 2/01/85 375

Linton, Stanley
Pintail drake, old working rpt, minor wear, J/G 4/24/86 104

Lipke, Paul (Whiting, IN)
Bluebill drake, fine orig pnt, minor flaking/wear, no structural flaws, retains orig stamped weight, rare, J/G 9/19/87 325
Bluebill drake, hollow, EX orig pnt, minor flaking on body/head, structurally EX, RWO 7/02/88 375
Bluebill drake, hollow w/detailed bill cvg, NM orig pnt, structurally EX, very rare/highly collectible, J/G 4/24/86 440
Bluebill pr, NM orig pnt, several sm pnt chips missing, weights missing, rare, J/G 9/20/86 650
Redhead drake, hollow w/detailed bill cvg, NM orig pnt, structurally EX, very rare/collectible, J/G 4/24/86 825

Lippencott, Charles; att
Black Duck, hollow, rpt w/minor wear, structurally sound, RWO 7/06/86 70

Lippincott, Gideon (New Jersey)
Black Duck, old rpt, average wear, age split in neck, RB 6/28/88 40

Lippincott, Gideon; att
Brant, hollow, fine old pnt, average wear, age check in neck, RB 3/11/88 225
Brant, hollow, head down & turned left, old pnt, average wear, age split in neck, early, RB 3/11/88 500

Litzenberg, Bill (Elkton, MD)
Bluebill pr, pnt by Jim Pierce, drake has hairline crack in neck, otherwise both are EX, ca 1963, RWO 7/05/85 130

Litzenberg, Bob (Elkton, MD)
Canvasback pr, working rpt, structurally good, ca 1932, RWO 7/05/85 275

Lockard, Henry (Elk Neck, MD)
Canvasback drake, old working rpt, average wear, structurally EX, RWO 2/12/88 200
Canvasback drake, old working rpt, average wear w/some flaking, structurally EX, ca 1920, RWO 11/11/87 160
Canvasback drake, rpt by Bob McGaw, average wear, structurally EX, RWO 11/11/87 400
Canvasback drake, rpt by Severin Hall, repair to neck, RWO 7/04/87 275
Canvasback pr, working rpt, average wear, both structurally VG, RWO 7/05/85 625
Canvasback pr, working rpt, average wear, chip to left side of drake's bill, RB 2/01/85 450

Lockard, Henry; att (Elk Neck, MD)
Canvasback drake, old rpt, average flaking/wear, age split in neck, RB 3/11/88 75
Canvasback drake, old rpt, average wear, age split in bill, RB 2/01/85 200

Lockhart, T.N.
Black Duck, hollow, fine old pnt, average wear, well preserved, 39, RB 7/08/85 125

Logal, Edward
Mallard drake, NM orig pnt, no structural flaws, rare, J/G 4/24/86 192
Pintail drake, cvd wing outline, EX orig pnt, no structural flaws, J/G 4/24/86 275

Loggie, Frank P. (Tabusintac, NB)
Brant, old pnt, heavy wear, thin checks to body, ca 1890, RWO 11/11/87 130

Lohrmann, William (Peoria, IL)

Bluebill drake, EX orig pnt w/fine combing on bk, rare, 22, J/G 4/24/85 440

Bluebill hen, NM orig pnt, hairline crack in bill, J/G 4/24/86 330

Bluebill hen, orig pnt, slight wear, structurally EX, J/G 4/23/87 350

Bufflehead drake, hollow, G orig pnt, average wear, EX condition, 193, RWO 7/02/88, 33% 250

Canvasback drake, slightly turned head, NM orig pnt, minor wear, no structural flaws, retains orig weight, J/G 9/19/87 325

Mallard drake, hollow, orig pnt, minor wear w/sm area of flaking on bk, G comb pnt, structurally sound, 210, RWO 2/12/88 450

Mallard drake, pnt taken down to mostly G orig, branded RLW, ms, from the rig of RL Weeks, J/G 4/24/86 220

Mallard hen, high quality working rpt, slight wear, hairline crack part way through neck, J/G 4/24/86 176

Pintail drake, orig pnt w/some crazing/wear, prof repair to end of bill, rare, J/G 4/24/86 440

Ringbill drake, hollow, old rpt, minor wear, structurally sound, RB 7/07/87 200

Scaup drake, early, old working rpt, minimal wear, structurally EX, 7, J/G 4/24/86 77

Long, Timothy

Black Duck, slightly turned head, several sm dents on underside of bodyblock, otherwise M, J/G 9/20/86 55

Greenwinged Teal drake, head in content position, cvd tail feathers w/raised primaries, J/G 9/20/86 65

Pintail drake, hairline crack part way down 1 side, otherwise M, J/G 9/20/86 50

Look, Clayton (South Addison, ME)

Black Duck, inlet head, orig pnt, moderate wear, minor crack on underside of bodyblock/bill rstr, oversize, J/G 9/20/86 350

Look, James (Martha's Vineyard, MA)

Canada Goose, old orig pnt, in-use flaking/wear, several age splits in neck, rare, 22/44, RB 5/02/86 1100

Redhead, early, extremely classy lines, very weathered/worn, RB 6/28/88 1800

Redhead drake, old pnt, in-use flaking/wear, some roughness to right side of bill, ms, 22/44, RB 5/02/86 750

Loring, Edgar (Kingston, MA)

Canada Goose, old pnt, average wear, artist brand, structurally EX, 22, RB 5/02/86 650

Losher, Jack (Remer, MN)

Bluebill drake, orig pnt, minor wear, no structural flaws, J/G 9/19/87 50

Louis, Frank (Ogdensburg, NY)

Bluebill drake, orig pnt, average wear, structurally EX, RWO 7/06/86 35

Goldeneye drake, Ogdensburg Humpback, orig pnt, average wear, structurally sound, RWO 7/06/86 45

Loveland, Ken

Bluebill, cvd wings, old rpt, average wear, age split in bottom/old repair to bill, RB 7/08/86 25

Gadwall drake, raised cvd wing tips, fine orig pnt, average wear, well preserved, RB 8/21/86 100

Greenwinged Teal pr, fine orig pnt, minor wear, well preserved, RB 8/21/86 100

Redbreasted Merganser drake, cvd w/open bill, EX pnt, RB 7/08/86 250

Snow Goose, hollow, raised wing tips, bill is open, minor wear, structurally sound, RB 8/27/87 225

Wood Duck pr, fine orig pnt, minor wear, well preserved, RB 8/21/86 225

Lurchin, Byron

Black Duck, early, old dry pnt, good style, 1886, RWO 11/06/85 25

Madara, Clark (Pitman, NJ)

Black Duck, head turned to the left, hollow, fine old pnt appears to be orig, minor wear, RB 3/11/88 650

Black Duck, hollow, EX orig flock pnt w/fine feather pnt on head, ca 1920's, RWO 11/06/85 550

Black Duck, hollow, old flock pnt, average wear, age split in neck, RB 3/11/88 225

Black Duck, hollow, old flock pnt, average wear, 189, RB 6/28/88 75

Black Duck, hollow, old working rpt, moderate wear, right eye missing, RB 8/25/88 60

Black Duck, hollow, orig pnt, average wear, 189, RB 6/28/88 300

Black Duck, hollow, rpt by Lem Ward, minor damage to bill, otherwise sound, ca 1920's, RWO 7/04/87 175

Black Duck, old working rpt by Lem Ward, minor wear, sm repair at base of neck/hairline crack in breast, J/G 9/19/87 650

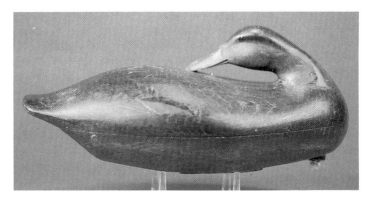

Madara, Clark
Black Duck, preening, EX condition, 50, RWO 11/06/85, $4,000.00.

Canada Goose, hollow w/dowelled-on head, rpt w/moderate wear, hairline crack in neck/breast, 107, J/G 4/23/87 .... **2100**
Redhead drake, hollow, orig pnt, heavy wear, age split at neck, otherwise structurally sound, 20, RB 12/06/85 .... **700**
Redhead pr, fine old pnt, average wear, both branded HH, age split in neck, RB 6/28/88 .... **600**

Madara, Clark; att (Pitman, NJ)
Black Duck, hollow, old pnt, moderate wear, both eyes missing, in-use repair to bill, RB 6/28/88 .... **80**
Black Duck, hollow, working rpt, structurally EX, RWO 7/05/85 .... **325**

Makesh, Gary
Black Duck, orig pnt, heavy wear, slight age split in bk, ls, RB 8/25/88 .... **50**
Bluebill drake, EX & orig condition, RB 8/25/88 .... **55**

Mann, Gordon (Accord, MA)
Black Duck, cvd crossed primary feathers, orig pnt, average wear, rare, 22/44, RB 5/02/86, 233% **1400**
Black Duck, cvd wing tips/primary feathers, old pnt, average wear, structurally sound, RB 7/09/85 .... **300**
Black Duck, stick-up, relief wing cvg w/feather outlines, orig pnt, minor wear, age line in bk, rare, J/G 9/19/87, 35% **700**
Mallard drake, dry old pnt, average wear, several sm age splits in body, RB 7/08/86 .... **75**
Mallard drake, pnt worn to natural wood, several age splits in body, right eye missing, sm tail chip, RB 7/08/86 .... **50**
Whitewinged Scoter, EX orig pnt, average wear, structurally sound, RB 7/07/87 .... **200**

Marchi, Mario (Martinez, CA)
Pintail hen, old working rpt, ls, J/G 4/23/87 .... **150**

Marksby, Mr. (Blenhiem, Ont)
Canvasback drake, G orig pnt w/scalloped pnt around breast, structurally EX, ca 1908, RWO 7/02/88 .... **155**

Marshall, Danny (Chincoteague, VA)
Brant, balsa body, artist signed/dated 1897, M condition, RWO 7/02/88 .... **100**

Marshall, John (Smith's Island, VA)
Pintail drake, worn old pnt, several narrow checks on bk/head, ca 1930, RWO 7/06/86 .... **250**

Marter, Reggie (Burlington, NJ)
Black Duck, hollow, cvd wing tips, EX old pnt, appears to be orig, minor wear, neck break reglued, RB 6/28/88, 131% **1050**
Black Duck, hollow w/raised cvd wing tips/tail feathers, fine orig pnt, average wear, well preserved, 39, RB 7/08/86 .... **1000**
Black Duck, low-head style, hollow, old working rpt, average wear, sliver of wood missing, otherwise sound, RWO 7/04/87 .... **210**
Black Duck, raised cvd primaries/secondaries, orig pnt w/feathering on 1 side, artist name tag, rare, J/G 9/19/87 .... **1025**

Marter, Reggie; att (Burlington, NJ)
Black Duck, hollow, old pnt, minor wear, RB 3/11/88 .... **250**

Martin, Oscar
Bluebill hen, fine orig pnt, minor wear, CHG cvd on bottom, chip on underside of bill, RB 8/25/88 .... **65**

Martin, Ralph
Mallard pr, feeding, raised cvd wing tips, fine orig pnt, hen has 1 dent/flaking to bk, ca 1930, RB 8/21/86 .... **900**

Mason, Charles E. (Beaufort, NC)
Bluebill pr, old working rpt, artist initialed, minor age lines, ls, 33, J/G 9/19/87 .... **850**

Massey, Bill
Bluebill drake, rpt, minor wear, RB 12/06/85 .... **55**

Mastins
Canada Goose, hollow, orig pnt, some in-use wear, rpr to neck/age split, 1 of 6 made, 36, RB 2/10/85, 47% **3750**

Matthews, William (Assawaman Island, VA)
Plover, cvd 'V' tail, EX orig pnt, average wear, ls, rare, 3, RB 3/06/87, 140% **1700**

Matthews, William
Dowitcher, twisted head/neck, old pnt which is partially orig, hairline crack on 1 side, otherwise EX, RWO 2/12/88, $2,300.00.

Matthews, William; att (Assawaman Island, VA)
Blackbellied Plover, old pnt, crazing/wear, bill is a replacement, RB 3/06/87 300
Curlew, cvd 'V' tail, old pnt appears to be orig, average flaking/wear, bill has been reglued, 3, RB 3/11/88, 138% 1100
Curlew, cvd wing tips, old working rpt, average wear, rare, RB 12/06/85 175
Mattie, Frank
Pintail drake, fine orig pnt, average wear, head appears to be working rpt w/minor wear, RB 8/27/87 175
Maxwell, Roy (Wading River, NJ)
Black Duck, hollow, orig pnt, average flaking/wear, NM condition, rare, RB 6/28/88, 66% 800
Brant, hollow, fine orig pnt, minor flaking/wear, well preserved, 186, RB 3/11/88, 160% 1600
Brant, hollow, working rpt, minor wear, branded HW Caine, bill repair, otherwise EX, ca 1915, RWO 7/02/88, 55% 550
Brant, swimming, hollow, G orig pnt w/some areas of flaking, branded, ca 1925, EX condition, RWO 07/06/86, 150% 2250
Canada Goose, hollow, EX orig pnt shows minor wear, 22/44, RB 5/02/86 2600
.Hutchins Goose, hollow, superb orig pnt, minor flaking, age split in neck, rare, 21, RB 2/01/85 900
Maxwell, Roy; att (Wading River, NJ)
Brant, hollow, old rpt, average wear, structurally sound, 20/50, RB 12/06/85 350
May, Robert (Smith's Falls, Ont)
Bluebill drake, cvd wing/feather detail, rpt w/average wear, RB 12/06/85 375
Bluebill drake, hollow w/cvd wing/feather detail, EX orig pnt, average wear, well preserved, RB 12/06/85 650
Bluebill hen, raised cvd wing outline, NM orig pnt, comb pnt on bk, structurally EX, J/G 4/23/87 415
Goldeneye drake, raised cvd wing tips, NM orig pnt, tiny chip in each wing tip, J/G 4/23/87 275
Mayhew, William
Goldeneye hen, VG orig pnt, average wear, age split in neck, 22/44, RB 5/02/86 500
McAlpin, Cline (Chicago, IL)
Bluewinged Teal drake, slightly turned head, M condition, J/G 4/24/86 605
Greenwinged Teal pr, hollow, M condition, RB 7/09/85 700
Greenwinged Teal pr, M pnt, retains orig weight, branded, RB 2/01/85 900
Greenwinged Teal pr, slightly turned heads, M condition, J/G 4/24/86 1210
Mallard drake, sleeping, hollow, M condition, RB 7/09/85 750
Mallard hen, sleeping, fine detailed feather pnt, M condition, rare, J/G 4/23/87 600
Mallard pr, sm dent on side of drake, hairline crack in neck, otherwise M, J/G 4/24/86 1045
Pintail drake, fine orig comb/feather pnt, minor wear, rpt to breast area, rpl head, J/G 4/23/87 1000
Pintail drake, highly detailed comb/feather pnt on bk/sides, white area on breast is rpt, otherwise M, 7, J/G 4/24/86 687
Pintail drake, preening, hollow, M condition, RB 12/06/85 550
Pintail hen, sleeping, M condition, orig weight on bottom, rare, J/G 4/24/86 770

McAlpin, Cline
Pintail pr, turned heads, very precise pnt patterns, extremely well executed, J/G 4/24/86, $2,970.00.

McAnney, John (New Gretna, NJ)
Black Duck, early, hollow, orig pnt, in-use wear, thin crack in neck, otherwise EX, 210, RWO 2/12/88 200
Golden Plover, G orig pnt, minor wear, sm crack in 1 side of head, J/G 4/24/86 275
McAnney, John; att (New Gretna, NJ)
Curlew, tack eyes, old rpt, average wear, bill is a replacement, ls, RB 3/11/88 650
McCarthy Family, att (Cape May, NJ)
Curlew, flat-sided, fine old pnt appears to be orig, left eye missing, RB 3/11/88, 66% 400
Yellowlegs, EX & orig condition, RB 3/11/88 700
McClellan, William
Brant, flying, NM pnt, canvas-framed wings, 1 of 6 made, 36, RB 2/01/85 8000
McCombs, Melvin (Peoria, IL)
Bluebill drake, old working rpt, minor crazing/wear, no structural flaws, 7, J/G 4/24/86 55

McCoy, Charlie (Tuckerton, NJ)
Greenwinged Teal pr, hollow, orig pnt, minor wear, EX condition, RB 3/11/88, 132% 3300
McCoy, Charlie; att (Tuckerton, NJ)
Bluebill drake, hollow, fine old pnt, appears to be orig w/average wear, 21, RB 2/01/85 275
McDonald, Zeke (MacDonald's Island, St. Clair Flats)
Black Duck, hollow, orig pnt, heavy wear w/areas on bk to bare wood, few cracks on bk, ca 1910, RWO 11/11/87 335
Black Duck, hollow, orig pnt, worn to bare wood on 1 side, structurally EX, ms, ca 1910, RWO 7/05/85 425
McGaw, Bob (Havre de Grace, MD)
Black Duck, EX scratch pnt, average wear, narrow check along 1 side of body/sm chunk out of tail, RWO 7/04/87 400
Black Duck, fine scratch pnt, M condition, RWO 7/02/88 1500
Black Duck, old working rpt, average wear, several thin cracks in neck, otherwise structurally sound, RWO 7/06/86 85
Black Duck, orig pnt w/few sm rubs, otherwise NM, ca 1930, RWO 11/06/85 775
Bluebill drake, old working rpt, average flaking/wear, thin cracks in neck/bk, ca 1925, RWO 7/06/86 80
Bluebill drake, old working rpt, average wear, crack in neck, ms, RWO 11/11/87 120
Bluebill drake, old working rpt worn to orig in many areas, age split in bk, 33, J/G 9/19/87 100
Bluebill drake, orig pnt, average wear, structurally sound, ca 1925, RWO 7/06/86 210
Bluebill drake, orig pnt, heavy wear to bare wood in several areas, structurally sound, RWO 7/06/86 120
Bluebill drake, orig pnt, in-use wear, thin hairline crack on 1 side, otherwise structurally EX, RWO 11/06/85 250
Bluebill hen, M condition, ca 1927, RWO 11/06/85 650
Bluebill pr, orig pnt, in-use wear, drake has few rough spots in bk, otherwise structurally sound, RWO 11/11/87 305

McGaw, Bob
Canada Goose, old McGaw rpt, average wear, sm age split in neck, otherwise EX, rare, RB 8/27/87, $3,000.00.

Canvasback drake, EX orig pnt, average wear, cracks in neck, otherwise structurally sound, 17, RWO 11/06/85 200
Canvasback drake, high-head, fine hairline check in bottom, otherwise M condition, RWO 7/02/88 1100
Canvasback drake, old working rpt, flaking/wear, artist brand, thin crack at base of neck, branded WLR, RWO 7/04/87 185
Canvasback hen, orig pnt, lg chip missing on 1 side/thin check on bk/crack runs through neck, ca 1925, RWO 11/06/85 250
Canvasback pr, M condition, hen is an extremely rare example, ca 1920's, RWO 11/11/87 1400
Canvasback pr, old working rpt, hen has different head, hairline crack in neck of drake, J/G 9/19/87 225
Coot, EX orig pnt, artist brand, extremely rare, ca 1930, RWO 11/11/87 1400
Coot, orig pnt, minor wear, artist brand, hairline crack running through neck, otherwise structurally EX, RWO 11/06/85 500
Mallard drake, EX orig pnt, average wear, thin crack in neck, otherwise structurally sound, ca 1940, RWO 11/06/85 550
Mallard drake, EX orig pnt, average wear w/in-use touchup on head, thin crack along 1 side, RWO 7/02/88 700
Mallard drake, G orig pnt, average wear, age check in bottom has been filled, ca 1920's, RWO 11/11/87 900
Mallard hen, EX orig pnt, artist brand, structurally EX, ca 1910, from the FW Krebbs rig, RWO 11/06/85 625
Pintail drake, high-head style, orig pnt, wear to bare wood on body, minor checks on bk, ca 1915-1920, RWO 11/11/87, 75% 675
Pintail drake, orig pnt, average wear, thin crack in neck, otherwise structurally sound, RWO 7/04/87 650
Pintail drake, orig pnt w/soft patina, M condition, RWO 11/06/85 475
Redhead hen, old working rpt, average wear, thin crack in neck, otherwise structurally sound, RWO 7/04/87 110
Redhead hen, orig pnt, average wear w/some flaking to bare wood, few dings on body/bill, otherwise sound, RWO 2/12/88 110
Redhead pr, drake has minor age line on bottom & dowel in head; hen is M, mounted on orig platforms, J/G 9/19/87, 200% 2200
Redhead pr, NM pnt, beautiful patina, NM condition, ca 1920's, RWO 11/11/87 4250
Widgeon drake, EX orig pnt, hairline crack in neck, otherwise structurally EX, ca 1930, RWO 11/06/85, 170% 1700
Wing duck, EX orig pnt, average wear, structurally EX, ca 1920's, rare, 41/75, RWO 11/11/87 1500
McGaw, Bob; att (Havre de Grace, MD)
Canvasback drake, old pnt worn to bare wood, part of bill missing/hs, RWO 2/12/88 95

McGlaughlin, Lawrence (Edgely, PA)

Black Duck, bears McGlaughlin's brass name tag on bottom, EX condition, ca 1950, J/G 4/24/86 440
Black Duck, cvd primaries/secondaries, orig pnt, minor wear, no structural flaws, J/G 9/19/87 450
Black Duck, cvd primaries/secondaries, orig pnt, minor wear, structurally EX, J/G 9/20/86 290
Bluebill drake, cvd tail feathers, orig pnt, sm crack on underside of tail, rare, J/G 9/20/86 210
Bluebill drake, low-head style, hollow, G orig pnt, brass tag bears maker's name, structurally EX, RWO 11/11/87 190
Bufflehead drake, hollow, G orig pnt, average wear, structurally EX, RWO 7/06/86 80
Canada Goose, hollow, EX orig pnt, average wear, brass tag bears maker's name, structurally EX, ca 1936, RWO 11/11/87 1300

McGloughlin, John (Bordentown, NJ)

Black Duck, balsa body, head tucked in content position, cvd raised wing tips, rpt shows minor wear, RB 6/28/88 175
Black Duck, cork body, EX & orig condition, made in 1973, RB 6/28/88, 133% 400
Black Duck, deep raised cvd primaries, orig pnt, average wear, structurally sound, ca 1930's, 50, RWO 11/06/85 1200
Black Duck, early, hollow, old orig pnt, average flaking/wear, rare, 50, RB 8/27/87 400
Black Duck, hollow, cvd raised crossed wing tips, rpt by McGloughlin in 1975, EX condition, RB 6/28/88, 125% 750
Black Duck, hollow, M condition, ca 1940's, RWO 7/05/85 875
Black Duck, hollow, old flocked pnt, average wear w/some areas worn to G orig, RB 3/11/88 175
Black Duck, hollow, old pnt, average wear, well preserved, RB 7/09/85 200
Black Duck, hollow, old pnt, minor wear, ca 1935, RB 6/28/88 300
Black Duck, hollow, signed, NM & orig condition, ca 1940's, RB 8/25/88 500
Black Duck, slightly turned head, cvd crossed wing tips, EX orig pnt, minor wear, RB 8/27/87 625
Black Duck, slightly turned head, hollow, cvd crossed wing tips, EX & orig w/minor wear, RB 9/27/87 625
Black Duck, slightly turned head, hollow, raised wing tips, orig pnt, average wear, inscribed/dated 1940, RB 3/06/87 650
Bluebill drake, slightly turned head, hollow w/raised crossed tail feathers, old working rpt, J/G 9/20/86 200
Bluebill hen, hollow, cvd crossed wing tips, rpt, minor wear, bill has been broken & repaired, RB 6/28/88 200
Brant, head slightly turned, hollow w/cvd raised wing tips/primary feathers, signed, NM condition, RB 8/25/88 1650
Brant, hollow, EX orig pnt, minor wear, signed/dated 1956, RB 7/08/86 550
Bufflehead drake, artist stamp, minor in-use wear, otherwise EX, RB 8/25/88 500
Canada Goose, hollow, EX orig pnt, signed/noted as 1 of his 1st 2 geese, ca 1930, slightly oversize, J/G 9/19/87 2750
Canvasback drake, early, hollow, old working rpt, average wear, structurally sound, RWO 7/02/88 200
Canvasback drake, early, hollow, old working rpt, traces of brand, average wear, sm tail chip, RWO 11/11/87 1150
Canvasback pr, high-neck style, signed, M condition, J/G 9/19/87 900
Canvasback pr, outstanding feather cvg/pnt detail, signed, sm rub on lower side of hen, otherwise M, J/G 9/19/87 1100
Goldeneye hen, EX orig pnt, signed on bottom, RB 7/07/87 650
Greenwinged Teal, slightly turned head, detailed pnt, signed on underside, M condition, J/G 9/20/86 300
Greenwinged Teal hen, slightly turned head, cvd wing tips, NM orig pnt, structurally EX, J/G 9/20/86 200
Herring Gull, raised cvd/crossed tail feathers, detailed bill cvg, M pnt, 63, J/G 9/20/86 650
Mallard drake, hollow, head slightly turned left, cvd crossed wing tips, signed, EX condition, RB 8/25/88 900
Mallard drake, slightly turned head, raised cvd crossed wing tips, M pnt, structurally EX, J/G 9/19/87 475
Mallard hen, early, hollow w/raised cvd primaries, orig pnt, several sm chips along tail, J/G 9/20/86 375
Pintail drake, fine comb pnt & feather detail, M condition, J/G 9/19/87 600
Pintail drake, preening, NM orig finely detailed feather/comb pnt, structurally EX, rare, J/G 9/19/87 625
Pintail hen, early, inserted tin primaries, old working rpt, average wear, artist signed, EX condition, RWO 7/02/88 400
Pintail hen, slightly turned head, EX orig pnt, minor flaking/wear, RB 7/07/87, 160% 1600

McGloughlin, John
Pintail pr, EX wing & tail cvg, cvd crossed wing tips, NM condition, RB 12/06/85, $850.00.

Pintail pr, hollow, signed on bottom, NM condition, RB 2/01/85 1050
Redhead drake, half-cvd, signed/dated 1945, EX & orig condition, RB 6/28/88 100
Redhead drake, hollow, relief cvg around primaries/tail, artist signed, M condition, RWO 7/02/88 525
Redhead drake, slightly turned head, hollow w/raised cvd primaries/secondaries, M pnt, slight wear, J/G 9/20/86 600
Shoveler hen, signed, EX orig condition, ca 1965, RWO 7/05/85 500
Wood Duck drake, slightly turned head, highly detailed cvd primaries/tail feathers, M pnt, J/G 9/20/86, 75% 750

McIntyre, Cameron (Port Royal, SC)
Black Duck, hollow, cvd wing tips, detailed feather pnt, RWO 7/02/88 105
McKenzie Brothers, Tom and John (Henry, IL)
    Mallard drake, early, G old pnt, minor wear, sm chip under bill, purchased directly from McKenzie family, J/G 4/23/87 275
    Pintail drake, orig pnt, minor crazing, working touchup on white areas, tail chip, retains weight, rare, J/G 4/23/87 900
    Pintail hen, hollow, EX orig pnt, RB 7/08/86 350
McKinney, Evans (Elkton, MD)
    Canvasback pr, fine comb pnt, M condition, RWO 11/11/87 170
    Redhead pr, comb pnt, signed/dated 1987, M condition, RWO 11/11/87 160
McLavan, William
    Bluebill hen, fine orig pnt, average flaking/wear, RB 6/28/88 100
McMillen, Stewart (Geneva, NY)
    Canvasback drake, old working rpt, average flaking/wear, structurally sound, RB 12/06/85 90
McNair, Mark (Old Lyme, CT)
    Black Duck, early, sleeper, hollow, signed MSM, EX condition, RWO 7/02/88 400
    Black Duck, preening, Connecticut style, initialed/dated 1976, M condition, J/G 9/20/86 800
    Black Duck, preening, Connecticut style, signed/dated 1976, EX & orig, RB 3/06/87 550
    Blackbellied Plover, Cobb Island style, EX in all respects, RWO 7/05/85 425
    Blackbellied Plover, initialed on bottom, EX condition, RB 3/06/87 175
    Bluewinged Teal drake, hollow, cvd in style of the Caines Bros, artist signed, EX condition, RWO 7/02/88 650
    Bluewinged Teal drake, swimming, hollow, EX orig pnt, branded MSM Old Lyme, RWO 2/13/87 1150
    Brant, Cobb Island style, unsigned, EX condition, RWO 2/13/87 700
    Bufflehead drake, orig pnt, artist signed, hairline cracks in left shoulder, signed, rare species, RWO 11/06/85 750
    Bufflehead drake, slightly turned head, tack eyes, NM orig pnt, 2 hairline cracks in bodyblock, rare, J/G 4/23/87 350
    Canada Goose, cvd in style of Nathan Cobb, cvd signature, outstanding orig condition, RWO 7/06/86, 50% 1250

McNair, Mark
Canada Goose, hollow, cvd in style of Nathan Cobb, M condition, lg/fat, RWO 2/12/88, 78%, $1,400.00.

Canada Goose, hollow, EX condition, rare, oversize, RWO 11/06/85 2200
Canada Goose, hollow, EX pnt, head has been broken off & reglued/2 hairline cracks in tail, oversize, RWO 7/06/86 1500
Canada Goose, stick-up, EX orig pnt, narrow check on underside, otherwise structurally sound, RWO 7/06/86, 50% 450
Canvasback drake, North Carolina style, EX orig pnt, signed, RWO 11/06/85 1000
Cormorant, inlet head, incised signature, EX & orig, RWO 11/06/85 105
Curlew, artist signed, EX condition, RWO 7/02/88, 65% 450
Curlew, Cobb Island style, M condition, RWO 7/05/85 450
Curlew, cvd raised wing tips, artist signed, minor age split in bottom, RB 3/11/88 800
Curlew, cvd wings, artist signed, EX condition, RB 3/11/88 700
Curlew, EX orig pnt, signed on bottom, RB 3/06/87 600
Curlew, feeding, highly stylized, EX orig condition, RWO 7/05/85 920
Curlew, McNair cvd in bottom, EX condition, RWO 7/02/88 500
Curlew, orig pnt, cvd signature, EX condition, RWO 11/11/87, 50% 450
Curlew, running, sm chip on tip of bill, signed/dated 1973, EX condition, RB 7/07/87 350
Curlew, signed, EX orig condition, RWO 7/05/85 475
Curlew, Virginia style, pnt worn away to bare wood, structurally EX, RWO 7/06/86 525
Dove, outstanding & orig in all respects, RWO 7/05/85 450
Dove, worn orig pnt, artist brand, few thin checks in body, RWO 2/13/87 400
Dowitcher, cvd in manner of Bill Bowman, EX orig pnt, signed, RB 3/06/87 400
Eider drake, EX orig pnt, G patina, narrow check at breast/thin tight check on 1 side of head, RWO 7/06/86 950
Eider drake, Monhegan style, inlet head, raised cvd wings/detailed bill cvg, M orig pnt, signed, EX, J/G 9/20/86 1000
Eskimo Curlew, EX pnt, signed, RB 7/07/87 350
Godwit, head/neck extended outward, EX pnt, initialed, 22, RB 7/07/87 500
Godwit, signed, M condition, RWO 11/06/85 500
Golden Plover, cvd signature, M condition, RWO 11/11/87 500

Golden Plover, early, pinned-on extended wing tips, orig pnt, minor wear, signed, structurally EX, J/G 4/23/87 400
Goldeneye drake, North Carolina style, EX orig pnt, RWO 11/06/85 525
Goldeneye drake, slightly turned head, NM orig pnt, signed, EX, 'For the Kirk Dows collection, 1980,' J/G 9/20/86 900
Goose, swimming, hollow, cvd in style of Nathan Cobb, EX orig pnt, 2 hairline cracks in body, J/G 4/24/86, 70% 1265
Greenwinged Teal drake, early, cedar body, hollow, M condition, RWO 11/06/85 1250
Hooded Merganser drake, early Delaware River style, slightly turned head, raised cvd primaries, NM orig pnt, J/G 9/20/86 900
Loon, early, open bill cvg, EX orig pnt, artist signed, RWO 7/06/86, 150% 450
Mallard drake, Delaware River style, raised cvd primaries, NM orig pnt, structurally EX, J/G 9/20/86 750
Mallard drake, hollow w/tucked head, M pnt, this decoy represents his finest work, 160, J/G 4/24/86, 57% 880
Mallard drake, signed/dated 1983, EX condition, RB 8/21/86 1000
Mallard hen, sleeping, finely formed, signed, pnt rubs/shrinkage, otherwise EX, J/G 9/20/86 1000

McNair, Mark
Mallard pr, drake: raised cvd wing tips; hen inscribed: From My Personal Rig 1984 PBS Broadcast, signed, EX, RB 7/07/87, $2,400.00.

Merganser drake, American; slightly turned head, hollow, NM orig pnt, signed, structurally EX, J/G 9/20/86 950
Merganser pr, EX orig pnt, signed, slight split in drake's neck, inscribed: Gunning Rig, 1980, Accomack VA, RB 7/07/87 950
Mourning Dove, hollow, hand-cvd cedar, artist brand, M condition, RWO 11/06/85 1000
Old Squaw drake, EX cvg in McNair tradition, signed, EX condition, RWO 7/06/86 1400
Old Squaw drake, hollow, artist signed, EX condition, RB 3/11/88 850
Old Squaw drake, preening, 1 raised wing, EX orig pnt, cvd signature, RWO 7/04/87 1300
Pintail drake, Cobb Island style, hollow, signed, EX condition, RWO 2/13/87 400
Pintail drake, hollow, artist signed, EX & orig condition, RB 3/11/88 800
Pintail drake, slightly turned head, hollow, outstanding comb pnt, artist signed, from his rig, oversize, J/G 4/24/86 1155
Pintail drake, superb comb pnt, outstanding details, signed, M condition, RWO 7/06/86 2200
Plover, Cobb Island style, EX pnt, artist brand, RWO 2/13/87 550
Redbreasted Merganser drake, early, preening, hollow, EX & orig, RB 3/06/87 1000
Redbreasted Merganser drake, folky, orig pnt, cvd signature, EX condition, RWO 11/11/87 900
Redbreasted Merganser drake, leather crest, signed, EX condition, retains McNair star weight, oversize, J/G 9/20/86 1200
Redbreasted Merganser drake, leather crest/tail, highly stylized pnt, artist signed, RWO 7/02/88, 55% 800
Redbreasted Merganser drake, signed, outstanding EX condition, RWO 11/06/85 1600
Redbreasted Merganser drake, very early, NM orig pnt, signed, slight age split in bk, J Beets cvd in bottom, J/G 9/20/86 850
Redhead drake, early, orig pnt, minor wear, artist initialed, hairline crack in side of breast, J/G 9/19/87 575
Robin Snipe, Cobb Island style, EX orig condition, RWO 7/05/85 300
Robin Snipe, Cobb Island style, EX orig pnt, signed, RB 7/07/87 350
Robin Snipe, cvd M on bottom, EX condition, RB 7/09/85 350
Robin Snipe, cvd wings, EX orig pnt, RB 7/07/87 450
Robin Snipe, EX pnt, signed, RB 7/07/87 550
Robin Snipe, folky, artist signed, orig condition, RWO 7/02/88 240
Robin Snipe, raised cvd wing outline, NM orig pnt, sm scratch on bk, J/G 4/23/87 400
Ruddy Duck, artist signed, EX & orig condition, RWO 7/02/88 475
Ruddy Duck, North Carolina style, EX orig pnt, signed, RWO 11/06/85 850
Ruddy Duck, thin tight checks on body, otherwise EX, RWO 11/11/87 600
Ruddy Duck hen, done in Lee Dudley style, artist signed, EX condition, RB 6/28/88 600
Ruddy Turnstone, raised cvd wing outline, orig pnt, minor wear, structurally EX, J/G 4/23/87 400
Ruddy Turnstone, raised cvd wings w/pinned-on wing tips, NM orig pnt, structurally EX, J/G 4/23/87 400
Ruddy Turnstone, raised wings, McNair cvd in bottom, EX condition, RWO 7/02/88, 58% 400
Sandpiper, cvd eyes, EX pnt, signed, RB 7/07/87 400

Sandpiper, early, orig pnt, minor wear, artist initialed, structurally EX, J/G 4/23/87 400
Surf Scoter, thin hairline crack running the length of the body, otherwise EX, artist signed, RWO 7/02/88 450
Tern, artist brand, EX condition, RWO 2/13/87 525
Tern, EX orig pnt, signed, 1 wing broken off & missing, RWO 7/06/86 350
Widgeon drake, slightly turned head, raised cvd primaries, M pnt, signed on bottom, from his personal rig, J/G 4/24/86 ... 770
Willet, feeding, raised cvd wings w/extended tips, NM orig pnt, structurally EX, J/G 4/23/87 450
Wood Duck, NM orig pnt, signed, structurally EX, exceptionally well made, J/G 9/19/87 1100
Wood Duck drake, hollow, cvd signature, EX orig condition, RWO 7/06/86, 125% 2500
Yellowlegs, early, preening, EX orig pnt, RWO 7/06/86 200
Yellowlegs, feeding, artist signed, EX condition, RWO 7/02/88, 60% 350
Yellowlegs, feeding, cvd w/a minnow in the throat, artist signed, RWO 2/12/88 300
Yellowlegs, feeding, raised cvd wing tips, NM detailed pnt, cvd signature, structurally EX, J/G 9/20/86 355
Yellowlegs, hollow, removable head, McNair cvd in bottom, EX condition, RWO 7/02/88 375
Yellowlegs, orig pnt, moderate wear w/some areas worn to bare wood, signed, structurally EX, RWO 7/06/86 325
Yellowlegs, preening, initialed MSM, EX orig condition, RWO 7/05/85 500
Yellowlegs, running, EX pnt, signed/dated 1973, RB 7/07/87 350

McNeal, Ed (Lansdown, Ont)
Black Duck, orig pnt, moderate wear, hairline crack in bk/tail, J/G 9/20/86 225

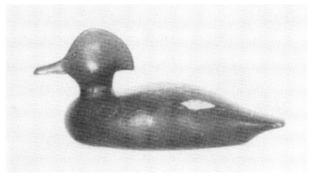

McNeal, Ed
Hooded Merganser hen, NM orig pnt, several sm dents on bk/sm amount of glue spilled on bk, otherwise EX, J/G 4/23/87, $1,300.00.

McPeak, Phil (New Jersey)
Black Duck, Delaware River style, hollow w/cvd raised wing tips, NM condition, RB 8/25/88 100
Meaher, Willie
Black Duck, old pnt, average wear, 21, RB 2/01/85 75
Widgeon drake, old pnt, average wear, sm chip on underside of bill, 21, RB 2/01/85 125
Mears, Roy
Bufflehead pr, both have minor age splitting, otherwise EX, RB 3/11/88 130
Meekins, Alvin (Cambridge, MD)
Bufflehead hen, orig pnt, average wear, structurally sound, RWO 7/06/86 75
Hooded Merganser drake, fine orig pnt, minor wear, signed, RB 8/25/88 35
Meldrum, Tobin (Fair Haven, MI)
Canvasback drake, hollow, old working rpt, average wear, structurally EX, RWO 7/02/88 165
Merkel, Fritz (Peoria, IL)
Bluebill drake, old working rpt, hairline crack in 1 side of neck, J/G 4/23/87 125
Michael, Wilson (Louisiana)
Bluewinged Teal pr, exagerated cvd raised wings, EX condition, RB 6/28/88 50
Miller, C.W. (Ontario)
Bluewinged Teal hen, low-head style, signed/dated 1965, M condition, RWO 7/05/85 475
Canada Goose, M condition, 1968, RWO 7/05/85 425
Miller, Clarence (Brockville, Ont)
Canvasback hen, cork body, fine orig pnt, minor flaking/wear, RB 8/25/88 60
Goldeneye drake, hollow, relief cvd primaries/tail, EX & orig condition, RWO 7/02/88 180
Miller, Fred (Beardstown, IL)
Mallard drake, G old pnt, minor wear, artist initials, no structural flaws, J/G 4/24/86 247
Miller, Fred; att (Beardstown, IL)
Mallard drake, EX orig pnt, no structural flaws, ca 1930, 7, J/G 4/24/86 247
Miller, Herb (Roebling, NJ)
Black Duck, hollow, EX orig pnt, minor in-use wear, well preserved, RB 7/09/85 250
Black Duck, raised cvd primaries/tail feathers, NM orig pnt, structurally EX, 65, J/G 9/20/86 275

Canvasback pr, low-head style, NM orig pnt, no structural flaws, J/G 9/19/87	575
Pintail drake, hollow, G orig pnt, average wear, RB 7/09/85	225
Misch, Otto	
Canvasback drake, high-neck style, hollow, detailed bill cvg, G old pnt, minor wear, no structural flaws, J/G 4/23/87	250
Redhead drake, hollow, old pnt, possibly orig w/average wear, RB 2/01/85	250
Mitchell, Madison (Havre de Grace, MD)	
Black Duck, early, fine orig pnt, minor wear, well preserved, RB 7/07/87	850
Black Duck, early, outstanding orig pnt, average wear, structurally EX, RWO 7/06/86	250
Black Duck, EX orig pnt, signed/dated on bottom, RB 2/01/85	200
Black Duck, fine orig pnt, average wear, age split in neck, RB 7/07/87	190
Black Duck, fine orig pnt, minor wear, well preserved, RB 3/06/87	450
Black Duck, fine orig scratch feather pnt, average wear, oversize, 22, RB 6/28/88	550
Black Duck, G orig pnt, minor wear, structurally sound, RWO 11/06/85	120
Black Duck, NM orig pnt, hairline crack on front side of neck, name James Lewis cvd on bottom, 33, J/G 9/19/87	325
Black Duck, old rpt, average wear, age split in neck/bill, RB 2/01/85	60
Black Duck, orig pnt, average wear, slight age split in neck, otherwise well preserved, RB 3/11/88	325
Bluebill drake, artist signed, orig pnt, minor wear, RB 6/28/88	175
Bluebill drake, early, orig pnt, average wear w/areas worn to bare wood along sides, structurally EX, RWO 11/11/87	245
Bluebill drake, fine orig pnt, average wear, RB 12/06/85	75
Bluebill drake, old rpt, heavy flaking/wear, lg knot missing from breast, age split in neck, RB 3/11/88	80
Bluebill drake, orig pnt, average flaking/wear, minor age split in bk, RB 6/28/88	150
Bluebill drake, orig pnt, minor wear w/nice age, structurally EX, ca 1950, RWO 07/06/86	130
Bluebill drake, rpt, average wear, RB 3/11/88	125
Bluebill drake, signed/dated 1966, M condition, RWO 11/11/87	325
Bluebill hen, early, orig pnt, average wear, structurally EX, RWO 7/06/86	120
Bluebill pr, half-body, drake has age split in neck, otherwise structurally EX, 22, RB 5/02/86	225
Bluebill pr, NM orig pnt, hen has sm area of dry rot on underside, J/G 9/19/87	475
Bluebill pr, orig pnt, average wear, structurally EX, RWO 7/04/87	425
Bluebill pr, orig pnt, minor wear, hen has sm chip in bill, otherwise structurally sound, ca 1941, RWO 11/06/85	450
Bluebill pr, orig pnt, minor wear, name James Lewis cvd in bottom, 33, J/G 9/19/87	600
Bluebill pr, rpt w/average wear, RB 2/01/85	80
Bluewinged Teal pr, EX orig pnt, minor wear, RB 12/06/85	300
Bluewinged Teal pr, turned heads, fine orig pnt, minor flaking, RB 8/27/87	650
Brant, cork body, minor wear, otherwise NM, rare, RB 8/25/88	550
Bufflehead pr, signed/dated 1977, NM condition, RWO 11/11/87	750
Canada Goose, early, G orig pnt, average wear, thin neck crack/check running along 1 side of body, 210, RWO 2/12/88	330
Canada Goose, EX orig pnt, average wear, structurally EX, 210, RWO 2/12/88, 210%	475
Canada Goose, fine old pnt, minor wear, age split in neck, 36, RB 2/01/85	300
Canada Goose, fine orig pnt, minor wear, signed/dated 1969, old neck break has been repaired, RB 8/25/88	325
Canada Goose, fine orig pnt, minor wear, slight age split in bk, RB 8/25/88	290
Canada Goose, fine orig pnt, minor wear, well preserved, RB 3/06/87	450
Canada Goose, G orig pnt, minor wear, RB 7/08/86	275
Canada Goose, M orig pnt, age split in neck, RB 2/01/85	200
Canada Goose, orig pnt, average wear, several age splits in neck, RB 3/06/87	350
Canada Goose, orig pnt, average wear, thin crack in neck/tight check in bk, otherwise structurally sound, RWO 7/06/86	225
Canada Goose, orig pnt, average wear, well preserved, RB 2/01/85	350
Canada Goose, orig pnt, average wear w/some rubs to bare wood on sides, cracks in bk, otherwise sound, RWO 7/02/88	200

Mitchell, Madison
Canada Goose, orig pnt, minor wear, structurally sound, RWO 2/13/87, 350%, $525.00.

Canada Goose, orig pnt, signed/dated 1958, outstanding orig condition, RWO 11/11/87 425
Canada Goose, rpt w/possible orig underneath, age split in neck, RB 3/11/88 225
Canada Goose, stick-up or floater, old rpt, average wear, RB 3/11/88 225
Canada Goose, swimming, rpt w/possible G orig underneath, RB 3/11/88 225
Canvasback drake, early, G old pnt, minor wear, hairline cracks in bk/neck, nailed rpr, J/G 4/23/87 225
Canvasback drake, G orig pnt, signed/dated 1942, crack in neck, otherwise structurally sound, RWO 7/04/87 275
Canvasback drake, old pnt, heavy wear, slight age splitting to body/end of bill has been chewed, RB 3/06/87 125
Canvasback drake, orig pnt, average wear, structurally sound, RWO 07/06/86 120
Canvasback drake, orig pnt, in-use wear, lg chunk of wood missing from head/some damage to bk, ca 1950, RWO 7/04/87 105
Canvasback drake, orig pnt, some areas worn to wood, NP cvd in bottom, signed/dated 1953, EX condition, RWO 2/12/88 190
Canvasback hen, NM orig pnt, 2 hairline cracks near a knot, 33, J/G 9/19/87 275
Canvasback hen, orig pnt, average wear, age split in bk, ls, RB 6/28/88 275
Canvasback hen, working rpt, average wear, signed/dated 1950, thin crack in neck, otherwise sound, RWO 7/0686 90
Canvasback pr, 'Up the River' model, orig pnt, hen has sm checks; drake has check on 1 side, 1950's, RWO 11/06/85 350
Canvasback pr, cvd X on underside of tail, rpt, average wear, age split in hen's neck, RB 6/28/88 275
Canvasback pr, drake has orig pnt w/minor wear, ls; hen has working rpt, minor lines in head/breast, 33, J/G 9/19/87 325
Canvasback pr, early, both signed/dated 1946, few tight checks in both, otherwise EX, RWO 7/04/87 475
Canvasback pr, EX orig pnt, hen has a 2 thin tight checks on breast, oversize, RWO 11/11/87 575
Canvasback pr, EX orig pnt, structurally NM, ca 1940, RWO 11/06/85 350
Canvasback pr, NM orig pnt, hen is signed & has 2 hairlines in side, J/G 9/19/87 400
Canvasback pr, old rpt, minor wear, well preserved, RB 8/27/87 230
Canvasback pr, old working rpt, hen has tight check on underside; drake has neck crack, 33/167, J/G 9/19/87 450
Canvasback pr, orig pnt, average wear, cracks running through necks, otherwise structurally sound, RWO 11/11/87 325
Canvasback pr, orig pnt, minor wear, well preserved, 39, RB 7/08/86 400
Canvasback pr, signed/dated 1971, M condition, RWO 11/11/87, 75% 425
Canvasback pr, unused, NM condition, RB 8/25/88 310
Canvasback pr, working rpt, minor wear, structurally EX, oversize, RWO 7/05/85 345
Coot, EX orig pnt, average wear, RB 7/08/86 275
Coot, EX orig pnt, signed/dated on bottom, RB 2/01/85 200
Coot, G orig pnt, average wear, 39, RB 7/08/86 185
Dove, early, M condition, RWO 2/12/88 325
Dove, signed/dated 1981, unused, RWO 11/11/87 500
Goldeneye drake, G orig pnt, average wear, some water staining on bottom, RB 7/08/86 175
Goldeneye hen, orig pnt, average wear, natural flaw on 1 side of body/check running from breast to bottom, RWO 7/04/87 295
Goldeneye pr, EX orig pnt, RB 2/01/85 300
Greenwinged Teal hen, signed/dated on bottom, M condition, RB 2/01/85 175
Greenwinged Teal pr, EX pnt pattern/patina, minor wear, made in the 1940's, NM condition, RB 8/25/88 1200
Mallard drake, G orig pnt, average wear, bottom half is water stained, RB 7/08/86 150
Mallard drake, head slightly turned to the right, orig pnt, minor flaking/wear, RB 8/25/88 170
Mallard drake, orig pnt w/some flaking & wear, some dry rot on bottom, RB 3/06/87 125
Mallard hen, tupelo wood body, G orig pnt, average wear, structurally EX, ca 1953, RWO 11/06/85 195
Mallard pr, EX orig pnt, average wear, structurally EX, signed/dated 1956, RWO 7/06/86 475
Mallard pr, NM orig pnt, drake has touchup over a knot in the side & name Lewis cvd on bottom, 33, J/G 9/19/87 900
Pintail, half-body, structurally EX, 22, RB 5/02/86 200
Pintail drake, slightly turned head, flat bottom, signed/dated 1951, rare, oversize, RWO 11/11/87 525
Pintail drake, tupelo wood body, orig pnt w/several areas worn to bare wood, ca 1953, RWO 11/06/85 210

Mitchell, Madison
Pintail pr, early, superb orig pnt, scratch feather pnt on hen; drake w/tight check on bk, EX, 41, RWO 11/11/87, 80%, $2,050.00.

Pintail pr, NM orig pnt, hairline crack part way through hen's bill, J/G 4/23/87 400
Redhead drake, old pnt, heavy flaking/wear, artist brand/dated 1941, structurally sound, RWO 7/06/86 90
Redhead drake, orig pnt, average wear, structurally sound, RWO 7/04/87 170
Redhead drake, orig pnt, minor wear, signed/dated 1952, crack in neck, RWO 2/13/87 200
Redhead drake, rpt, average wear, RB 2/01/85 40
Redhead drake, signed/dated 1958, M condition, RWO 11/11/87 270
Redhead drake, tupelo wood body, G orig pnt, average wear, crack in neck, otherwise EX condition, ca 1955, RWO 11/06/85 150
Redhead pr, EX & orig, RB 2/01/85 275
Redhead pr, EX orig pnt, average wear, signed/dated 1954, hen has long check on 1 side/gouge in bk, RWO 11/11/87 325
Redhead pr, fine orig pnt, average wear, signed/dated 1940 on each, well preserved, RB 3/06/87 450
Redhead pr, orig pnt, minor wear, hairline cracks in bodies, J/G 9/19/87 750
Redhead pr, orig pnt, signed/dated 1952, EX condition, RWO 7/06/86 300
Swan, artist signed & dated 1984, M condition, RWO 11/11/87 1150
Swan, early, EX orig pnt w/working touchup to bk, thin tight checks on body, RWO 11/11/87, 75% 1900
Swan, early, G orig pnt, average wear, damage to end-of-bill/thin checks in neck, otherwise EX, RWO 2/12/88 1700
Swan, early, orig pnt, minor crazing on bk, nice patina, thin crack in neck, otherwise structurally EX, RWO 7/06/86 2500
Swan, NM orig pnt, G age/patina, orig hinge weighted keel, exceptionally fine condition, J/G 9/20/86 3300
Swan, solid body w/keel, fine orig pnt, average wear, rare, RB 3/11/88 2900
Widgeon drake, EX orig pnt, hairline crack in neck, otherwise structurally EX, ca 1940's, RWO 11/06/85 200
Widgeon drake, EX orig pnt, RB 7/07/87 190
Widgeon drake, G orig pnt, minor wear, 39, RB 7/08/86 250
Widgeon drake, old working rpt stripped to reveal some orig, hairline crack in neck, ca 1970, RWO 7/06/86 80
Widgeon drake, orig pnt, average wear, thin crack along base of neck, otherwise structurally sound, RWO 7/04/87 210
Widgeon drake, signed/dated 1950, EX orig condition, RWO 7/04/87 350
Widgeon drake, tupelo wood, orig pnt, several areas flaking to bare wood, signed/dated 1955, neck crack, RWO 2/12/88 205
Widgeon hen, early, EX orig pnt, minor wear, structurally sound, RWO 7/06/86 220
Widgeon hen, early, G orig pnt, average wear, lg gouge out of 1 side of body, otherwise sound, ca 1930, RWO 11/06/85 100
Widgeon hen, EX orig pnt, average wear, nice patina, structurally EX, ca 1950's, RWO 7/06/86 225
Widgeon pr, M condition, RWO 2/12/88 375
Widgeon pr, NM orig pnt, several tiny dents on hen's bill, J/G 9/19/87 625
Widgeon pr, signed/dated 1972, M condition, RWO 11/11/87 500
Wood Duck pr, EX pnt, hen has natural flaw in wood on 1 side, does not detract, ca 1972, RWO 7/05/85 1575

Mittlesteadt, Robert (Buffalo, NY)
Goldeneye drake, deep solid body w/wide long flat tail, tack eyes, orig pnt, no structural flaws, 53, J/G 9/20/86 550
Goldeneye hen, head extended forward, full body, paddle tail, orig pnt, minor flaking/wear, 53, RB 7/07/87 700
Mallard pr, bold orig feather pnt, prof bill rstr, a few seam separations in drake, exceptional, rare, J/G 9/19/87, 75% 1100

Moak, Gus (Tustin, WI)
Bluebill drake, slightly turned head, hollow, old working rpt, minor wear, ls, rare, J/G 9/24/86 137
Bluebill hen, orig pnt, minor wear, sm area on underside where pnt has rubbed off, very rare, J/G 9/19/87 400

Moak, Gus
Canvasback drake, slightly turned low-head style, hollow, EX orig pnt, minor wear, well preserved, rare, RB 7/08/86, $750.00.

Canvasback hen, old working rpt, slight wear, ls, oversize, J/G 9/19/87 575
Canvasback hen, orig pnt, minor wear w/sm area removed from underside, ls, J/G 9/19/87 600
Canvasback pr, swimming, hollow, old working rpt worn to orig, oversize, J/G 4/24/86 660

Monroe, Don (Chalmette, LA)
Mallard drake, minor crazing w/some dry rot to left side of bill, otherwise EX, RB 6/28/88 50
Mallard pr, drake has orig pnt w/average wear & some cracking; hen has EX pnt, RWO 2/12/88 180

Morgan, Dick
Sea Gull, raised wing tips, old pnt, average wear, slight dry rot on bottom, RB 3/06/87 250

Morgan, J.H. (Holland, PA)
Black Duck, hollow w/raised cvd wings/primaries, artist brand, M/unused, RWO 11/11/87 100
Morrill, Charles
Black Duck, rpt, average flaking/wear, structurally sound, 22, RB 5/02/86 125
Morris, Harold C.
Canvasback drake, fine orig pnt, minor wear, artist brand, slight age split in neck, RB 8/27/87 125
Morris, John (Hamilton, Ont)
Bluebill hen, hollow, old working rpt, heavy wear, structurally sound, RWO 11/11/87 100
Morris, Lambert (Atlantic, NC)
Bluewinged Teal pr, balsa bodies, EX orig pnt, average wear, few dings/nicks, hardwood bottom board, RWO 11/11/87 575
Redhead pr, balsa bodies, orig pnt, in-use wear, few minor dings to body, hardwood bottom board, RWO 11/11/87 425
Robin Snipe, semi-flat, balsa body, orig pnt, average wear, structurally sound, RWO 7/02/88 180
Morse, Robert (Churches Island, NC)
Redhead hen, EX orig pnt, minor wear, several tight checks in breast area, very rare, 53, J/G 9/20/86, 50% 1000
Widgeon drake, old working rpt worn to orig in some areas, tight check in bk, ls, rare, 33, J/G 9/19/87 225
Morton, W.S. (Quincy, MA)
Golden Plover, EX orig condition, rigmates shown on pg 86 of New England Decoys by Delph, RWO 7/05/85 2500
Morton, W.S.; att (Quincy, MA)
Golden Plover, incised eyes, EX orig pnt, average wear, well preserved, rare, RB 7/08/86 700
Mosley, Douglas (Princeton, IL)
Mallard drake, early, pnt by Sara Mosley, DM pnt on bottom, EX condition, ca 1890, 193, RWO 7/02/88 2000
Pintail drake, early, pnt by Sara Mosley, heavy crazing to body, EX orig condition, ca 1890, rare, 193, RWO 7/02/88, 16% 400
Mosley, Douglas; att (Princeton, IL)
Canvasback drake, early, orig pnt, worn to bare wood on bk, bill rpr/crack in breast, otherwise sound, 193, RWO 7/02/88 200
Mossmier, Jim
Mallard pr, cvd wings/wing tips, EX orig pnt, 21, RB 2/01/85 3000
Mott, Fred Sr. (Pekin, IL)
Pintail drake, orig pnt, minor wear, hairline crack on underside, GAW stenciled on bottom, J/G 4/24/86 275
Pintail hen, orig pnt, moderate wear, touchup rstr to end of bill, rare, J/G 4/24/86 192
Mr. X (Peoria, IL)
Bluebill pr, turned heads/inlet hardwood bills, hollow, both have patent stamp, EX orig pnt & condition, J/G 4/24/86 1760
Pintail drake, turned head, hollow, inlet bill, feather/comb rpt by Edna Perdew, sm neck crack, 138, J/G 4/24/86 1210
Redhead drake, slightly turned head, hollow, inset bill, EX orig pnt, minor wear, ls, 39, RB 7/08/86, 140% 1700
Mueller, Keith (South Meriden, CT)
Black Duck, head in content position, NM pnt, no structural flaws, J/G 4/24/86 192
Black Duck, sleeping, hollow, EX orig pnt, minor in-use wear, structurally VG, contemporary, RWO 7/05/85 500
Black Duck, sleeping, orig pnt, EX condition, RWO 11/06/85 140
Bluebill drake, Stratford style, slightly turned head, NM orig pnt, sm chip out of 1 side of bill, J/G 4/24/86 66
Canvasback drake, EX orig pnt, signed on bottom, RB 8/27/87 100

Mueller, Keith
Eider, hollow, mussel in bill, EX pnt, artist stamp,
39, RB 7/08/86, $450.00.

Eider pr, slightly turned heads, hollow, drake has mussel in bill, signed on underside, J/G 4/24/86 275
Greenwinged Teal pr, cvd in Shang Wheeler style, EX condition, RWO 7/05/85 600
Merganser drake, head raised upward, hollow, M condition, RWO 11/06/85 60
Wood Duck pr, artist brand, M condition, RWO 11/06/85 400
Mueller, Ken
Widgeon drake, EX & orig, RB 7/09/85 250
Mulak, John
Surf Scoter, superb feather cvg, EX pnt detail, structurally EX, RB 7/07/87 350

Mulliken, Ted (Old Saybrook, CT)
Canvasback drake, early, orig pnt, crack in neck/1 eye missing, otherwise structurally sound, RWO 7/06/86 80
Mallard drake, raised cvd wing tips, signed/dated 1958, NM condition, RB 7/07/87 800

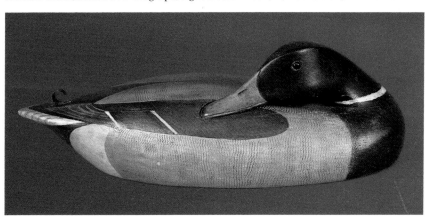

Mulliken, Ted
Mallard drake, sleeping, structurally EX, rare, 22/44, RB 5/02/86, 250%, $3,000.00.

Redhead drake, fine orig pnt, minor flaking, well preserved, rare, 22/44, RB 5/02/86, 233% 1400
Murphy, Henry (Davis Shores, NC)
Black Duck, cork body, worn orig pnt, weathered w/numerous age lines, 33, J/G 9/19/87 90
Canada Goose, cork body, orig pnt, average wear, working touchup to head, some dings to cork, bottom board, RWO 11/11/87 175
Greenwinged Teal drake, cork body, orig pnt, average wear, structurally sound, hardwood bottom board, RWO 11/11/87 130
Pintail drake, orig pnt, minor wear, branded HML, old working touchup on white areas, eyes missing, 33, J/G 9/19/87 900
Naquin, Nollie (Des Allemands, LA)
Bluebill drake, EX orig pnt, RB 7/07/87 80
Bluebill drake, NM orig pnt, no structural flaws, J/G 9/19/87 125
Redhead drake, fine orig pnt, minor wear, well preserved, RB 7/09/85 165
Ringbill drake, NM orig pnt, structurally EX, J/G 4/24/86 137
Neal, William (Black Point, CA)
Greenwinged Teal hen, cvd wing tips, artist signed, EX & orig, RB 7/09/85 175
Greenwinged Teal hen, cvd wing tips, artist signed, M condition, RB 7/09/85 120
Greenwinged Teal pr, EX pnt, artist brand, RB 8/21/86 250
Mallard pr, cvd primaries, EX pnt, artist signed, RB 7/09/85 315
Pintail drake, cvd primaries, EX rpt by Neal, RB 7/09/85 80
Pintail hen, cvd wings/primary feathers, G orig pnt, minor flaking, artist signed, RB 7/09/85 120
Widgeon pr, cvd wings/primary feathers, artist signed, M condition, RB 7/09/85 225
Nelo, Gus (Oshkosh, WI)
Canada Goose, crack in lower side, otherwise M, very rare, J/G 4/24/86 220
Canvasback drake, old working rpt, tight check on underside of bodyblock, oversize, J/G 4/24/86 192
Coot, high-neck style, old working rpt, several tight checks in breast, J/G 9/20/86 150
Snow Goose, NM orig pnt, no structural flaws, 1 of 6 known, J/G 9/19/87 450
Nelson, John
Canvasback drake, EX pnt, signed/dated 1984, RB 7/07/87 50
Swan, hollow, dovetailed head, M condition, RWO 11/11/87 225
Newman, Charles
Black Duck, G orig pnt, average wear, some age splitting to body, 22, RB 5/02/86 125
Nichols, Davey (Smith's Falls, Ont)
Black Duck, cvd primaries/secondaries, orig pnt, minor wear, sm rough area/reglued neck crack, ls, J/G 9/19/87 350
Black Duck, cvd wing tips/tail feathers, EX pnt, RB 2/01/85 250
Black Duck, EX orig pnt, in-use wear, sm sliver of wood missing from underside of bill, otherwise sound, RWO 7/04/87 295
Black Duck, fine feather cvg, NM condition, RB 12/06/85 340
Bluebill drake, EX orig pnt, structurally EX, RWO 7/04/87 450
Bluebill drake, slightly turned head, hollow, cvd wing tips/detailed feather cvg, NM feather pnt, ls, J/G 4/23/87, 140% 2550
Bluebill hen, cvd primaries/secondaries, orig pnt, minor wear, ls, J/G 9/19/87 325
Bluebill hen, cvd raised wing tips, feather detail on bk, orig pnt, average in-use wear, 189, RB 6/28/88 250
Bluebill hen, cvd wing tips/tail feathers, EX pnt, signed/dated on bottom, RB 2/01/85 200
Bluebill hen, early, raised cvd wing tips, orig pnt, minor wear, several short hairline cracks, J/G 4/23/87 375
Bluebill hen, fine orig pnt w/soft patina, NM condition, exceptional, RWO 7/05/85 1150

Bluebill hen, raised cvd primaries/secondaries, fine comb pnt w/minor wear, ls, J/G 9/19/87 425
Bluebill hen, raised cvd wing tips/detailed feather cvg, EX orig pnt, minor touchup, comb pnt on bk, J/G 4/23/87 300
Bluebill hen, relief cvg, orig pnt, minor chips at end of wings, ca 1920's, RWO 7/04/87 400
Bluebill pr, hollow w/raised cvd primaries/secondaries, NM exceptional comb pnt, very rare, J/G 9/19/87 1500
Bluewinged Teal hen, cvd wing tips/tail feathers, EX orig pnt, signed/dated on bottom, RB 2/01/85 200
Bluewinged Teal pr, artist signed/dated 1971, M condition, RWO 7/02/88 1400
Bufflehead pr, artist signed, hen is dated 1971; drake is dated 1972, M condition, RWO 7/02/88 1600
Canvasback drake, cvd wing tips/tail feathers, EX pnt, signed on bottom, RB 2/01/85 225
Canvasback hen, signed, outstanding original condition, ca 1940's, RWO 7/05/85 325
Canvasback pr, cvd wing tips/tail feathers, EX pnt, RB 2/01/85 450
Coot, cvd wing tips, EX pnt, signed/dated on bottom, RB 2/01/85 225
Goldeneye drake, cvd wing tips/tail feathers, EX pnt, RB 2/01/85 250
Goldeneye drake, cvd wing tips/tail feathers, ls, otherwise sound, RB 2/01/85 175
Goldeneye drake, fine old pnt, appears to be orig w/average wear, RB 2/01/85 150
Goldeneye hen, early, fine orig pnt, minor wear, 39, RB 7/08/86 150
Goldeneye hen, early, hollow w/raised cvd wings, old rpt by Nichols, minor wear, ls, J/G 9/19/87 400
Greenwinged Teal drake, artist signed, M condition, RWO 7/02/88 750
Greenwinged Teal pr, raised cvd primaries/tail feathers, highly detailed pnt, artist signed, M condition, J/G 9/20/86 1000
Greenwinged Teal pr, raised cvd wing tips/tail feathers, EX pnt, signed on bottom, RB 2/01/85 550
Redbreasted Merganser drake, artist signed/dated 1972, M condition, RWO 7/02/88, 35% 350
Redhead pr, both signed by artist, hen is dated 1970, M condition, RWO 7/02/88, 75% 1100
Ringbill drake, detailed cvg, M pnt, sm dent in top of bill, ms, rare, J/G 4/23/87 900
Ringbill drake, highly detailed cvd primaries/tail feathers, M orig pnt, G patina, J/G 9/20/86 650
Ringbill pr, cvd raised wing tips, fine orig pnt, minor wear, well preserved, RB 3/06/87 750
Ringneck pr, cvd wing tips/tail feathers, EX pnt, RB 2/01/85 650
Shoveler drake, inscribed/dated 1971, EX orig condition, RWO 11/06/85 275
Wood Duck drake, artist signed/dated 1972, M condition, RWO 7/02/88 1300
Wood Duck drake, cvd wing tips/tail feathers, EX pnt, ca 1958, RB 2/01/85 650
Wood Duck drake, raised cvd primaries/secondaries, detailed bill cvg, fine comb pnt, NM condition, rare, J/G 9/19/87 1850

Nichols, Davey; att (Smith's Falls, Ont)
Bluebill hen, fine orig comb feather pnt, minor wear, RB 8/25/88 175
Bluebill hen, raised cvd wing tips, combing on bk, NM orig pnt, cracks in eyes, J/G 4/23/87 450
Goldeneye hen, early, cvd wings, old working rpt, average wear, structurally sound, RWO 7/02/88 175

Nichols, F.M.
Yellowlegs, early, pnt flaking on bk/bill, artist brand, EX & orig condition, 193, RWO 7/02/88 400

Nickerson, Luther
Goldeneye drake, cvd wing pattern, orig pnt w/strengthening to white areas, 22, RB 5/02/86 900

Nickerson Family (Nova Scotia)
Goldeneye hen, hollow w/cvd wings, old pnt, heavy wear, RB 7/09/85 225
Merganser hen, cvd wings, extended paddle tail, fine old pnt w/some flaking, 22, RB 5/02/86 900

Nicks, Charles (Fort Erie, Ont)
Bufflehad pr, cedar, relief cvd primaries/tail, EX & orig condition, RWO 7/02/88 200
Bufflehead pr, cvd wing tips/tail feathers, artist signed, EX & orig condition, 189, RB 6/28/88, 37% 150

Noonen, Al (Bay Head, NJ)
Greenwinged Teal, hollow w/relief cvd primaries, orig pnt, minor wear, artist brand/dated 1964, RWO 7/06/86 70
Greenwinged Teal pr, raised cvd wing tips, EX orig pnt, RB 7/07/87 275

Nottingham, Luther (Cobb's Station, VA)
Curlew, early, cvd wings, iron bill, orig pnt, moderate wear, ca 1890, J/G 4/24/86 605

O'Connor, Richard
Bufflehead hen, cvd wing tips/tail feathers, EX condition, 189, RB 6/28/88 50

O'Neil, Callie (Churches Island, NC)
Widgeon drake, 3-pc body construction, orig pnt, minor wear, stamped TJ O'Connor, rare, 33, J/G 9/19/87 375

O'Neil, Pat (Churches Island, NC)
Canada Goose, canvas over wooden slat frame, orig pnt, minor wear, crack in neck is reglued, 28/33, J/G 9/19/87 500

O'Neil, Wallace (Churches Island, NC)
Battery Canvasback, old working rpt, 3 tight checks on underside of body, ls, 33, J/G 9/19/87 250

Odean, Lenas
Mallard drake, cvd wing tips/primary feathers, M pnt, signed/dated 1974 on bottom, RB 2/01/85 225

Ohnmacht, Bernard (Lafayette, IN)
Black Duck, 4 sm pnt rubs, otherwise M, orig storage bag included, rare, J/G 4/23/87 2200
Black Duck, cork body w/wooden swivel head, sm dent on side, otherwise M, skin-like body covering, rare, J/G 4/24/86 2750

Mallard drake, strong orig pnt w/some sm areas of flaking on 1 lower side, structurally EX, rare, J/G 9/20/86 1550
Mallard hen, EX orig pnt, slight shrinkage/flaking on tail, keel has been reapplied, rare, J/G 9/19/87 1700
Mallard hen, NM orig pnt, structurally EX, very rare, J/G 9/20/86 2000

Oler, William
Black Duck, headless feeder, EX orig pnt, minor wear on front, RWO 11/11/87 65
Black Duck, hollow, fine orig pnt, average in-use wear, artist brand, RB 8/25/88 90
Black Duck, hollow, fine orig pnt, average wear, artist brand, well preserved, RB 7/07/87 250
Brant, hollow, orig pnt, minor in-use wear, artist brand, age check at neck has been reglued, RB 8/25/88 80
Brant, preening w/slightly turned head, fine orig pnt, average wear, artist brand, well preserved, RB 7/07/87 150
Bufflehead drake, slightly turned head, hollow, fine orig pnt, minor wear, artist brand, well preserved, RB 7/07/87 110
Greenwinged Teal pr, hollow, orig pnt, minor in-use wear, artist brand, hen's neck has been reglued, RB 8/25/88 170
Gull, hollow w/raised crossed wing tips, orig pnt, minor wear, artist brand, no structural flaws, J/G 9/19/87 75
Mallard pr, hollow, fine orig pnt, minor in-use wear, artist brand, RB 8/25/88 160
Merganser pr, hollow, fine orig pnt, minor wear, artist brand, well preserved, RB 7/07/87 400
Redbreasted Merganser pr, hollow, orig pnt, minor wear, artist brand, nick on hen's crest, otherwise EX, 8/25/88 250
Redhead pr, hollow, orig pnt, average wear, artist brand, EX condition, RB 8/25/88 120

Olson, Fernie
Canvasback hen, fine orig pnt, minor wear, RB 2/01/85 75

Ortley, Dipper (Point Pleasant, NJ)
Black Duck, hollow, old working rpt, average wear, structurally sound, RWO 7/02/88 100
Black Duck, hollow, old working rpt, minor wear, structurally EX, ca 1950's, RWO 7/06/86 50
Bluebill drake, hollow, old pnt, average wear, structurally sound, RB 3/11/88 150
Bluebill hen, hollow, orig pnt, minor wear, old repair to bill, RB 7/08/86 130
Bluebill pr, hollow, EX condition, RB 3/11/88 250
Bluebill pr, hollow, fine orig pnt, average wear, RB 7/08/86 225

Ortley, Dipper; att (Point Pleasant, NJ)
Canada Goose, hollow, old rpt, average flaking/wear, structurally sound, RB 2/01/85 200

Orton, Drew; att (Burlington, IA)
Mallard drake, orig pnt, minor wear, detailed comb pnt on bk/sides, prof rstr to crack in neck, J/G 4/24/86 357

Osborne, Henry F. (Bellport, NY)
Blackbellied Plover, typical cvd wings, rpt w/minor wear, well preserved, 22/44, RB 5/02/86 550

Osborne, Henry F.; att (Bellport, NY)
Peep, early, cork body w/applied wings, several chips to cork/slight age split in body, 92, RB 7/08/86 300

Pape, Adam
Spoonbill drake, balsa body w/cedar head, M condition, J/G 4/24/86 99

Paquette, Joseph (Verdun, Que)
Bluebill hen, highly detailed feather/bill cvg, NM orig pnt w/scalloping & combing, ms, otherwise EX, J/G 4/23/87 600

Paquette, Robert (Verdun, Que)
Goldeneye drake, slightly turned head, highly detailed cvg on bill/wings/tail, NM pnt, J/G 9/20/86, 150%, $3,100.00.

Paquette, Robert; att (Verdun, Que)
Bluebill drake, relief cvg on bk, orig pnt w/touchup to black areas, structurally EX, RWO 7/04/87 80

Paquette Family (Quebec)
Bluebill hen, slightly turned head, EX feather cvg, fine orig pnt shows little wear, 39, RB 7/08/86 575
Greenwinged Teal drake, cvd wing/feather detail, EX orig pnt, average wear, rare, RB 12/06/85 350

Parez, Omar (Plaquemines Parrish, LA)
Pintail drake, old pnt, heavy wear, RB 7/08/86 325

Parker, Charles (Tuckers Island, NJ)
Brant, hollow, orig pnt, moderate wear, crack in neck has old repair, inset rectangular weight, J/G 9/20/86 120
Parker, Charles; att (Tuckers Island, NJ)
Redbreasted Merganser, dry orig pnt, minor wear, sm chip on bottom, inletted weight, ca 1900, 53, J/G 9/20/86 800
Parker, Ellis (Beach Haven, NJ)
Black Duck, hollow, EX orig pnt w/feather pnt on bk which is not orig, artist brand, well preserved, RB 8/21/86 185
Black Duck, hollow, fine orig pnt, average wear, chip under left side of bill, ls, RB 6/28/88 450
Black Duck, hollow, old working overpnt, average wear, chip of wood missing under bill, otherwise sound, RWO 07/06/86 160
Black Duck, hollow, orig pnt, heavy wear, structurally sound, 189, RB 6/28/88 150
Mallard pr, hollow, old working rpt, average wear, each have crack in neck, otherwise EX, ca 1920, RWO 07/06/86 375
Parker, Ellis; att (Beach Haven, NJ)
Black Duck, hollow, old orig pnt, average wear, RB 12/06/85 85
Brant, flying, canvas wings, EX orig pnt, designed to run down a wire to simulate flight, RWO 7/05/85 1500
Parker, George
Redbreasted Merganser drake, hollow, EX & orig condition, RB 7/09/85 175
Parker, Jay (Parkertown, NJ)
Black Duck, hollow, NM condition, RB 8/25/88 80
Bluebill drake, hollow, Jay C Parker cvd in bottom, orig pnt, average wear, well preserved, RB 3/11/88 350
Bluebill drake, hollow, working rpt w/traces of orig, thin crack in neck, otherwise structurally sound, RWO 11/11/87 110
Bluebill hen, hollow, old working rpt flaking to reveal some orig, structurally sound, RWO 11/11/87 90
Brant, hollow, fine orig pnt, average wear, age split in neck, RB 3/11/88 175
Brant, hollow, orig pnt, average wear, head shows heavy wear, age split in neck, RB 6/28/88 70
Canada Goose, balsa body, hollow, fine old pnt, average wear, well preserved, RB 7/09/85 175
Redbreasted Merganser drake, EX orig pnt, minor crazing/wear, 189, RB 6/28/88 70
Redbreasted Merganser drake, EX orig pnt, minor wear, well preserved, RB 6/28/88 150
Redbreasted Merganser drake, hollow, EX & orig condition, RB 3/11/88 175
Redbreasted Merganser drake, hollow, fine orig pnt, minor crazing/wear, 189, RB 6/28/88 65
Redbreasted Merganser drake, hollow, fine orig pnt w/some crazing, RB 3/11/88 250
Redbreasted Merganser pr, old pnt, average wear w/some crazing, no structural flaws, RWO 11/11/87 875
Parker, Jay; att (Parkertown, NJ)
Black Duck, hollow, old working flock pnt, average wear, minor tail chips, otherwise structurally sound, RWO 11/11/87 225
Black Duck, hollow, orig pnt, average wear w/overpnt on head, structurally sound, sm, RWO 11/11/87 160
Parker, Lloyd (Parkertown, NJ)
Black Duck, hollow, old pnt flaking to mostly natural wood, age split in neck, 21, RB 2/01/85 100
Black Duck, hollow, working rpt, average wear, slight separation where body halves join, 3, RWO 7/06/86 150
Black Duck, hollow, working rpt, crack at base of neck, otherwise structurally sound, RWO 7/06/86 90
Bluebill drake, hollow, tack eyes, fine orig pnt, minor wear, well preserved, RB 3/06/87 625
Bluebill hen, hollow, old working rpt, crack through neck, inset rectangular weight, J/G 9/20/86 90
Brant, hollow, NM orig pnt, minor wear w/some crazing to bk, age split in neck, rare, 21, RB 2/01/85 2250
Brant, hollow, old pnt, minor wear, old break in neck has been repaired, rare, 6, RB 7/07/87 550
Brant, hollow, old rpt, average wear, age split in neck, otherwise structurally sound, RB 3/11/88 800
Brant, hollow, old rpt, heavy flaking/wear, head needs to be reattached to body, 21, RB 2/01/85 325
Brant, hollow, orig pnt worn to bare wood in several areas, hairline crack in neck, otherwise EX, RWO 07/06/86 750
Brant, swimming, hollow, rpt, average wear, several age splits in neck/old repair to neck, 20, RB 12/06/85 300

Parker, Lloyd
Canada Goose, hollow, EX orig pnt, flaking around neck/tail, hairline crack in neck, exceptional, RWO 11/06/85, $3,250.00.

Canada Goose, hollow, NM orig pnt, minor flaking, RB 3/06/87, 125% 3100
Canada Goose, hollow, old working rpt, crack in neck, sm area of dry rot on underside, ca 1890, RWO 7/05/85 425

Canada Goose, hollow, old working rpt, possibly done by Parker, crack in neck, otherwise EX, RWO 7/02/88, 40%	600
Redhead drake, hollow, old rpt, average wear, thin tight crack in neck, otherwise structurally EX, RWO 07/06/86	225
Yellowlegs, cvd wing tips, fine old pnt by Lloyd Parker, average flaking/wear, ls, rare, 20/78, RB 12/06/85	1200
Yellowlegs, EX orig pnt, bill dowelled through to bk of head, tiny chip in tail/end of bill, J/G 4/24/86	770

Parker, Lloyd; att (Parkertown, NJ)

Canada Goose, swimming, relief cvd wings, old working rpt, crack in neck, J/G 9/19/87	450

Parker Family (Parkertown, NJ)

Black Duck, hollow, old rpt, average wear, roughness to end of bill, several age splits in neck, RB 6/28/88	40

Parker Family
Hutchins or Lesser Canada Goose, EX orig pnt, fine patina, fine crack in neck, otherwise EX, RWO 11/06/85, $800.00.

Parker Family, att (Parkertown, NJ)

Black Duck, hollow, old dry pnt, average wear, branded EDT, chip on underside of bill, RB 7/08/86	75
Black Duck, hollow, old pnt, average wear, branded EDT, structurally sound, RB 7/08/86	225
Brant, hollow, rpt w/minor wear, several age splits in neck, RB 7/08/86	100

Parsons, Tom (Oxford, MD)

Pintail drake, fine old pnt, in-use wear, structurally EX, rare, RWO 11/06/85	275

Patrick, Ralph (Cedarville, MI)

Bluebill pr, fine orig pnt, minor wear, signed on bottom, RB 12/06/85	30

Patterson, Ernie (Wellesley Island, NY)

Bluebill hen, G orig pnt, average wear, sm chip on underside of bill, otherwise structurally EX, ca 1930's, RWO 11/11/87	210

Patterson, Ernie; att (Wellesley Island, NY)

Bluebill hen, fine orig pnt, average in-use wear, ls, RB 7/09/85	100

Paul, Ammie (Davis, NC)

Black Duck, orig pnt, minor wear, several age lines, rare, 33, J/G 9/19/87	475
Pintail drake, orig pnt, average wear, thin crack in neck, RWO 11/11/87	600
Redhead drake, 3-pc laminated head, EX orig pnt, checks on underside, rare, 33/126, J/G 9/19/87	325

Paul, Joe (New Jersey)

Brant, hollow, evidence of G orig pnt underneath, otherwise old pnt w/average wear, 189, RB 6/28/88	150
Brant, hollow, orig pnt, heavy flaking/wear to natural wood in many areas, several age splits, 189, RB 6/28/88	100
Brant, hollow, rpt, average wear, age split in neck, end-of-bill chip, RB 6/28/88	75
Brant, swimming, hollow, old pnt, average wear, old break in neck, RB 7/08/86	90
Canada Goose, hollow, old rpt, average wear, age split in neck, RB 3/11/88	150
Canada Goose, hollow, rpt, average wear, age split in neck, RB 6/28/88	100

Paul, Joe; att (New Jersey)

Blackbellied Plover, rpt, average wear, bill is a replacement, RB 3/11/88	100
Brant, hollow, old rpt, average wear, age split in neck, 189, RB 6/28/88	125
Knot, fine old pnt, appears to be orig w/average wear, 189, RB 6/28/88	400
Knot, orig pnt, average flaking/wear, well preserved, RB 3/11/88, 157%	550
Pintail hen, hollow, rpt, average wear, age split in neck, RB 3/11/88	200
Ruddy Turnstone, flat-sided, old pnt, average wear, RB 3/11/88	100

Paulson, Dick (Massachusetts)

Brant, canvas-covered slat, G orig pnt, little wear, well preserved, 22, RB 5/02/86	325
Bufflehead pr, orig pnt, average flaking/wear, 22, RB 5/02/86	400

Pavlovich, Mike (Monroe, MI)

Canada Goose, hollow, old working rpt, swinging weight keel, no structural flaws, rare, 183, J/G 9/20/86	225
Canvasback drake, orig pnt, minor wear, structurally EX, J/G 9/20/86	175

Pellegrin, Arthur (Houma, LA)

Bluebill hen, EX & orig condition, RB 8/25/88	80

Bluewinged Teal pr, orig pnt, no structural flaws, J/G 9/20/86 300
Coot, EX & orig condition, RB 8/25/88 80
Coot, orig pnt, slight wear, sm crack in bill, J/G 9/20/86 35
Greenwinged Teal pr, cypress wood, NM condition, RWO 2/12/88 150
Greenwinged Teal pr, tupelo gum wood, EX pnt, initialed on bottom, RB 7/07/87 250
Mallard pr, orig pnt, minor wear, drake has hairline crack part way under tail, J/G 9/20/86 175
Mallard pr, orig pnt, NM condition, RWO 2/12/88 120
Merganser drake, American; AP cvd in bottom, EX condition, RB 6/28/88 70
Pintail pr, EX orig pnt, average wear, artist brand, structurally EX, RWO 11/11/87 250
Pintail pr, fine orig pnt, minor wear, RB 6/28/88 100
Redbreasted Merganser drake, G orig pnt, minor wear, RB 7/07/87 110
Redbreasted Merganser drake, signed AP on bottom, EX condition, RB 6/28/88 75
Ruddy Duck drake, EX orig pnt, RWO 11/11/87 130
Ruddy Duck pr, AP cvd in bottom, EX condition, RB 6/28/88 50

Pellegrin, Roy (Houma, LA)
Mallard drake, fine old pnt, minor wear, bill broken & reglued, slight age splitting to body, RB 7/09/85 150
Mallard pr, fine old pnt, minor wear, RB 7/07/87 225
Mallard pr, G orig pnt, minor wear, structurally sound, RWO 2/12/88 150
Mallard pr, orig pnt, minor wear, no structural flaws, J/G 4/24/86 247

Pelzer, Walter (Milwaukee, WI)
Mallard hen, slightly turned head, relief cvd wings, orig pnt, minor wear, structurally EX, J/G 9/19/87 800

Pember, H.
Black Duck, cork body, old pnt, average wear, structurally sound, RB 6/28/88 100
Pintail drake, cork body, fine old pnt, minor wear, RB 6/28/88 30

Penn, Jesse
Sandpiper, fine orig pnt, average wear, ca 1890, ls, RB 7/08/86 250

Penrose, Thorton Jr. (Burlington, VT)
Goldeneye hen, orig pnt, minor wear, structurally EX, ca 1940, J/G 9/20/86 85
Goldeneye hen, orig pnt, minor wear, tip of bill is slightly blunted, J/G 4/23/87 35

Perdew, Charles (Henry, IL)
Black Duck, early, deep 'V' body, orig pnt, old knot repair on breast/tail chip, retains orig weight, rare, J/G 4/24/86 990

Perdew, Charles
Black Duck, early, sleeping, 3-pc body, EX orig pnt by Edna,
detailed feathering, damage/rstr, ca 1910, J/G 4/24/86, $8,250.00.

Black Duck, hollow, minor pnt dings, sm areas of flaking on 1 side, otherwise M, retains orig weight, 193, RWO 7/02/88 1800
Black Duck, hollow, rpt, minor flaking/wear, branded Lorie Korsen, 39, RB 7/08/86 250
Black Duck, M condition, retains orig weight, rare, J/G 4/24/86 3300
Bluebill drake, boat-bk model, fine comb/feather pnt by Edna, minor wear, structurally EX, J/G 9/19/87 4250
Bluebill drake, early, outstanding wing cvg, NM orig pnt w/EX feather pnt, retains orig weight, J/G 4/24/86 4125
Bluebill drake, hollow, EX orig pnt, minor wear, structurally NM, outstanding, RWO 7/05/85 3100
Bluebill hen, hollow, G orig pnt by Edna, in-use wear, neck crack/sm tail rub, otherwise VG, 193, RWO 7/02/88 5250
Bluewinged Teal drake, NM pnt, minor flaking on head, structurally EX, rare, 193, RWO 7/02/88 6750
Bluewinged Teal hen, hollow, G orig pnt, flaking to bare wood on sides, crack in head/ms, rare, 193, RWO 7/02/88, 25% 850
Bluewinged Teal pr, slightly turned heads, highly detailed orig pnt, structurally EX/NM, rare, J/G 4/24/86 7700
Canada Goose, early, hollow, 3-pc body, slightly turned head, orig pnt w/some areas of flaking, rare, RB 3/06/87 3000
Canvasback drake, hollow w/raised cvd wings, superb, M condition, ca 1950's, RWO 11/06/85 1200
Canvasback pr, hen has minor flaking, otherwise M, both retain orig weight, structurally EX, J/G 4/24/86 3575
Crow, early, hollow, 3-pc laminated body, minor wear on tail/end-of-bill chip, otherwise EX & orig, 193, RWO 7/02/88 325
Crow, early, old rpt, average wear, age split at neck, 39, RB 7/08/86 300

Crow, early, solid body, turned head, wire legs added later, tight checks in breast, otherwise sound, 193, RWO 7/02/88 350
Crow, early, turned head, varnished, nicks/dings, checks in breast, otherwise EX & orig, 193, RWO 7/02/88 200
Crow, G orig pnt, age split at end of tail, slight roughness to end of bill, 39, RB 7/08/86 350
Crow, hollow, 3-pc laminated body, EX orig pnt, sliver of wood missing under bill, otherwise EX, rare, 193, RWO 7/02/88 250
Crow, orig pnt, average wear, structurally sound, RWO 7/06/86 350
Crow, slightly turned head, hollow, orig flock pnt, minor wear, crack in 1 side, rare, J/G 9/20/86 250
Golden Mallard pr, fine orig pnt, minor wear, hen has several hairline cracks in head, oversize, 68, J/G 4/24/86 3575

Perdew, Charles
Greenwinged Teal drake, EX detailed feather/comb pnt by Edna, stamped weight, structurally EX, 1930, 158, J/G 4/24/86, $8,800.00.

Greenwinged Teal hen, hollow, sm area on 1 side where pnt has peeled/neck crack, otherwise NM, rare, 193, RWO 7/02/88 6100
Mallard, hollow, rpt, minor wear, age split in neck has been reglued, RB 3/06/87 400
Mallard drake, early, hollow, G orig pnt by Edna, structurally EX, retains orig weight, ca 1935, RWO 7/04/87 1600
Mallard drake, early, hollow w/3-pc body construction, old rpt, average flaking/wear, 3, RB 7/07/87 500
Mallard drake, early, hollow 3-pc body, rpt, average wear, age split in neck/bill partly rstr/tail chip rstr, RB 8/25/88 375
Mallard drake, early, 3-pc body, EX orig pnt by Edna, EL cvd in bottom, neck crack, ca 1930's, 193, RWO 7/02/88, 56% 2000
Mallard drake, early, 3-pc body, worn orig pnt, branded WDB, J/G 4/24/86 467
Mallard drake, EX comb/feather pnt, 2 minor age lines in lower breast, retains orig weight, 1937, J/G 4/23/87 1750
Mallard drake, EX orig pnt by Edna, hairline crack in bk/sm chip on edge of bill, retains orig weight, J/G 9/19/87 1100
Mallard drake, fine comb pnt, M condition, retains orig weight, lot #282, J/G 9/19/87 1700
Mallard drake, fine comb pnt, M condition, retains orig weight, lot #288, J/G 9/19/87 1300
Mallard drake, hollow, EX orig pnt, minor wear, thin neck crack/head is loose, retains orig weight, RWO 7/02/88 1300
Mallard drake, hollow, few rubs to primer on head, otherwise NM, retains orig weight, RWO 7/02/88 1200
Mallard drake, hollow, fine orig pnt, average wear, structurally sound, 189, RB 6/28/88 1000
Mallard drake, hollow, fine orig pnt by Edna, average wear, well preserved, retains orig weight, 21, RB 2/01/85, 70% 1100
Mallard drake, hollow, M condition, orig weight on bottom, ca 1930, RB 7/09/85 1600
Mallard drake, hollow, NM orig pnt, retains orig weight, RB 7/07/87 2400
Mallard drake, hollow, old rpt, minor wear, structurally sound, RB 7/07/87 350
Mallard drake, hollow, raised cvd wings, orig pnt, heavy flaking/wear, crack in neck/head is loose, 1950's, RWO 11/06/85 190
Mallard drake, hollow, rpt, heavy flaking/wear, retains orig Perdew weight on bottom, 189, RB 6/28/88 175
Mallard drake, hollow, rpt by Helen Hageman w/flaking & wear, RB 8/21/86 225
Mallard drake, hollow, superb orig pnt, orig weight on bottom, NM condition, rare, RB 7/08/86 2750
Mallard drake, old working touchup by Charles, structurally EX, retains weight dated 1938, 3, RWO 7/05/85 875
Mallard drake, orig pnt, minor flaking/wear, in-use touchup, structurally EX, ca 1933, J/G 4/24/86, 75% 550
Mallard drake, pnt by Edna is EX w/some touchups, sm chip at base of neck, retains weight dated 1937, 131, J/G 9/19/87 550
Mallard drake, VG orig pnt by Edna, minor wear, structurally EX, retains orig weight dated 1937, RWO 7/05/85 1700
Mallard drake, 2 coats of pnt by Perdew, top coat is NM, 2 sm holes on underside/weight is missing, J/G 9/19/87 400
Mallard hen, early, EX orig pnt by Edna, average wear, retains orig weight, made in 1935, 193, RWO 7/02/88, 65% 2250
Mallard hen, early, EX orig pnt by Edna, 1 eye missing, retains orig weight, 1937, RWO 7/06/86 2750
Mallard hen, orig pnt w/wear to natural wood in some areas, age split in neck, rare, oversize, RB 2/01/85 350
Mallard hen, rpt, average wear, structurally EX, RWO 7/02/88 150
Mallard hen, rpt, structurally sound, retains Perdew weight, RWO 7/06/86 425
Mallard hen, sleeping, cvd wing tips, G orig pnt, lower half rpt, retains orig weight, rare, RB 2/01/85 2100

Perdew, Charles
Mallard hen, sleeping, several splatters of white pnt on bk, otherwise M, weight missing, slightly oversize, J/G 9/20/86, $4,500.00.

Mallard hen, slightly turned head, orig pnt, minor wear, Maxon brand, 2 tight neck cracks, orig weight, J/G 9/20/86, 65%	650
Mallard hen, taken down to mostly orig pnt, sm crack in neck, retains orig weight, J/G 4/24/86	467
Mallard hen, 2 coats of pnt by Perdew, top coat is M, retains orig weight, no structural flaws, J/G 9/19/87	550
Mallard pr, drake has slightly turned head, EX detailed orig pnt, both retain orig weight, structurally EX, J/G 9/20/86	2600
Mallard pr, early, EX orig pnt by Edna, few minor nicks/dings, otherwise structurally EX, 193, RWO 7/02/88, 150%	12000
Mallard pr, EX orig pnt by Edna w/touchup on each, few tight checks in neck of hen, orig 1937 weights, J/G 9/19/87	1450
Mallard pr, hen has slightly turned head, M/unused, both retain orig Perdew weight, J/G 9/20/86	3000
Mallard pr, hen has slightly turned head; drake has outstanding comb pnt, NM condition, J/G 9/20/86	3500
Mallard pr, hollow, raised cvd wings, hairline crack in neck, otherwise M, both retain orig weight, 1950's, RWO 11/06/85	2500
Mallard pr, hollow, rpt shows in-use flaking/wear, 39, RB 7/08/86	350
Mallard pr, NM orig pnt, drake has sm old neck repair, both retain orig weight, oversize, 7, J/G 4/24/86	2475
Mallard pr, orig pnt, minor flaking/wear, no structural flaws, both retain orig weight, J/G 4/24/86	1870
Mallard pr, orig pnt, minor wear, structurally EX, both retain orig Perdew weight, RWO 7/06/86	2400
Mallard pr, outstanding comb pnt on drake, M/unused, both retain orig weight, J/G 4/23/87	2600
Mallard pr, pnt by Edna, each has some working touchup, hen has neck crack, retains orig 1937 weight, 131, J/G 9/19/87	2400
Mallard pr, slightly turned heads, fine pnt details, both retain orig weight, M/unused, J/G 4/23/87	2750
Pintail drake, early, orig pnt on bk, otherwise rpt, old neck repair/sm chip on side of bill, J/G 4/24/86	357
Pintail drake, early, 3-pc body, EX orig comb pnt by Edna, average wear, hairline crack in neck, 193, RWO 7/02/88, 38%	1500
Pintail drake, early working rpt by Perdew, average wear, structurally EX, weight missing, ca 1940, RWO 7/04/87	2250
Pintail drake, fine orig pnt, minor wear, retains orig weight, rpr chip, stamped: Made for S Kowalski, 1930, J/G 4/24/86	4400
Pintail drake, flaking rpt over G orig w/combing, minor touchup, orig weight dated 1941, sm neck crack, 131, J/G 9/19/87	850
Pintail drake, flaking rpt reveals strong orig w/comb & feather pnt, crack in neck, 1941 weight, 131, J/G 9/19/87, 75%	650
Pintail drake, flaking rpt shows strong orig w/comb & feather detail, neck hairlines, has 1941 weight, 131, J/G 9/19/87	1100
Pintail drake, hollow, fine orig pnt, average wear w/some minor flaking, age split in neck, ls, rare, RB 3/06/87	600
Pintail drake, hollow, orig pnt w/some white areas of overpnt, orig weight on bottom, 6, RB 7/07/87	1500
Pintail drake, hollow, rpt w/minor wear, bill may have some rstr, branded Lorie Korsen, 39, RB 7/08/86	250
Pintail drake, hollow, wht areas/head/bill are working overpnt, pnt on bk by Edna, orig Perdew weight, RWO 7/02/88, 47%	700
Pintail drake, orig pnt w/fine combing/feather detail on bk, artist stamp, orig weight, ca 1930, 177, J/G 9/20/86, 75%	1100
Pintail hen, EX orig pnt w/touchup, hairline through neck/chip on underside of bill, very rare, 131, J/G 9/19/87, 25%	500
Pintail hen, EX orig pnt/touchup, artist-stamped weight dated 1944, tight check in neck, ls, rare, 131, J/G 9/19/87, 70%	2500
Pintail hen, hollow, retains orig weight, M condition, 193, RWO 7/02/88	1850
Pintail pr, hollow, drake has narrow crack in neck, otherwise M condition, 193, RWO, 7/02/88	2500
Pintail pr, sleeping, old working rpt w/traces of orig, structurally sound, rare, 193, RWO 7/02/88, 52%	1800
Wood Duck pr, hen: slightly turned head, raised cvd wings/crests, finely detailed pnt, hen: M; drake: NM, J/G 4/24/86	2860

Perdew, Charles; att (Henry, IL)
Coot or Mudhen, early, hollow, old pnt, in-use wear, sm crack at base of neck/prof bill rstr, 193, RWO 7/02/88	275

Perdew, Hadden (Henry, IL)
Crow, raised cvd wing tips, NM orig pnt, structurally M, J/G 4/23/87	75

Pernie, Dr. Miles
Mallard hen, G orig pnt, minor wear, well preserved, RB 12/06/85	250
Ringbill pr, old pnt, minor wear, well preserved, RB 8/21/86	375
Widgeon drake, raised cvd wing tips, G orig pnt, average wear, age split in neck, ls, RB 7/07/87	325

Perry, Royal (Burlington, VT)
Black Duck, orig pnt, minor wear, structurally sound, J/G 4/23/87	300
Goldeneye hen, cork body, orig pnt, minor wear, shallow dent in breast, ls, J/G 9/19/87	100

Pertuit, Dewey (Raceland, LA)
Bluewinged Teal drake, orig pnt, minor wear, hairline crack in bk, 33, J/G 9/19/87 175
Bluewinged Teal hen, orig pnt shows some flaking, ls, otherwise sound, RWO 2/12/88 130
Bluewinged Teal pr, G orig pnt, average wear, structurally sound, RWO 11/06/85 100
Coot, early, old working rpt, moderate wear, structurally EX, J/G 4/24/86 88
Mallard hen, EX orig pnt, slight age split in neck/sm chip at top of wing tips, RB 7/09/85 250
Mallard hen, orig pnt, minor wear, reglued crack in neck, prof rstr to bill/lower check, J/G 4/23/87 75
Ringbill drake, fine old pnt, average wear, age split in neck, ls, RB 8/25/88 70
Ringbill drake, made from tupelo gum wood, old rpt, average wear, slight age split in bill, RB 7/07/87 75
Ringbill drake, old pnt, average wear, structurally sound, RB 7/09/85 175
Ringbill drake, old pnt, moderate flaking/wear, RB 6/28/88 40
Ringbill drake, old working rpt, structurally EX, J/G 4/24/86 110
Ringneck, orig pnt, average wear w/few spots to bare wood on white areas, structurally EX, RWO 7/06/86 70
Peterman, Frank (Henry, IL)
Mallard drake, raised touched wing tips, old working rpt/strong orig underneath, High & Sibley brands, rare, J/G 4/23/87 600
Peterson, Emil
Sprig drake, fine dry pnt, EX & orig condition, RB 8/25/88 550
Peterson, Oscar
Mallard drake, old pnt, heavy wear, structurally sound, 39, RB 7/08/86 150
Peterson, Pete (Cape Charles, VA)
Bufflehead drake, artist signed/dated 1983, EX & orig condition, RWO 7/02/88 160
Curlew, orig pnt, cvd Pete on bottom, signed/dated 1985, EX & orig, RB 3/06/87 150
Greenwinged Teal pr, NM pnt, artist brand, RB 3/06/87 200
Hooded Merganser pr, EX pnt, artist brand/dated, RB 7/09/85 375
Mallard drake, EX pnt, artist brand, RB 8/21/86 200
Mallard pr, hollow, EX orig pnt, artist brand, signed/dated on bottom, RB 7/09/85 275
Mudhen, hollow, Hog Island style, artist brand, M condition, RWO 7/06/86 95
Old Squaw pr, inlet heads, hollow, artist brand, dated 1986, M condition, RWO 7/06/86 150
Pintail pr, hollow, signed/dated 1985, hen inscribed: My prettiest decoy in 28 yrs of cvg, RWO 7/05/85 425
Redbreasted Merganser pr, inscribed/dated 1982, M condition, RWO 11/11/87 375
Ruddy Duck, G orig pnt, ca 1965, RWO 7/06/86 115
Ruddy Duck, hollow, artist brand, M condition, sm, RWO 7/06/86 100
Swan, hollow, signed, unused, RWO 11/11/87 325
Widgeon pr, artist brand, M condition, RWO 11/06/85 400
Widgeon pr, inlet heads, hollow, Hog Island style, artist brand, M condition, RWO 7/06/86 225
Petre, Claude (Golden Meadow, LA)
Greenwinged Teal pr, slightly turned heads, raised cvd primaries/cvd tail feathers, J/G 4/24/86 257
Phillips, Capt. Ike (Wachepague, VA)
Black Duck, orig scratch pnt, minor wear, sm rough area on bill/minor age lines, J/G 4/23/87 300
Bluebill pr, EX orig pnt, average wear, slight age split in neck of hen, 49, RB 7/09/85, 40% 300
Phillips, Ed (Cambridge, MD)
Black Duck, orig pnt, average wear, structurally EX, ca 1930's, RWO 7/05/85 600
Black Duck, orig pnt, average wear w/some flaking on bk, minor repair to underside of bill, ms, rare, RWO 11/11/87 675
Bluebill drake, EX orig pnt, fine structural condition, ca 1930's, RWO 7/05/85 550
Bluebill drake, hollow, EX orig pnt, minor wear, sm chip on underside of bill, otherwise EX, 69, RWO 7/02/88 1100
Pintail drake, EX orig pnt, structurally EX, ca 1930's, RWO 7/05/85 1350

Phillips, Ed
Pintail drake, orig pnt, pnt flaking on sm area of tail, structurally EX, 1930's, RWO 7/06/86, $2,250.00.

Pice, Charles (Astoria, OR)
Mallard drake, hollow, old pnt, moderate wear, end-of-tail chip, RB 8/25/88 175
Mallard drake, hollow, orig pnt, average wear, minor age split at neck, otherwise EX, RB 8/25/88 450
Pintail hen, hollow, orig pnt, heavy wear, structurally sound, RWO 7/06/86 190
Piecor, Gordon
Canvasback pr, balsa w/pine keels, NM orig pnt, structurally EX, ca 1955, J/G 9/20/86 135
Pierce, Earl
Pintail drake, NM pnt, slight age split in neck, otherwise structurally EX, RB 8/21/86 300
Pierce, Jim (Havre de Grace, MD)
Black Duck, preening, NM, RB 7/07/87 125
Black Duck, sleeping, M condition, ca 1980, RWO 7/05/85 140
Bluewinged Teal drake, orig pnt, average wear, artist stamp, RB 3/06/87 150
Bluewinged Teal drake, sleeping, EX orig pnt, minor flaking/wear, well preserved, RB 7/08/86 225
Bluewinged Teal pr, G orig pnt, minor wear, RB 7/08/86 120
Brant, unused condition, ca 1979, RWO 7/05/85 60
Canada Goose, preening, unused condition, RWO 7/02/88 160
Mallard drake, EX orig pnt, RB 7/07/87 75
Pintail drake, orig pnt shows some flaking & wear, ls, RB 3/11/88 175
Piggott, Melvin (Merlin, ON)
Redbreasted Merganser drake, detailed bk/tail cvg, branded MP, M condition, lg, RWO 2/12/88 120
Pigott, Robert (Gloucester, NC)
Bluebill drake, G old orig pnt, hairline crack in bk, rare, 33, J/G 9/19/87, 275% 1400
Pinkham, Capt. (Yarmouth, ME)
Eider drake, inlet neck, gracefully cvd head, fine orig pnt, average weathering/wear, ls, rare, RB 7/09/85, 40% 1000
Eider hen, fine orig pnt, average wear, some minor age splitting, 22, RB 5/02/86 1500
Eider pr, inlet heads, EX orig pnt, minor age splits, made from salvage of schooner, ca 1898, 44/22, J/G 9/19/87, 55% 2250

Pinkham, Capt.
Eider pr, inlet heads, G orig pnt, minor age splitting, oversize, 22/44, RB 5/02/86, $4,000.00.

Piolotti, Mario (Spring Valley, IL)
Mallard pr, NM old pnt w/outstanding feather pnt, no structural flaws, rare, 7, J/G 4/24/86 2035
Piolotti, Mario; att (Spring Valley, IL)
Mallard drake, hollow, rpt w/minor wear, structurally sound, 6, RB 7/07/87 300
Pirnie, Miles
Bluewinged Teal drake, cvd wing tips, fine orig pnt, average wear, well preserved, RB 7/08/86 200
Ringneck drake, orig pnt, average wear, old working repair to neck, RWO 11/11/87 120
Ruddy Duck, EX pnt, artist brand, RB 7/09/85 300
Widgeon pr, EX pnt, artist brand on keel, RB 7/09/85 575
Pitman, Peter
Goldeneye hen, hollow, orig pnt, structurally sound, RWO 11/11/87 50

Greenwinged Teal drake, raised cvd primaries/secondaries, artist brand, J/G 9/20/86 70

Pitzer, Louis (Half Moon Island, Pistakee Lake, IL)

Redhead drake, orig pnt, heavy wear, crack running through neck/end-of-bill chip, hs, RWO 7/02/88 95

Plickta, Fred

Canvasback drake, G orig pnt, average wear, RB 2/01/85 125

Redhead drake, pnt taken down to orig w/heavy wear, structurally sound, RB 2/01/85 150

Pomir, Byron

Bluebill hen, hollow, old dry pnt, heavy flaking/wear, most of bill broken off & missing, 2, RB 12/06/85 75

Powers, Chris (Peru, IL)

Mallard pr, hollow, outstanding orig pnt, drake has chip on underside of bill, otherwise sound, ca 1935, RWO 7/05/85 3500

Pozzini, Charles (Detroit, MI)

Black Duck, hollow, EX orig pnt, 77, RB 12/06/85 800

Pratt, Norris (Kemblesville, PA)

Canvasback drake, high-head style, EX orig pnt, minor wear, structurally NM, ca 1968, rare, RWO 11/11/87 260

Canvasback drake, hollow w/cvd primary feathers, EX orig pnt by Ned Mayne, oversize, RB 7/07/87 100

Canvasback hen, hollow w/cvd wing tips/primary feathers, EX orig pnt by JC Reed, oversize, Rb 7/07/87 125

Canvasback pr, cedar bodies, pnt by Lem Ward, slight pnt rubs, signed/dated 1961, structurally EX, J/G 9/19/87 700

Canvasback pr, EX orig pnt, signed/dated 1961, RB 7/09/85 750

Mallard pr, orig pnt, minor wear, never weighted, RWO 11/11/87 290

Merganser hen, EX orig pnt by Delbert 'Cigar' Daisy, RB 7/07/87 300

Redbreasted Merganser pr, pnt by Lem Ward, both in outstanding condition, RWO 7/05/85 385

Redhead drake, EX orig pnt by Dick Dobbs, tiny bit of crazing at top of head, RB 7/07/87 150

Predmore, Cooper

Canada Goose, hollow, rpt, minor wear, age split in neck, RB 6/28/88 225

Price, Liberty (Manahawkin, NJ)

Black Duck, hollow, old pnt, heavy wear, age split in neck, 189, RB 6/28/88 100

Black Duck, hollow, old rpt, average flaking/wear, minor age split in neck, chip on underside of bill, RB 3/11/88 200

Black Duck, hollow, rpt, average wear, age split in neck/top of head, RB 3/11/88 125

Price, Liberty; att (Manahawkin, NJ)

Black Duck, hollow, old flocked pnt, average wear, age split in neck, 189, RB 6/28/88 55

Black Duck, hollow, rpt, average wear, age check in neck, otherwise structurally sound, RB 3/11/88 150

Black Duck, hollow, working rpt, minor wear, artist brand, structurally EX, 3/11, RWO 7/06/86 325

Pringle, Peter; att

Black Duck, EX orig pnt, minor wear, stamped Ross Munger, well preserved, RB 7/07/87 450

Pryor, Leonard (Chesapeake City, MD)

Black Duck, hollow w/raised cvd wings/primaries, NM condition, ca 1915, RWO 11/06/85, 160% 4000

Pryor, Leonard
Canvasback drake, fine orig pnt w/soft patina, structurally EX, ca 1910, rare, RWO 11/06/85, $1,050.00.

Pintail drake, hollow, orig pnt, average wear w/some flaking to bare wood, structurally EX, ca 1910, RWO 11/11/87, 50% 475

Pryor, Leonard; att (Chesapeake City, MD)

Canvasback drake, working rpt, average flaking/wear, RB 2/01/85 200

Pudvar, Reginald (St. Albans, VT)

Black Duck, old working rpt, sm age line in top of head, 62, J/G 4/23/87 55

Purdo, Nick (Detroit, MI)

Canvasback drake, EX orig condition, RWO 11/06/85 50

Canvasback drake, hollow, relief cvd primaries/secondaries, signed, 3rd place winner Davenport IA 1967, M, J/G 4/23/87 600

Redhead drake, fine orig pnt, well preserved, RB 2/01/85 100

Redhead hen, balsa body, cvd wing tips, EX orig pnt, overpnt to white areas on sides of body, RB 2/01/85 125

Purnell, Bill (Ocean City, MD)
Pintail drake, low-head style, orig pnt, average wear, structurally EX, RWO 7/06/86 90
Purnell, Charles (Churches Island, NC)
Canvasback pr, orig pnt, drake: old working rpt to wht area on head, body checks; hen: check in neck, RWO 2/12/88 700
Purnes, Allen
Canvasback drake, fine orig pnt, minor wear, RB 7/08/86 75
Quillen, Nate (Rockwood, MI)
Bluebill drake, hollow, old rpt, average wear, branded WTB, part of bill missing, chip on tail, 6, RB 7/07/87 250
Bluebill drake, hollow, orig pnt, average wear, thin check in neck, otherwise EX, 68, RWO 7/05/85 2650
Bluebill hen, old working rpt, moderate wear, branded ED, crack in neck, J/G 9/20/86 175
Bluebill pr, inlet heads, orig pnt, hen has hairline check/both have neck cracks, 193, RWO 7/02/88 1750
Goldeneye hen, low-head style, hollow, old orig pnt, structurally EX, 53/61, J/G 9/20/86 300
Mallard drake, early, inlet head, hollow, old pnt taken down to orig, no structural flaws, ca 1900, J/G 9/19/87 700
Mallard hen, inlet head, hollow, EX orig pnt, branded HHB for Harvey Brown, Cleveland OH, EX, ca 1885, J/G 4/24/86, 50% 1265
Mallard hen, orig pnt, minor wear, branded JCM for JC Morse, tight check in neck, ca 1894, rare, J/G 4/23/87 2200

Quillen, Nate
Pintail drake, early, hollow, pnt taken down to orig w/moderate wear, several age splits in neck, RB 7/07/87, 30%, $750.00.

Pintail drake, inlet head, hollow, prof pnt rstr, artist brand, prof rstr to part of bill, ls, rare, J/G 9/20/86 350
Pintail drake, inlet head, hollow, prof pnt rstr, branded WTB, crack in neck has been reglued, J/G 9/19/87 300
Pintail drake, inlet neck, hollow, orig pnt, moderate wear, branded WLB, rpr bill/neck, ls, rare, RB 7/07/87, 50% 950
Pintail hen, inlet head, hollow, pnt taken down to orig/in-use rpt, hairline crack in neck, WTB brand, J/G 4/23/87 750
Pintail hen, inlet head, orig pnt, minor crazing/wear, crack in neck, ls, made for JC Morse, 150, J/G 9/20/86 2000
Redhead drake, inlet neck, hollow, overpnt w/average wear, branded CVH, age split in neck, 6, RB 7/07/87 600
Redhead drake, low-head style, hollow, fine orig scratch feather pnt, average wear, ls, rare, RB 12/06/85 3000
Redhead pr, low-head style, orig pnt, average wear, hen has tight crack in head, EX, ca 1880's, 150, RWO 7/06/86, 160% 4000
Quimet, Emile
Bluebill pr, feather cvg on bk, EX pnt, artist brand, RB 2/01/85 100
Bluebill pr, fine wing/feather cvg on bk, NM pnt, RB 7/07/87 250
Quinn, William (Yardley, PA)
Black Duck, hollow w/raised 'V' tail cvg, orig pnt, average wear, weight stamped by maker, RWO 7/06/86, 165% 1400
Black Duck, sleeping, hollow, fine orig pnt, only 1 existent, EX-collection Bob White & Hal Sorensen, 1940, RWO 11/06/85 3500
Bluebill pr, low-head style, EX orig pnt, artist brand, both retain keel weights, ca 1950's, RWO 11/11/87 3600
Mallard pr, hen's head is slightly tucked, raised cvd wing tips, EX orig pnt, RB 7/09/85 4000
Redhead pr, hollow, artist brand, EX & orig condition, bears maker's weight, RWO 2/12/88 2650
Widgeon hen, head tucked, hollow w/raised wing tips, EX orig pnt, signed, 1 eye missing, signed, rare, RB 3/06/87 1650
Quintel, Tony
Brant, hollow, w/detailed feather cvg on wings, M condition, 60, J/G 9/20/86 150
RaFuse, Gilbert (Chester Basin, NS)
Redbreasted Merganser drake, leather crest, M condition, ca 1980, RWO 7/04/87 130
Redbreasted Merganser drake, M condition, ca 1980, RWO 7/04/87 120
Redbreasted Merganser drake, preening, artist brand, M condition, ca late 1970's, RWO 7/04/87 120
Ramsay, John (Summerside, PEI)
Brant, early, old working rpt, minor wear, age split in bk/minor age lines/3 holes drilled in underside, ls, J/G 9/19/87 175
Rathel, Joseph (Leach Lake Indian Reservation, MN)
Wood Duck pr, NM orig pnt, structurally EX, half-size, J/G 4/23/87 100
Rathmann, Jake (Wreck Lead, LI, NY)
Golden Plover, fine orig condition, branded Jake's Point, RWO 7/05/85 500
Rathmell, Lou (Stratford, CT)
Black Duck, cork body, G orig pnt, average wear, sm chip on underside of bill, 22/44, RB 5/02/86 3500
Black Duck, cork body, head has EX orig pnt, fine old washed pnt on body, artist brand on weight, rare, RB 12/06/85 2500

Black Duck, cork body, NM orig pnt, minor wear, underside of bill has been rstr, orig weight dated 1941, RB 3/06/87 .... **2900**
Black Duck, cork body, slightly turned head, unused/NM condition, RB 6/28/88 .... **3250**
Black Duck, cork body, slightly turned head/high & alert, EX feather detail, EX orig pnt, well preserved, RB 3/06/87 .... **2800**

Rathmell, Lou

Top: Black Duck, cork body, tucked head, 'LC Rathmell' on metal plate, overall NM condition, RWO 7/04/87, $7,250.00.
Bottom: Black Duck, cork body, turned head, '1941, LC Rathmell' on metal plate, NM condition, RWO 7/04/87, $6,000.00.

Black Duck, working rpt, artist brand, from artist's own hunting rig, RWO 11/06/85 .... **2000**
Canvasback hen, slightly turned head, hollow w/raised wing tips, 2 dents in bk, extremely rare, J/G 9/19/87 .... **5000**
Canvasback pr, hollow, EX orig comb/feather pnt, branded 1944, exceptional, rare, RWO 7/05/85 .... **8750**
Rawlings, William (Musquadoboit Harbour, NS)
Yellowlegs, root-head, NM orig pnt, crack in 1 side, J/G 4/24/86 .... **275**
Ray, Davis (East Peoria, IL)
Bluebill hen, NM orig pnt by Edna Perdew, structurally EX, J/G 9/20/86 .... **300**
Reed, Corbin (Chincoteague, VA)
Black Duck, EX pnt, RB 7/09/85 .... **650**
Reed, Don (Hamilton, Ont)
Bluebill hen, early, orig pnt, minor wear, several scratches, J/G 4/24/86 .... **280**
Reed, Dr. (Dunnville, Ont)
Canvasback drake, hollow, M condition, RWO 11/11/87 .... **170**
Canvasback drake, hollow, NM pnt, structurally EX, ca 1920, RWO 11/11/87 .... **100**
Reeves, Charles (Port Rowan, Ont)
Pintail drake, hollow, orig pnt, average wear, 2 thin checks in neck/minor damage to bottom of bill, RWO 11/06/85 .... **150**
Reeves, Jack (Long Point, Ont)
Canvasback drake, hollow w/stretched canvas over bk, old working rpt w/some orig, J/G 4/24/86 .... **302**
Reeves, John (Long Point, Ont)
Canada Goose, hollow, orig pnt, average wear, structurally EX, RWO 7/05/85, 65% **2000**
Pintail drake, old rpt w/some orig on lower sides, prof rstr to part of bill, very rare, 179, J/G 9/20/86 .... **850**
Reeves, Phineas (Toronto, Ont)
Canada Goose, thin-shelled, hollow, orig pnt, hairline crack in bk/tail chip, otherwise EX, ca 1870, 193, RWO 7/02/88 .... **5750**
Reghi, Ralph (Detroit, MI)
Bluebill drake, fine old pnt, average flaking/wear, RB 8/25/88 .... **160**
Canvasback drake, bull-neck, old working rpt w/orig showing in some areas, structurally EX, J/G 4/24/86 .... **385**
Canvasback drake, early, orig pnt, structurally EX, ca 1938, RWO 7/04/87 .... **1100**
Canvasback drake, high-head style, fine orig pnt, average wear, ms, 53, RB 7/09/85 .... **350**
Canvasback drake, old rpt, partially taken down to orig w/heavy wear, RB 2/01/85 .... **125**
Canvasback drake, sleeping, balsa body w/pine head, NM orig pnt, structurally EX, J/G 9/19/87 .... **375**
Reghi, Ralph; att (Detroit, MI)
Bluebill drake, fine old pnt, average wear, RB 2/01/85 .... **125**
Reid, Corb (Chincoteague, VA)
Shoveler drake, raised wing cvg/detailed bill cvg, artist brand, EX orig condition, RWO 11/06/85 .... **525**
Reimenschneider, Rich
Pintail drake, EX condition, RB 8/25/88 .... **60**
Widgeon, EX condition, RB 8/25/88 .... **40**

Reineri, Lou (Chincoteague, VA)
Pintail pr, cvd in style of Ward brothers 'pinch-breast,' M condition, RWO 11/11/87 310
Pintail pr, G orig condition, RWO 7/02/88 200
Reitgraff, Herman (Peru, IL)
Mallard drake, hollow, fine orig pnt, average wear, most of bill is rstr, RB 3/06/87 200
Mallard drake, orig pnt, minor wear, minor working touchup, structurally EX, J/G 9/20/86 350
Pintail drake, orig pnt, minor wear, white area may be rpt, tiny chip on 1 side of bill, rare, J/G 4/24/86 247
Reitmeyer, Fred
Barrows Goldeneye drake, hollow, feather cvg w/cvd wing tips, branded WFR, minor bill chip, otherwise EX, RB 3/11/88 130
Black Duck, feather cvg w/cvd wing tips, branded WFR, EX condition, RB 3/11/88 70
Bluebill drake, hollow, feather cvg w/cvd wing tips, branded WFR, EX condition, RB 3/11/88 110
Canvasback drake, hollow, feather cvg w/cvd wing tips, branded WFR, EX condition, RB 3/11/88 110
Goldeneye drake, feather cvg w/cvd wing tips, branded WFR, EX condition, RB 3/11/88 120
Greenwinged Teal drake, feather cvg w/cvd wing tips, pnt shows minor wear, branded WFR, RB 3/11/88 140
Redhead drake, hollow w/cvd wing tips, overall feather cvg, branded WFR, EX condition, RB 3/11/88 140
Reitz, Al (Tullytown, PA)
Black Duck, hollow, orig pnt, average flaking/wear, structurally EX, RWO 7/04/87 500
Bluebill hen, low-head, hollow, 'V' cvd wings, metal tag on bottom bears maker's name/hometown, M, RWO 7/02/88 600
Reitz, Al; att (Tullytown, PA)
Black Duck, hollow, fine old pnt, appears to be orig w/average wear, RB 8/21/86 350
Reitz, William (Columbia, PA)
Canvasback pr, orig pnt, average wear, hen has chew marks on bill/check on bottom, otherwise sound, 69, RWO 11/11/87 260
Remus, Samuel P.
Bluebill pr, orig pnt, minor wear, artist stamp, hairline crack in neck of hen, rare, J/G 4/23/87 200
Mallard pr, hollow w/canvas bottoms, orig pnt, minor wear, artist stamp, structurally sound, rare, J/G 4/23/87 350
Reneson, Chet (Old Lyme, CT)
Bluebill drake, G pnt, average wear, cvd initials on bottom, RB 7/09/85 80
Bluebill drake, working rpt, average wear, comb pnt on bk, structurally sound, ca 1950, RWO 11/11/87 150
Pintail drake, hollow, EX orig pnt, RB 7/09/85 200
Widgeon drake, hollow, EX orig pnt, RB 7/09/85 200
Rhodes, David (Absecon, NJ)
Brant, hollow, signed/dated 1970, 1970 US National Decoy Show sticker on bottom, EX condition, RB 3/11/88, 60% 150
Greenwinged Teal pr, hollow, EX condition, RWO 7/06/86 80
Loon, hollow, artist brand, M condition, RWO 7/06/86 200

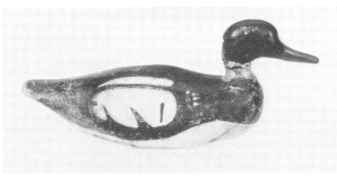

Richardson, Frank (Edgartown, MA)
Redbreasted Merganser drake, hollowed from bottom w/cvd crest, old pnt, average wear, split in neck, 23, RB 7/07/87, 70%, $700.00.

Rider, Jack (Port Clinton, OH)
Crow, raised cvd wing outline/thigh cvg, M condition, J/G 4/23/87 400
Riley, Nelson (Absecon, NJ)
Black Duck, low-head, hollow, raised 'V' cvd wings/tail cvg, detailed feather pnt, M condition, RWO 7/02/88 250
Greenwinged Teal pr, hollow, signed/dated 1972, M condition, RWO 7/06/86 60
Roberts, George (Long Island, NY)
Black Duck, cork body, head is orig pnt, minor wear, body is natural cork w/pnt speculum, RB 8/21/86 50
Bluebill drake, cork body, fine orig pnt, average wear, artist brand, ls, RB 3/06/87 75
Bluebill drake, cork body, old pnt, average wear, age split in neck, RB 7/07/87 40
Bluebill hen, cork body, fine orig pnt, minor wear, old break in bill has an in-use repair, RB 7/07/87 50
Bluebill hen, preening, cork body, EX orig pnt, branded Manning, rare, RB 7/08/86 175
Canvasback drake, cork body, orig pnt, average wear, some minor natural checks in cork on bk, otherwise EX, RWO 7/06/86 80
Yellowlegs, relief cvd wings, cvd eyes, working rpt, sm tail chip, ls, ca 1880, J/G 4/23/87 425

Roberts, Rufus (Coinjock, NC)
Bluebill drake, old orig pnt, structurally sound, RWO 11/06/85 400
Robertson, Gerald (Blue Hills, ME)
Black Duck, early, cvd wings, old pnt, average wear, RB 6/28/88 500
Black Duck, inlet head turned to left/angled forward, hollow, raised cvd wings, EX condition, RB 7/07/87, 310% 3100
Black Duck, inlet neck, raised cvd wing tips, rpt, minor wear, structurally sound, RB 7/07/87 500
Robin, Charlie (Delacroix, LA)
Bluewinged Teal drake, orig pnt, structurally sound, RWO 7/06/86 90
Robin, Herbert; att
Mallard drake, cvd wings, old orig pnt, heavy flaking/wear, 21, RB 2/01/85 350
Robinson, Sleighter (Bishop's Head, MD)
Redbreasted Merganser hen, orig pnt, in-use wear, unusual inserted bill, ca 1900, RWO 11/06/85 200
Robinson, Thomas (New Jersey)
Black Duck, hollow, fine orig pnt, average wear, RB 3/11/88 150
Black Duck, hollow, G orig pnt, minor flaking/wear, well preserved, RB 2/01/85 50
Black Duck, hollow, orig pnt, average wear, retains orig weight, RB 3/06/87 350
Black Duck, hollow, rpt, average wear, RB 6/28/88 75
Rodrique, Vic (Vacherie, LA)
Canvasback drake, working rpt, flaking/wear, structurally sound, RWO 2/12/88 90
Ringbill or Bluebill drake, G orig pnt, average wear, thin cracks on top of head, sm, RWO 2/12/88 80
Roeders, Ken (Sonoma, CA)
Canvasback pr, fine old pnt, some appearing to be orig w/average wear, well preserved, RB 8/27/87 225
Greenwinged Teal drake, cvd primary feathers, EX & orig, RB 8/27/87 90
Greenwinged Teal hen, cvd primary feathers, fine orig pnt, minor wear, RB 8/27/87 65
Rogers, Augustus
Goldeneye hen, EX orig pnt, average wear, ls, RB 12/06/85 60
Rogers, H.M. (Quincy, MA)
Canada Goose, cork body, G orig pnt, average wear, artist stamp, orig bottom board has dry rot, oversize, RB 7/08/86 60
Rogers, Skee (Louisiana)
Canvasback drake, orig pnt, average wear, reglued hairline crack in bill, J/G 4/23/87 100
Ringbill, EX orig pnt, no structural flaws, rare, J/G 4/24/86 121
Ringbill drake, break at end of bill has been reglued, otherwise EX, RB 6/28/88 50
Ringbill drake, EX orig pnt, minor wear, signed on bottom, RB 7/07/87 75
Ringbill drake, G orig pnt, minor flaking/wear, signed/dated 1965 on bottom, RB 7/08/86 150
Rollin, Cecil (Harbor Beach, MI)
Mallard pr, signed/dated 1978, M condition, RWO 11/06/85 70
Roseling, Joseph (Almeda, CA)
Sprig drake, old pnt, moderate flaking/wear, end of tail has been cvd down, RB 8/25/88 175
Ross, Douglas
Bluebill hen, old pnt, average wear, well preserved, RB 12/06/85 70

Ross, Harold
Goldeneye hen, EX orig pnt, won prize at Nat'l NY Show in 1951, rare, 22/44, RB 5/02/86, 200%, $1,600.00.

Ross, Harry A.
Bluewinged Teal drake, mahogany, EX orig pnt, RB 7/07/87 175
Ross, Willie (Chebeague Island, ME)
Black Duck, dowelled inlet head, NM orig pnt, structurally EX, rare, J/G 4/24/86 192
Black Duck, EX orig pnt, narrow crack running through neck, RWO 7/04/87 240
Goldeneye drake, old working rpt, minor wear, hairline cracks in head/body, oversize, J/G 9/19/87 175
Goldeneye hen, inlet head, orig pnt, minor wear w/old working touchup on white areas, ls, J/G 9/19/87 400

Goldeneye hen, orig pnt, average wear, ls, rare, RB 2/01/85 .... **600**
Goldeneye pr, rpt w/average wear, several age splits, 22/44, RB 5/02/86 .... **1000**
Merganser hen, inlet head, orig pnt, minor wear, 2 sm hairline cracks in lower breast, ls, J/G 9/19/87, 50% **700**
Merganser hen, early, inlet head, pnt eyes, NM orig pnt, tight check on bottom, rpl ostrich plume crest, 48, J/G 4/24/86 .... **3410**
Merganser pr, inlet heads, EX orig pnt, drake has prof bill rstr, several hairline cracks, ms, J/G 4/23/87 .... **2300**
Redbreasted Merganser drake, inlet neck, fine orig pnt, average wear, overpnt to white areas, otherwise EX, RB 7/07/87 .... **1500**
Redbreasted Merganser drake, orig pnt w/touchup to white areas, structurally sound, RWO 7/06/86 .... **1000**

Ross, Willie
Redbreasted Merganser pr, EX orig pnt, minor flaking, retain orig peacock plume crests, 1940, EX condition, RWO 7/06/86, $5,750.00.

Redbreasted Merganser pr, inlet necks, G orig pnt, average wear, age splits, 22, RB 5/02/86 .... **1400**
Redbreasted Merganser pr, orig pnt, prof bill repairs, drake has sm chips in tail; hen has crack in neck, RWO 7/06/86 .... **1300**
Yellowlegs, NM orig pnt, sm chip on side of tail, 1 shot mk, J/G 9/19/87 .... **300**
Ross, Willie; att (Chebeague Island, ME)
Yellowlegs, G orig pnt, old repair to neck, ca 1910, rare, RB 2/01/85 .... **400**
Rossiter, Harry; att (Vinal Haven, ME)
Old Squaw drake, fine orig pnt, average wear, cvd initials, RB 7/09/85 .... **90**
Roth, John (Oshkosh, WI)
Bluebill drake, orig pnt, minor wear, hairline crack on underside extending part way up breast, J/G 9/20/86 .... **175**
Coot, orig pnt, average wear, structurally EX, 15, RWO 7/06/86 .... **110**
Roussell, Reme (Raceland, LA)
Bluewinged Teal hen, EX orig pnt, NM condition, rare, RB 12/06/85 .... **675**
Mallard drake, early, orig pnt, average wear, half of bill prof rstr, chips in end of wing tips, J/G 4/23/87 .... **200**
Mallard pr, raised cvd wing tips, EX condition, 21, RB 2/01/85 .... **750**
Ringbill pr, raised cvd wing tips, fine orig pnt, minor wear, 21, RB 2/01/85, 250% **1000**
Roust, Zan (Ganaque, Ont)
Black Duck, orig pnt, minor wear, ls, J/G 9/20/86 .... **85**
Rovello, Joe
Coot, hollow, raised wing tips/relief cvg on primaries, M condition, RWO 7/06/86 .... **25**
Rowe, Jimmy L. (Norfolk, VA)
Coot, orig pnt, average wear, structurally EX, ca 1938, RWO 7/06/86 .... **135**
Rowe, Tim (Norfolk, VA)
Coot, metal head, orig pnt, minor wear, no structural flaws, 28, J/G 9/19/87 .... **350**
Rucker, Larry
Golden Plover, EX pnt, signed/dated on bottom, 36, RB 2/01/85 .... **70**
Hooded Merganser, EX pnt, signed/dated 1968 on bottom, 36, RB 2/01/85 .... **125**
Rue, Ben (Locustville, VA)
Bluebill pr, orig pnt, average wear, drake has worm holes near breast/both have tail damage, otherwise G, RWO 7/02/88 .... **250**
Rue, Ron (Cambridge, MD)
Black Duck, balsa body, EX orig pnt, average wear w/few pnt dings, structurally sound, RWO 11/11/87 .... **200**
Canvasback drake, M condition, RWO 7/06/86 .... **325**
Widgeon drake, G orig pnt, average wear, RB 7/08/86 .... **200**
Ruggles, Charles (Henry, IL)
Canvasback drake, prof rstr to pnt on body, old working rpt on head, chips missing at tail/bill, ca 1890, RWO 2/13/87 .... **375**
Mallard hen, prof rpt, worn area on underside, J/G 4/23/87 .... **200**
Rule, John (Beardstown, IL)
Pintail drake, old working rpt w/some orig, branded FAM, tight crack in neck/bill, 7, J/G 4/24/86 .... **165**
Pintail pr, drake has slightly turned head, NM orig pnt, both have hairline crack in neck, J/G 4/23/87 .... **1050**

Rumble, William (Bloomfield, Ont)
Bluebill hen, hollow, orig pnt, average wear, structurally sound, 3/76, RB 3/06/87 750
Rumble, William; att (Bloomfield, Ont)
Bluebill hen, hollow, orig pnt, average wear, bears Mackey stamp, thin crack in neck, otherwise sound, 3, RWO 7/06/86 300
Runyan, George D. (Bordentown, NJ)
Mallard drake, hollow, old working rpt, reglued crack in bill, 65, J/G 4/23/87 350
Ruppel, Walter (Portland, OR)
Black Duck, cork body, EX orig pnt, average in-use wear, wooden bottom, ca 1950, half-size, RWO 11/11/87 10
Greenwinged Teal pr, slightly turned heads, signed, NM condition, ca 1970, RB 8/27/87 250
Mallard pr, balsa bodies, orig pnt, average wear, dents/marring, drake has sm age split in neck, 1940, lg, RB 8/27/87 175
Russell, Burrley (Stockton, CA)
Canada Goose, canvas-covered, cvd raised wing tips, EX orig pnt, tears at neck/minor tear on tail, ca 1935, RB 8/25/88 175
Sprig drake, canvas-covered, minor wear to end of tail/bill, neck slightly loose, otherwise NM, ca 1935, RB 8/25/88 90
Rutter, Bob (West Creek, NJ)
Bluewinged Teal pr, hollow, artist brand, M condition, RWO 11/11/87 220
Redbreasted Merganser pr, hollow, signed/artist brand, structurally M, RWO 11/11/87 100
Ryder, Tom (Tuckerton, NJ)
Black Duck, hollow, G orig pnt, minor wear, artist brand, RB 8/27/87 60
Rymal, John
Black Duck, fine feather cvg, fine orig pnt, minor wear, RB 12/06/85 170
Canvasback drake, feather cvg/wing detail, EX condition, RB 2/01/85 175
Rys, Walter
Canvasback drake, hollow, orig pnt, minor wear, branded W-RYS, RB 6/28/88 75
Sabatini, Michael
Black Duck, hollow, NM condition, RWO 11/06/85 325
Sabatini, Pat
Brant, hollow, EX orig pnt, slight age check in bill, RB 7/07/87 225
Mallard pr, hollow, cvd raised wing tips, signed on weight on bottom, minor flaking/wear, otherwise EX, RB 6/28/88, 58% 350
Sabatini, Pat; att
Bluebill pr, hollow, fine orig pnt, average wear, RB 3/11/88 250
Sabatini, Ralph (Bristol, PA)
Black Duck, swimming, hollow, M condition, RWO 7/05/85 135
Shoveler pr, hollow, M condition, RWO 7/05/85 140
Widgeon pr, M condition, RWO 11/06/85 170
Sabatini, Ron (Burlington, NJ)
Widgeon drake, raised cvd primaries/tail feathers, NM orig pnt, ls, J/G 9/20/86 160
Widgeon hen, hollow w/raised cvd primaries, M condition, RWO 2/13/87 80
Sacchi, Nick (Bristol, PA)
Black Duck, hollow w/raised cvd primaries, M condition, rare, 7, J/G 4/24/86 165
Pintail drake, hollow w/raised cvd primaries, M condition, rare, 7, J/G 4/24/86 330
Sallette, Lou (Detroit, MI)
Canvasback drake, old working rpt, artist brand, crack in neck, J/G 4/23/87 80
Salmons, Bradford (Mayetta, NJ)
Black Duck, hollow, fine old pnt, average wear, branded H Hoffman-Thorofare NJ, RB 6/28/88, 58% 175
Canada Goose, hollow, old orig pnt, heavy wear, age check along 1 side of body, RWO 07/06/86 525
Redhead drake, hollow, old pnt, in-use wear, age split in neck, RB 2/01/85 250
Salmons, Bradford; att (Mayetta, NJ)
Canada Goose, swimming, hollow, old rpt, average flaking/wear, several age splits in neck/bill chip, RB 3/11/88, 60% 600
Salmons, Joel
Redbreasted Merganser drake, hollow, old pnt, average wear, structurally sound, RB 3/11/88 500
Salter, Elmer; att
Bufflehead drake, fine old pnt, appears to be orig w/heavy flaking/wear, RB 7/09/85 100
Salvatore, Dominick (Paulsboro, NJ)
Black Duck, hollow, fine orig flocked pnt, stamped weight, age split at neck, 20/50, RB 12/06/85, 50% 750
Mallard hen, preening, hollow, fine orig flock pnt, minor wear, well preserved, ca 1920, rare, 20/50, RB 12/06/85 1500
Samindi, David (Caro, MI)
Mallard drake, swimming, incised wing cvg, orig pnt, minor wear, minor age line in 1 side, J/G 4/23/87 225
Sammis, Andrew (Babylon, LI, NY)
Bluebill hen, orig pnt, average wear, structurally EX, RWO 7/05/85 500
Sammis, Capt. (Bellport, NY)
Bluebill drake, swimming, G old pnt, rough area on 1 side, J/G 4/24/86 275

Sanborn, Herb
Eider, hollow, EX pnt, copy of Eider by EW Lyford, 39, RB 7/08/86 200
Sanpier, Budgeon; att
Bluebill, hollow, old pnt, average wear, ls, RB 2/01/85 275
Sapone, Nick (North Carolina)
Swan, canvas-covered, EX orig pnt, RB 8/21/86 175

Sattler, Carl (Burlington, IA)
Mallard hen, low-head style, orig pnt, average wear, structurally
sound, ca 1940, 53, RWO 2/13/87, 70%, $1,050.00.

Savoie, Amateur (Neguac, N.B.)
Black Duck, NM orig pnt, feather-stamped surface, hairlines/sm chip in bill, J/G 9/19/87 205
Black Duck, sleeping, artist signed/dated, M condition, ca 1960's, RWO 2/12/88 375
Black Duck, sleeping, narrow check running length of the bottom, otherwise M condition, RWO 2/12/88 375
Sawler, Stan (Western Shore, NS)
Eider drake, orig pnt, minor wear, several sm tight checks in bodyblock, oversize, J/G 9/20/86 300
Merganser drake, orig pnt, old working rpt on white areas, minor wear, prof rstr to part of bill, J/G 4/23/87 500
Merganser hen, orig pnt, minor wear, prof bill rstr, 53, J/G 9/20/86 400
Schifferl, Lou (Green Bay, WI)
Barn Owl, signed, EX condition, RB 2/01/85 900
Dove pr, M condition, RWO 7/02/88 45
Goldeneye drake, EX pnt, minor wear, signed on bottom, RB 7/09/85 275
Merganser drake, American; EX orig pnt, artist brand, chip at end of tail has been reglued, otherwise sound, RB 3/06/87 350
Pintail drake, EX pnt, artist signed, RB 7/09/85 150
Sea Gull, cvd wing tips, orig pnt w/nice scratch pnt, structurally EX, RWO 7/04/87 230
Schmidt, Ben (Detroit, MI)
Black Duck, feather cvg, fine orig pnt, average wear, ms, RB 7/09/85 250
Black Duck, fine orig pnt, average wear, sm chip on underside of bill, ls, oversize, RB 7/07/87 275
Black Duck, orig pnt, average wear, sm tight check along 1 side, otherwise sound, RWO 7/06/86 350
Black Duck, orig pnt, minor wear, minor hairline crack in bill, J/G 4/23/87 450
Black Duck, raised extended wing tips/feather-cvd throughout, hollowed out from bottom, EX orig pnt, chips, J/G 9/19/87 575
Black Duck, worn orig pnt, hairline crack in bill/tail, otherwise structurally sound, RWO 7/02/88 250
Bluebill drake, content, hollow, EX orig pnt w/minor specks of white pnt on bk, branded GEB, RB 8/27/87 150
Bluebill drake, hollow, fine orig pnt, minor wear, minor age splits in back, RB 8/25/88 370
Bluebill drake, NM orig pnt, hairline crack part way through bill, J/G 4/24/86 385
Bluebill hen, slightly turned head, highly detailed feather/wing cvg, NM orig pnt w/touchup on bill/face, J/G 9/20/86 350
Canada Goose, EX feather cvg on body, fine orig pnt, average flaking/wear, well preserved, RB 7/07/87 650
Canvasback drake, early, G orig pnt, average wear, thin hairline crack in neck, otherwise EX, RWO 7/02/88 275
Canvasback drake, EX orig pnt, minor flaking/wear, RB 7/07/87 500
Canvasback drake, G orig pnt, average wear, sm chip under bill, otherwise structurally EX, RWO 7/02/88 300
Canvasback drake, hollow, EX orig pnt, structurally EX, RWO 7/06/86 350
Canvasback drake, old pnt, average wear, structurally sound, RB 7/07/87 150
Canvasback drake, old pnt, heavy wear, several age splits in body, RB 12/06/85 75
Canvasback drake, orig pnt, heavy flaking/wear, age splits in body, 6, RB 6/28/88 210
Canvasback drake, orig pnt, minor wear, structurally EX, RWO 11/06/85 220
Canvasback drake, outstanding orig pnt w/nice patina, structurally M, RWO 7/02/88 500
Canvasback drake, rpt w/average wear, old bill repair, RB 7/09/85 175
Canvasback hen, orig pnt, average wear, signed, structurally EX, RWO 7/06/86 350
Canvasback hen, orig pnt, minor wear, repair to 1 edge of tail, rare, J/G 4/23/87 525
Canvasback hen, rpt by Len Carneaghi, age split in neck, RB 2/01/85 160
Canvasback pr, EX orig condition, RWO 7/05/85 725
Canvasback pr, fine orig pnt, minor wear, RB 7/09/85 650
Canvasback pr, slightly turned heads, both bear Nicholson's JRN stamp on bottom, unused, M condition, RB 8/25/88 1050

Mallard drake, EX orig pnt, minor wear, structurally EX, RWO 7/04/87 .... **600**
Mallard drake, fine orig pnt, average wear, well preserved, RB 7/09/85 .... **450**
Mallard drake, NM orig pnt, sm dent in side of bill, J/G 4/23/87 .... **300**
Mallard drake, slightly turned head, hollow, EX orig pnt, minor wear, no structural flaws, J/G 4/23/87 .... **525**
Mallard hen, allover feather cvg, EX orig pnt, sm chip at end of tail, RB 7/08/86 .... **600**
Mallard hen, NM orig pnt, sm chip missing from 1 side of bill, rare, J/G 4/23/87 .... **500**
Pintail drake, old working rpt, several tight checks in bodyblock, J/G 4/23/87 .... **300**
Pintail hen, orig pnt, minor wear, 2 tight checks/3 sm holes in body, rare, J/G 4/23/87 .... **500**
Redhead drake, EX orig pnt, minor wear, minor age split in bill, 189, RB 6/28/88, 78% **275**
Redhead drake, hollowed out from underside, NM orig pnt, no structural flaws, J/G 4/23/87 .... **325**
Redhead drake, rpt taken down to orig w/heavy wear, RB 2/01/85 .... **275**
Redhead hen, orig pnt w/working touchup to bill, structurally EX, RWO 11/11/87 .... **300**
Redhead pr, EX orig condition, RWO 7/05/85 .... **400**
Redhead pr, orig pnt, minor wear, hairline crack in tails/part way down bk of drake, J/G 4/23/87 .... **550**
Widgeon drake, orig pnt, heavy in-use wear, ls, rare, RB 7/09/85 .... **450**
Widgeon hen, hollow, bill has been broken off & reglued, otherwise M, very rare, J/G 4/24/86 .... **550**

Schmidt, Ben
Wood Duck pr, detailed feather cvg/raised wing tips, NM orig pnt, hen has chip on top of tail, rare, RB 2/01/85, $1,800.00.

Schmidt, Ben; att (Detroit, MI)
Canvasback drake, balsa body, rpt w/average wear, RB 7/09/85 .... **50**
Widgeon drake, G orig pnt, average wear, ls, RB 7/08/86 .... **200**
Schmidt, Frank (Detroit, MI)
Black Duck, fine feather cvg, NM pnt, age split in neck, RB 2/01/85 .... **125**
Bluebill pr, fine orig pnt, average wear, structurally sound, RB 7/07/87 .... **200**
Canada Goose, feather cvg, G orig pnt, average wear, several age splits to body/neck, otherwise sound, RB 12/06/85 .... **250**
Canvasback drake, old working rpt, average wear, structurally sound, RWO 7/04/87 .... **90**
Canvasback pr, EX orig pnt, drake has thin check on bk, otherwise structurally sound, RWO 11/11/87 .... **450**
Canvasback pr, G orig pnt, drake has hairline check on 1 side, RWO 7/04/87 .... **200**
Canvasback pr, pnt worn to bare wood on bk of hen, otherwise EX orig condition, ca 1954, RWO 7/04/87 .... **275**
Mallard drake, G orig pnt, average wear, well preserved, 39, RB 7/08/86 .... **200**
Ringbill pr, cvd primaries/secondaries, M pnt, J/G 4/23/87 .... **750**
Schmidt, Frank; att (Detroit, MI)
Canvasback hen, orig pnt, average wear, structurally sound, RWO 7/04/87 .... **70**
Schmiedlin, Jim (Bradford Woods, PA)
Whitewinged Scoter, hollow w/bill cvg, raised shoulder cvg, EX orig pnt, artist brand, structurally sound, RWO 7/06/86 .... **400**
Schoenheider, Charles (Peoria, IL)
Bluebill drake, early, G old working rpt, sm chip under bill, J/G 4/23/87 .... **275**
Bluewinged Teal drake, old rpt, minor wear, ls, ca 1900, rare, J/G 4/23/87 .... **400**
Bluewinged Teal hen, hollow, precise bill cvg, EX feather pnt, orig weight, hairline in head, ls, rare, J/G 9/19/87, 75% **3000**
Canada Goose, standing, hollow, EX orig pnt, minor flaking on head, thin neck crack, otherwise EX, 193, RWO 7/02/88 ...... **60000**
Goldeneye drake, orig pnt, in-use wear w/some flaking to bare wood, EX condition, ca 1900, rare, 193, RWO 7/02/88, 17% **500**
Mallard drake, hollow, G orig pnt, average flaking/wear, chip at right underside of bill, RB 7/09/85 .... **250**
Mallard hen, early, hollow, old working rpt, in-use wear, structurally sound, RWO 2/13/87 .... **220**
Mallard pr, M condition, magnum, J/G 4/23/87 .... **450**
Pintail hen ice duck, 3-pc laminated body, early rpt flaking to orig, neck crack, otherwise sound, 193, RWO 7/02/88, 69% **3500**
Ringbill drake, rpt w/minor wear, 21, RB 2/01/85 .... **275**
Ringneck drake, early, hollow, EX orig pnt, minor wear, structurally EX, rare, 193, RWO 7/02/88, 57% **2000**
Schoenheider, Charles; att (Peoria, IL)
Mallard drake, hollow, old working rpt, average wear, thin crack in neck is the only structural flaw, RWO 2/12/88 .... **110**
Merganser pr, American; hollow, stripped & rpt by Lou Schifferl, in the manner of Schoenheider, EX, RWO 7/02/88 ...... **250**
Pintail drake, hollow, orig pnt, minor chips to end of bill, otherwise structurally EX, rare, RWO 11/06/85 .... **1650**

Ringbill hen, hollow, EX & orig condition, RB 7/09/85, 50% **400**

Schramm, Butch (Burlington, IA)
Bluebill hen, G orig pnt, average wear, chip out of bill, otherwise sound, RWO 11/06/85 .... **30**
Bluebill pr, drake is hollow, orig pnt, average wear, artist brand, structurally sound, RWO 11/06/85 .... **80**
Bluebill pr, orig pnt, artist brand, structurally sound, RWO 11/06/85 .... **90**
Mallard drake, early, hollow, tack eyes, old working rpt, no structural flaws, J/G 4/24/86 .... **110**
Redhead drake, G orig pnt, average wear, structurally sound, RWO 11/06/85 .... **25**

Schroeder, Tom (Detroit, MI)
Canvasback drake, low-head style, cork body, EX pnt, signed on bottom/dated 1960, RB 7/09/85 .... **400**
Canvasback hen, sleeping, cork body, EX pnt, artist brand/dated 1960, rare, RB 7/09/85 .... **190**
Coot, fine old orig pnt, average wear, branded Hy Dahlka, RB 7/07/87 .... **400**
Redhead pr, body is composition, mounted on wooden bottom board, G orig pnt, minor wear, artist brand, RWO 7/02/88 .... **1100**

Schroeder, Tom; att (Detroit, MI)
Canvasback drake, bob-tail style, old pnt, average wear, RB 8/25/88 .... **40**

Schultz, William (Milwaukee, WI)
Bufflehead drake, NM orig pnt, signed, EX condition, 1st place winner in 1968 Midwest Decoy Contest, J/G 4/23/87, 218% **1300**
Mallard drake, G pnt w/flaking to varnished finish, 22, RB 5/02/86 .... **450**
Pintail pr, hollow w/highly detailed bill/wing cvg, cvd eye lids, orig pnt, minor wear, keels missing, J/G 9/20/86, 32% **800**
Widgeon drake, slightly turned head, detailed raised extended wing tips, cvd for Rex Roupe/1966, M, J/G 9/19/87 .... **1000**

Schurada, Mike
Mallard hen, thin-shelled, EX orig pnt, structurally EX, RWO 7/06/86 .... **350**

Schuyler, Mallon; att (Bordentown, NJ)
Mallard drake, raised cvd primaries/secondaries, NM orig pnt, no structural flaws, J/G 9/20/86 .... **125**

Schwartz, Jack (Lacon, IL)
Bluebill drake, early, hollow, orig pnt by Edna Perdew, minor nicks/dings, otherwise EX, ca 1920's, 193, RWO 7/02/88 .... **1200**
Mallard drake, old rpt, average wear, well preserved, 39, RB 7/08/86 .... **200**
Mallard pr, hollow, rpt w/average wear, both have old neck repairs, 39, RB 7/08/86 .... **425**

Schwartz, Jack
Wood Duck pr, early, hollow 2-pc body, pnt by Charles Perdew, neck cracks, ca 1920's, rare, 193, RWO 7/02/88, 145%, $14,500.00.

Schweikart, John (Detroit, MI)
Bluebill hen, hollow, EX old working rpt, no structural flaws, very rare, 43, J/G 4/23/87 .... **650**
Bluebill hen, old working rpt, minor wear, ls, J/G 9/19/87 .... **550**
Bluebill hen, pnt prof taken down to orig w/minor wear, ls, rare, J/G 9/20/86 .... **250**
Canvasback drake, early, bull-neck/turned-down fan tail/cvd eyes, orig pnt, hairline down bk, ca 1900, rare, J/G 9/19/87 .... **850**
Canvasback drake, low-head, hollow w/bottom board, metal wings/wing tips, orig pnt, minor wear, NM, 113/146, RWO 7/02/88 .... **8500**
Canvasback hen, EX orig pnt, minor wear, brass keel arrangement on bottom, exceptional, rare, RB 7/09/85 .... **4100**
Canvasback hen, EX orig pnt, minor wear, minor flaw at end of bill, structurally sound, ca 1910, 68, RWO 7/05/85 .... **5000**
Canvasback hen, hollow, raised tin wing tips, orig pnt, prof touchup, orig folding copper keel, very rare, J/G 9/20/86 .... **3100**

Canvasback hen, low-head style, EX orig pnt, minor in-use wear, structurally EX, rare, exceptional, RWO 7/05/85, 66% **4000**
Coot, swimming, hollow, EX old pnt, slight wear, tight crack in bill, J/G 9/20/86 .... **350**
Goldeneye hen, old working overpnt, average wear, structurally EX, rare, ca 1900, RWO 7/06/86, 75% **2250**
Redhead hen, hollow, old pnt, average wear w/minor flaking, structurally sound, RB 7/07/87 .... **550**
Redhead hen, old working rpt w/some orig, no structural flaws, very rare, J/G 9/20/86 .... **700**
Redhead hen, orig pnt w/in-use touchup, structurally sound, rare, RWO 7/06/86 .... **2700**

Scriven, Dannie (Detroit, MI)
Canvasback drake, bob-tail style, old rpt, average flaking/wear, age split at neck, well preserved, RB 12/06/85 .... **50**

Sedlo, Otto
Redbreasted Merganser hen, hollow, EX orig pnt, minor wear, well preserved, RB 7/07/87 .... **100**

Seebt, Warren (New Orleans, LA)
Greenwinged Teal drake, cvd primaries, EX old pnt, no structural flaws, dated 1950, J/G 4/24/86 .... **110**
Pintail drake, cvd wings, EX & orig, RB 7/09/85 .... **150**

Selig, Frank (Voglers Cove, NS)
Black Duck, EX orig pnt, average wear, break in neck has been rpt, sm chip in tail is repaired, RB 8/21/86, $275.00.

Sellers, Robert (Silver Springs, PA)
Canvasback, old working rpt, minor wear, hairline cracks in body, ls, 33, J/G 9/19/87 .... **200**
Canvasback pr, high quality working rpts, no structural flaws, 33, J/G 9/19/87 .... **350**
Redhead pr, cvd 'X' in tail, fine orig pnt, in-use wear, well preserved, 69, RB 7/09/85, 75% **900**

Sellers, Walter (Pennsylvania)
Bluebill pr, old working rpt, minor wear, hen has several hairline cracks, ls, 33, J/G 9/19/87 .... **300**
Canvasback drake, working rpt, average wear, structurally sound, RWO 11/11/87 .... **175**

Senecal, Tony (Alexandria Bay, NY)
Redhead drake, early hump-back style, orig pnt, minor wear, old working touchup on black areas, 33, J/G 9/19/87 .... **115**

Seneno, Bill
Yellowlegs, 2-pc body construction, fine orig pnt, minor wear, sm end-of-tail chip, otherwise sound, 189, RB 6/28/88 .... **250**

Senick, Frank
Greenwinged Teal, fine old pnt, average flaking/wear, slight age split at neck, 22, RB 5/02/86 .... **60**

Serigny, Joseph (Golden Meadow, LA)
Bluewinged Teal drake, cypress root, raised cvd wing tips/tail feathers, orig pnt, no structural flaws, J/G 9/20/86 .... **130**
Mallard drake, fine orig pnt, average wear, age split in bk, RB 6/28/88 .... **125**
Pintail drake, orig pnt, average wear, minor repair to 1 wing tip, otherwise structurally EX, RWO 11/11/87 .... **160**

Sexton, W.
Bluebill drake, early, old working rpt, bears Mackey stamp, crack in neck/part way through head, J/G 9/20/86 .... **100**

Shaddack, Wayne (Trenton, Ont)
Mallard drake, detailed wing cvg, NM orig comb pnt, hairline at base of neck, from Shaddack hunting rig, J/G 9/19/87 .... **550**

Sharon, John (Toledo, OH)
Black Duck, cork body, stenciled w/his name & address on keel, NM condition, 189, RB 6/28/88 .... **50**
Mallard pr, cork body, stenciled signature, minor flaked areas on bodies, otherwise NM condition, RB 8/25/88 .... **80**

Shaw, William (Lacon, IL)
Mallard hen, orig pnt, minor shrinkage/wear, tight check in neck has been repaired, rare, J/G 9/19/87 .... **800**
Mallard pr, old working rpt, hen has sm tail chip, rare, 7, J/G 4/24/86 .... **550**

Shaw, William; att (Lacon, IL)
Pintail drake, hollow, old working rpt flaking to reveal orig, crack running through neck, RWO 11/11/87 .... **80**

Sheerman, Wendell
Wood Duck, hollow, EX pnt, signed on bottom, RB 7/08/86 .... **50**

Sheldon, Charles (Tiskilwa, IL)
Mallard drake, hollow, orig pnt, keel weight, ca 1930's, RWO 11/06/85 .... **800**

Sherman, Sandy (Marshfield, MA)
Black Duck, G orig pnt, average wear, artist brand, well preserved, 22, RB 5/02/86 225
Shipman, Harold; att
Merganser drake, old orig pnt, average flaking/wear, slight age split in neck, RB 3/06/87 500
Shourds, Alvin M.
Redbreasted Merganser drake, orig pnt, minor wear, some surface staining, RB 7/07/87 100
Redbreasted Merganser drake, orig pnt, minor wear, structurally EX, RB 7/07/87 210
Shourds, Harry M. (Parkertown, NJ)
Black Duck, hollow, old rpt, average flaking/wear, age split in neck, RB 3/11/88 275
Black Duck, hollow, old rpt, average wear, age split in neck, 189, RB 6/28/88 240
Black Duck, hollow, old rpt, average wear, age split in neck, bill has been rstr, RB 3/06/87 325
Black Duck, hollow, old rpt, average wear, chip on right underside of bill, RB 6/28/88 90
Black Duck, hollow, old rpt, average wear, RB 3/11/88 300
Black Duck, hollow, old rpt w/flaking/wear, otherwise well preserved, RB 3/06/87 200
Black Duck, hollow, orig pnt worn to natural wood in several areas, age split in neck, bill is a replacement, RB 3/11/88 200
Black Duck, hollow, rpt worn to reveal some orig, branded FW Cassedy, age split in neck, RB 3/11/88 225
Black Duck, hollow, slightly extended neck, G orig pnt, moderate in-use wear, minor age split in tail/neck, RB 3/11/88 1150
Bluebill drake, hollow, old pnt, average wear, age split in neck, 20, RB 12/06/85 225
Bluebill drake, hollow, old working rpt, crack in neck, inset rectangular weight, J/G 9/20/86 175
Pintail drake, hollow, rpt, average wear, rare, RB 3/11/88 1000
Pintail drake, hollow, rpt partially taken down to orig, heavy in-use wear, age split in neck, RB 3/11/88 600
Redbreasted Merganser drake, hollow, antiqued washed pnt, minor wear, RB 3/11/88 450
Redhead drake, hollow, rpt, average wear, RB 3/11/88 250
Shourds, Harry V. (Tuckerton, NJ)
Black Duck, early, hollow, artist signed, EX & orig condition, RB 3/11/88 175
Black Duck, hollow, EX condition, RB 7/07/87 210
Black Duck, hollow, fine old pnt, moderate wear, age split in neck, RB 3/11/88 450
Black Duck, hollow, fine old pnt, some of which is orig, moderate flaking/wear, bill chip/age split in neck, RB 6/28/88 300
Black Duck, hollow, old flocked pnt, minor wear, structurally sound, RB 3/11/88 350
Black Duck, hollow, old pnt, moderate flaking/wear, age split in head/sm chip at top of head, ls, RB 3/11/88 250
Black Duck, hollow, old rpt, average flaking/wear, chip on underside of bill, 20, RB 12/06/85 125
Black Duck, hollow, old rpt, average flaking/wear, old repair to right side of neck, RB 7/07/87 100
Black Duck, hollow, old rpt, average wear, chip on underside of bill has been rstr, RB 3/11/88 300
Black Duck, hollow, old rpt, average wear, RB 6/28/88 200
Black Duck, hollow, old rpt, minor wear, age split in neck, otherwise structurally sound, RB 8/21/86 375
Black Duck, hollow, old working rpt, average wear, age split in bk of body/neck, RB 3/11/88 300
Black Duck, hollow, pnt stripped to mostly natural wood, age split in neck, RB 6/28/88 150
Black Duck, hollow, rpt by David Rhodes, tail chip/neck crack, otherwise VG, ca 1900, RWO 7/06/86, 80% 140
Black Duck, orig pnt, touchups, minor wear, tight age split, several sm holes in underside, J/G 4/23/87 450
Black Duck, preening, hollow, body has fine orig pnt, average wear, RB 6/28/88 275
Black Duck, rpt, heavy flaking/wear, minor age splitting, 189, RB 6/28/88 175
Black Duck, worn orig pnt w/some old rpt, Starr collection stamp on underside, crack in tail, J/G 4/24/86 412
Blackbellied Plover, early, orig pnt, Fall plumage, average wear, bill has been put in upside down, RWO 7/02/88, 70% 1250
Blackbellied Plover, EX orig pnt, average wear, ls, rare, RB 7/09/85 2000
Blackbellied Plover, full body, fine orig pnt, rare emerging plumage, average wear, ms, 77/9, RB 12/06/85 2000
Blackbellied Plover, full body, G orig pnt, average wear, ls, RB 12/06/85 1700
Bluebill, hollow, pnt stripped to natural wood, structurally sound, RB 6/28/88 140
Bluebill drake, early, hollow, old working rpt, average flaking/wear, RB 7/09/85 400
Bluebill drake, fine orig pnt, average flaking/wear, branded, old break in neck has been reglued, RB 3/06/87 800
Bluebill drake, hollow, old rpt, average flaking/wear, underside of bill has been replaced, RB 12/06/85 200
Bluebill drake, hollow, some old working rpt taken off to reveal orig, minor tail damage/crack in neck, RWO 2/12/88 260
Bluebill drake, old working rpt, average wear, structurally sound, RWO 7/05/85 280
Bluebill drake, old working rpt, thin crack in neck, sm chip in tail, repair to bill, ca 1910, RWO 7/06/86 90
Bluebill hen, hollow, EX rpt in Shourds' style, structurally sound, RWO 11/11/87 220
Bluebill hen, hollow, old pnt appears to be orig, average wear, several sm tail chips, rstr bill, RB 3/11/88, 70% 350
Bluebill hen, hollow, rpt, minor wear, age split in neck/old break in bill has been reglued, RB 3/06/87 175
Bluebill hen, hollow, rpt taken down to orig, average wear, age split in neck, 21, RB 2/01/85 500
Bluebill hen, working rpt on body has been stripped to reveal traces of orig, structurally sound, RWO 11/11/87 225
Bluebill pr, hollow, old pnt, average flaking/wear, drake has sm age split in neck, RB 7/07/87 850
Bluebill pr, hollow, old pnt w/areas of orig, average wear, age split in neck of drake, RB 12/06/85 1100
Bluebill pr, NM rpt, structurally EX, J/G 9/19/87 450

Bluebill pr, rpt, heavy flaking/wear, 21, RB 2/01/85 325
Brant, flying, canvas wings, working rpt, flaking/wear, chip on underside of bill/end of tail, rare, 21, RB 2/01/85 1100
Brant, flying, canvas wings are torn, old pnt, average flaking/wear, rare, 22/44, RB 5/02/86 1400
Brant, flying, orig pnt w/extensive rstr, prof rstr to split on bk, wing tip missing, rare, J/G 9/19/87 1000
Brant, head slightly turned to the right, branded HVS, EX condition, RB 3/11/88 175
Brant, hollow, EX pnt, minor flaking, artist brand, RB 3/11/88 100
Brant, hollow, old rpt, heavy flaking/wear, head needs to be reattached to body, 21, RB 2/01/85 300
Brant, hollow, old working rpt, average flaking/wear, age split in neck, RB 7/07/87 400
Brant, hollow, orig pnt, minor wear, structurally EX, inset rectangular weight, J/G 4/24/86 1375
Brant, hollow, pnt stripped to natural wood, minor age splitting, otherwise structurally EX, 189, RB 6/28/88 350
Brant, hollow, rpt, average flaking/wear, several age splits in neck, RB 3/11/88, 120% 600
Brant, hollow, rpt, average wear, age split in neck, shallow chip on underside of bill, RB 3/11/88 400
Brant, hollow, rpt, average wear, chip on underside of bill, age split in neck, ls, 189, RB 6/28/88 425
Brant, hollow, rpt, average wear, structurally sound, RB 3/11/88 550
Brant, hollow, rpt by Chris Sprague, average wear, well preserved, 20, RB 12/06/85 700
Brant, preening, hollow, NM pnt, minor flaking to bk of neck, branded HVS, RB 3/11/88 85
Brant, rpt, minor wear, rstr crack in neck, J/G 9/19/87 450
Brant, rpt in style of Shourds, branded F Vandergrift, hairline in bk/underside, J/G 9/19/87 575
Bufflehead hen, hollow, orig pnt worn to bare wood on much of body, sm tail chips/neck crack, rare, RWO 7/02/88, 70% 550
Canada Goose, hollow, fine orig pnt, average wear, age splits in neck, rare, RB 7/07/87 1700
Canada Goose, hollow, old rpt, average wear, age split in neck/bill, ms, RB 3/06/87 650
Canada Goose, hollow, old rpt, average wear, slight age splitting, old repair to end of bill, RB 6/28/88 250
Canada Goose, hollow, old working rpt, average flaking/wear, RB 2/01/85 800
Canada Goose, hollow, rpt, minor wear, bill is an old replacement, left eye missing, 6, RB 7/07/87 500
Canada Goose, mahogany, hollow, body pnt orig w/strengthening to white areas, rstr to bill, rare, 20, RB 12/06/85 2200
Canada Goose, mahogany, hollow, EX orig pnt/touchup, 2 minor cracks, ca 1910, 1 of 3 existent, 53/54/55/56, J/G 9/20/86 4500
Canada Goose, old pnt, some wear, branded John Furlow, prof bill rstr, reglued crack in bill, J/G 9/19/87 950
Canada Goose, swimming, hollow, old working rpt, average wear, structurally EX, 193, RWO 7/02/88 2500
Canada Goose, swimming, rpt by artist, some shrinkage/wear, prof rstr to base of neck, rare, J/G 9/19/87 700
Canada Goose, swimming, shoe-button eyes, worn to natural wood w/some overpnt, splits/bill chip, RB 3/11/88, 52% 1050

Shourds, Harry V.
Curlew, EX orig pnt, structurally outstanding, RWO 7/02/88, $6,000.00.

Curlew, fine orig pnt, average wear, head has an old repair, rare, 10, RB 12/06/85 2200
Curlew, fine orig pnt, slight wear, bill is a prof replacement, J/G 4/24/86, 55% 1155
Curlew, G orig pnt, average wear, bill is a prof replacement by Kenneth DeLong, rare, RB 12/06/85, 65% 1000
Goldeneye, hollow, signed/dated, EX condition, RB 6/28/88 100
Goldeneye drake, hollow, fine orig pnt, average wear, 1 side slightly skinned, RB 3/11/88 500
Goldeneye drake, hollow, old pnt, average wear, age split in neck, 3, RB 7/08/86 600
Goldeneye drake, hollow, old working rpt taken down to orig, thin crack through neck, otherwise EX, RWO 11/11/87, 70% 525
Goldeneye drake, hollow, outstanding orig pnt, average wear, thin crack on side of head, otherwise superb, RWO 7/05/85 3500
Goldeneye drake, taken down to mostly orig pnt, slight rough area on edge of bill, J/G 4/24/86 550
Goldeneye drake, working rpt, structurally sound, RWO 11/06/85 130
Goldeneye hen, hollow, G orig pnt, worn/bubbled, bill broken off & reglued/age split in neck, rare, RB 7/09/85 600
Goldeneye hen, hollow, outstanding orig pnt, average wear, structurally EX, RWO 7/05/85 3600
Goose, swimming, EX rpt, several age lines on underside, hairline crack in bk, minor roughness on tail, J/G 9/19/87 1500
Greenwinged Teal pr, signed/dated 1973, EX condition, RB 3/11/88 275
Hooded Merganser drake, hollow w/detailed feather cvg on bk, signed/dated 1973, EX condition, RB 3/11/88 175
Hudsonian Curlew, orig pnt, weathered/worn, age splits, bill is complete/orig, rare, RB 7/09/85 2000
Knot, EX orig pnt, minor wear, ls, rare, 10, RB 12/06/85, 70% 1100
Merganser drake, hollow, rpt in Shourds' style, thin crack in neck, otherwise sound, ca 1900, RWO 7/02/88 850

Merganser hen, working rpt, head is a replacement, neck has age split, 21, RB 2/01/85 200
Old Squaw pr, hollow, orig pnt, heavy wear, age split in neck of drake, 20/50/82, RB 12/06/85 9500
Pintail drake, hollow, rpt by Mark McNair, thin tight check in neck, otherwise structurally EX, rare, RWO 11/11/87, 65% 975
Pintail drake, signed/dated 1970, EX condition, half-size, RB 3/11/88 75
Redbreasted Merganser drake, hollow, EX orig pnt, average wear, minor age split in tail/bill is reglued, RB 3/11/88 2500
Redbreasted Merganser drake, hollow, orig pnt, in-use wear, minor flaking, structurally VG, RWO 7/05/85 3000
Redbreasted Merganser drake, orig pnt, minor wear, overpnt has been removed, no structural flaws, J/G 9/19/87 2925
Redbreasted Merganser pr, hollow, rpt, average wear, structurally sound, 6, RB 7/07/87 1900
Redbreasted Merganser pr, hollow, signed/dated 1979, EX condition, RB 3/11/88 275
Redbreasted Merganser pr, hollow, tack eyes, orig pnt, moderate wear, structurally EX, rare, 6, RB 7/07/87 4400
Redhead drake, EX orig pnt, average wear, several tail chips/thin crack down bk/chip at bill, exceptional, RWO 7/05/85 3000
Redhead drake, hollow, fine orig pnt, in-use wear, age split in neck, RB 2/01/85 1000
Redhead drake, hollow, NM orig pnt on bk/sides, minor wear, inset rectangular weight, rare, J/G 4/24/86 1485
Redhead drake, hollow, pnt taken down to mostly natural wood, age split in neck, RB 8/25/88 225
Redhead drake, hollow, rpt, average wear, branded JAH & JWA on bottom, age split in neck, RB 6/28/88 175
Redhead drake, pnt worn to mostly natural wood, slight age split in neck, 6, RB 7/07/87 200
Redhead drake, prof pnt rstr, sm chip on side of tail, J/G 9/19/87 450

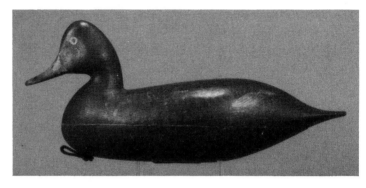

Shourds, Harry V.
Redhead hen, slight separation where body halves join, otherwise outstanding orig condition, extremely rare, RWO 7/05/85, $4,000.00.

Robin Snipe, cvd in style of HV Shourds Sr, orig condition, RWO 7/02/88 100
Robin Snipe, early, orig pnt, heavy wear, worn to bare wood on bk, thin neck crack, otherwise sound, RWO 7/02/88 700
Robin Snipe, orig pnt, minor wear, sm chip under tail, bill may be an old replacement, J/G 4/23/87 950
Swan, hollow, signed/dated 1983, M condition, RWO 11/11/87 325
Widgeon drake, EX condition, artist brand, RB 7/07/87 130
Wood Duck hen, slightly turned head, hollow, EX orig pnt, slight age splitting in neck, RB 8/27/87 110
Wood Duck pr, hollow, cvd raised wing tips, drake signed/dated 1973, hen is artist branded, RB 3/11/88 150
Yellowlegs, early, flat-sided, G orig pnt, average wear, RB 7/08/86 750
Yellowlegs, early, G orig pnt, average wear, bill has been chewed, ms, RB 7/08/86 450
Yellowlegs, early, G orig pnt, average wear, ls on breast/bill, otherwise EX, 193, RWO 7/02/88, 55% 650
Yellowlegs, early, some old working rpt w/much orig showing, bill may be a replacement, RWO 7/02/88 400
Yellowlegs, EX pnt w/fine patina, bill is a fine replacement, 3, RB 3/06/87 1400
Yellowlegs, fine orig pnt, average wear, ls, bill is a replacement, RB 7/09/85 1700
Yellowlegs, G orig pnt, average wear, ms, 9, RB 12/06/85 1000
Yellowlegs, G orig pnt, average wear w/some crazing to bk, 10, RB 12/06/85 1100
Yellowlegs, superb orig pnt, minimal wear, well preserved, RB 12/06/85, 125% 1900
Shourds, Harry V.; att (Tuckerton, NJ)
Ruddy Turnstone, fine orig pnt, average wear, ls, rare, RB 2/01/85 1900
Shourds, Ross
Canada Goose, hollow, EX orig pnt, artist brand, RB 7/09/85 300
Showell, Dan (New Jersey)
Black Duck, hollow, cvd eyes, old rpt, moderate flaking/wear, age split in neck, RB 6/28/88 130
Black Duck, hollow, old rpt, heavy in-use wear, minor age split to body, RB 6/28/88 200
Blackbellied Plover, old pnt, average wear, head chip has been reglued, bill is a replacement, RB 3/11/88, 150% 450
Showell, Dan; att (New Jersey)
Black Duck, hollow, cvd eyes, rpt, average wear, chip on underside of bill, RB 3/11/88 200
Blackbellied Plover, old rpt, average wear, bill is a replacement, RB 3/11/88 225
Blackbellied Plover, running, cvd eyes, orig pnt, heavy wear, bill is a replacement, RB 3/11/88, 250% 375
Shuler, George
Wood Duck drake, fine orig pnt, minor flaking, signed on underside of wing, RB 7/07/87 125

Shurts, George H.
Pintail drake, hollow, EX orig pnt, average wear, bill is a prof replacement, age split in neck, 39, RB 7/08/86, $550.00.

Shurtz, Edward (Henry, IL)
Pintail drake, early, EX orig pnt, minor wear, no structural flaws, retains orig weight, J/G 4/24/86 935
Pintail drake, hollow, fine old pnt, heavy wear, structurally sound, RB 7/09/85 450
Pintail drake, hollow, orig pnt, heavy flaking/wear, age split in neck, sm chip at end of tail, RB 7/07/87 200

Shutte, George
Canvasback drake, fine orig pnt w/EX patina, shallow chip on underside of bill, ls, RB 8/25/88, 66% 200

Sichik, J. Jr. (New Jersey)
Pintail hen, wing/primary feather cvg, artist brand, EX & orig condition, RWO 2/12/88 105

Sidebotham, Frank (Andalusia, PA)
Black Duck, cork body, slight amount of cork missing from tail, RB 12/06/85 60
Canvasback drake, hollow, orig pnt, average wear, bill broken off & reglued, otherwise EX, ca 1930, RWO 11/11/87 450

Sieger, Henry (Bayshore, LI, NY)
Redbreasted Merganser drake, old pnt, average wear, artist brand, structurally sound, RWO 11/06/85 110

Siloski, Jerry
American Avocet, signed on bottom, M condition, RWO 2/12/88 70
Crow, orig pnt, artist brand, tip of bill broken off, otherwise structurally EX, RWO 7/06/86 90

Simmonds, Godfrey
Black Duck, cork body, head has orig pnt, average wear, sm chip at end of tail, 22, RB 5/02/86 250
Black Duck, sleeping, cork body, orig pnt on head, minor flakes, lg chip on breast/end of tail chewed, 22/44, RB 5/02/86 225

Simmons, Bill (Hamilton, Ont)
Canvasback drake, hollow, NM condition, RWO 11/11/87 50

Simpson, Wilbur (Moorehead City, NC)
Bluebill hen, orig pnt, minor wear, no structural flaws, 33, J/G 9/19/87 350

Sirois, Pillippe (Maine)
Mallard pr, flying, EX orig condition, RWO 7/05/85 675

Slack, Jim (Pekin, IL)
Bluebill pr, hen is sleeping, orig pnt, EX condition, RWO 11/06/85 130
Sea Gull, standing, cvd in style of Gus Wilson, M condition, J/G 9/20/86 70

Smith, Ben (Martha's Vineyard, MA)
Merganser drake, rpt, RB 7/09/85 300
Merganser hen, hollow, orig pnt, 2 tail chips, otherwise structurally sound, 48, RWO 7/06/86 3000
Redbreasted Merganser drake, orig pnt, heavy in-use wear, old repair to neck, rare, RB 7/09/85 1300

Smith, Capt. Gerald B.
Black Duck, hollow, EX orig pnt, artist brand, RB 12/06/85 50
Bufflehead drake, cvd w/open bill, fine orig pnt, minor wear, artist brand, RB 12/06/85 175
Eider drake, fine orig pnt, minor wear, slight chip on underside of bill, ls, RB 12/06/85 60
Goldeneye drake, fine orig pnt, minor wear, artist stamp, well preserved, RB 12/06/85 100
Surf Scoter pr, EX pnt, artist brand, copied from Fabin's Scoters, RB 12/06/85 425

Smith, Capt. John (Ocean City, MD)
Black Duck, preening, old working rpt, little wear, structurally VG, ca 1940, RWO 7/05/85 240
Brant, early, old root-head style, old pnt, average wear, several age splits/ls, ca 1920, RB 8/25/88 150
Canada Goose, natural flaw in wood on 1 side of body, otherwise unused condition, RWO 7/02/88 275
Canvasback, G orig pnt w/flaking around base of neck, RWO 11/11/87 75
Pintail drake, stylish form, EX orig pnt, ca 1920, RWO 7/05/85 350
Pintail hen, M orig pnt, minor in-use wear, 21, RB 2/01/85 600

Pintail pr, EX orig pnt, minor wear, hen has crack running through neck/check on bottom; drake is sound, RWO 11/11/87 250

Smith, Capt. John; att (Ocean City, MD)
Knot, fine orig pnt, average wear, ls, bill has been slightly shortened from wear, RB 8/21/86 60

Smith, Capt. Percy (South River, MD)
Bluebill drake, old working rpt, minor wear, hairline crack in breast, ca 1895, J/G 9/19/87 175

Smith, Cassius (Milford, CT)
Black Duck, hollow, EX orig pnt, average wear, structurally sound, RWO 7/04/87 1100
Bluebill drake, hollow, old rpt, average flaking/wear, age split in neck/bk of head, 1 eye missing, 22, RB 5/02/86 100
Bluebill drake, taken down to mixture of orig pnt/rpt, artist brand, rstr to tip of bill, J/G 9/19/87 375

Smith, Cassius
Gadwall hen, hollow, prof touchup has been added to orig pnt, branded, ca 1890, EX condition, RWO 7/06/86, 46%, $2,250.00.

Goldeneye drake, hollow, old working rpt, minor wear, artist brand, hairline crack in bill, J/G 9/20/86 300
Goldeneye hen, old working rpt, artist brand, old repair to crack in bill, J/G 9/19/87 225

Smith, Cassius; att (Milford, CT)
Black Duck, hollow, old pnt, in-use flaking/wear, structurally VG, 39, RB 7/08/86 900

Smith, Charles (Liverpool, IL)
Mallard drake, old working rpt, no structural flaws, 7, J/G 4/24/86 165
Pintail drake, hollow, old working rpt, no structural flaws, 7, J/G 4/24/86 99

Smith, Chris (Lake St. Clair, MI)
Bluebill drake, low-head style, old working rpt, minor wear, prof rstr to end of bill, J/G 9/20/86 250
Canvasback drake, folky, hollow, orig pnt, average wear, ls, otherwise sound, RWO 7/02/88 325
Redhead drake, hollow, old pnt, average wear, chip at end of tail, RB 2/01/85 200

Smith, Chris; att (Lake St. Clair, MI)
Canvasback drake, laminated balsa body, old pnt, average flaking/wear, oversize, RB 12/06/85 85

Smith, Del (Canby, OR)
Redbreasted Merganser drake, signed/dated on bottom, tiny nick on underside of bill, otherwise EX, 36, RB 2/01/85 175

Smith, Ernie; att
Brant, hollow, old working rpt, average wear, age splits in neck, RB 2/01/85 150

Smith, Forman
Canada Goose, feeding, laminated body construction, rpt w/minor wear, well preserved, 9, RB 12/06/85 700

Smith, George and Minor (Milford, CT)
Bluebill drake, early, EX old working rpt by Shang Wheeler, artist brand, several minor age lines, J/G 9/19/87 225
Old Squaw hen, hollow, old working rpt, average flaking/wear, old repair to bill, 21, RB 2/01/85 600

Smith, George and Minor; att (Milford, CT)
Broadbill, hollow, old working rpt, average flaking/wear, 21, RB 2/01/85 300

Smith, Gil (Patchogue, NY)
Brant, root-head, old working rpt, minor wear, 2 minor age lines in bk, J/G 9/19/87 200

Smith, Gilbert M.; att (Long Island)
Bluebill hen, cork body, orig pnt w/G patina, minor wear, structurally sound, RWO 7/02/88 65

Smith, Holger (Massachusetts)
Canada Goose, EX pnt, artist brand, signed/dated 1977 on bottom, RB 8/21/86 225

Smith, Lawrence
Bufflehead drake, slightly turned head, relief cvd wings, orig pnt, minor wear, no structural flaws, J/G 9/19/87 175

Smith, Lysander (Marshfield, MA)
Black Duck, swimming, fine orig scratch pnt w/minor wear, no structural flaws, J/G 9/19/87 125

Smith, Miles (Marine City, MI)
Redbreasted Merganser drake, G orig pnt, structurally sound, RWO 11/06/85 90

Smith, Neil
Bluebill hen, old pnt, minor wear, old repair to bill, RB 12/06/85 75

Smith, Sam (Amityville, NY)
Black Duck, rpt by George Coombs, minor wear, RB 7/09/85 90

Bluebill drake, EX old pnt, minimal wear, branded CGS, structurally EX, ca 1915, very rare, J/G 4/24/86 330
Canada Goose, early, hollow, early working rpt, in-use wear, sm chip on underside of bill, RWO 7/02/88 350

Smith, Samuel Ernest (Tuckerton, NJ)
Bluebill, hollow, old rpt, heavy flaking/wear, age split in head, RB 2/01/85 70

Smith, Seymour (Seneca Lake, NY)
Bluebill drake, orig pnt, minor wear, crack in lower breast/neck, J/G 4/23/87 240
Bluebill drake, orig pnt, minor wear, hairline crack in breast, J/G 9/20/86 225
Canvasback drake, head has been broken off & reglued, ca 1920, RWO 11/11/87 140
Redhead drake, orig pnt, slight wear, hairline crack part way up breast, J/G 9/20/86 225

Smith, Stanley
Goldeneye, cheeky head, hollow w/bottom board, VG orig pnt, artist initial, VG condition, ca 1910, RWO 7/04/87 950

Smith, Wendall (Chicago, IL)
Bluebill drake, hollow, EX orig pnt, average wear, NM condition, 193, RWO 7/02/88 375
Bluebill drake, hollow w/fine combing on bk/sides, pnt flecks around seam in bodyblock, otherwise EX, 7, J/G 4/24/86 330
Bluebill drake, orig pnt, comb pnt on bk/sides, touchup to white areas, magnum, J/G 4/23/87 250
Coot, hollow w/detailed combing, raised cvd wing tips, J/G 4/23/87 250
Coot, hollow w/raised primaries, flipped-up tail, orig pnt, minor wear, 2 sm dents in 1 side of breast, J/G 4/24/86 330
Coot, raised primaries, orig comb pnt, minor wear, bill has been slightly trimmed, J/G 9/20/86 175
Mallard pr, EX orig comb pnt, minor wear, no structural flaws, J/G 4/24/86 467
Mallard pr, orig pnt, minor wear, highly detailed combing on bk/sides, both varnished, no structural flaws, J/G 9/20/86 700
Wood Duck pr, hollow, appl crests, VG orig scratch feather pnt, EX condition, rare, 193, RWO 7/02/88, 75% 3000

Smith, Will; att (Stony Brook, LI, NY)
Goldeneye hen, fine old pnt, average flaking/wear, age split at bk of head/ls, RB 12/06/85 125

Smith Brothers
Bluebill drake, outstanding Shang Wheeler rpt, EX patina, artist brand, J/G 0/20/86 400

Snow, Dexter (Powell's Point, NC)
Bluebill drake, worn old working rpt w/some orig showing, tight crack in neck, rare, oversize, J/G 4/24/86 165
Swan, canvas over wire frame, old working rpt, no structural flaws, 33, J/G 9/19/87 300

Snyder, Ed
Pintail pr, sleeping, EX pnt, RB 8/21/86 600

Somme, Leon
Ringbill drake, old pnt, average wear, old break in neck has been reglued, RB 8/21/86 90

Sorby, Henley (Gores Landing, Ont)
Goldeneye hen pr, EX old orig dry pnt, M condition, ca 1930, RWO 7/06/86 500

Soule, George (Freeport, ME)
Black Duck, cork body, orig pnt shows flaking & wear, some separation to laminated tail, 22, RB 5/02/86 80
Eider drake, cork body, EX orig pnt, 22, RB 5/02/86 170
Redbreasted Merganser, half-bodied, EX condition, 22, RB 5/02/86 45

Soule, Guy (Duxbury, MA)
Black Duck, body is a wood block covered w/cloth, head is orig pnt w/average wear, age split at neck, 22, RB 5/02/86 60
Goldeneye pr, orig pnt, average flaking/wear, some age splitting, 22, RB 5/02/86 250

Southard, William (Long Island, NY)
Yellowlegs, cvd eyes/wings, fine old pnt shows average wear, ls, RB 3/11/88 450
Yellowlegs, cvd eyes/wings, old pnt appears to be orig, average wear, bill is a replacement, ls, RB 3/11/88 450
Yellowlegs, cvd wings/eyes, G orig pnt, average wear, rstr to part of tail, bill is a replacement, RB 12/06/85 700
Yellowlegs, fine cvd wings, orig pnt, average wear, old in-use repair to top of head, rare, RB 7/09/85 1100

Southard, William; att (Long Island, NY)
Blackbellied Plover, cvd wings, rpt, average wear, old repair to head, RB 7/08/86 100

Southard, William
Turnstone, orig pnt, average wear w/areas worn to bare wood, structurally EX, RWO 2/13/87, 160%, $4,000.00.

134

Spiller, John (Peoria, IL)
Canvasback drake, hollow, NM orig pnt, structurally EX, J/G 9/19/87 100
Spiron, Charles (Goldsboro, NC)
Black Duck, hissing, folky style, hollow, signed, EX pnt, RWO 7/06/86 80
Black Duck, hollow w/raised wing cvg, EX feather pnt, signed, EX condition, RWO 7/06/86 80
Black Duck, sleeping, artist brand, M condition, RWO 11/06/85 200
Greenwinged Teal pr, hen w/turned head & bill buried in feathers, hollow w/raised primaries, M condition, J/G 4/24/86 302
Mallard drake, head tucked down, hollow, EX condition, RB 7/09/85 175
Pintail drake, head tucked down, hollow, dovetailed separate pintail, EX & orig, RB 7/09/85 275
Wood Duck pr, slightly turned heads, raised cvd primaries, M condition, J/G 4/24/86 275
Spongia, Anthony
Redhead pr, slightly turned heads, cvd wing tips, EX pnt, signed on bottom, RB 8/21/86 200
Sprague, Chris (Beach Haven, NJ)
Black Duck, hollow, open bill, fine orig pnt, minor wear, 9, RB 12/06/85 800
Brant, hollow, old pnt, average wear, rare, 6, RB 7/07/87 375
Brant, hollow, old pnt, average wear, well preserved, RB 7/08/86 275
Brant, hollow, old rpt, average flaking/wear, RB 3/11/88 250
Brant, hollow, old working rpt, average flaking/wear, separation where body halves join/gouge out of bk, RWO 2/13/87 140
Canada Goose, hollow, fine orig pnt, minor wear, structurally sound, RB 6/28/88 325
Goldeneye hen, hollow, G orig pnt, minor wear, well preserved, RB 8/27/87 170

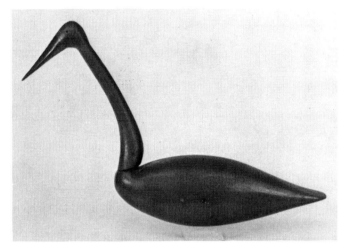

Sprague, Chris
Great Blue Heron, old pnt shows minor wear, 6, RB 7/07/87, $12,000.00.

Sanderling, flattie, orig pnt, minor wear, structurally sound, RWO 7/02/88 25
Yellowlegs, EX condition, 6, RB 7/07/87 175
Yellowlegs, EX orig pnt, signed/dated 1946 on underside of tail, RB 3/06/87 300
Sprague, Chris; att (Beach Haven, NJ)
Brant, orig pnt, minor wear/touchup, sm crack on lower breast/underside, J/G 9/19/87 350
Mallard drake, hollow, 3-pc body, old pnt, moderate flaking/wear, RB 3/11/88 110
Sprague, Jonas (Beach Haven, NJ)
Curlew, EX orig pnt, slight age split in bodyblock, rare, 20/50/83, RB 12/06/85 1600
Curlew, fine old pnt appears to be orig, bill is a replacement, age split in left side of body, RB 3/11/88 850
Curlew, fine orig pnt, average wear, bill is a replacement, well preserved, rare, 39, RB 7/08/86, 65% 650
Curlew, G old orig pnt, average wear, bill is a replacement, rare, 50, RB 12/06/85 1600
Yellowlegs, cvd eyes, old rpt, average wear, bill may be an old replacement, 189, RB 6/28/88 200
Sprague, Jonas; att (Beach Haven, NJ)
Blackbellied Plover, cvd eyes, old rpt, average wear, bill is a replacement, ls, RB 3/11/88 275
Squire (Long Island, NY)
Blackbellied Plover, running, cvd wings/wing tips, old pnt, much in-use wear, ms, ca 1880, RB 7/09/85 1200
Curlew, cvd wings/raised wing tips, orig pnt, average wear, bill replaced by DeLong, rare, RB 7/09/85 1400
Stachowiak, Ignatius (LaSalle, IL)
Black Duck, NM orig pnt, no structural flaws, rare, 7, J/G 4/24/86 605
Mallard drake, NM pnt (2 coats), hairline crack in neck, from his personal rig, J/G 4/24/86 550
Mallard hen, orig pnt, minor wear, sm pnt spill on neck/breast, reglued neck crack, from A Lenski rig, 1938, J/G 4/24/86 935

Mallard hen, 2 coats of pnt by Stachowiak, minor flaking, structurally EX, from his personal rig, J/G 4/24/86 440

Stanley, Capt. James (Cape Vincent, NY)

Goldeneye drake, orig pnt, minor wear, structurally EX, rare, 35/53, J/G 9/19/87 1225

Goldeneye hen, NM orig pnt on body, NM second coat of pnt on head, hairline crack down bk, rare, J/G 9/19/87 475

Greenwinged Teal drake, hollow, orig pnt, heavy wear w/some areas to bare wood, ca 1910, rare, RWO 7/02/88, 135% 800

Greenwinged Teal drake, old pnt, average wear, break in bill has been cleanly repaired, RB 3/11/88 300

Greenwinged Teal hen, EX orig pnt, minor wear, structurally sound, 189, RB 6/28/88, 145% 1450

Stanley, Joe

Bluebill drake, fine old pnt, possibly orig, average flaking/wear, ls, RB 7/08/86 70

Stannard, Bill (Branford, CT)

Bluebill drake, old pnt, heavy flaking/wear, ms, 2, RB 12/06/85 100

Bluebill hen, old pnt, heavy flaking/wear, repair to chip at end of tail/age split in neck, RB 12/06/85 170

Stannard, Bill; att (Branford, CT)

Bluebill drake, hollow, old rpt, heavy flaking/wear, age split in neck, RB 3/06/87 75

Redhead drake, hollow, old rpt, heavy flaking/wear, age split in neck, RB 3/06/87 200

Starr, George Ross (Duxbury, MA)

Black Duck, cork body, bill is chipped w/an in-use repair, otherwise structurally sound, 22, RB 5/02/86 100

Black Duck, cork body, EX condition, oversize, 22, RB 5/02/86 225

Black Duck, cork body, pnt shows average wear, both eyes missing, chip on left side of bill, 22, RB 5/02/86 450

Black Duck, hollow, finely cvd primaries/tail feathers, NM elaborate feather pnt, artist brand, 22, RB 5/02/86, 120% 2900

Black Duck, hollow, orig pnt, in-use wear, structurally sound, 22, RB 5/02/86 450

Starr, George Ross
Black Duck, preening, cvd wing tips/primaries, EX pnt, artist brand, minor nicks at end of tail, 22, RB 5/02/86, 210%, $4,200.00.

Black Duck, sleeping, cork body, artist brand, EX condition, 22, RB 5/02/86 250

Black Duck, slightly turned head, EX primary/tail cvg, EX orig pnt, artist brand, sm nick in tail, 22, RB 5/02/86, 150% 3000

Bluebill drake, hollow, cvd primary feathers, structurally EX, 22, RB 5/02/86 250

Bluebill drake, sleeping, hollow, EX condition, 22, RWO 5/02/86 500

Bluebill drake, slightly turned head, hollow, EX pnt, artist brand, 'Made w/Wheeler Pattern 1978,' 22, RWO 5/02/86 400

Canada Goose, preening, separate feather cvgs on wings, artist brand, 22/52, RB 5/02/86 1400

Canvasback drake, hollow, EX pnt, artist brand/dated 1971, 22, RB 5/02/86 500

Eider drake, cvd wings/primary feathers, orig pnt, heavy flaking, several age splits, 22, RB 5/02/86 650

Goldenyeye pr, orig pnt, minor flaking, artist brand/dated 1953, well preserved, RB 5/02/86 800

Mallard, sleeping, hollow, cvd wing/tail feathers, NM pnt, artist brand, 22, RB 5/02/86 1100

Mallard drake, hollow, cvd primary/tail feathers, orig pnt w/some flaking, signed/1961, end-of-tail chip, 22, RB 5/02/86 700

Steck, E.

Canada Goose, 6-pc body, old pnt, minor wear, body is varnished, RB 7/09/85 90

Sterling, Lloyd (Crisfield, MD)

Bluebill drake, orig pnt worn to mostly natural wood, some slight age splitting, RB 7/07/87 650

Bluebill pr, cork body, wooden bottom boards have been attached, unused, RWO 11/11/87 75

Bluewinged Teal pr, EX orig pnt, minor wear, old repair to drake's tail, rare, 21, RB 2/01/85, 240% 3600

Brant, fine orig scratch feather pnt, average wear, rstr to underside of bill, rare, 49, RB 7/09/85 650

Canvasback hen, balsa body, orig pnt, average wear, thin crack runs through neck, otherwise sound, signed, RWO 2/13/87 190

Goldeneye drake, old pnt, average wear, age split in neck, RB 7/08/86 100

Pintail drake, early, banjo-tail, old pnt, heavy flaking/wear, several age splits to body, RB 12/06/85 950

Pintail drake, old rpt, average flaking/wear, several age splits, bill has been rstr, ca 1932, RB 7/09/85 400

Pintail drake, old working rpt, average wear, 2 age lines in head/body, eyes missing, prof rstr chip, J/G 9/19/87, 205% 1025

Pintail drake, orig pnt, hairline crack down bk, otherwise structurally sound, 1920's, RWO 11/06/85 450

Sandpiper, EX & orig, 10, RB 12/06/85 125
Widgeon drake, orig pnt, heavy wear, some slight age splitting, otherwise structurally sound, RB 7/07/87 600

Sterling, Lloyd; att (Crisfield, MD)
Bluebill pr, cork body, rpt w/minor wear, 21, RB 2/01/85 100

Sterling, Noah (Crisfield, MD)
Bluebill drake, early, old working rpt, several age lines, prof rstr to most of bill, 33, J/G 9/19/87 175
Goldeneye hen, old pnt may be orig, average wear, head is loose/checks in bill/breast, RWO 11/11/87 130

Sterling, Noah; att (Crisfield, MD)
Goose, early, old working rpt in the Ward style, several tight age splits in body & neck, J/G 9/19/87 550

Sterling, Will (Crisfield, MD)
Goldeneye drake, old pnt, appears to be orig w/heavy flaking/wear, several age splits, rare, RB 2/01/85 450
Goldeneye hen, fine old pnt, average wear, age split in neck, RB 7/09/85 250

Sterling, Will; att (Crisfield, MD)
Pintail drake, EX & orig condition, 69, RB 3/11/88 850

Sterling Family, att (Crisfield, MD)
Goldeneye drake, fine old pnt, average wear, sm chip at top of tail, RB 7/09/85 90

Sterling Family (Crisfield, MD)
Canvasback hen, early, pnt by Lem Ward, average wear, some age splits/bill has been rstr, RB 7/08/86, 190% 2300
Goldeneye drake, old rpt, heavy flaking/wear, RB 3/11/88 375

Stevens, Ivey (Knott's Island, NC)
Bluebill drake, old working rpt, minor wear, hairline crack in bk, rare, 33, J/G 9/19/87 600
Canvasback drake, old working rpt, average wear, several tight checks in underside, ls, rare, 33, J/G 9/19/87 375

Strey, Frank (Oshkosh, WI)
Black Duck, orig pnt, minor wear, minor age split on underside/hairline crack in bk, rare, oversize, J/G 9/19/87 450
Bluebill drake, orig pnt, minor wear, structurally EX, J/G 9/19/87 250
Canvasback pr, orig pnt, minor wear, minor discoloration on bks/several sm checks in bodies, oversize, J/G 4/23/87 . 425
Coot or Mudhen, orig pnt, minor wear, unnoticeable check in bottom, otherwise structurally sound, ca 1940, RWO 7/02/88 375
Redhead drake, thin check in bottom, otherwise EX & orig condition, ca 1930's, RWO 2/12/88 325
Redhead pr, working rpt, structurally EX, RWO 11/06/85 160

Strey, Frank; att (Oshkosh, WI)
Bluebill drake, G orig pnt, average wear, lg tail chip/sm chunk of wood out of bk, RWO 7/02/88 85

Struebing, Walter
Redhead drake, fine orig pnt, minor wear w/flaking around sides of body, RB 2/01/85 300
Redhead pr, G orig pnt, drake has overpnt on head/breast, RB 2/01/85 350

Stuart, Allen
Merganser drake, incised cvg where bill meets head, fine orig pnt, minor wear, old tail repair, 22, RB 5/02/86, $2,000.00.

Stump, George
Black Duck, sleeping, fine feather pnt done in Connecticut style, M condition, J/G 9/20/86 450
Black Duck, sleeping, hollow, detailed feather pnt, M condition, J/G 4/23/87 550
Mallard drake, low-head Delaware River style, M condition, not an early decoy, RWO 7/04/87 100
Ruddy Turnstone, feeding, cvd in the style of Lothrop Holmes, EX & orig condition, nicely aged, RWO 2/12/88 150

Sutton, Bob
Grebe, slightly turned head, hollow w/EX feather cvg, signed/dated 1976, EX condition, RB 8/25/88 175

Swain Family (Cape May County, NJ)
Hudsonian Curlew, EX orig pnt, minimal wear, structurally EX, ca 1900, RWO 11/11/87 800

Swiderski, Ron (Burlington, NJ)
Black Duck, low-head style, raised cvd primaries/tail feathers, orig pnt, minor wear, structurally EX, 65, J/G 4/24/86 137
Bufflehead drake, slightly turned head, hollow w/raised cvd wings, NM pnt, J/G 9/20/86 245

Canada Goose, hissing, hollow w/raised primaries, orig pnt, average wear, structurally EX, RWO 11/11/87 330

Swift, William (Sagamore Beach, MA)
Merganser drake, American; cvd eyes, fine old pnt, average in-use wear, tail chip/old neck repair, RB 7/09/85 800

Talbot, Fred (Pekin, IL)
Mallard drake, early, slightly turned head, hollow, orig pnt, minor wear, retains orig weight, J/G 9/19/87 150

Tax, John (Osakis, MN)
Bluebill drake, canvas-covered, tack eyes, orig pnt, in-use wear, minor tears in canvas, ca 1920, RWO 7/04/87 120
Bluebill drake, filled canvas construction, NM orig pnt, tax stamp, sm tear in canvas, rare, J/G 4/23/87 125
Canada Goose, hollow w/laminated construction, orig pnt, minor wear, slight separation/cracking in body, J/G 9/20/86 5750

Tax, John
Snow Goose, stick-up, hollow, vertical laminated construction, leather carrying strap, EX & orig, rare, RWO 7/02/88, $24,500.00.

Taylor, Clarence
Redbreasted Merganser drake, EX orig pnt, signed/dated 1972 on bottom, RB 7/09/85 150

Taylor, Hamilton (Portsmouth Island, NC)
Brant, rpt as a Bluebill drake, numerous age lines/long chip missing from 1 side, 33, J/G 9/19/87 525

Teeter, Maurice
Bluebill pr, hollow, fiberglass-covered, orig pnt, average wear, hen has flaking, ms, otherwise sound, RWO 11/11/87 115

Terry, Albert (Riverhead, NY)
Goldeneye hen, fine old pnt, average wear, some slight age splitting/shallow chip on underside of bill, RB 7/07/87 400
Merganser hen, body has old orig pnt, average wear, head is rpt, RB 7/07/87 125
Scoter, early, orig pnt, prof rstr to bill, otherwise structurally EX, artist initials, ca 1865, very rare, J/G 4/24/86 880

Thayer, Capt. (Assinippi, MA)
Yellowlegs, cvd split tail, EX orig pnt, minor flaking, ls, RB 7/08/86 150
Yellowlegs, feeding, fine orig pnt, average flaking/wear, hs, RB 8/21/86 150
Yellowlegs, G orig pnt, average wear/moderate flaking to right side, ms, RB 7/08/86 250
Yellowlegs, slightly turned head, G orig pnt, average flaking/wear, hs, RB 8/21/86 200

Thomas, Al (Aberdeen, MD)
Bluebill drake, orig pnt, average wear, structurally sound, ca 1935, RWO 11/06/85 60
Canvasback drake, orig pnt w/thin coat of shellac, ls, otherwise structurally sound, ca 1935, RWO 11/06/85 50
Canvasback hen, old working rpt, structurally sound, ca 1930, RWO 11/06/85 55

Thomas, Charles (Assinippi, MA)
Blackbellied Plover, balsa body, cvd wings, G orig pnt, average wear, well preserved, 22/44, RB 5/02/86 500
Blackbellied Plover, split tail, tack eyes, orig pnt, minor wear, bill is an old replacement, J/G 9/20/86 300
Greater Yellowlegs, raised wing tips, tack eyes, EX orig pnt, filled split, very lg, 105, J/G 4/23/87 1550
Willet, cvd wing tips, rpt by Thomas, average wear, ls, rare, RB 7/08/86 400
Willet, orig pnt, average wear, slight curve in bill, age split on bottom, 22/44/46, RB 5/02/86 2700
Yellowlegs, fine orig pnt, minor wear, ls, chip in tail, 22, RB 5/02/86 500
Yellowlegs, old pnt, heavy flaking/wear, chip at top of tail/bill is possible replacement, RB 7/09/85 200

Thomas, Joe
Brant, fine old pnt, minor wear, branded CSA, age splits in neck, otherwise well preserved, 98, RB 2/01/85 150

Thompson, George
Goldeneye drake, orig pnt, minor wear, structurally sound, J/G 4/23/87 85
Yellowlegs, feeding, signed on bottom, RB 7/07/87 100

Tilghman, Richard (Talbot County, MD)
Canvasback pr, orig pnt, drake w/heavy wear to bare wood in areas, structurally EX, inscribed, ca 1925, RWO 11/06/85 325

Tillet, Alphonso D. (Kitty Hawk, NC)
Bluebill drake, working rpt, minor wear, neck crack/several hairlines in body, very rare, 122/33, J/G 9/19/87 750
Tillett, Allen (Kitty Hawk, NC)
Bluebill drake, orig pnt, minor wear, age split in bk, 33, J/G 9/19/87 425
Coot, root-head, orig pnt, minor wear, no structural flaws, 33, J/G 9/19/87 225
Tillett, Clay (Kitty Hawk, NC)
Bufflehead drake, orig pnt, thin tight check in body, ca 1940, RWO 7/04/87 240
Tillinghast, Charles (East Greenwich, RI)
Black Duck, old pnt, 2 neck cracks, 1 eye missing, retains Dr Starr's label, ca 1890, 44, RWO 7/04/87 425
Black Duck, 4-pc lamination construction, old pnt, top piece needs reattached to body, 22/44, RB 5/02/86 300
Tillinghast, Charles; att (East Greenwich, RI)
Merganser, American; 4-pc body, cvd crest, old pnt may be working rpt, bill is a replacement, ca 1890, RWO 7/04/87 475
Tilton, Lauren
Redhead drake, head tucked down, hollow w/cvd tail feathers, EX orig pnt, RB 8/21/86 225
Tilton, Pokey (Brick, NJ)
Hooded Merganser hen, EX & orig, RB 7/08/86 150
Tocchini, Leo
Canvasback drake, EX orig pnt, minor wear, branded LT on bottom, ms, RB 8/25/88 125
Pintail drake, balsa body, EX orig pnt, minor wear, some age splitting to bk, RB 8/27/87 220
Sprig pr, fine old pnt, average flaking/wear, RB 8/25/88 400
Tocchini, Leo; att
Pintail drake, orig pnt, average wear, slight age split in right side of body, RB 12/06/85 110
Tooker, Jim
Blackbellied Plover, hollow 2-pc body, JET cvd in bottom, separation where body joins, otherwise EX & orig, RWO 2/12/88 70
Tern pr, split tails, EX orig pnt, JET cvd in bottom, RWO 2/12/88 100
Yellowlegs, JET cvd in bottom, EX & orig condition, RWO 2/12/88 5500
Toothacher, Sam (Brunswick, ME)
Merganser hen, preening, orig pnt, some touchup to white area, exceptional, RWO 7/05/85 1500
Torrey, Benjamin Franklin (Braintree, MA)
Sandpiper, split tail cvg, orig pnt, minor flaking, bill is an old replacement, 22/44, RB 5/02/86 800

Totman, Arthur
Wood Duck, G orig pnt, crazing around head/breast, ca 1900, rare, RWO 7/06/86, 166% $5,000.00.

Townsend, Ollie (Friendship, TX)
Pintail pr, EX orig pnt, minor flaking, artist brand, RB 8/21/86 250
Townsend, Otis
Yellowlegs, cvd wings, old pnt, heavy wear, bill appears to be orig but reduced in length, 20, RB 12/06/85 150
Trader, Claude Jr. (Florence, NJ)
Black Duck, raised extended wing tips, old working rpt, minor wear, J/G 9/19/87 400
Trader, Stanley (Florence, NJ)
Black Duck, raised cvd primaries/tail feathers, EX working rpt, no structural flaws, rare, J/G 4/24/86 220
Travers, Capt. Josiah; att (Vienne, MD)
Canvasback drake, old working rpt, average wear, structurally sound, RWO 7/06/86 110
Travers, Josiah (Vienna, MD)
Canvasback drake, old pnt, may be orig w/average wear, thin neck crack, otherwise sound, ca 1930's, RWO 7/02/88 130
Tremblay, Gerald (Alburg Springs, VT)
Goldeneye hen, early, old working rpt, sm chip on edge of tail, J/G 9/19/87 80
Tribadeau, H. (Valley Field, Que)
Bluebill hen, feather cvg on bk/wings/tail, EX detailed comb pnt, artist brand, hairline crack in neck, J/G 9/20/86 175

Truex, Rhodes (Atlantic City, NJ)

Black Duck, early, hollow, old rpt, moderate flaking/wear, ms, RB 3/11/88	200
Black Duck, hollow, added glass eyes, orig pnt, average wear, repair to base of neck, RWO 11/11/87	140
Black Duck, hollow, fine orig pnt, average wear, bill appears to have some overpnt, branded HW Cain, RB 3/11/88	475
Black Duck, hollow, NM orig flock pnt, 20, RB 12/06/85	400
Black Duck, hollow, old pnt appears to be taken down to orig, average wear, age split in neck, RB 3/11/88	275
Black Duck, hollow, old pnt w/touchup around speculum/tail, minor crack at base of neck, otherwise sound, RWO 11/11/87	235
Black Duck, hollow, old rpt, average flaking/wear, branded HW Cain, age split in neck, 189, RB 6/28/88	170
Black Duck, hollow, old rpt, average wear, minor age split in neck, bill has an old repair, RB 3/11/88	275
Black Duck, hollow, old rpt, moderate wear, chip on underside of tail, age split in neck, RB 6/28/88	175
Black Duck, hollow, old working rpt, heavy flaking/wear, structurally sound, 1920's, RWO 7/06/86	50
Black Duck, hollow, rpt, average wear, age split in neck, RB 6/28/88	250
Black Duck, hollow, rpt, average wear, minor age split in neck, RB 3/11/88	250
Blackbellied Plover, EX orig pnt, bill has been prof replaced by Kenneth DeLong, rare, RB 8/25/88, 45%	225
Blackbellied Plover, EX orig pnt, minor wear, ms, RB 7/07/87	400
Blackbellied Plover, EX orig pnt, 20/50, RB 12/06/85	500
Blackbellied Plover, minor wear, otherwise NM, RB 6/28/88	700
Blackbellied Plover, orig pnt, minor wear, structurally EX, J/G 9/19/87	500
Blackbellied Plover, orig pnt, minor wear, well preserved, rare, RB 3/11/88	1150
Bluebill drake, hollow, EX orig pnt, minor wear, NM condition, RB 3/11/88	600
Bluebill drake, hollow, fine orig pnt, minor wear, structurally sound, RB 6/28/88	150
Bluebill drake, hollow, orig pnt, flaking/wear, structurally sound, RWO 11/11/87	180
Bluebill pr, old pnt, appears to be orig w/average flaking/wear, structurally sound, RB 6/28/88, 50%	200
Bluebill pr, old working rpt, no structural flaws, J/G 9/19/87	425
Canada Goose, hollow, NM orig condition, rare, 20/81, RB 12/06/85, 130%	2300
Curlew, pnt worn to natural wood & varnished, bill is a replacement, RB 3/11/88	400
Goldeneye pr, hollow, NM orig pnt, EX condition, 50, RB 12/06/85	2400
Merganser pr, hollow, NM/outstanding condition, 20/81, RB 12/06/85, 130%	4600
Redbreasted Merganser drake, hollow, EX orig pnt, minor wear, bill replaced by Kenneth DeLong, rare, 21, RB 2/01/85	1000
Redbreasted Merganser drake, hollow, rpt, some blistering on bk, cracks on bk/head, otherwise EX, RWO 7/02/88	325
Redbreasted Merganser drake, prof pnt rstr, sm old tail chip repair, J/G 9/20/86	200

Truex, Rhodes
Merganser pr, NM orig pnt, G patina, some smudges of brown pnt under hen's tail, 50/81, J/G 9/19/87 $7,000.00.

Redbreasted Merganser pr, NM orig pnt, minor wear, prof bill replacement on drake, rare, 21/50, RB 2/01/85	2500
Yellowlegs, EX orig pnt, minor wear, left eye missing, RB 3/11/88	600
Yellowlegs, EX orig pnt, minor wear, well preserved, RB 3/11/88	650
Yellowlegs, feeding, EX orig pnt, orig bill has some wear, otherwise NM, RB 3/06/87, 125%	1500
Yellowlegs, fine orig pnt, average wear, RB 3/11/88	575

Yellowlegs, fine orig pnt, minor wear, bill has been prof replaced by Kenneth DeLong, RB 8/25/88 200
Yellowlegs, ls, otherwise EX, 189, RB 6/28/88 400
Yellowlegs, NM orig pnt, ls, J/G 9/19/87 475
Yellowlegs, NM pnt, EX condition, 189, RB 6/28/88 600
Yellowlegs, orig pnt, minor wear, age check on right side of body, sm portion of orig bill remains, 189, RB 6/28/88 250
Yellowlegs, slight age check on left side of body, otherwise NM, 189, RB 6/28/88, 75% 375

Truex, Rhodes; att (Atlantic City, NJ)
Black Duck, hollow, old pnt, average wear, sm age split in neck/sm chip at end of tail, RB 8/27/87 140

Tull, Randy (Hayward, IL)
Greenwinged Teal drake, M condition, by world championship carver, J/G 4/23/87 450

Tullner, William
Yellowlegs, cvd wings, G orig pnt, average wear, bill is a replacement, ls, RB 3/11/88 130

Tully, J.D. 'Bud' (Peterborough, Ont)
Bluebill drake, head slightly turned, cvd wings/crossed wing tips, superb feather & bill cvg, NM, 53, RB 7/07/87, 130% 2600

Tuxis Family (Madison, CT)
Whitewinged Scoter, fine orig pnt, average flaking/wear, RB 6/28/88 75

Tyler, Lloyd (Crisfield, MD)
Black Duck, old working overpnt flaked away to reveal orig, flaws in wood on 1 side, otherwise sound, RWO 7/06/86 300
Black Duck, very old pnt, heavy wear, structurally sound, ca 1920's, RWO 11/06/85 200
Bluebill drake, old rpt, average flaking/wear, minor age splitting, RB 3/11/88 70
Bluebill drake, orig pnt, heavy wear, part of bill missing/narrow check on 1 side of bk, RWO 7/06/86 120
Bluebill drake, worn orig pnt, dings out of wood on bk, otherwise structurally sound, RWO 11/06/85 120
Bluebill hen, orig pnt, average wear, minor age splits in bottom of body, RB 3/11/88 50
Bufflehead drake, orig pnt, minor wear, signed/dated 1968, structurally sound, J/G 4/23/87 425
Bufflehead hen, old pnt, in-use flaking/wear, chip at end of bill/left side of tail, RB 7/09/85 125
Canada Goose, G orig pnt, average wear, thin crack in top of head/slight damage to end of bill, RWO 7/06/86 425
Canada Goose, orig pnt, average wear, slight dry rot to right side of body/sm tail chip, RB 3/11/88 100
Canvasback drake, orig pnt, average wear w/some areas to bare wood, few narrow cracks in bk, otherwise EX, RWO 2/12/88 170
Canvasback drake, orig pnt, 1 eye missing/splinter of wood missing under bill, RWO 7/06/86 180
Curlew, bill has been broken off & reglued, RWO 11/06/85 60

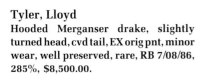

Tyler, Lloyd
Hooded Merganser drake, slightly turned head, cvd tail, EX orig pnt, minor wear, well preserved, rare, RB 7/08/86, 285%, $8,500.00.

Pintail drake, early, fine orig pnt, average wear, age split to body/head, RB 7/09/85 700
Pintail drake, orig pnt, average wear, vertical split running through neck, otherwise sound, ca 1925, RWO 7/06/86 550
Pintail drake, rpt by Lem Ward, tight check in breast/head, tail chip/defect on underside, J/G 9/19/87 325
Pintail hen, G orig pnt, average wear, moderate check along 1 side/thin tight check near bottom of neck, RWO 11/11/87 300
Pintail hen, orig pnt, worn to bare wood in several areas, prof bill rstr, hairlines on bk, RWO 7/04/87 350
Widgeon drake, EX orig pnt, average wear, sm chip out of bill/minor tail chips, otherwise structurally EX, RWO 7/04/87 650
Widgeon drake, G orig pnt, average wear, slight age splits, RB 12/06/85 550
Widgeon drake, orig pnt, average wear, lg band worn to bare wood, otherwise EX, RWO 11/11/87 500
Widgeon drake, raised cvd wings, orig pnt, minor wear, RWO 2/13/87 400

Tyler, Lloyd; att (Crisfield, MD)
Black Duck, long body, orig scratch pnt, average wear, no structural flaws, J/G 9/20/86 350

Canada Goose, early, fine orig pnt, average wear, scratch feather detail, chip on bottom of bill, RB 8/21/86, 125% 1100
Pintail drake, old pnt, average wear, old repair to bill, RB 7/08/86 90
Plover, old working rpt, average wear, head has been broken off & reattached, RWO 11/11/87 170

Udell, Larry
Bluebill drake, cork body, G orig pnt, minor wear, artist brand, 22, RB 5/02/86 90

Uhle, Jack
Mallard hen, hollow, G orig pnt, average flaking/wear, ca 1920, RB 7/09/85 225

Uhlendorf, P.L.
Wood Duck drake, EX orig pnt, branded, RB 12/06/85 120

Unger, Robert
Canvasback drake, hollow, old working rpt, prof bill rstr, applied bottom board, J/G 9/20/86 250

Updike, Jack; att (New Jersey)
Black Duck, hollow, old rpt, average wear, 189, RB 6/28/88 60

Updike, John (Green Bank, NJ)
Black Duck, hollow, old rpt, moderate flaking/wear, structurally sound, 189, RB 6/28/88 90
Black Duck, hollow, old sand pnt, average wear, sm chip on underside of bill, 21, RB 2/01/85 100
Black Duck, hollow, old working rpt, average wear, crack running through neck, otherwise sound, RWO 11/11/87 200
Black Duck, hollow, orig sand pnt, RWO 2/13/87 120
Black Duck, lg body, hollow, old flock pnt, moderate flaking/wear, ls, RB 6/28/88 75
Black Duck pr, hollow, old working touchup w/traces of orig, heavy wear, 1 has thin crack in neck, RWO 7/06/86 175

Updike, John; att (Green Bank, NJ)
Black Duck, hollow, fine old flock pnt, average wear, well preserved, 21, RB 2/01/85 100

Urie, Capt. Jess (Rock Hall, MD)
Black Duck, headless feeder, EX orig pnt, minor wear on front, RWO 11/11/87 65
Bluebill drake, old working rpt, average wear, structurally sound, RWO 7/06/86 80
Canvasback drake, early orig pnt, average wear, structurally sound, RWO 11/11/87 130
Canvasback pr, old working rpt, in-use wear, minor hairline checks, used at Cedar Point Club, RWO 7/04/87 200
Coot, working rpt, average wear, hairline crack in neck, RWO 11/11/87 75
Goldeneye pr, signed, M condition, RWO 11/11/87 275
Pintail drake, EX orig pnt, prof rstr to neck, J/G 4/24/86 176

Urie, Capt. Jess
Pintail pr, EX orig pnt, average wear, hen has check running down bk, otherwise structurally EX, ca 1940, RWO 11/11/87, $850.00.

Redhead drake, working rpt, average wear, spike driven down through top of head, RWO 11/11/87 70

Uzee, Frances T.
Mallard pr, cvd wing tips, G orig pnt, age split in drake's bill, 21, RB 2/01/85 450

Vallero, Michael (Spring Valley, IL)
Mallard drake, old working rpt, branded DWV, tight check in neck, J/G 4/24/86 165
Mallard hen, old working rpt by Vallero, touchup on underside, J/G 4/23/87 175
Pintail drake, hollow, EX orig pnt by Edna Perdew, some varnish appl, bill rpr, otherwise EX, 193, RWO 7/02/88, 58% 550
Pintail drake, old working rpt, old bill repair, 7, J/G 4/24/86 220

Van Brunt, Les (Manahawkin, NJ; Middleborough, MA)
Black Duck, head slightly turned to the right, hollow, fine orig pnt, minor wear, well preserved, RB 6/28/88 75
Black Duck, hollow, fine old pnt, average flaking/wear, RB 8/25/88 30
Black Duck, hollow, old pnt, average wear, RB 7/08/86 60
Black Duck, hollow, old rpt, average wear, age split in neck, RB 8/25/88 55
Black Duck, hollow, orig pnt, in-use wear/flaking, putty falling out between seams, otherwise sound, RWO 2/12/88 90
Black Duck, swimming, hollow, rpt w/minor wear, thin cracks in neck, otherwise sound, 1930's-1940's, RWO 7/06/86 60
Brant, hollow, old pnt, average wear, age split in neck, RB 7/08/86 50
Brant, hollow, old pnt, average wear, RB 3/11/88 150
Merganser drake, hollow, old working rpt, average wear, thin crack through bill, otherwise sound, RWO 07/06/86 100

Van Brunt, Les; att (Manahawkin, NJ; Middleborough, MA)
Pintail drake, hollow, old pnt, in-use wear, artist information, well preserved, RB 2/01/85 400
Redbreasted Merganser pr, hollow, old working rpt, branded T Maxwell, bill damage, otherwise sound, RWO 7/02/88 325
Van Lew, Gerald
Shoveler pr, artist signed, M/unused condition, RWO 2/12/88 50
Van Ness, Dirk
Canvasback pr, hollow, EX orig pnt, minor wear, artist initials, ca 1955, 20, RB 12/06/85 850
Vandeboesch, Teddy (Mt. Clemens, MI)
Canvasback hen, preening, orig pnt, average wear, fine check on lower side, otherwise EX, 114, RWO 7/05/85 700
Veasey, William
Redbreasted Merganser pr, hollow, EX orig condition, RWO 7/05/85 450
Verdin, Alfonse (Pointe au Chien, LA)
Bluewinged Teal pr, EX orig pnt, structurally EX, RWO 11/11/87 80
Greenwinged Teal pr, EX & orig condition, RWO 2/12/88 70
Verdin, Joseph
Greenwinged Teal pr, EX condition, RB 6/28/88 100
Verdin, Laurent Jr. (Marrerd, LA)
Canvasback pr, tucked heads, M condition, RWO 2/12/88 160
Gadwall drake, preening, M condition, RWO 2/12/88 110
Pintail drake, tupelo wood, M condition, RWO 11/11/87 160
Verdin, Laurent Sr. (Pointe au Chien, LA)
Bluewinged Teal hen, orig pnt, minor damage to end of bill/gouge of wood missing from bk, very sm, RWO 11/11/87 75
Bluewinged Teal pr, EX condition, RB 6/28/88 150
Greenwinged Teal pr, EX condition, RB 6/28/88 100
Mallard drake, cypress wood, old rpt, average wear, structurally sound, RB 7/07/87 75
Pintail hen, orig pnt, average wear, structurally EX, ca 1940, RWO 11/11/87 100
Verity, Alonzo; att
Black Duck, cork body, orig pnt, average wear, structurally sound, RB 7/07/87 180
Verity, Andrew (Seaford, LI, NY)
Bluebill drake, cork body, old rpt, average wear, RB 7/07/87 30
Bluebill drake, EX orig pnt, average wear, ls, otherwise structurally sound, RWO 7/06/86 50
Redbreasted Merganser drake, cork body, fine old orig pnt, average wear, well preserved, RB 7/07/87 100
Verity, Andrew; att (Seaford, LI, NY)
Yellowlegs, EX orig pnt, average wear, some splintering at end of bill, ms, RWO 7/04/87, 70% 900
Verity, John Henry (Seaford, LI, NY)
Golden Plover, 3-pc body construction, G orig pnt, minor wear, structurally sound, RWO 11/06/85 625
Verity, Obediah (Seaford, LI, NY)
Blackbellied Plover, cvd eyes/wings, orig pnt, moderate wear, ms, very lg, J/G 9/20/86 1500
Blackbellied Plover, cvd wings/eyes, EX orig pnt, minor flaking/wear, well preserved, rare, RB 7/09/85 3000
Blackbellied Plover, fine raised cvd wings, EX orig pnt, minor wear, age split in breast, rare, J/G 4/24/86 1210
Blackbellied Plover, orig pnt, touchup to black, EX, ca 1880, deaccessioned from Stony Brook LI museums, RWO 7/06/86 6200

Verity, Obediah
Blackbellied Plover, orig pnt w/minor touchup, structurally EX, deaccessioned by Stony Brook museums, 1880, RWO 7/05/85, $3,650.00.

Blackbellied Plover, orig pnt w/rpt on belly, average wear, structurally EX, ca 1870-1880, RWO 7/04/87, 62% 2500
Blackbellied Plover, orig pnt worn away to bare wood, wedge missing from head, initialed DM, ca 1880, RWO 7/05/85 1450

Blackbellied Plover, plump, orig pnt, average wear, ms, otherwise structurally EX, lg, RWO 11/06/85 1600
Blackbellied Plover, raised cvd wings, cvd eyes, orig pnt w/touchup, some wear, rstr to chip in bill, ls, J/G 4/23/87 925
Blackbellied Plover, worn orig pnt, orig bill, hs, ca 1800, RWO 7/05/85 1500
Blackbellied Plover, 2-pc laminated construction, prof pnt rstr, structurally sound, RWO 7/02/88 450
Curlew, bold pnt pattern, black-speckled feathering on bk, EX orig condition, ca 1875, 15" long, RWO 7/05/85 12000
Curlew, cvd eyes, deeply incised wings, orig pnt worn to fine patina, bill is a replacement, ls, early, RB 3/11/88, 69% 5500
Peep, cvd wings/eyes, EX orig pnt, ls, rare, RB 7/09/85 4400
Peep, detailed cvd wings/eyes, NM orig pnt, minor wear on bill, minor bloodstain on 1 side, very rare, J/G 9/20/86 4500
Plover, relief cvd wings, cvd eyes, G old pnt, minor wear, ls, 105, J/G 4/23/87 2000
Robin Snipe, fine orig pnt, minor wear, ms, well preserved, rare, rare, RB 7/09/85 5000
Robin Snipe, typical cvd wings/eyes, old pnt, heavy wear, bill is a replacement, ms, 22, RB 5/02/86 1350
Sanderling, prof rstr pnt, RWO 7/05/85 600

Verity, Obediah; att (Seaford, LI, NY)
Sanderling, cork body, EX orig pnt, structurally fine, RWO 7/05/85 575

Verity, Steven (Seaford, LI, NY)
Black Duck, early, hollow, glass eyes, G old pnt, minor wear, sm crack under tail/in breast, J/G 9/19/87 550
Canvasback hen, hollow w/relief cvd wings, old working rpt, structurally sound, branded JJ Doyle, ca 1890, RWO 7/04/87 ... 200
Mallard drake, worn old pnt, branded Lockwood/Webb/Burdy, end of tail/bill rpr w/epoxy, 33, J/G 9/19/87 525

Verity Family (Seaford, LI, NY)
Blackbellied Plover, cvd wings/eyes, orig pnt worn to mostly natural wood, roughness to top of head, hs, RB 7/08/86 600
Brant, EX orig pnt, average wear, structurally sound, RB 7/08/86 1600
Brant, root-head, EX orig pnt, average wear, structurally EX, ca 1890, RWO 7/04/87 225
Goldeneye hen, G orig pnt, minor wear/shrinkage, ls, J/G 9/19/87 250
Peep, cvd wings, fine orig pnt, average wear, ms, RB 12/06/85 1200

Verity Family
Left: Ruddy Turnstone, feeding, cvd wings/eyes, detailed feather pnt, outstanding, rare RWO 7/04/87, $16,000.00.
Right: Ruddy Turnstone, running, pnt eyes, detailed feather pnt, EX patina, rare, RWO 7/04/87 $9,000.00.

Yellowlegs, flat-sided, cvd wings/eyes, G old pnt, minor wear, crack in bill, ls, JG 4/24/86 440
Yellowlegs, 2 coats of Verity pnt, minor wear, ls, J/G 9/19/87 600

Verity Family, att (Seaford, LI, NY)
Tern, tack eyes, dowelled-on bill, worn orig pnt, sm tail chip/2 minor age lines, ca 1880, very rare, J/G 4/23/87 750

Vickers, John (Cambridge, MD)
Swan, EX & orig, RWO 11/06/85, 70% 1100
Swan, feeding, orig pnt, average wear, thin crack along side of body, otherwise EX, RWO 7/05/85 1250
Swan, sleeping, orig pnt, minor wear, structurally EX, RWO 7/06/86 600

Vidacovich, Ernest (Avondale, LA)
Greenwinged Teal, cypress root, raised cvd wings, orig pnt, minor wear, no structural flaws, J/G 4/24/86 715
Mallard pr, drake has slightly turned head/orig pnt w/minor wear; hen has worn orig pnt, glued rpr, J/G 4/23/87 300

Vidacovich, Paul (Louisiana)
Pintail drake, cvd wings, EX orig pnt, bill has old age split which has been repaired, rare, RB 8/21/86 500
Pintail drake, cvd wings/wing tips, EX orig pnt, average wear, rare, RB 7/09/85 1300

Pintail drake, G orig pnt, average wear, some overpnt to white areas, RB 12/06/85 850
Pintail drake, incised wings, orig pnt, average wear, some sm mars to wood, repair to tail, RB 12/06/85 400
Pintail drake, slightly turned head, cvd wings/wing tips, EX orig pnt, average wear, rare, RB 7/09/85, 140% 2100
Pintail drake, slightly turned head, incised wings, G orig pnt, average wear, bill is a replacement, rare, RB 12/06/85 750
Pintail drake, tip-up, EX orig pnt, minor wear, RB 7/08/86 100
Tip-up, EX orig pnt, ls, RB 7/09/85 300
Vincent, Carrol (New Orleans, LA)
Coot, orig pnt, slight wear, no structural flaws, J/G 9/20/86 45
Visier, Odee (Louisiana)
Pintail drake, old working rpt, average wear, tight checks on bottom/tiny bill flaw, otherwise sound, 193, RWO 7/02/88 150
Vizier, Clovis (Gilliano, LA)
Greenwinged Teal hen, fine orig pnt, minor wear, 21, RB 2/01/85, 400% 1000
Mallard pr, cvd wing tips/tail feathers, hen has separately cvd feathers along the wings, EX pnt, 21, RB 2/01/85, 200% 1000
Vorhees, Clark
Blackbellied Plover, split tail w/raised wing tips, CV cvd in bottom, EX & orig condition, RB 8/25/88 80
Waguspack, Richard (Louisiana)
Bluewinged Teal drake, cvd raised wing tips, EX condition, RB 6/28/88 70
Greenwinged Teal pr, EX condition, RB 6/28/88 75
Walker, Charles (Princeton, IL)
Mallard drake, early, hollow, EX orig pnt, minor wear, structurally EX, 193, RWO 7/02/88 4500
Mallard drake, hollow, cvd wings, EX orig pnt, average in-use wear, EX condition, rare, 193, RWO 7/02/88, 46% 3250

Walker, Charles
Top: Mallard drake, hollow, EX orig pnt, minor wear, Jolley cvd in bottom, NM condition, ca 1940, 199, RWO 7/02/88, $12,000.00.
Bottom: Mallard hen, hollow, EX orig pnt, minor wear, Jolley cvd in bottom, EX condition, ca 1940, 193/199, RWO 7/02/88, $19,500.00.

Mallard drake, hollow, EX orig pnt w/working touchup to head, structurally EX, RWO 7/06/86 4500
Mallard drake, hollow, G orig pnt, average wear, well preserved, RB 7/09/85 1800
Mallard drake, preening, hollow w/cvd wings, overpnt taken down to orig w/heavy wear, rare, RB 12/06/85 4000
Mallard drake, round body, orig pnt, minor wear, traces of overpnt, no structural flaws, rare, 7, J/G 4/24/86 1155
Mallard drake, several coats of pnt by Walker, top coat has EX combing w/minor wear, tail chip rpr, J/G 4/23/87 1150
Mallard drake, short body, several coats of pnt by Walker, moderate wear, from Princeton Fish & Game Club, J/G 4/23/87 650
Mallard drake, silhouette, EX bill cvg, NM orig pnt on duck, minor wear on base, structurally EX, rare, J/G 9/19/87 2500
Mallard drake, slightly turned head, raised cvd wings, NM orig pnt/touchups, no flaws, from Zearing rig, 7, J/G 4/24/86 2750
Mallard drake, slightly turned head, raised cvd wings, NM orig pnt, no structural flaws, 147, J/G 4/24/86 4950
Mallard hen, early, NM bright orig pnt, sm rough area on 1 side of bill, J/G 4/24/86 4950
Pintail drake, NM orig pnt on body, head is a prof replacement, retains orig weight, rare, J/G 9/20/86 450
Walker, Charles; att (Princeton, IL)
Mallard drake, early, hollow, raised wings, working rpt taken down to orig, appl wax, G condition, 193, RWO 7/02/88, 22% 450
Walker, Dave (Havre de Grace, MD)
Mallard pr, several sm rubs on pnt, otherwise M, artist stamp, J/G 9/19/87 225
Walker, Wilton (Tull's Bay, NC)
Battery Bluebill, old working rpt, minor wear, age split in underside/tail chip/hairline cracks in body, 33, J/G 9/19/87 200

Battery Widgeon, orig pnt, minor wear, old working touchup on lower sides, crack in neck, 33, J/G 9/19/87 200

Wallace, Alton (West Point, ME)
Redbreasted Merganser drake, orig pnt, in-use flaking/wear, several chips to bk of breast, ls, 22, RB 5/02/86 800
Skunkhead Coot, inlet head, NM orig pnt, minor checks, ca 1940, J/G 9/19/87 350
Whitewinged Scoter, G orig pnt, average wear, sm chip on bk /underside of bill, 22, RB 5/02/86 350
Whitewinged Scoter drake, fine orig pnt, average wear, some slight age splits, 22, RB 5/02/86 550

Wallace, Amos (West Point, ME)
Merganser hen, fine orig pnt, average wear, slight age split in bill, 22/44, RB 5/02/86 1600
Redbreasted Merganser drake, long body w/inlet neck, fine orig pnt, average wear, ls, rare, 22/44, RB 5/02/86 1700

Wallace, Floyd (Small's Point, ME)
Scoter, orig pnt, heavy wear, crack in neck has separated, ca 1900, RWO 11/06/85 100

Wallace, G.E. (Barnegat, NJ)
Herring Gull, full-bodied juvenile stick-up, cvd eye sockets/wing tips/split tail, EX pnt, artist stamp, 53, J/G 9/20/86 3000

Wallace, John (Damriscotta, ME)
· Goldeneye hen, incised bill, cvd eyes, EX orig pnt, minor wear, chip on underside of bill, RB 6/28/88 425

Wallace, Orrin (Waldoboro, ME)
Goldeneye drake, rpt, average wear, 22, RB 5/02/86 110

Wallace Family
Merganser pr, inlet heads/horsehair crests, EX orig pnt, reglued crack in 1 bill/ minor age splits, J/G 9/19/87, $2,250.00.

Wallach, Carl
Canvasback drake, bob-tail style, old working rpt, average wear, RWO 7/04/87 625
Canvasback drake, fine old pnt orig pnt, G patina, no structural flaws, J/G 4/24/86 330

Walsh, John and Todd
Bluebill drake, fine old pnt, minor wear, signed/dated 1924, age split in neck, RB 2/01/85 130

Walter, August
Mudhen, orig pnt w/touchup on bill, crack at base of neck, ms, ca 1915, RWO 7/06/86 80

Walters, Hank (Algonac, MI)
Black Duck, fine feather cvg, G orig pnt, minor wear, RB 2/01/85 225
Canada Goose, hollow, G orig pnt, average wear, RB 2/01/85 250
Mallard drake, fine orig pnt, RB 2/01/85 200
Mallard hen, hollow, orig pnt, average wear, ms, otherwise structurally sound, ca 1940-1950, 53, RWO 7/04/87 400

Waquespack, Richard (Thidoux, LA)
Dove, EX orig pnt, ls, 22, RB 5/02/86 275

Ward, Albert (Toronto, Ont)
Canvasback drake, orig pnt, moderate wear, fine comb pnt on bk/sides, prof rstr to edge of bill, rare, J/G 4/24/86 247

Ward, David (Essex, CT)
Black Duck, sleeper, hollow, made in 1979 & used in his own gunning rig, EX & orig condition, RWO 7/02/88 400
Black Duck, sleeping, artist stamp/dated 1984, M condition, J/G 9/19/87 275

Black Duck, sleeping, cork body, EX pnt, artist brand, RB 7/09/85 250
Black Duck, sleeping, cork body, orig pnt, artist stamp, EX condition, RWO 11/06/85 140
Black Duck, sleeping, superb example, M condition, RWO 11/06/85 475
Blackbellied Plover, finely detailed raised cvd wing tips, orig pnt, minor wear, oversize, J/G 4/24/86 165
Blackbellied Plover, raised wings/feather detail, NM orig pnt, artist brand, structurally EX, J/G 4/23/87 100
Canvasback drake, hollow, rpt as a hen showing flaking/wear, RB 7/09/85 100
Curlew, EX pnt, initials cvd in bottom, RB 7/09/85 100
Curlew, sickle bill, artist brand/dated 1977, M condition, RWO 7/04/87 190
Golden Plover, orig pnt, artist stamp, EX condition, RWO 11/06/85 30
Greenwinged Teal drake, EX antiqued pnt, artist brand/dated 1978, RB 8/21/86 425
Greenwinged Teal drake, sleeping, EX orig pnt, minor wear, artist stamp/signed DBW-'78, structurally EX, J/G 9/20/86 275
Knot, raised cvd wings/EX feather detail, NM orig pnt, artist stamp/dated 1982, structurally EX, very rare, J/G 4/23/87 175
Loon, EX pnt, minor flaking, artist brand, RB 7/09/85 300
Redbreasted Merganser drake, EX pnt, artist brand, RB 7/09/85 100
Ruddy Turnstone, NM orig pnt, artist brand/dated 1977, structurally EX, J/G 4/23/87 150
Sanderling, cvd wings, cvd in manner of Elmer Crowell, EX condition, RWO 7/02/88 150
Sanderling, orig pnt, artist stamp, EX condition, RWO 11/06/85 120
Sea Gull, hollow, EX pnt, artist brand, RB 7/09/85 150
Surf Scoter, sleeping, cork body, EX pnt, signed/dated 1976, RB 8/21/86 425
Wood Duck, hollow, EX pnt, artist brand, RB 7/09/85 475
Yellowlegs, orig pnt, artist stamp, structurally sound, RWO 11/06/85 50

Ward, Gary
Bluewinged Teal pr, hollow w/raised cvd wings, signed/dated 1982, M condition, RWO 11/11/87 260

Ward, Tony
Pintail, hollow, EX condition, RB 8/27/87 150

Ward, Travis (Crisfield, MD)
Black Duck, orig pnt, heavy wear, inscribed/signed/dated 1916, several age checks/chips/dry rot, RWO 11/11/87 400
Canada Goose, early, old working rpt, average wear, bill is old replacement, a few tight checks in body, 33, J/G 9/19/87 400
Canvasback, early, orig pnt on body, head is rpt, moderate flaking/wear, tight check in bk/chip on bill, 33, J/G 9/19/87 600
Canvasback drake, early, worn old pnt, several tight age splits on sides, ca 1917, J/G 9/20/86 475
Canvasback drake, rpt by Ward brothers, moderate flaking/wear, 2 age lines in bk/1 on head, 33, J/G 9/19/87 500

Ward Brothers (Crisfield, MD)
Black Duck, balsa body, cedar head/tail, cvd wing tips, NM orig pnt, sm separation at neck, ca 1948, J/G 4/23/87 4000
Black Duck, balsa body, G orig pnt, minor wear, signed/dated 1948, repair to tip of bill, otherwise sound, RWO 11/06/85 1400
Black Duck, balsa body, orig pnt, heavy wear, signed/dated 1948, head slightly loose/split through bill, RWO 7/06/86 675
Black Duck, balsa body, orig pnt w/some worn working rpt, signed/dated 1948, thin crack on head, RWO 7/02/88, 73% 875
Black Duck, EX orig pnt, minor wear, sm separation at neck/1 eye missing, otherwise EX, ca 1930, 174, RWO 11/06/85 3750

Ward Brothers
Top: Black Duck, high tail, turned head/lifted bill, EX scratch pnt, signed Lem/dated 1921, EX structure, 69, J/G 9/19/87, $20,500.00.
Bottom: Black Duck, slightly turned head w/wide round bill, signed/dated 1936, NM orig pnt & condition, 33/169, J/G 9/19/87, $11,500.00.

Black Duck, hollow, orig pnt, moderate wear, tight age checks on bk, otherwise sound, ca 1930, rare, RWO 11/06/85, 65% 1900
Black Duck, hollow, signed Lem & Steve/dated 1968, M condition, RWO 11/11/87, 130% 1800
Black Duck, humpback w/low breast, turned head, scratch feather pnt, structurally EX, ca 1920, rare, RB 7/09/85, 420% 38000
Black Duck, NM orig pnt, signed/dated 1945/To My Friends Heis & Margaret, hairlines/sm dents, 33, J/G 9/19/87 4000
Black Duck, old working rpt, average wear, structurally sound, classic 1936 model, RWO 2/12/88, 75% 1100
Black Duck, orig pnt worn away in many areas, signed Lem/dated 1934, neck crack/loose head, both eyes gone, RWO 7/06/86 2750
Black Duck, pinch-breast, signed, working rpt, average wear, signed Lem & Steve/dated 1933, photo w/lot, RWO 11/11/87 1600
Black Duck, pnt taken down to EX orig, signed Steve/dated 1928, structurally VG, 33, J/G 9/19/87, 55% 700
Black Duck, rpt by Lem, signed Lem & Steve/dated 1929, tight check along side of bk, from Lem's rig, RWO 7/06/86 1600
Black Duck, rpt by Ward Brothers, little wear, gunning decoy from ca 1932, well preserved, RB 3/06/87, 165% 2000
Black Duck, standing, detailed wing/feather cvg, cvd webbed feet, NM orig pnt, very rare, J/G 9/20/86, 50% 4000
Black Duck, worn old pnt, signed/dated 1934, several checks/age lines, neck chip, eyes missing, 33, J/G 9/19/87 850
Bluebill drake, balsa body, orig pnt, heavy wear, slight separation where head joins body, RWO 7/04/87 425
Bluebill drake, balsa body, orig pnt, some flaking/wear, signed/1948, bill broken off & reglued, RWO 7/06/86 650
Bluebill drake, early, fat-jaw model, old working rpt, minor wear, signed/dated 1918, filled age lines, 33, J/G 9/19/87 875
Bluebill drake, early, fat-jaw model, raised cvd wings, rpt by Lem in 1967, structurally EX, ca 1918, RWO 11/11/87 1100
Bluebill drake, early, fat-jaw model, rpt by Lem in 1969, rare, ca 1918-1920, 69, RWO 7/04/87, 75% 1100
Bluebill drake, early, old working rpt, bill is an old replacement, J/G 9/20/86 200
Bluebill drake, early, slightly turned head, cedar construction, old rpt/possible touchup, well preserved, J/G 9/20/86 1100
Bluebill drake, early, slightly turned head, EX form, traces of orig pnt worn mostly to natural wood, 192, RB 6/28/88 2300
Bluebill drake, EX orig pnt, signed/dated 1970 on bottom, RB 12/06/85 1300
Bluebill drake, fine orig pnt, average flaking/wear, slight age splits in bk, rpl bill, ca 1936, RB 7/07/87 1600
Bluebill drake, G orig pnt, crack in bill has been reglued/touched up, otherwise sound, 1936 model, RWO 7/02/88, 45% 1500
Bluebill drake, head turned right, pnt may be orig, minor wear, minor age split, gunning decoy from 1930's, RB 3/06/87 1700
Bluebill drake, orig pnt, minor wear, sm worn area on 1 cheek, signed/dated 1932, 33/164, J/G 9/19/87, 78% 3500
Bluebill drake, pinch-breast style, rpt taken down to orig, signed LT Ward/dated 1929, hs, RWO 7/04/87 1300
Bluebill drake, slightly turned head, old working rpt, signed/dated 1928, several tight checks in bodyblock, J/G 4/23/87 850
Bluebill drake, turned head, raised cvd wing tips, Ward Bros rpt, slight wear, extremely stylish, ca 1920's, J/G 9/20/86 2000
Bluebill hen, balsa body, fine old pnt, appears to be orig, average wear, att to Steve, RB 7/09/85 225
Bluebill hen, fat-jaw/turned head, EX 1970 rpt signed Lem/dated 1918, thin cracks/filler added, 33, J/G 9/19/87, 70% 1400
Bluebill pr, cedar body, signed/dated 1972, M condition, RWO 7/02/88 2750
Bluebill pr, hen is sleeping; drake has slightly turned head, NM pnt, signed Lem & Steve/dated 1972, RB 7/08/86 2750
Bluebill pr, sharply turned heads, M orig pnt, signed/dated 1973, drake has crack on 1 side of breast, J/G 4/23/87 2250
Bluebill pr, slightly turned head, signed/dated 1972 on bottom, EX & orig, 39, RB 7/08/86, 125% 3800
Bluebill pr, slightly turned heads, drake has raised cvd wing tips, signed/1967, Shooting Stool label, M, J/G 4/23/87 2200
Bluebill pr, slightly turned heads, finely blended pnt, signed Lem & Steve, dated 1972, M condition, 33, J/G 9/19/87 2300
Bluebill pr, slightly turned heads, signed/dated 1972, age split in hen's neck, otherwise M, RB 2/01/85 2400
Brant, swimming, slightly turned head, hollow, signed/dated 1968, 33/165, M condition, J/G 9/19/87 2400
Bufflehead pr, signed/dated 1966, M condition, RWO 11/06/85 2400
Canada Goose, balsa body, old working rpt, flaking/wear, thin tight checks to head/body, otherwise sound, RWO 2/12/88 625
Canada Goose, balsa body, orig pnt, average wear, minor chips in tail, otherwise sound, ca 1948, RWO 7/06/86 1900
Canada Goose, balsa body, orig pnt, average wear/few dings, signed/inscribed, EX condition, ca 1940's, RWO 11/11/87, 62% 2500
Canada Goose, balsa body, orig pnt w/minor touchup, signed by both brothers/dated 1948, structurally EX, RWO 2/13/87 3500
Canada Goose, balsa body, pnt worn to natural wood in several areas, some age splitting, ca 1936, RB 3/11/88, 64% 450

Ward Brothers
Canada Goose, cedar, EX orig blended feather pnt on bk/sides, signed/dated 1929, filled knothole in tail, J/G 4/24/86, $6,875.00.

Canada Goose, early, old working rpt, average wear, some neck filler missing/several age lines in body, 33, J/G 9/19/87 550
Canada Goose, early, old working rpt, minor wear, artist stamp, several minor age lines in head, J/G 9/19/87, 70% 1100

Canada Goose, early, orig pnt, w/some working rpt, thin cracks in bk/neck, ca 1930, 193, RWO 7/02/88 6500
Canada Goose, EX orig blended/feathered pnt, signed/1938, tight check in bk, sm crack in head, 33, J/G 9/19/87, 75% 3000
Canada Goose, feather/wing/tail cvg, signed Lem/dated 1975, poem/inscribed: Made for Jack Parks, RWO 11/11/87 4750
Canada Goose, hollow, EX orig pnt, average wear, signed/dated 1940, 2 tight checks running down bk, RWO 7/04/87 2500
Canada Goose, hollow, EX orig pnt, stamped/signed/1965, minor split in breast/tail, Shooting Stool decoy, RWO 7/06/86 1850
Canada Goose, old working rpt flaking to reveal G orig, signed/dated 1933, EX w/nailed neck seam, 33, J/G 9/19/87, 65% 2250
Canada Goose, slightly turned head, balsa body, EX orig pnt, minor wear, signed, RB 7/09/85 3000
Canada Goose, slightly turned head, cvd wing tips, fine feather pnt pattern, signed/dated 1968, NM, 5, RB 7/07/87 2900
Canada Goose, slightly turned head, old rpt, average wear, several age chips at end of tail, rare, RB 7/08/86 1250
Canada Goose, swimming, orig pnt, average wear, minor touchup, signed/1931, hairlines/rstr bill, 120, J/G 9/19/87, 66% 2000
Canada Goose, working rpt, signed Steve/dated 1932, structurally sound, RWO 7/06/86, 70% 700
Canvasback drake, balsa body, artist signed/dated 1948, M condition, 193, RWO 7/02/88, 75% 1350
Canvasback drake, balsa body, EX orig pnt, signed/dated 1948, filled age split/hairlines in breast, 33, J/G 9/19/87 500
Canvasback drake, balsa body, orig pnt, minor wear, EX condition, ca 1848, RWO 2/12/88 1800
Canvasback drake, balsa body, orig pnt, signed Lem & Steve/dated 1948, structurally EX, RWO 7/05/85 1100
Canvasback drake, balsa body, orig pnt w/touchup to black areas, RWO 7/04/87 550
Canvasback drake, balsa body, orig pnt w/working rpt on body, signed/dated 1948, bill broken & reglued, RWO 7/06/86 575
Canvasback drake, balsa body, rpt by Lem, signed/dated 1948, structurally sound, RWO 7/06/86 750
Canvasback drake, balsa body, rpt by Lem in 1977, structurally sound, 207, RWO 7/02/88 500
Canvasback drake, balsa body, signed/dated 1951, M condition, RWO 2/12/88 2400
Canvasback drake, cedar, overpnt taken down to orig w/minor wear, hairline through neck, 1936 model, J/G 4/24/86, 210% 1870
Canvasback drake, cvg at base of bill, orig pnt, average wear/prof touchup, EX condition, 1936 model, RWO 11/11/87, 45% 2750
Canvasback drake, early, rpt, tiny chip at end of tail, RB 7/09/85 525
Canvasback drake, early, rpt by Lem, signed by Lem & Steve, crack in neck/2 tail chips, ca 1936, RWO 7/06/86 1250
Canvasback drake, EX orig pnt, signed/identified/dated 1967, never weighted, RWO 7/04/87 1400
Canvasback drake, head tucked down, hollow cedar, cvd wing tips/tail feathers, orig pnt, signed/dated 1963, RB 8/21/86 2250
Canvasback drake, head turned right, orig pnt, EX patina, age split in bottom, gunning decoy ca 1930's, RB 3/06/87, 130% 2300
Canvasback drake, inserted tail, working overpnt to black areas/tail, artist signed/dated 1936, RWO 7/02/88, 95% 2250
Canvasback drake, orig pnt, minor wear, signed/dated 1932, hairlines on bk/part way through neck, 33, J/G 9/19/87 3350
Canvasback drake, orig pnt, signed by Lem/dated 1970, hairline crack in neck, otherwise EX, RWO 11/11/87, 65% 900
Canvasback drake, sleeping, signed by both brothers/dated 1973, M condition, RWO 7/04/87 1700
Canvasback drake, slightly turned head, cedar body, M pnt, signed/dated 1974, oversize, J/G 4/24/86 1100
Canvasback drake, slot-bk model, EX orig pnt, signed/stamped, 1 eye broken, appears unused, EX, RWO 7/04/87, 50% 1500
Canvasback hen, balsa body, old pnt, average wear, artist stamp, slight age splitting/head is loose, RB 8/21/86 850
Canvasback hen, cedar body, made by Steve/pnt by Lem/dated 1967, M condition, RWO 11/11/87, 80% 1100
Canvasback hen, early, rpt, heavy flaking/wear, both eyes missing, minor age spit in bottom, ca 1928, RB 3/11/88, 125% 625
Canvasback hen, head turned left, rpt by Ward Brothers, minor wear, bill is prof rpl, gunning decoy, 1930's, RB 3/06/87 2300

Ward Brothers
Canvasback hen, orig pnt w/touchup on head, signed '1 of 12,' tail chip/thin body checks, ca 1925, RWO 11/11/87, $9,500.00.

Canvasback hen, pristine rpt by Lem, signed/1940, crack in neck/thin crack in bill, RWO 7/06/86, 66% 1000
Canvasback hen, sleeping, balsa, hollowed out from bottom, added keel weight, signed/1954, 69, RWO 11/06/85 6500
Canvasback pr, balsa bodies, EX orig pnt, signed/dated 1948, chip on hen's bill; drake has neck crack, 33, J/G 9/19/87 1500
Canvasback pr, balsa bodies, G orig pnt, average wear, signed/dated 1948, few dings on wood to both, RWO 11/11/87 2700
Canvasback pr, balsa bodies, outstanding orig pnt, minor wear, structurally NM, ca 1948, RWO 11/11/87 4200

Canvasback pr, balsa bodies, signed Lem & Steve/dated 1952, both are in EX orig condition, RWO 7/05/85 4500
Canvasback pr, both have turned heads & finely detailed pnt, signed/dated 1968, M condition, J/G 4/23/87 2800
Canvasback pr, cedar bodies, hollow, minor dings to pnt, otherwise M, signed by both/dated 1968, RWO 11/11/87 3000
Canvasback pr, cedar body, hollow, signed/dated 1972, M condition, RWO 7/02/88 2200
Canvasback pr, EX pnt, signed/dated 1936, filled split, tail chip/crack on hen, minor neck separations, 120, J/G 9/19/87 11000
Canvasback pr, hollow, cedar body, M orig pnt, signed Lem & Steve/dated 1967, drake has hairline in bill, RWO 7/05/85 2000
Canvasback pr, hollow, heads slightly turned, signed/dated 1966, EX orig condition, RB 9/27/87 2700
Canvasback pr, hunting model, slightly turned heads, G orig pnt, hairline in neck of hen, ca 1948, oversize, J/G 4/24/86 1650
Canvasback pr, knot heads, old working rpt, signed/dated 1932, half of drake's bill is a prof rpl, rare, 33, J/G 9/19/87 5500
Canvasback pr, orig pnt, signed Lem & Steve/dated 1929, each have prof bill rstr, RWO 7/06/86 9500
Canvasback pr, raised wing model, orig pnt, signed Lem/dated 1925, EX condition, rare, RWO 11/06/85 20000
Canvasback pr, signed/dated 1973, M condition, 33, J/G 9/19/87, 72% 1800
Canvasback pr, slightly turned heads, balsa bodies, EX orig pnt, 21, RB 2/01/85 3000
Canvasback pr, slightly turned heads, cvd wing tips, NM orig pnt/structure, signed/dated 1967, poem, J/G 4/23/87, 70% 2500
Canvasback pr, slightly turned heads, finely detailed pnt, signed/dated 1968, M condition, J/G 4/23/87, 80% 2800
Canvasback pr, slightly turned heads, hollow w/fine wing cvg, cedar bodies, dated 1971, M condition, 161, J/G 4/24/86 4125
Gadwall pr, hollow, signed Lem/dated 1971, M condition, RWO 7/06/86 4250
Goldeneye drake, balsa body, EX orig pnt, signed/dated 1956, minor crazing/bill damage, otherwise EX, RWO 7/06/86 1750
Goldeneye drake, balsa body, rpt w/minor wear, ca 1948, RB 7/09/85 350
Goldeneye drake, cedar body, signed/dated, 1966, M/unused, RWO 7/06/86, 66% 1000
Goldeneye drake, fat-jaw humpback, slightly turned head, paddle tail, EX orig pnt, eyes missing, 33, 1920, J/G 9/19/87 7000
Goldeneye drake, fat-jaw model, rpt by Lem in 1967, photo w/lot, ca 1925, RWO 11/11/87 1000
Goldeneye drake, hollow, orig pnt, signed/dated 1967, NM condition, never weighted, RWO 2/13/87 2500
Goldeneye drake, old working rpt, average wear, age line/chip, rough area on underside, eyes missing, 33, J/G 9/19/87 525
Goldeneye drake, signed/dated 1967, minor check in bk, slight separation on side of neck seam, 33, J/G 9/19/87 700
Goldeneye drake, slightly turned head, fat-jaw humpback, paddle tail, eyes missing, VG condition, ca 1920, J/G 9/19/87 7000

Ward Brothers
Goldeneye hen, early, beaver tail, orig pnt, EX scratch pnt, ms/ pc of wood missing from tail, 205, RWO 7/02/88, $25,000.00.

Goldeneye hen, fat-jaw humpback, slightly turned head, paddle tail, EX/VG orig pnt, 1 eye gone, 1920, 33, J/G 9/19/87 4000
Goldeneye pr, signed/dated 1965, each w/poem by Lem, M condition, RWO 11/11/87 2500
Greenwinged Teal drake, slightly turned head, cedar body, EX feather pnt, stamped, NM condition, ca 1936, RB 8/21/86 17500
Greenwinged Teal hen, NM orig pnt, signed/dated 1952, hairline down bk, otherwise structurally NM, RWO 7/04/87, 50% 1750
Greenwinged Teal pr, balsa body, signed/dated by Lem in 1952, M condition, RWO 7/02/88 4750
Greenwinged Teal pr, NM orig pnt, both signed/dated 1966, half-size, 28, J/G 9/19/87 1100
Greenwinged Teal pr, sharply turned heads, relief wing tip cvg, signed/dated 1909, M condition, rare, 33, J/G 9/19/87 3000
Greenwinged Teal pr, slightly turned heads, EX orig pnt, signed/dated 1969, RB 7/09/85 3100
Hutchins Goose, rpt w/average wear, signed Lem & Steve/branded, cracks in neck, rare, ca 1929-1932, 69, RWO 7/04/87 1400
Mallard drake, balsa body, EX orig pnt, average wear, signed/dated 1945, sm separation at bk joint, RWO 11/11/87 1400
Mallard drake, balsa body, EX orig pnt, signed/dated 1948, bill rpl by Wards/reglued chip, ls, 33, J/G 9/19/87 875
Mallard drake, balsa body, orig pnt, minor wear w/rubs to top of head, structurally EX, ca 1948, RWO 11/11/87 1400
Mallard drake, balsa body, orig pnt shows minor wear, identified/signed, EX condition, RB 8/21/86 1000
Mallard drake, EX orig pnt, average wear, prof rstr to underside of bill, otherwise EX, 1936 model, RWO 11/11/87, 63% 4750

Mallard drake, outstanding orig pnt, sm repair to side of bill/few hairline cracks, otherwise EX, ca 1936, RWO 7/06/86 .... **8000**
Mallard drake, signed Lem & Steve/dated 1971, M condition, RWO 7/04/87 .... **1700**

Ward Brothers
Top: Mallard drake, slightly turned head, EX orig pnt, minor wear, ca 1936, 29, J/G 4/24/86, $10,450.00.
Bottom: Mallard hen, slightly turned head, cedar body, NM orig pnt, tail has prof rpr/pnt touchup, J/G 4/24/86, 145%, $8,800.00.

Mallard drake, slightly turned head, slight age split in bottom, otherwise NM, unused, ca 1936, rare, RB 8/21/86 .... **9000**
Mallard hen, EX orig pnt, minor wear, prof repair to crack in neck, otherwise EX, 1936 model, rare, RWO 11/11/87, 50% **4500**
Mallard hen, swimming, slightly turned head, balsa body, detailed feather pnt, signed/dated 1962, half-size, J/G 9/19/87 .... **425**
Mallard pr, balsa bodies, cedar heads/tails, orig pnt, minor wear, several sm dents in balsa, ca 1948, J/G 4/23/87 .... **3100**
Mallard pr, sleeping, turned heads, balsa, cvd wing tips w/prof rstr, NM orig pnt, signed/dated, 1954, 34, J/G 9/19/87 .... **7000**
Mallard pr, slightly turned heads, balsa bodies, M pnt, drake w/2 age splits, sign/dated 1972 w/verse, 21, RB 2/01/85 .... **4000**
Old Squaw drake, balsa body, NM & orig condition, 216, RWO 2/12/88 .... **2400**
Pintail drake, balsa body, EX orig pnt, minor wear, artist signed/dated 1939, EX condition, 193, RWO 7/02/88 .... **2500**
Pintail drake, balsa body, EX orig pnt, minor wear, identified/signed, well preserved, RB 8/21/86 .... **1750**
Pintail drake, balsa body, EX orig pnt, wear on end of bill, signed/dated 1951, EX condition, RWO 7/02/88 .... **2200**
Pintail drake, balsa body, orig pnt, average wear, few nicks/dings to wood, otherwise VG, RWO 2/12/88, 55% **1100**
Pintail drake, balsa body, orig pnt, considerable wear, separation where head joins body, RWO 7/04/87 .... **1400**
Pintail drake, balsa body, orig pnt, minor wear, structurally sound, RB 7/07/87 .... **1500**
Pintail drake, balsa body, rpt, minor wear, age split in neck, RB 7/07/87 .... **200**
Pintail drake, balsa body, signed Lem & Steve/dated 1952, hairline crack on head, otherwise EX, RWO 7/05/85 .... **2200**
Pintail drake, balsa body, slightly turned head, outstanding orig pnt, M condition, 1948 hunting model, J/G 9/20/86 .... **5250**
Pintail drake, beaver-tail model, signed Lem/dated 1935, rpt by Lem, rpr to bill/thin cracks in neck, RWO 7/06/86 .... **1150**
Pintail drake, cedar body, orig pnt, average wear, artist's rubber stamp, age checks on bk/1 near tail, RWO 7/02/88 .... **1100**
Pintail drake, early, EX orig pnt, average wear, slight age split in bottom, RB 7/09/85 .... **500**
Pintail drake, early, old rpt, average wear, some orig pnt on body, slight separation at neck, RB 3/06/87 .... **1700**
Pintail drake, early, old working rpt, minor wear, several age lines in body/head, J/G 9/19/87 .... **425**
Pintail drake, early, old working touchup/minor wear, signed/1925, minor check/tail was planed, ls, 33, J/G 9/19/87 .... **1750**
Pintail drake, EX orig pnt, minor wear, prof rpr to narrow check in bk, otherwise EX, RWO 2/12/88, 80% **2000**
Pintail drake, EX orig pnt, minor wear, slight age split in bk/chip on underside of bill, ca 1936, rare, RB 8/21/86 .... **4000**
Pintail drake, EX orig pnt, minor wear, sm tail chip/rpr to side of tail, otherwise EX, 1936 model, RWO 11/11/87, 63% **4750**
Pintail drake, glass eyes, rpt by Lem, signed Lem, check running down bottom, 1935 model, RWO 7/06/86, 75% **850**
Pintail drake, high-neck style, pnt worn to bare wood, signed Lem/dated 1920, cracks/chip/hairline, ls, 33, J/G 9/19/87 .... **750**
Pintail drake, humpback style, rpt, minor wear, age split on side of body/neck, ca 1936, RB 7/09/85 .... **500**
Pintail drake, NM orig pnt w/varnish, signed/dated 1954, age split in side, 33, J/G 9/19/87, 65% **1300**
Pintail drake, old working rpt, average wear, age split in head/bill has been rstr, ca 1930, RB 7/09/85 .... **300**
Pintail drake, preening, lifted wings, detailed feather cvg, NM pnt finished by F Finney, signed, rstr tail, J/G 9/19/87 .... **2000**
Pintail drake, signed Lem/dated 1956, NM condition, never weighted, RWO 7/06/86 .... **2400**
Pintail drake, slightly lifted head, NM orig pnt w/fine feathering, crack on bottom, sm chips to bill, J/G 4/24/86 .... **4125**

Pintail drake, VG orig pnt, signed w/rubber stamp, wide crack on bk/check on breast, ca 1940's, RWO 7/05/85 1075
Pintail drake, VG orig pnt, thin neck crack strengthened with nail, gouge on bill, unsigned, ca 1936, RWO 7/05/85 3250
Pintail hen, balsa body, orig pnt, average wear, artist stamp/signed/dated 1946, narrow crack in neck, RWO 7/04/87 1000
Pintail hen, early, old working rpt, average wear, signed/dated 1920, thin tight cracks/damage to head, RWO 11/11/87 600
Pintail hen, early, orig pnt/some rpt by Lem, signed/dated 1930, fine hairline cracks, otherwise EX, 69, RWO 11/11/87 3600
Pintail hen, early pinch-breast style, rpt by Lem w/traces of orig, narrow neck crack, otherwise EX, 69, RWO 11/11/87 3000
Pintail hen, EX orig pnt, minor wear, check running from 1 side to bottom, otherwise EX, 1936 model, RWO 11/11/87, 60% 4500
Pintail hen, EX pnt, inscribed/made/pnt (rpt?) by Lem in 1930, structurally EX, RWO 7/04/87, 50% 3000
Pintail hen, orig pnt, considerable wear, signed Lem/dated 1936, structurally sound, 45, RWO 7/05/85 3750
Pintail hen, orig pnt worn to bare wood in many areas, crack in neck/bill, ca 1932, RWO 7/06/86 675
Pintail hen, rpt by Lem, signed Lem/dated 1935, structurally VG, RWO 7/05/85 850
Pintail hen, sleeping, balsa body, M pnt, G patina, 1948 hunting model, J/G 9/20/86 6750
Pintail hen, slightly turned head, balsa body, old rpt, hairline crack in neck, ca 1948, J/G 9/19/87 275
Pintail pr, balsa bodies, hen has raised wings w/minor damage, signed/dated 1940 by Lem for Roy Walsh, RWO 7/04/87 3100
Pintail pr, pinch-breast style, high alert heads, EX orig pnt primaries/sponging, chewed bill, ca 1930's, 39, RB 8/21/86 45000
Pintail pr, rpt by Lem, signed/dated 1938, structurally EX, RWO 7/06/86 2100
Pintail pr, worn orig pnt w/old touchup, signed/dated 1930, hen has nailed crack/sm tail chip, ls, 33, J/G 9/19/87 2500
Pintail pr, 1936 model, EX orig pnt, both have in-use bill rpr/age checks/sm neck cracks, otherwise EX, RWO 7/02/88 6500
Redbreasted Merganser drake, cedar, thin-shelled, hollow, EX & orig condition, 215, RWO 2/12/88, 75% 1900
Redbreasted Merganser pr, hollow, cedar, signed/dated 1967, drake has bill crack, otherwise EX & orig, 205, RWO 7/02/88 4500
Redbreasted Merganser pr, hollow, cedar body, pnt by Lem/made by Steve/1967, inscribed: Shooting Stool, M, RWO 7/06/86 4250

Ward Brothers
Redbreasted Merganser pr, signed Lem & Steve/dated 1967, inscribed: Shooting Stool, M condition, RWO 7/04/87, $4,700.00.

Redhead drake, balsa body, G orig pnt, minor wear, structurally sound, ca 1948, RB 7/07/87, 170% 1700
Redhead drake, early pinch-breast style, slightly turned head, rpt w/some orig, structurally sound, 39, RB 7/08/86 2100
Redhead drake, G pnt on bk/lower sides, minor touchup, signed Lem/dated 1938, ls, 33, J/G 9/19/87 1800
Redhead drake, orig pnt on bk, some rpt on speculum/base of neck, thin checks around breast, RWO 7/04/87 275
Redhead drake, slightly turned head, balsa body, EX orig pnt, signed/dated 1948, structurally EX, 33, J/G 9/19/87, 160% 3250
Redhead hen, balsa body, NM orig pnt, no structural flaws, signed/dated 1948, 33, J/G 9/19/87 1750
Redhead hen, balsa body, old working rpt, average wear, signed Lem & Steve/dated 1945, structurally sound, RWO 7/04/87 900
Redhead hen, hollow, signed Lem/dated 1977, inscribed: To Eben Waterfield, M condition, RWO 7/06/86, 55% 1100
Redhead pr, signed/dated 1966, M condition, RB 3/06/87, 150% 2700
Redhead pr, signed/dated 1966, M condition, RWO 7/06/86 3500
Ruddy Duck, head tucked/slightly turned, cvd primary feathers, inscribed: 1 of 2/Lem/dated 1969, NM, 32, RB 7/07/87 3900
Sea Gull, hollow, EX orig pnt, sm chip out of top of bill/thin check in bk, otherwise EX, 1968, 175, RWO 11/06/85, 140% 1700
Sea Gull, hollow, orig pnt, minor wear, signed Lem & Steve/dated 1966, structurally EX, RWO 7/04/87 1500
Surf Scoter, NM well-blended pnt on bk, signed Lem/dated 1970, minor age line on underside, 33, J/G 9/19/87 1600
Widgeon, balsa body, overpnt w/some traces of orig, heavy wear, neck has been reglued/head is loose, RB 8/25/88 425
Widgeon drake, balsa body, EX orig pnt, average wear, minor pit marks on body, ca 1948, w/photo of Lem, RB 7/07/87 3600
Widgeon drake, balsa body, M pnt, minor rub at tip of tail w/pnt dabbed over it, dent along 1 side, RWO 7/06/86 2000
Widgeon drake, preening, raised cvd wings, cvd feather detail to tail/wings, EX & orig, ca 1960, RB 7/09/85 3100
Widgeon drake, preening, raised wings, pnt incomplete, lacking wing detail, signed Lem/dated 1977, RB 3/06/87 3000
Widgeon drake, working model, slightly turned head, balsa body, signed/dated 1954, M condition, J/G 4/24/86 2200
Widgeon hen, balsa body, EX orig pnt, ca 1956, RB 7/09/85 1800
Widgeon hen, balsa body, EX orig pnt, minor wear, body has been varnished, ca 1945, RB 7/09/85 1400
Widgeon hen, balsa body, EX orig pnt, minor wear, well preserved, RB 8/21/86 1750
Widgeon hen, sleeping, balsa body, fine orig pnt, minor wear, slight age splitting, from Lem's rig, 21, RB 2/01/85 3000
Widgeon hen, working model, slightly turned head, balsa body, signed/dated 1954, M condition, J/G 4/24/86 2200
Widgeon pr, hen has 2 sm areas where pnt has flaked away, signed Lem & Steve/dated 1969, outstanding, RWO 7/05/85 4600
Ward Brothers, att (Crisfield, MD)
Canada Goose, hollowed from bottom, old pnt, average wear, dated 1920, thin cracks in neck/body, 193, RWO 7/02/88 270

Canada Goose, laminated body construction, G working rpt, head may be an old replacement, 193, RWO 7/02/88, 50% 300
Canada Goose, old rpt, average flaking/wear, some slight age splitting, old repair to base of neck, RB 7/07/87 200
Pintail drake, balsa body, old pnt, moderate flaking/wear, bill chip has been reglued, RB 3/11/88, 133% 400

Warin, George (Toronto, Ont)
Black Duck, early, low-head style, hollow, G orig pnt on head, orig pnt/minor working touchup on body, 181, J/G 9/20/86 850
Black Duck, low-head style, old working rpt, chip missing from 1 side of bill, bottom board replaced, J/G 9/19/87 550
Black Duck, low-head style, old working rpt taken down to orig, minor wear, ls, 181, J/G 9/20/86 500
Black Duck, low-head style, thin-shelled, pnt has been rstr, from St Clair Flats Shooting Club, 1889-1908, RWO 7/04/87 800
Bluebill drake, fine head cvg, orig comb pnt, minor wear, no structural flaws, J/G 9/19/87 950
Bluebill hen, fine orig pnt, minor flaking/wear, 189, RB 6/28/88 225
Bluebill hen, orig pnt w/fine feathering on bk/lower sides, minor wear, no structural flaws, J/G 9/20/86 1150
Canada Goose, EX orig feather pnt, average wear, sm portion of bill missing/lg chip at tail, ca 1875, RWO 7/06/86, 63% 7500
Canvasback drake, low-head style, orig pnt, minor wear, most of bill is prof rpl, branded AL, ca 1880, rare, J/G 4/23/87 650
Redhead drake, hollow, EX orig pnt, average wear, ls, otherwise well preserved, rare, RB 7/09/85 1800
Redhead drake, hollow, fine comb pnt on bk & sides, crack in side of head has been filled, ls, rare, J/G 9/19/87 850
Redhead drake, orig pnt, moderate wear, fine feather pnt on wing tips, sm knothole on 1 side, rare, 180, J/G 9/20/86 900

Warin, George; att (Toronto, Ont)
Black Duck, early, hollow, orig pnt, moderate wear, ls, oversize, J/G 9/20/86 550
Mallard drake, low-head style, hollow, old working rpt, structurally EX, ca 1900, RWO 7/04/87 450

Waterfield, J.; and Beasley, W. (Knott's Island, NC)
Ruddy Duck, working rpt, minor age lines/rough area on 1 edge of tail, rare, 33, J/G 9/19/87 1400

Waterfield, Reggie (Knott's Island, VA)
Greenwinged Teal hen, orig pnt, bill broken off & reglued, ca 1940, RWO 7/04/87 50

Watson, Dave (Chincoteague, VA)
Black Duck, feeding, balsa body, headless, orig pnt, EX condition, RWO 2/13/87 225
Black Duck, hollow w/cvd 'V' tail, EX orig pnt, minor wear, slight age split in side of head, rare, 76, RB 7/09/85 4200
Black Duck, hollow w/cvd wing tips, orig pnt, heavy wear, old repair to bill, rare, RB 12/06/85 1100
Black Duck, sleeping, balsa body, rpt in style of Watson, structurally sound, RWO 2/12/88 500

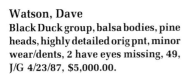

Watson, Dave
Black Duck group, balsa bodies, pine heads, highly detailed orig pnt, minor wear/dents, 2 have eyes missing, 49, J/G 4/23/87, $5,000.00.

Brant, hollow, old working rpt, average wear, hairline crack in bill, otherwise EX, ca 1920's, rare, RWO 11/11/87, 70% 1100
Brant, hollow, rpt in Watson style, structurally EX, ca 1920's, RWO 7/05/85 1050
Canada Goose, balsa 2-pc body, old working rpt, several tight age splits in head/neck, rare, J/G 4/23/87, 75% 1000
Canada Goose, hollow, working rpt, average wear, age check down bk/thin crack in neck, ca 1920's, RWO 7/05/85 1600
Pintail drake, hollow, old rpt in the Watson style, structurally VG, RWO 7/05/85 700
Pintail drake, old pnt taken down to orig w/average wear, rare, J/G 9/19/87 625
Redhead drake, hollow, orig pnt, underside of bill has a lg chip, ms, RB 8/21/86 450

Watson, Dave; att (Chincoteague, VA)
Black Duck, solid body, old pnt, heavy wear, lg chip running down bk/2 lesser cracks in body & head, RWO 7/04/87 120
Plover, old pnt, average wear, some slight dry rot to 1 side, bill is a replacement, RB 8/21/86 375

Redhead drake, cvd 'V' tail, old pnt worn to natural wood in many areas, several age splits to body, 3, RB 7/09/85 275
Watson, Dick
Merganser pr, fine orig pnt, artist brand/dated 1978, RB 3/06/87 150
Watson, Milton (Chesapeake City, MD)
Canvasback drake, fine orig pnt, minor wear, RB 2/01/85 275

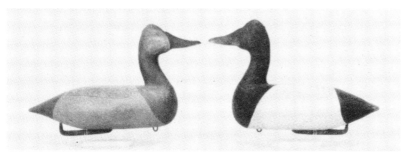

Watson, Milton
Canvasback pr, fine orig pnt, minor wear, RB 3/06/87, $500.00.

Canvasback pr, high-heads, M/unused, ca 1950's, RWO 11/11/87 750
Canvasback pr, orig pnt, few dings to wood, otherwise structurally EX, ca 1950, RWO 11/06/85 210
Watts, Vanentine (Lawrence, LI, NY)
Ruddy Turnstone, NM orig pnt, ls, ca 1890, very rare, J/G 9/19/87, 60% 3500
Webber, Fred (Peru, IL)
Pintail drake, early, old working rpt, no structural flaws, J/G 4/24/86 192
Weeks, Robert (Bureau, IL)
Greenwinged Teal pr, NM orig detailed pnt, artist stamp, structurally EX, J/G 9/19/87 425
Mallard drake, old working rpt, old chip in top of tail, J/G 4/23/87 175
Mallard pr, M condition, 7, J/G 4/24/86 440
Mallard pr, sleeping, hollow, M pnt, artist stamp, J/G 9/20/86 275
Pintail drake, sm chip out of tip of tail, otherwise M, tight crack in neck, 7, J/G 4/24/86 330
Weeks, William
Teal, pnt in white primer w/flaking & some slight age splitting, 22/44, RB 5/02/86 375
Weir, A.
Black Duck, hollow, EX condition, RB 8/25/88 50
Bluebill drake, hollow, fine orig pnt, minor wear, RB 8/25/88 75
Welles, Ralph
Black Duck, hollow, outstanding orig condition, ca 1945, RWO 7/05/85 675
Wells, C.V. (Milwaukee, WI)
Canvasback drake, canvas over cork body w/wooden head, old working rpt, no structural flaws, oversize, J/G 4/24/86 99
Wells, Charles R. (Stratford, CT)
Black Duck, cork body, chips around tail area/shallow chip on right side of bill, ls, RB 3/06/87 50
Black Duck, hollow, old working rpt, average wear, major crack in neck is secured w/nails, head is loose, RWO 2/12/88 ... 150
Black Duck, hollow, orig pnt, average wear w/rubs to bare wood on head, artist brand, EX condition, RWO 7/06/86 230
Black Duck, sleeping, hollow, EX & orig condition, RWO 2/12/88 700
Bluebill drake, early, hollow, orig pnt, artist brand, ls, otherwise sound, 95, RWO 7/04/87 200
Bluebill drake, early, hollow, orig pnt, in-use wear, artist brand, ls, structurally sound, oversize, RWO 11/11/87 310
Bluebill drake, slightly turned head, hollow, old working rpt, bill has been broken off & reglued, J/G 9/20/86 140
Bluebill hen, hollow, old working rpt, artist brand, no structural flaws, J/G 9/20/86 65
Bluebill hen, hollow w/raised wing cvg, orig scratch pnt, average wear, artist brand, structurally EX, RWO 11/11/87 175
Bluebill hen, raised cvd wings, orig pnt, average wear, artist brand, RWO 7/04/87 375
Bluebill pr, hollow, working rpt, average wear, structurally sound, RWO 2/12/88 120
Broadbill, hollow, orig pnt, average wear, artist brand, bill is an old replacement, RB 3/06/87 150
Mallard drake, hollow, fine orig pnt, minor wear, RB 3/06/87 325
Mallard drake, hollow, working rpt, average wear, comb pnt on bk, artist brand, 1940's, EX condition, RWO 7/06/86 190
Whistler, hollow, EX pnt, artist brand, 39, RB 7/08/86 500
Wells, Gene
Black Duck, old pnt worn to natural wood in many areas, structurally sound, RB 7/09/85 750
Wells, John (Toronto, Ont)
Black Duck, EX orig pnt, minor wear, fine feathering on bk of head, chip at end of tail, 53/68, RB 7/07/87, 75% 1100
Black Duck, hollow, G old pnt, moderate wear, tight age split at base of neck, J/G 9/20/86 200
Black Duck, NM orig pnt, artist brand, crack running part way up bk/tiny tail chip, J/G 4/24/86 550

Black Duck, old pnt, heavy wear, age split in neck, branded C Cook, 39, RB 7/08/86	50
Black Duck, orig pnt, average wear, ls, J/G 4/24/86	300
Black Duck, solid body w/thick bottom board, old pnt, some of which may be orig, ms, otherwise sound, RWO 7/02/88	180
Bluebill drake, NM orig pnt, EX combing on bk/feather pnt on sides, tight crack in base of neck, J/G 4/24/86	742
Bluebill drake, orig pnt w/fine feathering, minor wear, J/G 9/20/86	350
Bluebill hen, hollow, orig pnt, minor wear & touchup, ls, ca 1895, J/G 4/23/87	500
Bluebill hen, rpt as Redhead by Chas Reeves, structurally sound, branded JR Wells, ca 1920, J/G 4/23/87	105
Canvasback, old rpt, heavy wear, left eye is a replacement, ms, RB 7/07/87	175
Canvasback drake, G old rpt, branded AS Ward, eyes are missing, ls, J/G 9/19/87	325
Canvasback drake, hollow, working rpt, minor crazing/wear, artist brand, structurally EX, rare, J/G 4/23/87	700
Canvasback drake, NM orig pnt, CE Chandler's brand, prof rstr to edge of bill, J/G 9/19/87	600
Canvasback drake, orig pnt, minor wear, branded, no structural flaws, J/G 4/24/86	495
Canvasback drake, orig pnt, rpt to wht areas, minor wear, old rpr to edge of bill, ca 1915, J/G 4/23/87	650
Canvasback hen, hollow, EX orig comb/feather pnt, separation where head/body meet, ls, EX, 193, RWO 7/02/88, 155%	14000
Mallard drake, hollow, pnt taken down to orig w/minor wear, branded Buck, ls, J/G 9/19/87	1050
Mallard drake, hollow, working overpnt taken down to reveal much orig, branded JRW, structurally sound, RWO 7/02/88	1200
Mallard drake, old pnt, average wear, artist stamp, structurally sound, RB 12/06/85	300
Pintail drake, hollow, orig pnt, average wear, artist brand, thin neck crack, otherwise EX, ca 1920's, RWO 7/06/86, 375%	3750

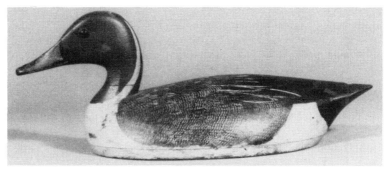

Wells, John
Pintail drake, orig pnt, average wear, branded JRW/EN pnt in red, lg tail chips/hs, otherwise EX, RWO 2/12/88, $2,950.00.

Redhead drake, EX orig pnt, minor wear, artist brand, no structural flaws, J/G 9/20/86	300
Redhead drake, fine comb/feather pnt, structurally sound, branded AL, J/G 4/23/87	500
Redhead drake, hollow, old pnt, may be orig, artist brand, 1 eye missing, bill is a prof replacement, ls, RWO 11/11/87	170
Redhead drake, orig pnt w/areas of working touchup, branded, half of bill is a replacement, 1920's, RWO 11/06/85	220
Redhead hen, EX orig pnt, average wear, hairline crack on side of bk, ca 1920, EX condition, RWO 11/06/85	140
Shoveler drake, EX orig pnt w/fine feathering on bk/sides, minor wear to head, artist brand, rare, J/G 9/20/86, 122%	7950
Shoveler hen, body is in fine orig pnt, minor wear, artist brand, head is a prof replacement, rare, J/G 9/20/86	200

Wells, John; att (Toronto, Ont)

Redhead drake, hollow, EX orig pnt, old blk wash on bk, ls, otherwise EX, branded TH Newberry, 163, J/G 4/23/87, 125%	1500
Redhead drake, low-head, hollow, G working rpt, RWO 7/02/88	120

Wells, Ollie; att (Long Island, NY)

Canada Goose, early, old working rpt, minor wear, 2 cracks in neck/minor age lines in body/neck chip, 33, J/G 9/19/87	250

West, James (Bordentown, NJ)

Bluebill hen, hollow, fine old pnt, average flaking/wear, well preserved, RB 8/21/86	150
Bluewinged Teal drake, raised cvd wings, signed/dated 1965, hairline crack through neck, otherwise EX, RWO 7/06/86	130
Goldeneye drake, cvd primaries/secondaries, signed, M condition, 65, J/G 9/19/87	650
Greenwinged Teal pr, cvd crossed wings, signed/dated, M condition, RB 2/06/85	575
Hooded Merganser drake, fine orig pnt, minor wear, sm chip on underside of bill, RB 3/11/88	150
Redhead drake, old working rpt, minor wear, no structural flaws, J/G 9/19/87	100
Widgeon drake, slightly turned head, hollow w/cvd tail feathers/raised crossed wings, J/G 9/20/86	550

West, Joseph (Bordentown, NJ)

Black Duck, low-head, old working rpt, flaking/wear, structurally sound, RWO 7/02/88	175
Bluebill pr, hollow, drake orig pnt; hen working rpt w/some areas flaking to bare wood, structurally sound, RWO 7/04/87	130
Goldeneye drake, cvd primary feathers, EX pnt, signed/dated 1918 on bottom, RB 7/08/86	150
Pintail pr, hollow, orig pnt, average wear, structurally EX, ca 1925, RWO 7/05/85	225

Whealton (Virginia)

Dowitcher, early, old pnt appears to be orig w/some areas worn to bare wood, W cvd in bottom, EX & orig, 3, RWO 2/12/88	1250

Wheeler, Charles (Stratford, CT)

Black Duck, cork body, head has orig pnt, average wear, 22/44, RB 5/02/86, 170%	2600

Black Duck, cork body, orig pnt, heavy wear to body/EX on head, 1 glass eye missing, othewise EX, ca 1940's, RWO 7/05/85 .... **2250**
Black Duck, cork body, pnt worn to natural cork on body, ls, chip on underside of bill, 98, RB 2/01/85, 60% **1250**
Black Duck, cork body, working rpt, ca 1920's, 18/74, RWO 11/06/85, 65% **2000**
Black Duck, early, full body w/slightly turned head, hollow , old pnt, average wear, rare, RB 3/06/87, 50% **2000**

Wheeler, Charles
Black Duck hollow, handwritten presentation, M condition, slightly oversize, RWO 2/12/88, $35,000.00.

Black Duck, sleeping, cork body, fine old pnt, average wear, structurally EX, rare, 39, RB 7/08/86 .... **8000**
Black Duck, sleeping, cork body, orig pnt, 2 sm chunks missing from tail, otherwise sound, rare, 8, RWO 7/06/86 .... **3250**
Black Duck, sleeping, early overpnt to black areas, head & speculum may be orig, ca 1895, EX condition, RWO 7/05/86 .... **9500**
Black Duck, sleeping, fine old pnt, minor wear, chip on tail/slight age split in neck, 21, RB 2/01/85 .... **5000**
Black Duck, sleeping, hollow, fine old pnt, average flaking/wear, age split in neck, rare, 22/44, RB 5/02/86 .... **9000**
Black Duck, slightly turned highly detailed head, NM orig pnt, ls, made for mayor of Milford CT, 48, J/G 4/24/86 .... **6600**
Bluebill drake, balsa body w/pine head, NM orig pnt, EX comb pnt on bk, several sm dents in balsa, rare, J/G 4/23/87 .... **3200**
Bluebill drake, cork body, fine old pnt, average wear, old break in neck has been reglued, 22, RB 5/02/86 .... **1250**
Bluebill drake, early, cork body, cedar head/tail, never weighted or used, 27, J/G 9/20/86 .... **6500**
Bluebill hen, cork body, head has orig pnt, minor wear, 22, RB 5/02/86 .... **450**
Bluebill hen, cork body, head retains fine orig pnt, body is natural cork, RB 6/28/88 .... **775**
Bluebill hen, cork body, pnt speculum, head has orig w/some overpnt, average wear, 22, RB 5/02/86 .... **600**
Bluebill hen, cork body, some pnt flaking on bill, no major structural flaws, orig condition, RWO 7/02/88 .... **500**
Bluebill pr, slightly turned heads, cork body w/pine heads/keels, NM orig pnt, structurally EX, rare, 95/27, J/G 9/19/87 .... **6500**
Bufflehead, early, rpt as Goldeneye, few chips at tail/few dings, retains orig teardrop weight, 17, RWO 7/06/86, 32% **1100**
Bufflehead hen, hollow, NM pnt w/EX feather pnt pattern, rare, Ex-collection CT Audubon Society, RB 8/21/86 .... **7000**
Mallard drake, hollow w/raised cvd wing tips, EX orig scratch feather pnt, RB 7/08/86, 75% **6000**
Old Squaw, hollow, old rpt, average flaking/wear, signed by Tom Marshall, structurally sound, RB 6/28/88 .... **5500**
Passenger Pigeon, full body, raised wings, EX pnt, sm rough area on wing tip edge, otherwise M, 16", 27/95, J/G 9/20/86 .... **15000**
Pintail drake, slightly turned head, intricate comb pnt, M/unused, 111/134, J/G 9/20/86 .... **13000**
Redhead pr, drake is asleep; hen has slightly turned head, exceptional feather & comb pnt, ls, rare, 95/11, J/G 4/23/87 .... **23000**
Surf Scoter, hollow, NM condition, pictured in 1948 photo National Decoy Makers Contest in 'Shang,' 111/134, J/G 9/20/86 .... **6500**
Surf Scoter, outstanding orig condition, rare, RWO 7/05/85 .... **7000**
Whistler, hollow, rpt as a Black Duck by Ben Holmes, minor wear, old break in bill, 39, RB 7/08/86 .... **900**
Widgeon drake, bill/pnt prof rstr by Kenneth DeLong, made for Cornelius Vanderbilt, rare, RWO 7/02/88, 17% **1000**
Wheeler, Charles; att (Stratford, CT)
Bluebill hen, cork body, head has orig pnt w/minor wear, RB 12/06/85 .... **250**
Wheeler, Chauncey (Alexandria Bay, NY)
Black Duck, high-head style, orig pnt w/minor touchup, slight separation where body halves join, ca 1930, RWO 7/04/87 .... **800**
Black Duck, hollow, EX orig pnt, minor wear, tail chip, ls, J/G 4/24/86 .... **935**
Black Duck, old working rpt, 2 tight checks in body/several sm chips, J/G 4/23/87 .... **225**
Bluebill drake, fine orig pnt, average wear, EX comb feather pnt on bk, 189, RB 6/28/88 .... **800**
Bluebill drake, G orig scratch pnt, average wear w/few rubs to bare wood, structurally EX, ca 1930, RWO 7/06/86 .... **525**
Bluebill drake, old pnt, average wear, minor age splitting to body, ls, RB 8/25/88 .... **425**
Bluebill hen, fine old pnt, average wear, well preserved, RB 3/06/87, 185% **950**
Bluebill hen, fine orig pnt, average wear, RB 3/06/87 .... **550**

Bluebill hen, NM orig pnt, minor wear, superb shadowing/feather pnt, minor age split along breast/bk, RB 8/25/88 1350
Bluebill pr, M orig pnt, head on hen has been broken off & reglued, RB 7/08/86 1050
Bluebill pr, rpt w/heavy wear, old repair to hen's bill, RB 7/08/86 200

Wheeler, Chauncey
Brant, cvd wings/tail feathers, fine orig feather pnt branded WFB prof chip rpr, otherwise NM, J/G 9/19/87, $3,950.00.

Brant, relief cvg on bk, EX orig pnt, average wear, slight short check on bk, otherwise EX, ca 1920's, RWO 11/11/87, 47% 950
Canvasback drake, balsa body w/cedar head/tail, NM orig pnt w/EX combing, slight separation on bk, oversize, J/G 9/20/86 1700
Canvasback drake, slightly turned head, NM orig pnt, comb-pnt bk/sides, structurally VG, branded, oversize, J/G 4/23/87 1250
Canvasback drake, traces of orig pnt w/heavy wear, several age splits/dry rot on breast, end-of-tail chip, RB 3/11/88 70
Canvasback pr, NM orig pnt w/fine combing on drake, both have slightly blunted tail tips/cracks, 21" long, J/G 4/23/87 6350
Goldeneye drake, orig pnt, minor wear, ls, rare, J/G 4/23/87 400
Goldeneye hen, EX orig pnt, minor wear, structurally NM, RB 7/07/87, 200% 2000
Goldeneye hen, EX orig pnt, w/some overpnt, some flaking to side/bk, otherwise average in-use wear, RB 8/25/88 700
Goldeneye hen, old rpt in Wheeler's style, average wear, slight age split in neck, RB 2/01/85 125
Old Squaw hen, slightly turned head, comb pnt, minor wear, branded WFB, 2 hairlines/checks, rare, J/G 9/19/87 2750
Redhead drake, EX orig pnt w/fine comb pnt on bk, ls, otherwise EX, ca 1930-1940, RWO 7/02/88, 125% 2200
Redhead drake, flying, exceptional NM comb pnt, sm chip ea side of ft/1 on wing tip, very rare, full-size, J/G 9/19/87 3250
Redhead drake, old rpt, considerable wear, RB 12/06/85 65
Redhead hen, orig pnt, minor wear on extremeties, ls, otherwise structurally EX, J/G 4/23/87 925
Wheeler, Chauncey; att (Alexandria Bay, NY)
Black Duck, EX orig pnt, minor wear, RB 7/07/87 700
Black Duck, fine orig pnt, average wear, 39, RB 7/08/86 350
Bluebill hen, old rpt, average wear, RB 12/06/85 50
Whipple, Mark (Bourg, LA)
Canvasback drake, G orig pnt, minor flaking/wear, sm rough area on edge of tail, rare, J/G 4/24/86 220
Mallard drake, orig pnt, average wear, bill broken off & missing/thin check on bk, otherwise sound, RWO 7/04/87 775
Pintail drake, orig pnt, moderate flaking/wear, slight age splitting to body/bill has been reglued, rare, RB 7/07/87 500
Ringbill drake, fine old pnt, possibly orig, somewhat flaked, RB 7/09/85 250
Ringbill drake, fine orig pnt, average flaking/wear, structurally sound, RB 3/11/88 750
Whipple, Roy
Mallard drake, old rpt, average wear, old break in neck, RB 8/21/86 150
White, Al (East Sandwich, MA)
Blackbellied Plover, EX pnt, signed on bottom, RB 7/09/85 100
Blackbellied Plover, slightly turned head, EX pnt, signed on bottom, RB 7/09/85 90
Curlew, EX pnt, signed on bottom, RB 7/09/85 175
White, Bob (Tullytown, PA)
Black Duck, low-head, hollow, cvd primaries, EX & orig condition, RWO 7/02/88 220
Bluebill, hollow, EX & orig, RB 7/09/85 400
Bluebill drake, low-head style, orig pnt, minor wear, structurally EX, RWO 7/04/87 150
Bluebill drake, relief wing cvg, NM orig pnt, inscribed: Bob White 1892 Shooting Stool, structurally EX, J/G 9/19/87 325
Brant, hollow, orig pnt, minor blistering from heat exposure, artist brand, ca 1960's, RWO 7/04/87 210
Brant, hollow, orig pnt w/minor blistering on bottom due to sun exposure, structurally sound, RWO 2/13/87 185
Brant, hollow, swimming, EX orig pnt, artist stamp, RB 3/06/87 250
Canvasback drake, hunting model, orig pnt, minor wear, slight separation where neck joins body, J/G 4/23/87 175

Canvasback drake, sleeping, hollow, cvd tail feathers, EX orig pnt, signed R White Decoys on weight, RB 8/27/87 .... **300**
Canvasback pr, heads tucked down, hollow, orig pnt, minor flaking/wear, otherwise EX, RB 6/28/88, 50% **200**
Gadwall, early, slightly tucked head, Delaware River style, artist logo, triangular weight, RWO 7/04/87 .... **280**
Gadwall drake, hollow w/raised cvd wing/tail feathers, orig weight on underside, rare, J/G 9/20/86 .... **600**
Gadwall hen, cvd raised wing tips, fine orig pnt, signed/dated 1983, rare, RB 6/28/88, 50% **150**
Greenwinged Teal hen, swimming, EX condition, RB 3/11/88 .... **200**
Greenwinged Teal pr, hollow, cvd raised wing tips, EX orig pnt, minor flaking/wear, signed/dated, RB 6/28/88, 62% **375**
Hooded Merganser pr, artist's oval brand, EX & orig condition, RWO 2/12/88, 150% **600**
Hooded Merganser pr, cvd in Delaware style, artist's oval brand, EX & orig condition, RWO 7/02/88 .... **600**
Pintail drake, hollow, EX orig pnt, signed on bottom, RB 7/08/86 .... **350**
Pintail hen, hollow, EX & orig condition, 3, RB 6/28/88 .... **350**
Plover, orig pnt, minor wear, signed, ls, J/G 4/23/87 .... **75**
Ruddy Turnstone, signed/dated 1981, M condition, RWO 7/04/87 .... **95**
Widgeon hen, hollow, cvd raised wing tips, fine orig pnt, signed/dated 1976, RB 6/28/88 .... **150**
Wood Duck, early, styrofoam body, orig pnt, structurally sound, RWO 11/06/85 .... **100**

White, Roy (Knott's Island, NC)
Canvasback pr, drake has raised wings, structurally EX, RWO 7/04/87 .... **110**

White, Windsor
Bufflehead drake, old pnt, heavy flaking/wear, structurally sound, 22, RB 5/02/86 .... **275**

Whitmore, Charles (New Boston, IL)
Bluebill drake, slightly turned head, hollow, old working rpt, minor wear, no structural flaws, J/G 4/24/86 .... **100**

Whitney, James (Falmouth, ME)
Black Duck, EX pnt, artist brand, RB 7/09/85 .... **100**
Black Duck, preening, EX pnt, RB 12/06/85 .... **225**
Black Duck, preening, orig pnt, average wear, artist brand, RWO 7/02/88 .... **75**
Black Duck, slightly turned head, EX pnt, artist brand, oversize, RB 7/09/85 .... **150**
Black Duck, swimming, branded JH Whitney, age split in bottom, otherwise EX & orig condition, RB 6/28/88 .... **200**
Black Duck, swimming, fine orig pnt, minor wear, artist brand, RB 7/09/85 .... **140**
Black Duck, working rpt, average wear, structurally sound, RWO 11/06/85 .... **90**
Canada Goose, branded Whitney, EX & orig condition, oversize, RWO 2/12/88 .... **130**

Whittington, Hector (Oglesby, IL)
Black Duck, EX orig pnt, artist stamp/signed, no structural flaws, ca 1935, rare, J/G 9/19/87 .... **1000**
Black Duck, orig pnt, minor crazing/wear, rstr chip on side of bill/hairline at neck base, ca 1935, J/G 4/23/87 .... **1100**
Bluebill drake, early, G working rpt, no structural flaws, ca 1926, J/G 4/24/86 .... **110**
Bluebill drake, early, old pnt, average wear, shallow chip on left side of bill, ca 1935, RB 7/09/85 .... **200**
Coot, artist stamp/dated 1979, M condition, J/G 4/23/87 .... **225**
Coot, hollow, signed/stamped/dated 1979, M condition, RB 12/06/85 .... **400**
Greenwinged Teal hen, hollow, EX pnt, artist stamp, dated 1974, RB 7/07/87 .... **650**
Mallard drake, hollow, EX orig condition, ca 1936, RWO 7/05/85 .... **900**
Mallard drake, hollow, fine orig pnt, heavy in-use wear, chip on underside of bill, RB 7/09/85 .... **300**
Mallard drake, old working rpt, signed on bottom, structurally sound, ca 1926, J/G 4/23/87 .... **350**
Mallard drake, slightly turned head, orig pnt, moderate crazing on head/wings, retains orig weight, 7, J/G 4/24/86 .... **770**
Mallard drake, thick comb pnt, streamlined, sm rough area on bill, rstr/rpt chip, ca 1930's, rare, J/G 9/19/87, 50% **650**
Mallard hen, head slightly tilted down, hollow, fine orig pnt, average wear, ms, RB 7/09/85 .... **250**
Mallard hen, slightly turned head, hollow, EX orig pnt, minor flaking/wear, 39, RB 7/08/86 .... **525**
Mallard hen, slightly turned head, hollow, VG orig pnt, flaking/wear, 39, RB 7/08/86 .... **400**
Mallard pr, slightly turned heads, artist stamp, hairline crack under bill, otherwise M, J/G 9/20/86 .... **750**
Merganser drake, American; slightly turned head, hollow, cvd wing tips, artist stamp/1957, oversize, M, J/G 4/23/87, 55% **1000**
Old Squaw pr, slightly turned heads, artist stamp, M condition, rare, J/G 4/23/87 .... **1000**
Old Squaw pr, slightly turned heads, artist stamp/dated 1973, M condition, J/G 9/20/86 .... **750**
Pintail drake, early, hollow, old pnt, average wear, well preserved, RB 8/21/86 .... **850**
Pintail drake, hollow, EX orig pnt, average wear, age split in neck, ms, ca 1930, rare, RB 7/09/85, 50% **450**
Pintail drake, hollow, EX orig pnt, minor crazing around head, structurally EX, ca 1950, RWO 7/04/87 .... **1900**
Pintail drake, hollow, EX orig pnt, minor wear, thin crack in neck/ls, ca 1925-1928, 193, RWO 7/02/88, 40% **800**
Pintail drake, hollow, fine orig pnt, average wear, chip at end of tail/age split at neck, 7/20, RB 12/06/85 .... **425**
Pintail drake, 2 sm pnt flakes off of head, otherwise M, ca 1970's, 7, J/G 4/24/86 .... **385**
Pintail hen, fine orig pnt, average wear, rstr to tip of bill, crack in neck is reglued, rare, J/G 4/24/86 .... **385**
Pintail hen, hollow, G orig pnt w/some flaking along 1 side/bk, ca 1920's, 193, RWO 7/02/88, 25% **300**
Pintail hen, hollow, G pnt, minor in-use wear, structurally EX, RWO 7/05/85 .... **380**
Pintail pr, hen is sleeping, NM condition, both signed/dated 1966, RB 7/09/85 .... **900**
Pintail pr, hollow w/highly detailed bill cvg, drake has sm rub on top of head, otherwise M, J/G 9/20/86 .... **850**

Pintail pr, NM orig pnt, artist stamp, signed/dated 1970, structurally EX, J/G 4/23/87 750

Wickerson, R.

Goldeneye hen, hollow, fine old orig pnt, no structural flaws, J/G 4/24/86 110

Wilbur, Charles (Island Heights, NJ)

Brant, hollow, artist brand, M condition, RB 12/06/85 80

Brant, hollow, fine orig pnt, minor wear, artist brand, RB 7/08/86 125

Brant, hollow, NM orig pnt, artist brand, no structural flaws, J/G 9/19/87 150

Brant, hollow, orig pnt, average wear, RB 3/11/88 175

Brant, NM orig pnt, artist brand, no structural flaws, J/G 4/24/86 395

Brant, preening, hollow, EX orig pnt, crack in neck, otherwise structurally sound, ca 1950's, RWO 11/11/87 200

Crow, cvd thighs/split tail, orig pnt, structurally EX, RWO 7/06/86 150

Wilbur, Pete (Island Heights, NJ)

Bluebill pr, G orig pnt, average wear, ls, RB 7/08/86 175

Bluebill pr, hollow, fine orig pnt, minor flaking/wear, slight age split in drake's neck, RB 8/27/87 150

Gull, hollow, EX pnt, branded HCM, RB 2/01/85 325

Wilbur, Pete; att (Island Heights, NJ)

Brant, hollow, fine orig pnt, minor wear, well preserved, 39, RB 7/08/86 175

Brant, hollow, old pnt, average flaking/wear, end of bill broken off & reglued, RB 7/08/86 60

Wilbur Family (Island Heights, NJ)

Canada Goose, old working rpt w/some orig showing through, sm crack in bill/part way through neck, J/G 9/19/87 250

Wilcoxen, Charles (Liverpool, IL)

Mallard drake, hollow, orig pnt, average wear w/few rubs to bare wood, structurally sound, ca 1930, RWO 7/04/87 130

Wilcoxen, Chester (Liverpool, IL)

Canvasback drake, early, hollow, old working rpt, in-use wear, bill has been broken & reglued, neck crack, RWO 7/02/88 70

Wilcoxen, Perry (Liverpool, IL)

Canvasback drake, hollow, EX orig pnt, minor wear, branded Rawling, structurally NM, ca 1930's, RWO 7/04/87 375

Canvasback drake, old working rpt, no structural flaws, retains orig weight, J/G 4/24/86 302

Coot, hollow, old working rpt, minor wear, structurally EX, J/G 4/24/86 330

Greenwinged Teal drake, hollow, rpt w/minor wear, 39, RB 7/08/86 350

Mallard drake, early, orig pnt, minor wear, ls, oversize, 168, J/G 9/19/87 385

Mallard drake, hollow, deep body, EX orig pnt, fine structural condition, ca 1930, RWO 7/05/85 475

Mallard drake, hollow, fine orig pnt, average wear, RB 12/06/85 450

Mallard drake, hollow, orig pnt, average wear, structurally EX, ca 1930's, RWO 7/02/88 180

Mallard drake, hollow, orig pnt w/old working touchup around bottom, structurally sound, RWO 2/13/87 170

Mallard drake, NM orig pnt, structurally EX, 7, J/G 4/24/86 412

Mallard drake, old pnt, minor flaking/wear, structurally sound, 21, RB 2/01/85 150

Mallard drake, old working rpt, heavy flaking/wear, crack in neck/sm dings to wood on body, RWO 7/04/87 60

Pintail drake, hollow, G orig pnt, average wear, thin crack in neck, otherwise structurally EX, ca 1935, RWO 7/06/86 475

Pintail drake, hollow, NM orig comb pnt on bk/sides, structurally EX, rare, oversize, J/G 4/23/87 350

Pintail drake, old working rpt, worn to reveal orig, crack through neck, otherwise sound, ca 1930's, RWO 11/11/87 165

Ringneck, EX orig pnt, average wear, no physical flaws, rare, RWO 7/05/85 200

Wilcoxen, Perry; att (Liverpool, IL)

Mallard hen, hollow, old working rpt, average wear, crack in neck/1 glass eye missing, otherwise sound, RWO 2/12/88 170

Wilcoxen, Richard (Liverpool, IL)

Canvasback hen, hollow, orig pnt w/working touchup to sides, structurally sound, ca 1920, RWO 11/11/87 245

Greenwinged Teal drake, hollow, orig pnt w/crazed varnish, head is reglued, otherwise sound, ca 1920, RWO 7/02/88 475

Wilcoxen, Richard
Greenwinged Teal pr, hollow, fine comb/feather pnt, minor wear, ca 1910, used at Crane Lake IL Gun Club, J/G 4/23/87, $2,050.00.

Wilcoxen, Wilmer (Liverpool, IL)

Canvasback drake, early, hollow, old working rpt, in-use wear, working rpr to bill, ca 1919, RWO 7/02/88 70

Mallard drake, old working rpt, no structural flaws, rare, J/G 4/24/86 165

Wilkenson, H.W. (Owen Sound, Ont)
Bluebill drake, NM orig pnt, 3 hairlines in breast/1 has nailed repair, rare, J/G 9/19/87 150
Williams, John (Cedar Island, VA)
Bluebill, old working rpt worn to orig pnt & bare wood in many areas, tight cracks in neck, rare, 33/124, J/G 9/19/87 2950
Ruddy Duck, early, orig pnt worn to mostly natural wood, ls, RB 7/08/86, 160% 4000
Ruddy Duck, old working rpt, tight check on bk/minor dings, otherwise structurally sound, ca 1890, RWO 7/04/87 2800
Ruddy Duck, prof bill rstr, otherwise VG condition, ca 1880's to 1890's, extremely rare, RWO 11/06/85 5500
Swan, bill is doweled into head, old rpt w/minor wear, filled-in age split, 33, J/G 9/19/87, 70% 4500
Swan, rpt, minor wear, head is a replacement, several minor age splits, well preserved, 9, RB 12/06/85 350
Williams, T.; att
Merganser drake, early, cvd eyes, orig pnt, heavy flaking, artist brand, some dry rot on bottom, rare, RB 7/09/85 2200
Merganser hen, early, cvd eyes, orig pnt, heavy flaking/wear, some dry rot on bottom, rare, RB 7/09/85 2000
Willis, Eldon (Stacey, NC)
Pintail drake, orig pnt, average wear, 2 age splits, several age lines, rare, 33/120, J/G 9/19/87 950
Willis, M. Wayne
Greenwinged Teal pr, cvd wing tips/primary feathers, M pnt, signed/dated 1955 on bottom, 21, RB 2/01/85 500

Wilson, Charles
Black Duck, hollow, orig pnt, narrow check running through neck, EX form/grace, ca 1880, rare, RWO 11/11/87, $7,000.00.

Wilson, Gus (South Portland, ME)
Black Duck, fine orig pnt, average wear, head has been prof reattached by Delong, 22, RB 5/02/86 700
Black Duck, full body, inlet head, cvd eyes, raised cvd wings, fine orig pnt, well preserved, RB 2/01/85 600
Black Duck, head to side & slightly lifted, EX orig pnt, some areas worn to bare wood, structurally VG, RWO 7/05/85 2250
Black Duck, high-head style, stylish, minor rpt, hairline crack in neck, otherwise EX, RWO 7/05/85 1650
Black Duck, inlet head, cvd wings/eyes, orig pnt, minor wear, several tight checks in body/neck, ls, J/G 4/24/86, 195% ... 1980
Black Duck, inlet head, raised wing outline, cvd eyes, old working rpt, well done neck rpr, J/G 4/23/87 250
Black Duck, inlet head, well defined wing cvg, cvd eyes, EX & orig, RB 12/06/85 1500
Black Duck, open bill, wooden fish in its mouth, EX orig pnt, thin neck crack/minor split in bill, rare, RWO 7/05/85 11000
Black Duck, orig pnt, average wear, thin checks on bk/2 cracks in neck, otherwise sound, 1930's, RWO 2/13/87 550
Black Duck, preening, head turned bk/bill tucked under wing, cvd wings (1 raised), EX orig pnt, rare, RB 7/07/87, 165% ... 16500
Black Duck, rocking head, cvd wings/eyes, fine orig pnt, minor wear, age split in neck, rare, RB 7/09/85, 160% 1750
Black Duck, rocking head, raised cvd wing tips, old pnt, average wear, some age splits on neck, rare, 22/44, RB 5/02/86 .. 2400
Black Duck, sleeping, cvd wings, fine old pnt, average wear, 22/44, RB 5/02/86, 130% 6500
Black Duck, slightly turned head, hollow, G orig pnt, average wear, structurally sound, RWO 7/06/86 600
Black Duck, slightly turned head, inlet neck, cvd moulded wings, NM orig pnt, branded JB Chase, rare, RB 7/07/87, 50% .. 1000
Black Duck, slightly turned inlet head, raised cvd wings, fine orig pnt, slight wear, sm neck crack, J/G 4/24/86, 175% ... 1760
Black Duck, slightly turned inlet head, raised wings, cvd eyes, G old pnt, minor wear, ms, 114, J/G 4/24/86, 200% 2420
Bufflehead drake, flying, overpnt taken down to orig, age check runs down breast, prof rpl foot, RWO 11/06/85 1500
Common Scoter, swivel head, cvd eyes/fluted tail/slightly raised wings, NM/never used, 114, J/G 4/24/86, 225% 2750
Eider drake, EX orig pnt, alligatoring to white pnt, fine tight checks, RWO 7/02/88 2500
Eider drake, neck outstretched, hollow, some overpnt removed to reveal orig, prof rpr bill/tail chip, RWO 7/05/85 7500
Eider drake, slightly turned inlet head, hollow, cvd bill/eyes, old working rpt, tight check in neck, ls, J/G 4/23/87 1600
Eider drake, wide/inlet head touches breast, rpt taken down to orig, check on side, horseshoe weight, RWO 7/06/86, 130% ... 18000
Eider hen, early, inlet head, G working rpt, pc of wood on wing is secured by nail/sm tight checks, RWO 7/02/88, 38% ... 2250
Eider pr, cvd wings/bills, hen's head turned/age split in neck, EX orig pnt, minor wear, from JC Pike rig, RB 7/09/85 4750
Eider pr, drake's body was made in 2 pcs to cover a flaw in the wood, otherwise EX & orig condition, RWO 7/02/88 3500

Eider pr, EX orig condition, ca 1932, exceptional, 30, RWO 11/11/87 .... **4500**
Eider pr, EX orig pnt, drake has tight crack on side; hen has tight checks, from the Pike rig, EX, 30, RWO 7/06/86 .... **2500**
Eider pr, hen has slightly turned head, EX orig pnt, minor wear, age split in hen's neck, RB 7/08/86, 37% **2250**
Goldeneye drake, EX orig pnt, average wear, structurally EX, RWO 7/06/86 .... **475**
Goldeneye drake, inlet neck, cvd wings/eyes, fine orig pnt, average wear, RB 7/09/85, 70% **700**
Goldeneye hen, inlet head, outstanding orig pnt w/minor flaking, structurally EX, RWO 7/06/86 .... **275**
Goldeneye hen, orig pnt, average wear, thin crack on bk of head/along base, ms, RWO 7/06/86 .... **500**
Goldeneye pr, inlet heads, raised cvd primaries, white is old working rpt, minor splits, rare, 114, J/G 4/24/86, 165% **4950**
Goldeneye pr, inlet necks, cvd wings/eyes, orig pnt, average wear, RB 7/08/86 .... **1250**
Goldeneye pr, inlet necks/cvd wings, hen w/cvd tail feathers, EX orig pnt, rstr/age split in hen, 22/44, RB 5/02/86 .... **6000**
Goldeneye pr, slightly turned heads, inlet necks, EX pnt, RB 7/08/86 .... **2750**
Goldeneye pr, swivel heads, slightly raised wings, fluted tails, cvd eyes, M pnt, G patina, rare, 114, J/G 4/24/86, 200% ... **4950**
Gull, inlet head/open mouth, raised cvd primaries/tail feathers, worn orig pnt, rpr upper bill, J/G 9/20/86, 60% **1500**
Mallard drake, flying, EX orig pnt, average wear, few thin age checks on bk/wing, otherwise EX, RWO 7/02/88, 50% **1750**
Mallard drake, flying, EX orig pnt, narrow splits in body/damage to 1 foot, otherwise structurally sound, RWO 7/04/87 ...... **4250**
Mallard drake, flying, few thin tight checks on body/sm dent on underside of bill, otherwise M, RWO 11/11/87 .... **2750**
Mallard drake, flying, outstanding orig condition w/no structural flaws, RWO 7/02/88, 46% **1600**
Mallard drake, flying, relief cvg on wings/tail, outstanding orig pnt, no structural flaws, RWO 7/06/86 .... **4000**
Mallard drake, inlet head, wire feet, cvd wings/eyes, leather tail, NM pnt, EX, two thirds-size, rare, J/G 9/19/87, 70% **1750**
Mallard pr, flying, cvd eyes/bills/tail/wing feathers, hen: head extended/cocked; drake: head extended/rstr, RB 12/06/85 ... **13500**
Old Squaw drake, head turns on lg spike, raised shoulder cvg, EX condition, RWO 7/05/85 .... **2800**
Old Squaw drake, inlet head, hardwood insert tail, EX orig pnt, 2 sm checks on sides, EX, rare, RWO 7/06/86 .... **1750**
Old Squaw drake, slightly turned head, orig pnt/average wear, orig made as Goldeneye, structurally EX, RWO 11/06/85 ...... **4000**
Old Squaw pr, swivel heads, cvd eyes, raised wings, hen has fluted tail, never weighted, NM, 114, J/G 4/24/86 .... **8250**
Old Squaw pr, swivel heads, cvd wings/eyes, EX orig pnt, rare, RB 7/08/86, 58% **3500**
Old Squaw pr, swivel heads, M condition, never weighted, rare, RWO 7/06/86 .... **4000**
Rail, running, raised cvd wings, tack eyes, NM orig pnt, structurally EX, extremely rare, J/G 9/20/86 .... **1750**
Redbreasted Merganser drake, EX orig dry pnt, prof rpr to bill/crest by F Finney, otherwise EX, rare, RWO 7/02/88, 28% ... **4250**
Redbreasted Merganser drake, EX orig pnt, artist stamp, checks in head, otherwise sound, rare, 30, RWO 7/04/87 .... **5750**
Redbreasted Merganser drake, EX orig pnt, average wear, retains horsehair crest/Wilson stamp, EX, 30/152, RWO 7/06/86 ... **5500**
Redbreasted Merganser drake, EX orig pnt, minor wear, bears the Pike stamp & a rare Gus Wilson stamp, 30, RWO 2/12/88 ... **3350**
Redbreasted Merganser drake, leather crest, glass eyes have been added, VG orig pnt, rpl bill, RWO 7/05/85 .... **2750**
Redbreasted Merganser drake, preening, inlet head, raised cvd wings, cvd eyes w/added copper tacks, VG/EX, J/G 9/20/86 ... **30000**
Redbreasted Merganser drake, slightly turned head, cvd eyes, moulded wings, EX orig pnt, rare, 48, RB 7/07/87 .... **3250**
Redbreasted Merganser drake, turned inlet head, cvd wings, EX orig pnt, slight age split in body, RB 2/01/85 .... **4750**

Wilson, Gus
Redbreasted Merganser pr, drake's head turned/bk; hen preening, brass tack eyes, rstr orig pnt, 140/141, RWO 11/06/85, $56,000.00.

Scoter, American; swivel head, fluted tail/raised wings, NM/never used or weighted, 3 tight checks in side, J/G 4/24/86 .... **2420**
Scoter, calling, inlet head, cvd eyes/wings, G pnt/touchup, several tight checks at base of neck, ls, rare, J/G 9/20/86 .... **2250**
Scoter, EX orig pnt, sm area at base where dry rot is visible, otherwise EX, very rare, RWO 7/06/86, 55% **1100**
Scoter, Monhegan style, inlet head, cvd eyes, rpt is peeling, separation at body joints, J/G 9/20/86 .... **1050**
Scoter, Monhegan style, slightly turned inlet head, cvd wings/eyes, old working rpt, oversize, J/G 4/23/87, 75% **1200**
Scoter, swivel head, fluted tail/raised wings, NM orig pnt, tight checks in side, never weighted, 114, J/G 4/24/86, 160% **2420**

Scoters, set of 8, floating shadow, Surf/Whitewing/American included, orig pnt, minor age splits, 3/76/90, RWO 7/06/86 3750
Skunkhead Scoter, rare swivel-head style, slightly raised wings, fluted tail, orig pnt, EX condition, J/G 9/20/86, 55% 650
Surf Scoter, inlet neck, cvd/moulded wings, cvd eyes, orig pnt, minor wear, some age splitting to neck, rare, RB 7/07/87 750

Wilson, Gus
Surf Scoter, mussel in mouth, superb orig pnt, crack in neck/ls, otherwise structurally EX, RWO 11/06/85, 185%, $28,000.00.

Surf Scoter, swivel head, deep shoulder cvg, EX orig pnt, no structural flaws, rare, RWO 7/06/86 850
Whitewinged Scoter, bold EX orig pnt, w/possible touchup, narrow crack in neck/thin crack in bill, RWO 7/04/87, 45% 1100
Whitewinged Scoter, early, G orig pnt, average wear, lg check along 1 side of body/lg tail chip, RWO 2/12/88, 78% 700
Whitewinged Scoter, early, inlet head, orig pnt, heavy wear to bare wood on body, thin check on bk, RWO 7/04/87 800
Whitewinged Scoter, EX orig pnt, minor wear, thin crack in neck/sm chip on side of bill, otherwise EX, RWO 7/06/86, 135% 700
Whitewinged Scoter, EX orig pnt, thin tight checks on bk, RWO 7/04/87 525
Whitewinged Scoter, full body, inlet head, cvd wings/eyes, hollow, EX orig pnt, oversize, J/G 4/23/87, 45% 900
Whitewinged Scoter, G orig pnt, average wear, narrow checks in bk of head/tight check along 1 side, 30, RWO 7/06/86 550
Whitewinged Scoter, high-head style, EX orig pnt, half of bill has been prof rstr, narrow check on bk, RWO 2/13/87 1550
Whitewinged Scoter, inlet head, cvd wings/eyes, EX old pnt, minor wear, age split on bottom, J/G 9/20/86 1450
Whitewinged Scoter, Monhegan style, worn orig pnt, sm tight checks in head, otherwise EX, 8, RWO 7/06/86, 80% 2000
Whitewinged Scoter, preening, EX orig pnt, minor wear, 2 tight checks on bk/bottom, well preserved, RWO 7/04/87, 200% 10000
Whitewinged Scoter, preening, old orig pnt worn to bare wood in some areas, structurally EX, rare, 8/48, RWO 7/06/86 4250
Whitewinged Scoter, rocking head, cvd wings, old pnt, average wear, prof rstr on neck, rare, 22/44/46, RB 5/02/86, 66% 2000
Whitewinged Scoter, superb cvg, some overpnt on bill, white removed from breast, some wear, EX condition, RWO 7/05/85 1850
Whitewinged Scoter, swivel head, EX orig pnt, never weighted, rare, RWO 7/06/86 550
Whitewinged Scoter, swivel head, raised cvd wings/tail, orig pnt, minor wear, EX/never used, rare, J/G 9/20/86, 35% 700
Whitewinged Scoter, 2-pc body w/inlet head, relief wing cvg, cvd eyes, old working rpt, VG condition, J/G 9/19/87 350
Whitewinged Scoter drake, orig pnt on bk/speculum, working rpt on black areas, structurally sound, RWO 7/06/86 600
Wilson, Michael (New Orleans, LA)
Mallard pr, relief raised wings, G orig condition, sm, RWO 2/12/88 140
Wilson, Summerfield; att (Havre de Grace, MD)
Canvasback drake, 2-pc body construction, working rpt, average wear, age split in neck, ms, RB 2/01/85 70
Wilson, Thomas (Ipswich, MA)
Blackbellied Plover, early, deep relief cvd wings w/raised wing tips, orig pnt, minor wear, 22/44, RB 5/02/86, 140% 2000
Winslow, John (Nantucket, MA)
Curlew, fine orig pnt, poor rstr to bill, rare, RB 12/06/85 400
Curlew, orig pnt, minor wear, bill is a replacement, ca 1890, J/G 4/24/86 467
Witherspoon, Leigh (North Haven, ME)
Merganser hen, cvd primaries/secondaries/sm crest, open mouth w/mussel, prof rstr bill/mussel, 22/44, J/G 9/19/87, 50% 5000
Redbreasted Merganser drake, fine orig pnt, average wear, ls, 39, RB 7/08/86 500
Surf Scoter drake, orig pnt, average wear, sm chip on underside of bill, ls, 39, RB 7/08/86 70
Surf Scoter hen, orig pnt, average wear, ls, 39, RB 7/08/86 65
Woodington, C. (Prince Edward Island)
Canada Goose, feeding, age split in back, CW cvd under tail, EX condition, 22, RB 5/02/86 550
Woodman, Stanley (Wolf Island, Ont)
Bluebill pr, old working rpt w/nice scratch pnt on bks, thin cracks in necks, ca 1930, RWO 7/04/87 120
Woodring, Carl (Cotuit, MA)
Merganser pr, folky form, old pnt crazed & worn, RB 3/11/88 1600
Woodring Family, att (Ipswich, MA)

Merganser drake, American; upright head, brass tack eyes, old pnt, moderate flaking/wear, neck rpr, EX form, RB 9/27/87 1050

Woodside, Susan (Erieville, NY)

Mallard drake, raised cvd wing tips, primary cvg, superb pnt pattern, structurally EX, RB 7/07/87 250

Wozny, Eddie (Cambridge, MD)

Canada Goose, crooked neck, relief cvg around wings, lg check on 1 side/narrow bk check, RWO 7/02/88 120

Curlew, feeding, EW cvd in bottom, M condition, RWO 2/12/88 200

Dove, raised wings/primary cvg, W cvd in bottom, EX condition, RWO 7/02/88 140

Dowitcher, short bill, detailed primary cvg, M condition, RWO 7/02/88 310

Swan, hollow, artist initial, narrow check on bottom, otherwise structurally EX, RWO 11/11/87 270

Tern, W cvd in bottom, M condition, RWO 2/12/88 110

Yellowlegs, raised cvd primaries, cvd in Bill Bowman style, W cvd into bottom, RWO 11/11/87 240

Wragg, Al; att (Michigan)

Wood Duck drake, EX orig pnt, average wear, structurally EX, RWO 11/11/87 205

Wright, Alvirah (Duck, NC)

Canvasback drake, high alert head, wide body, old working rpt, a few hairlines/ls, rare, oversize, 33, J/G 9/19/87, 135% 6750

Wright, Alvirah
Canvasback hen, outstanding form/full body, EX old pnt, hairlines in bottom/1 has nails, oversize, 33, J/G 9/19/87, 200%, $23,500.00.

Ruddy Duck, delicately cvd tail, check running down bk, otherwise EX, ca 1880-1890, RWO 7/05/85 4050

Ruddy Duck, full body, G old pnt, average wear, hairline in breast, sm chip on top of tail, 33/122, J/G 9/19/87, ... 19000

Wright, Franklin Pierce

Redbreasted Merganser drake, cvd wings, folky, 3-color breast feathers, EX orig/minor touchup, EX, 48, RB 7/7/87, 215% 15000

Redbreasted Merganser drake, cvd wings, horsehair comb, folky, 3-color feather pnt, minor wear, EX, RB 7/07/87, 265% 8000

Wright, Winfield (Seabright, NJ)

Goldeneye hen, rpt, average flaking/wear, ca 1850, 9/77, RB 12/06/85 220

Wyer, Capt. (Nantucket, MA)

Eskimo Curlew, fine orig pnt, average wear, ls, ca 1880, rare, RB 7/08/86 750

Yellowlegs, baleen bill, EX orig pnt, minor wear, RB 7/09/85 350

Yellowlegs, baleen bill, fine orig pnt, average wear, RB 2/01/85 900

Yeargan, Ben (St. Louis, MO)

Canada Goose, hollow, EX orig pnt, minor wear, well preserved, rare, RB 8/21/86 850

Yearwood, Adam

Bluebill drake, fine feather cvg on bk, G orig pnt, average wear, RB 7/07/87 100

Young, Otto (Atlantic City, NJ)

Yellowlegs, early, pnt appears to be orig w/some flaking on bk, structurally sound, RWO 7/02/88 50

Young, Wallace (Lacon, IL)

Mallard hen, orig pnt, minor wear, sm crack in breast/tiny chip on 1 side of tail, J/G 4/23/87 300

Zackmann, John F. (Michigan)

Black Duck, hollow w/cvd primaries, fine feather pnt, structurally EX, oversize, 102, J/G 4/23/87, 150% 1500

Canvasback drake, hollow, fine orig pnt, minor wear, well preserved, oversize, rare, RB 3/06/87, 200% 4000

Zender, Joseph (Fairbury, IL)

Greenwinged Teal hen, hollow, EX orig pnt, minor wear, well preserved, 39, RB 7/08/86 450

Greenwinged Teal hen, hollow, G orig pnt, average wear, 39, RB 7/08/86 200

Mallard drake, slightly turned head, NM orig pnt, structurally EX, J/G 4/24/86 330

Factory Decoys

Airite Decoy Company
Owl, canvas-covered, button eyes, all orig, orig wooden stake, ca 1925, rare, RWO 7/04/87 145

Bean, L.L.
Black Duck, cork body, orig pnt, flaking on head, structurally fair, RWO 11/11/87 35
Black Duck, cork body w/wooden head, NM orig pnt, several sm chips in cork, early, J/G 4/24/86 66

Dodge Company
Black Duck, glass eyes, EX orig pnt, slight factory-filled crack on bk, rare, J/G 4/24/86 357
Black Duck, glass eyes, strong orig pnt, minor wear, hairline crack in underside/neck filler missing, J/G 4/23/87 175
Black Duck, hollow, very old pnt, heavy wear, Mackey stamp, split at base of neck/flat spot on head, rare, RWO 7/05/86 200
Black Duck, old working rpt, moderate wear, tight age split in bk, J/G 9/20/86 60
Bluebill drake, canvas-covered stuffed body w/wooden bottom board & head, EX orig pnt, minor wear, 21, RB 2/01/85 350

Dodge Company
Bluebill drake, EX orig pnt, minor flaking/wear, well preserved, RB 7/08/87, $550.00.

Bluebill drake, orig pnt, minor wear, minor bill rpr, neck filler may be a replacement, RWO 7/02/88 120
Bluebill drake, orig pnt, moderate flaking/wear, end of bill has been chewed by a dog, RB 6/28/88 75
Bluebill drake, tack eyes, fine orig pnt, average flaking/wear, RB 8/25/88 170
Bluebill drake, tack eyes, orig pnt, average wear on head/breast, most of the neck filler is missing, J/G 9/20/86 300
Bluebill hen, EX orig pnt, minor wear, age split in bodyblock, 21, RB 2/01/85 200
Bluebill hen, EX orig pnt, minor wear, minor flaking around neck, sm age split in left side of body, RB 7/08/87 250
Bluebill pr, detailed orig pnt, minor wear, some neck filler missing, ca 1890, rare/highly collectible, J/G 4/24/86 715
Bluebill pr, orig pnt, minor wear, hairline crack in lower side of hen, neck filler missing from drake, J/G 9/19/87 400
Bluewinged Teal drake, EX orig pnt, minor wear, hairline crack in neck, otherwise structurally EX, rare, RWO 7/02/88 450
Canada Goose, hollow, orig pnt, separation where head/neck join, well preserved, ca 1880's, rare, RWO 7/02/88, 46% 700
Canvasback drake, tack eyes, orig pnt, moderate wear, sm crack on tip of tail, J/G 9/19/87 175
Dowitcher, minor wear on end of tail, otherwise NM, 193, RWO 7/02/88 1500
Gadwall, most of the neck filler is missing, otherwise M, rare, RWO 7/05/86 600
Gadwall drake, EX orig pnt, average wear, much of the neck filler missing/rough area on breast, rare, RWO 7/02/88 250
Gadwall drake, orig pnt, average wear, some neck filler missing, otherwise structurally sound, rare, RWO 11/06/85 225
Goldeneye drake, orig pnt, heavy wear w/lg areas on bk worn to bare wood, structurally fair, rare, RWO 7/05/85 55
Goose, old working rpt, average wear, age check in bk/bill has been replaced, RWO 7/05/86 300
Greenwinged Teal drake, EX orig pnt, structurally superb, ca 1890, very rare, RWO 7/06/85 500
Greenwinged Teal hen, EX orig pnt, NM condition, extremely rare, RB 2/01/85 950
Hooded Merganser drake, EX orig pnt, average flaking/wear, rare, RB 7/08/87 1000
Mallard drake, EX orig pnt, average wear, sm chips out of neck filler, otherwise structurally sound, 93, RWO 7/04/87 375
Mallard drake, EX orig pnt, average wear, structurally EX, RWO 7/02/88 425
Mallard drake, NM orig pnt, several chips in neck filler, ca 1880's, J/G 9/19/87 800
Mallard drake, orig pnt, average wear, bill broken & repaired, rare, RB 3/06/87 200
Mallard drake, orig pnt, average wear, 2 sm tail chips/several hairline cracks in bodyblock, rpl eyes, J/G 4/23/87 125
Mallard drake, orig pnt, heavy wear, factory brand, neck filler missing, otherwise structurally sound, RWO 11/06/85 130
Mallard drake, rpt by Charles Walker, average wear, well preserved, 39, RB 7/08/86 150
Mallard drake, superb orig pnt, minor flaking/wear, factory brand, sm age split in right side of body, RB 7/08/87 375
Mallard pr, glass eyes, orig pnt, minor wear, neck filler missing, hen has tight check in bodyblock, J/G 4/23/87 575
Mallard pr, tack eyes, EX orig pnt, minor wear, sm tail chips, neck filler missing, J/G 9/20/86 600
Merganser, overpnt taken down to some orig, head nailed in place/1 eye missing/bill damage, rare, 113, RWO 7/05/85 325

Merganser drake, American; orig pnt, average wear w/several dings/dents, working repair, rare, 3/76, RWO 7/04/87 .... **4250**
Pintail drake, rpt, average wear, RB 8/25/88 .... **85**
Pintail hen, orig dry pnt, heavy flaking, age split in neck, rare, RB 7/09/85 .... **600**
Plover, orig pnt, heavy wear, structurally sound, RB 7/08/86 .... **200**
Plover or Dowitcher, orig pnt, average wear, some of the bill may have worn away, 193, RWO 7/02/88 .... **225**

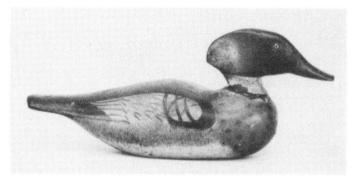

Dodge Company
Redbreasted Merganser drake, EX orig pnt, minor wear,
neck, filler missing, extremely rare, RB 2/01/85, 285%,
$8,500.00.

Redhead drake, hollow, orig pnt, minor wear, some neck filler missing/rough area on edges of bill, J/G 9/20/86 .... **275**
Redhead drake, hollow w/highly detailed cvg, orig pnt, minor wear, sm crack in 1 side, ca 1890, J/G 4/24/86 .... **577**
Robin Snipe, orig pnt, minor wear on body, pnt worn off bill, tip of bill is slightly blunted, J/G 4/23/87 .... **450**
Ruddy Turnstone, orig pnt, structurally EX, rare, RWO 7/06/85 .... **375**
Spoonbill hen, orig pnt, heavy wear, chip out of tail/crack in neck, head is dovetailed to body, very rare, RWO 7/05/85 .... **425**
Widgeon drake, orig pnt, minor wear, neck filler has been prof rstr/sm crack on top of head, very rare, J/G 4/24/86 .... **385**
Widgeon hen, tack eyes, EX orig pnt, minor wear, factory line in bk, ca 1880's, rare, J/G 4/24/86 .... **660**
Yellowlegs, EX orig pnt w/fine patina, minor flaking on breast, structurally EX, early, 193, RWO 7/02/88 .... **325**
Yellowlegs, old working rpt, average wear, sm gouges out of wood, otherwise structurally sound, RWO 11/11/87 .... **180**
Yellowlegs, old working rpt, in-use wear, hs, 1 eye missing, bill is replaced, bears Mackey stamp, RWO 7/04/87 .... **180**
Yellowlegs, orig pnt, heavy wear, bill is an old replacement, RB 7/08/86 .... **225**
Down East Decoy Company
Black Duck, factory stamp, minor age splitting, otherwise NM, RB 6/28/88 .... **225**
Black Duck, hollow, old working rpt, average wear, structurally sound, RWO 7/02/88 .... **50**
Black Duck, hollow, orig pnt, average wear, well preserved, RB 7/08/86 .... **250**
Black Duck, sleeping, orig pnt, average wear, well preserved, RB 7/08/86 .... **350**
Black Duck, swimming, orig pnt, average wear, thin tight check on bk, RWO 2/12/88 .... **140**
Mallard drake, sleeping, thin hairline in bottom, M/unused, RWO 7/04/87 .... **275**
Mallard drake, slight age split in bk, otherwise M, RB 7/08/86 .... **175**
Mallard drake, swimming, M/unused, RWO 7/04/87 .... **325**
Mallard hen, head slightly turned, hollow, slight flaking on bk, otherwise NM, 39, RB 9/08/86 .... **300**
Mallard pr, drake has minor age splitting, otherwise EX, RB 6/28/88 .... **325**
Evans Duck Decoy Company
Bluebill drake, EX orig pnt, average wear w/traces of varnish on bk/sides, factory stamp, EX condition, RWO 7/02/88 .... **160**
Bluebill drake, EX orig pnt, factory stamp, NM condition, ca 1920's, RWO 7/05/86 .... **300**
Bluebill drake, orig pnt, minor wear, factory stamp, RWO 7/02/88 .... **150**
Bluebill drake, orig pnt, minor wear, sm worn area on edge of tail, J/G 9/19/87 .... **150**
Bluebill hen, G orig pnt, average wear, factory stamp, sm check on 1 side, otherwise structurally EX, RWO 7/05/86 .... **120**
Bluebill pr, EX orig pnt, average wear, hen has hairline crack down bk/drake has gouge along 1 side, RWO 7/02/88 .... **225**
Bluebill pr, hollow, orig pnt, minor wear, factory stamp, ls, J/G 9/19/87 .... **450**
Bluebill pr, orig pnt, minor wear, factory stamps, bill repair on drake, J/G 4/24/86 .... **357**
Bluewinged Teal drake, orig pnt, average wear, sm dent on head/tail, otherwise structurally sound, RWO 7/05/86 .... **200**
Canvasback drake, Mammoth Grade, EX orig pnt, minor wear, factory stamp, ls, J/G 9/20/86 .... **500**
Canvasback drake, Mammoth Grade, orig pnt, average wear, factory stamp, RWO 7/04/87 .... **230**
Canvasback drake, orig pnt, average wear w/some flaking around head/tail, structurally sound, RWO 7/05/86 .... **200**
Canvasback drake, orig pnt almost completely worn away, factory stamp, structurally sound, RWO 7/05/85 .... **25**
Canvasback drake, working touchup, average wear, factory stamp, age check along 1 side of body, RWO 7/05/85 .... **150**
Canvasback drake, worn orig pnt, average wear, factory stamp, body cracks have been filled/pnt, RWO 7/02/88 .... **140**
Canvasback hen, Mammoth Grade, orig pnt, average wear, ls, J/G 4/23/87 .... **200**
Canvasback hen, orig pnt, average wear, shallow chip on underside of bill, RB 7/08/87 .... **75**
Canvasback hen, worn orig pnt, check on the bottom/bill is broken, RWO 7/05/85 .... **70**
Canvasback pr, orig pnt, heavy wear, factory stamp, structurally sound, RWO 7/05/85 .... **350**

Coot, old pnt, possibly orig, in-use wear, 36, RB 2/01/85 180
Coot, orig pnt, minor wear, tight check in lower side, factory stamp, ls, J/G 4/24/86 522
Mallard drake, hollow, EX orig pnt, average wear w/some crazing to breast, structurally EX, RWO 7/02/88 100
Mallard drake, Mammoth Grade, outstanding orig pnt, minor wear, factory stamp, structurally EX, RWO 7/05/86 400
Mallard drake, orig pnt, in-use wear, factory stamp, sm chips on tail/head, otherwise structurally sound, RWO 7/05/86 170
Mallard hen, EX orig pnt, minor wear, factory stamp, tight check on bottom, otherwise EX, RWO 7/02/88 250
Mallard hen, orig pnt, average wear, factory stamp, poor repair to bill/sm tight check running down bottom, RWO 7/05/86 180
Pintail drake, EX orig pnt, minimal wear, factory stamp, ls, RB 2/01/85 475
Pintail drake, hollow, EX orig pnt, prof bill rpr, artist stamp/branded from the rig of DB Day, RWO 2/12/88 475
Pintail drake, Mammoth Grade, EX orig pnt, minor wear, factory stamp, old repair to bill, ls, rare, RB 8/27/87 500
Pintail drake, old working rpt, age splits in bodyblock, tight crack in neck/bill, hairline crack in neck, J/G 9/20/86 65
Pintail drake, orig pnt, heavy wear, factory stamp, nickel-size gouge out of neck, flaw in wood near tail, RWO 11/11/87 170
Redhead drake, EX orig pnt, little wear, factory brand, well preserved, RB 3/06/87 375
Redhead drake, orig pnt, moderate wear, RB 8/25/88 80

Hays Decoy Factory
Black Duck, EX orig pnt, little wear, RB 7/08/86 230
Bluebill drake, orig pnt w/old varnish, average wear, head is loose/tight checks on body/check in bottom, RWO 2/12/88 100
Bluewinged Teal drake, orig pnt, average wear, narrow crack running the length of the body, otherwise EX, RWO 7/02/88 350
Canvasback drake, NM orig pnt, part of the neck filler is missing, rare, J/G 4/23/87 225
Coot or Mudhen, orig pnt, average wear, lg check along 1 side of body, sm chip on underside of bill, RWO 7/02/88 185
Mallard drake, orig pnt, minor wear, factory stamp, sm crack at base of neck, J/G 9/19/87 225
Redhead drake, EX orig pnt w/minor flaking, tight age split extends part way up breast/under tail, rare, J/G 4/23/87 200
Shoveller drake, orig pnt, slight wear/flaking, stamped Hays #271, tight check in body/2 sm tail cracks, J/G 4/23/87 550

Herters, Inc.
Black Duck, sleeping, canvas over balsa, EX orig condition, retains old Herters anchor, RWO 2/12/88 120
Black Duck, sleeping, lithographed canvas covering, EX orig pnt, several tiny tears on bk, early, oversize, J/G 4/24/86 145
Blackbellied Plover, M condition, somewhat rare, RWO 11/11/87 125
Bluebill drake, orig pnt, minor in-use flaking/wear, RB 6/28/88 70
Bluewinged Teal drake, factory brand, M condition, RWO 11/11/87 90
Bufflehead drake, factory brand, EX orig condition, RWO 11/11/87 80
Canada Goose, balsa body, orig pnt, heavy flaking/wear, RB 8/25/88 60
Canada Goose, canvas body/wooden head, average wear, otherwise EX, RB 8/25/88 170
Canada Goose, lithographed canvas covering, NM pnt, no structural flaws, early, J/G 4/24/86 275
Canvasback hen, orig pnt, average flaking/wear, RB 3/11/88 60
Crow, balsa body, worn orig pnt, chipping at the tail, made to be used in clutches of owl or separately, RWO 11/11/87 190
Crow, balsa body w/wire legs, orig pnt, minor wear, no structural flaws, J/G 9/19/87 100
Dove, orig pnt, minor flaking/wear, several hairline cracks, J/G 4/23/87 150
Galdwall drake, M condition, J/G 4/23/87 120
Great Horned Owl, pressed styrofoam, minor pnt dings, otherwise EX, ca 1960, RWO 7/04/87 50
Mallard drake, lithographed canvas covering, EX orig pnt, 2 sm tears, early, J/G 4/24/86 145
Mallard drake, stick-up, EX condition, RB 7/09/85 160
Mallard pr, sleeping, lithographed canvas covering, minor rpt, ea has few tiny tears, early, oversize, J/G 4/24/86 385
Merganser drake, American; M condition, RB 7/09/85 110
Owl, G orig pnt, average wear, minor repair to 1 ear, otherwise EX, early, RWO 7/02/88 700

Herters, Inc.
Owl, NM RB 3/11/88, 150%, $1,350.00.

Shoveler drake, factory brand, EX orig condition, RWO 2/13/87	**200**
Swan, cvd wings, M condition, J/G 4/24/86	**275**
Widgeon drake, M condition, J/G 4/24/86	**80**
Widgeon drake, M orig pnt, factory brand, crack in 1 side of bk, J/G 4/23/87	**170**
Wood Duck drake, early factory stamp, M condition, RWO 11/11/87	**150**

Mason Factory

Black Duck, Challenge Grade, EX orig pnt, minor tail chip, otherwise structurally sound, RWO 7/05/86	**625**
Black Duck, Challenge Grade, EX orig pnt, minor wear w/several rubs on 1 side, sm tail chip/head reglued, J/G 9/20/86	**425**
Black Duck, Challenge Grade, EX orig pnt w/areas of working touchup, no structural flaws, early, J/G 4/24/86	**605**
Black Duck, Challenge Grade, EX orig pnt w/sm scratches, varnished, head is slightly loose, RWO 7/05/85	**180**
Black Duck, Challenge Grade, G orig pnt, average flaking/wear, age split refilled on right side of body, RB 7/09/85	**350**
Black Duck, Challenge Grade, G orig pnt, faint factory stamp, 2 tight checks, otherwise sound, RWO 7/04/87	**725**
Black Duck, Challenge Grade, G orig pnt, minor wear, old repair to tail chip, 36, RB 2/01/85	**600**
Black Duck, Challenge Grade, G orig pnt w/areas of working touchup, branded AF Hayden, RWO 11/06/85	**260**
Black Duck, Challenge Grade, hollow, EX orig pnt, minor wear, age split in neck, eyes damaged, rare, RB 3/06/87	**450**
Black Duck, Challenge Grade, NM orig pnt, Challenge stamp, hairline crack in underside, J/G 9/19/87	**1125**
Black Duck, Challenge Grade, NM orig pnt, factory stamp, age split extending up breast/under tail, J/G 4/23/87	**750**
Black Duck, Challenge Grade, snaky head, EX orig pnt, spots on breast/around tail worn to bare wood, early, RWO 2/02/88	**800**
Black Duck, Challenge Grade, snaky head, fine orig pnt, chip at end of tail, otherwise NM, RB 8/27/87	**500**

Mason Factory
Black Duck, Challenge Grade, snaky head, M dry orig pnt, structurally EX, 2 staples added, RWO 2/13/87, $2,050.00.

Black Duck, Challenge Grade, snaky head, orig pnt, minor wear, factory stamp, sm crack on underside, J/G 9/19/87	**375**
Black Duck, Premier Grade, EX orig pnt, average wear, ls, otherwise structurally sound, 39, RB 7/08/86	**800**
Black Duck, Premier Grade, EX orig pnt, average wear, structurally EX, RWO 7/05/85	**505**
Black Duck, Premier Grade, EX orig pnt, flaking to bk, minor repair, RWO 7/04/87	**550**
Black Duck, Premier Grade, EX orig pnt, minimal wear, Premier stamp, tiny chip/ls, exceptional, RWO 7/05/85	**900**
Black Duck, Premier Grade, EX orig pnt, minor wear, EX swirling, factory stamp, sm chip at end of tail, RB 3/06/87	**700**
Black Duck, Premier Grade, hollow, NM orig pnt, seam in bodyblock has separated on 1 side, J/G 9/19/87, 50%	**750**
Black Duck, Premier Grade, hollow, orig pnt, average wear, factory stamp, chip in the tail, RWO 2/13/87	**725**
Black Duck, Premier Grade, hollow, orig pnt, in-use wear, thin crack in bill, minor repair, RWO 7/04/87	**390**
Black Duck, Premier Grade, NM orig pnt, sm rough area on tip of bill/ls, rare, J/G 4/24/86	**385**
Black Duck, Premier Grade, old pnt, minor wear, chip at end of tail has been reglued, rare, oversize, RB 7/07/87	**225**
Black Duck, Premier Grade, old rpt taken down to orig w/heavy wear, chip in tail has been reglued, oversize, RB 7/09/85	**300**
Black Duck, Premier Grade, old working rpt, moderate wear, traces of orig Premier stamp on underside, J/G 4/23/87	**250**
Black Duck, Premier Grade, orig pnt, in-use wear, 36, RB 2/01/85	**400**
Black Duck, Premier Grade, orig pnt, minor wear, heavy crazing to overall surface, ls, RB 6/28/88	**325**
Black Duck, Premier Grade, orig pnt, minor wear, slight separation to body halves, ls, RB 3/06/87	**225**
Black Duck, Premier Grade, orig pnt w/working touchup at base of neck, RWO 7/05/85	**375**
Black Duck, Premier Grade, underside of bill has slight cvg, EX orig pnt, minor wear, tiny nicks on tail, RB 7/07/87	**675**
Black Duck, Standard Grade, glass eyes, EX orig pnt, average wear, 1 eye missing/age split in bottom, RB 7/09/85	**150**
Black Duck, Standard Grade, glass eyes, EX orig pnt, average wear, RB 7/09/85	**225**
Black Duck, Standard Grade, glass eyes, EX orig pnt, averagewear, ls, RB 8/27/87	**350**
Black Duck, Standard Grade, glass eyes, EX orig pnt, minor wear, branded Barron, sm age split on side, RB 8/28/87	**300**
Black Duck, Standard Grade, glass eyes, G orig pnt, minor wear, ls, RB 3/11/88	**175**
Black Duck, Standard Grade, glass eyes, NM orig pnt, sm chip on 1 side of bill, J/G 9/20/86	**300**

Black Duck, Standard Grade, glass eyes, orig pnt, in-use wear, ms, RB 7/09/85 170
Black Duck, Standard Grade, pnt eyes, NM orig pnt, minor flaking in filler around neck, RB 8/21/86 210
Black Duck, Standard Grade, pnt eyes, NM orig pnt w/few minor dings, NM condition, RWO 7/04/87 260
Black Duck, Standard Grade, pnt eyes, NM orig pnt w/no wear, sm amount of neck filler missing on 1 side, J/G 4/24/86 330
Black Duck, Standard Grade, tack eyes, EX orig pnt, average wear, neck filler missing/thin check on bk, RWO 2/12/88 250
Black Duck, Standard Grade, tack eyes, EX orig pnt, minor wear, Barron brand, structurally EX, RWO 11/11/87 385
Black Duck, Standard Grade, tack eyes, EX rpt, tight check in underside part way up breast/under tail, J/G 4/23/87 275
Black Duck, Standard Grade, tack eyes, M orig pnt, tight crack on underside of bodyblock, J/G 4/24/86 412
Black Duck, Standard Grade, tack eyes, narrow crack on underside, otherwise M, RWO 7/02/88 300
Black Duck, Standard Grade, tack eyes, rpt by Crowell, typical feather pnt/blue speculum, 2 sm age splits, RB 8/21/86 350
Black Duck, Standard Grade, tack eyes, rpt in Mason style, no structural flaws, J/G 9/19/87 155
Black Duck pr, Premier Grade, orig pnt w/minor wear, ms, ends of tails slightly shaved down, RB 3/06/87 300
Black Duck pr, Standard Grade, glass eyes, rpt w/orig pnt on head, 1 has chip in bill, structurally sound, RWO 7/05/86 150
Blackbellied Plover, EX orig pnt, minor wear, tiny chips missing from end of tail, ls, early, rare, RB 7/09/85, 75% 1400
Blackbellied Plover, full body, spike bill, glass eyes, G orig pnt, ls, age split in bottom, 36, RB 2/01/85, 60% 1250
Blackbellied Plover, glass eyes, orig pnt, minor wear, sm age split on left side of body, RB 7/07/87 450
Blackbellied Plover, orig pnt, average wear, structurally EX, RWO 7/06/85 950
Blackbellied Plover, overpnt taken down to orig, average wear, ls, well preserved, RB 12/06/85 1100
Blackbellied Plover, tack eyes, G orig pnt w/wear around bill, structurally EX, RWO 7/06/85 800
Blackbellied Plover, tack eyes, NM pnt, ls, early, 39, RB 7/08/86 1500
Blackbellied Plover, tack eyes, orig pnt, minor wear, ls, rare, 105, J/G 4/23/87 1300
Blackbellied Plover, VG orig pnt in Spring plumage, structurally EX, early, 113, RWO 7/06/85 650
Bluebill drake, Challenge Grade, EX orig pnt, structurally EX, RWO 11/06/85 400
Bluebill drake, Challenge Grade, flat-bottom, G orig pnt, average wear, hs, otherwise EX, RWO 7/02/88, 42% 325
Bluebill drake, Challenge Grade, G orig pnt, minor wear on head/neck/bk, several cracks in bk/head, J/G 4/24/86 247
Bluebill drake, Challenge Grade, high-head style, orig pnt, minor wear, several minor age lines, J/G 4/23/87 450
Bluebill drake, Challenge Grade, hollow, G orig pnt, sm repair to right side of tail, rare, RB 7/09/85 800
Bluebill drake, Challenge Grade, low-head style, slight wear on edge of bill, ms, otherwise M, 100, J/G 4/23/87 2750
Bluebill drake, Challenge Grade, NM condition, 36, RB 2/01/85 1100
Bluebill drake, Challenge Grade, snaky head, orig pnt, minor wear & touchup, sm crack, ms, J/G 9/19/87 400
Bluebill drake, Premier Grade, EX orig pnt, age split on left lower side of body, ls, RB 6/28/88, 70% 350
Bluebill drake, Premier Grade, G orig pnt, age split in bk has been repaired, RB 7/07/87 450
Bluebill drake, Premier Grade, low-head, EX orig pnt, tight check on side/head, ls, tail chip, rare, 193, RWO 7/02/88 2100
Bluebill drake, Premier Grade, low-head style, orig pnt, average wear/touchup, crack, ms, early, rare, 87, J/G 9/19/87 700
Bluebill drake, Premier Grade, NM pnt, minor wear, 36, RB 2/01/85 850

Mason Factory
Bluebill drake, Premier Grade, low head, EX orig pnt, 2 rubs to bare wood, RWO 2/12/88, 72%, $2,550.00.

Bluebill drake, Premier Grade, orig pnt, heavy wear, crack running up bk of head, neck rpr, RWO 7/06/85 100
Bluebill drake, Premier Grade, orig pnt, in-use wear, ls, RB 7/09/85 300
Bluebill drake, Premier Grade, orig pnt, minor wear, sm crack in tail/separation at seams in bodyblock, J/G 9/20/86 600
Bluebill drake, Premier Grade, orig pnt, minor wear, tight check in tail/worn on underside, J/G 4/23/87 400
Bluebill drake, Premier Grade, orig pnt, moderate flaking/wear, no structural flaws, J/G 4/23/87 400
Bluebill drake, Premier Grade, orig pnt, worn to bare wood in some areas, ms, otherwise sound, early, 193, RWO 7/02/88 300
Bluebill drake, Premier Grade, orig pnt w/overpnt on breast, in-use wear, ls, structurally sound, RWO 7/05/86 325
Bluebill drake, Premier Grade, orig pnt worn to bare wood on most of body, few nicks, otherwise sound, RWO 7/02/88 130
Bluebill drake, Standard Grade, EX orig pnt, average wear, sm end-of-bill chips/tight check on 1 side, RWO 2/12/88 200
Bluebill drake, Standard Grade, glass eyes, EX orig pnt, average wear, ms, RB 12/06/85 90
Bluebill drake, Standard Grade, glass eyes, EX orig pnt, average flaking, RB 12/06/85 250
Bluebill drake, Standard Grade, glass eyes, EX orig pnt, minor wear, ls, J/G 9/20/86 300
Bluebill drake, Standard Grade, glass eyes, old working rpt, wood on underside slightly shaved, J/G 4/23/87 80

Bluebill drake, Standard Grade, glass eyes, orig pnt, minor wear, most of neck filler missing, J/G 9/19/87	**170**
Bluebill drake, Standard Grade, glass eyes, orig pnt w/some overpnt, moderate flaking/wear, RB 7/08/87	**90**
Bluebill drake, Standard Grade, glass eyes, outstanding orig pnt, structurally sound, RWO 7/05/86	**200**
Bluebill drake, Standard Grade, hollow, glass eyes, mostly orig pnt w/overpnt to wht areas, left eye broken, RB 3/11/88	**75**
Bluebill drake, Standard Grade, pnt eyes, NM condition, RB 7/09/85	**175**
Bluebill drake, Standard Grade, pnt eyes, NM orig pnt, minor discoloration, hairline crack in bodyblock, J/G 4/23/87	**375**
Bluebill drake, Standard Grade, pnt eyes, NM orig pnt, several nail holes in underside of bodyblock, J/G 9/20/86	**125**
Bluebill drake, Standard Grade, tack eyes, G orig pnt, average wear, sm age split in bk, RB 12/06/85	**100**
Bluebill drake, Standard Grade, tack eyes, G orig pnt, average wear, RB 7/08/86	**170**
Bluebill drake, Standard Grade, tack eyes, G orig pnt, flaking/wear, some age splitting to bottom, RB 8/21/86	**80**
Bluebill drake, Standard Grade, VG orig pnt, tight checks on bk/1 on cheek, narrow crack in bottom, RWO 7/02/88	**200**
Bluebill hen, Challenge Grade, low-head style, orig pnt, minor flaking, hairline on underside, rare, 100, J/G 4/23/87	**1300**
Bluebill hen, Challenge Grade, low-head style, orig pnt w/some working touchup, 2 checks on side, RWO 11/06/85	**245**
Bluebill hen, Challenge Grade, NM orig pnt w/old touchup, checks on bottom, rare, oversize, J/G 4/24/86	**357**
Bluebill hen, Challenge Grade, orig pnt, heavy wear, ms, otherwise structurally sound, RB 8/21/86	**150**
Bluebill hen, Challenge Grade, orig pnt, minor wear w/touchup to bill, head has been reglued, early, RWO 7/06/85	**450**
Bluebill hen, Challenge Grade, snaky head, EX orig pnt, strong feathering/swirling, sm age split in bottom, RB 8/27/87	**600**
Bluebill hen, Challenge Grade, snaky head, EX orig pnt w/minor flaking on lower side, J/G 9/20/86	**435**
Bluebill hen, Premier Grade, G orig pnt, in-use wear, crack in body/bill chip/ms, otherwise sound, 193, RWO 7/02/88	**425**
Bluebill hen, Premier Grade, low-head style, orig pnt, minor wear, rare, J/G 4/24/86	**825**
Bluebill hen, Premier Grade, NM condition, 21, RB 7/09/85	**1000**
Bluebill hen, Premier Grade, NM pnt, minor wear, 36, RB 2/01/85	**800**
Bluebill hen, Premier Grade, orig pnt, heavy wear, left eye missing, ms, RB 3/06/87	**200**
Bluebill hen, Premier Grade, orig pnt, heavy wear, structurally sound, RWO 7/05/86	**200**
Bluebill hen, Premier Grade, orig pnt worn to bare wood on most of body, crack in bk, otherwise sound, RWO 7/02/88	**100**
Bluebill hen, Standard Grade, glass eyes, EX orig pnt, average wear, sm age split in bottom, RB 8/27/87	**225**
Bluebill hen, Standard Grade, glass eyes, EX orig pnt, average wear, ls, RB 2/01/85	**225**
Bluebill hen, Standard Grade, glass eyes, EX orig pnt, sm crack in bottom/neck filler missing, otherwise EX, RWO 7/05/86	**375**
Bluebill hen, Standard Grade, glass eyes, extra thick orig pnt, hairline crack in neck, J/G 9/20/86	**500**
Bluebill hen, Standard Grade, glass eyes, most of pnt worn away, thin body checks, otherwise sound, RWO 2/12/88	**70**
Bluebill hen, Standard Grade, glass eyes, NM pnt, slight age split in bottom, 39, RB 7/08/86	**325**
Bluebill hen, Standard Grade, glass eyes, old rpt worn to natural wood in many areas, RB 12/06/85	**50**
Bluebill hen, Standard Grade, glass eyes, VG orig pnt, average wear, slight age split in bottom, 39, RB 7/08/86	**175**
Bluebill hen, Standard Grade, tack eyes, fine orig pnt, average wear, sm age split in bottom, RB 7/07/87	**375**
Bluebill hen, Standard Grade, tack eyes, orig pnt w/some overpnt showing flaking/wear, split in bottom, RB 7/07/87	**80**
Bluebill pr, Challenge Grade, G orig pnt, weathered/some wear/EX patina, sm age split in body of each, 1, RB 12/06/85	**350**
Bluebill pr, Challenge Grade, low-head style, EX orig pnt, hen shows flaking/ms; drake is NM, rare, RWO 7/05/86	**2500**
Bluebill pr, Challenge Grade, orig pnt, minor wear, prof rstr to chip on drake's bill, J/G 9/19/87	**1000**
Bluebill pr, Challenge Grade, snaky heads, EX orig pnt, minor flaking/wear, 36, RB 2/01/85	**1100**
Bluebill pr, Premier Grade, orig pnt, heavy wear, hen's bill has been rstr, ms, RB 7/09/85	**350**
Bluebill pr, Premier Grade, orig pnt, minor wear, branded HED, seams have been refilled, J/G 9/19/87	**625**
Bluebill pr, Premier Grade, orig pnt, minor wear, hen has sm checks on breast/tail, ls, J/G 9/19/87	**900**
Bluebill pr, Premier Grade, orig pnt w/touchup to breast of drake, filled check, RWO 7/06/85	**350**
Bluebill pr, Standard Grade, glass eyes, fine orig pnt, average wear, 36, RB 2/01/85	**400**
Bluebill pr, Standard Grade, glass eyes, NM orig pnt, both have cracks on underside of bodyblock, J/G 4/24/86	**605**
Bluebill pr, Standard Grade, glass eyes, orig pnt, minor wear, hairline cracks, drake: 3; hen: 37, J/G 4/23/87	**700**
Bluebill pr, Standard Grade, glass eyes, VG orig pnt, rubs to primer, hen's neck filler gone/age check, RWO 7/02/88	**350**
Bluebill pr, Standard Grade, pnt eyes, drake has fine orig pnt, minor wear; hen has orig pnt w/heavy wear, RB 7/09/85	**250**
Bluebill pr, Standard Grade, pnt eyes, NM orig pnt, hen has filled crack on head & worn area on bottom, ls, J/G 9/19/87	**400**
Bluebill pr, Standard Grade, pnt eyes, orig pnt, in-use wear, neck filler missing/hen's head is loose, RWO 11/11/87	**190**
Bluebill pr, Standard Grade, tack eyes, drake has a sm crack running down bk, otherwise EX & orig, RWO 7/06/85	**525**
Bluebill pr, Standard Grade, tack eyes, EX orig pnt, minor wear/shellac, structurally sound, RWO 7/05/86	**210**
Bluebill pr, Standard Grade, tack eyes, factory brand, M condition, RB 2/01/85, 150%	**1050**
Bluebill pr, Standard Grade, tack eyes, NM orig pnt, several chips in neck filler, J/G 9/20/86	**525**
Bluebill pr, Standard Grade, tack eyes, orig pnt, minor wear, some neck filler missing, branded Barron, J/G 9/19/87	**650**
Bluewinged Teal, Standard Grade, pnt eyes, EX orig pnt, neck filler missing on both, otherwise EX, RWO 2/12/88	**800**
Bluewinged Teal drake, Challenge Grade, hollow, G orig pnt, minor flaking/wear, ls, 36, RB 2/01/85, 65%	**1200**
Bluewinged Teal drake, Challenge Grade, hollow, NM orig pnt, structurally outstanding, 113, RWO 7/06/85	**1650**
Bluewinged Teal drake, Challenge Grade, orig pnt, minor wear, no structural flaws, rare, J/G 9/19/87, 45%	**550**
Bluewinged Teal drake, Challenge Grade, snaky head, orig pnt, branded MR Bingham, neck rpr/tail chips, RWO 2/12/88	**500**
Bluewinged Teal drake, Challenge Grade, VG orig pnt, some rubs to primer, tail rpr/crack in bottom, 193, RWO 7/02/88	**1100**

Bluewinged Teal drake, Premier Grade, G orig pnt, average wear, rare, 36, RB 2/01/85 600
Bluewinged Teal drake, Premier Grade, hollow, EX orig pnt, ls/2 head cracks, otherwise EX, 193, RWO 7/02/88, 67% 2000
Bluewinged Teal drake, Standard Grade, glass eyes, EX orig pnt, average wear, age split in bk, RB 12/06/85 300
Bluewinged Teal drake, Standard Grade, glass eyes, EX orig pnt, moderate flaking/wear, rare, RB 12/06/85 400
Bluewinged Teal drake, Standard Grade, glass eyes, EX orig pnt, 30% neck filler missing, J/G 9/20/86 550
Bluewinged Teal drake, Standard Grade, glass eyes, EX orig pnt, minor flaking, sm crack part way down bk, J/G 4/24/87 962
Bluewinged Teal drake, Standard Grade, glass eyes, EX orig pnt, minor wear, structurally sound, early, RWO 7/02/88 600
Bluewinged Teal drake, Standard Grade, glass eyes, EX orig pnt, minor wear, separation/split/hairline, J/G 4/23/87 700
Bluewinged Teal drake, Standard Grade, glass eyes, G orig pnt, average wear, replaced neck filler, EX, RWO 7/04/87 425
Bluewinged Teal drake, Standard Grade, glass eyes, G orig pnt, average wear, RB 7/09/85 550
Bluewinged Teal drake, Standard Grade, glass eyes, NM orig pnt, structurally EX, never weighted, 193, RWO 7/02/88 1050
Bluewinged Teal drake, Standard Grade, glass eyes, orig pnt, average wear, filler in bottom, ls, RB 6/28/88, 233% 700
Bluewinged Teal drake, Standard Grade, orig pnt, average wear, crack on bk/one-half of bill missing, RWO 7/02/88 100
Bluewinged Teal drake, Standard Grade, pnt eyes, fine orig pnt, average wear, RB 3/11/88 325
Bluewinged Teal drake, Standard Grade, pnt eyes, G orig pnt, average wear, age split in body, ls, RB 3/11/88 300
Bluewinged Teal drake, Standard Grade, tack eyes, NM orig pnt, bears Mackey stamp, J/G 4/23/87 1050
Bluewinged Teal drake, Standard Grade, tack eyes, orig pnt, average wear, neck filler missing, RWO 11/06/85 325
Bluewinged Teal drake, Standard Grade, tack eyes, orig pnt, neck filler missing/tight check/bill chip, RWO 2/12/88 350
Bluewinged Teal hen, Challenge Grade, G orig pnt, minor wear, strengthening to pnt on breast/head, 36, RB 2/01/85, 60% 600
Bluewinged Teal hen, Challenge Grade, orig pnt, heavy wear, old bill repair, eyes are a replacement, RB 7/09/85 200
Bluewinged Teal hen, Challenge Grade, snaky head, G orig pnt, branded DB Day, EX condition, 193, RWO 7/02/88 1450
Bluewinged Teal hen, Premier Grade, EX orig pnt, age split in neck has been prof repaired, rare, 36, RB 2/01/85 2500
Bluewinged Teal hen, Premier Grade, hollow, orig pnt, crack part way along side to tail, otherwise EX, 193, RWO 7/02/88 2700
Bluewinged Teal hen, Standard Grade, glass eyes, EX orig pnt, minor flaking, 2 age splits, RB 7/07/87 1400
Bluewinged Teal hen, Standard Grade, glass eyes, EX orig pnt, several defects in wood, hs, J/G 4/23/87 275
Bluewinged Teal hen, Standard Grade, glass eyes, EX orig pnt w/areas of flaking, structurally EX, RWO 7/04/87 1200
Bluewinged Teal hen, Standard Grade, glass eyes, EX orig pnt, minor wear, most of the neck filler missing, J/G 4/23/87 650
Bluewinged Teal hen, Standard Grade, glass eyes, NM orig pnt, minor check on lower side, J/G 9/19/87 650

Mason Factory
Bluewinged Teal hen, Standard Grade, glass eyes, outstanding orig pnt w/some flaking, EX condition, RWO 7/04/87, 120%, $1,200.00.

Bluewinged Teal hen, Standard Grade, tack eyes, EX orig pnt, minor wear, structurally EX, 39, RB 7/08/86 850
Bluewinged Teal pr, Challenge Grade, rpt in Mason style, minor flaking, structurally sound, RWO 7/04/87 375
Bluewinged Teal pr, Challenge Grade, rpt w/flaking, structurally EX, RWO 11/06/85 210
Bluewinged Teal pr, Premier Grade, G orig pnt, average wear, RB 12/06/85 1700
Bluewinged Teal pr, Standard Grade, glass eyes, EX orig dry pnt, minor flaking/wear, rare, J/G 9/19/87 1200
Bluewinged Teal pr, Standard Grade, glass eyes, G orig pnt, average wear, 36, RB 2/01/85 900
Bluewinged Teal pr, Standard Grade, glass eyes, G orig pnt, average wear, minor age line in hen's head, J/G 4/23/87 700
Bluewinged Teal pr, Standard Grade, tack eyes, orig pnt, average wear, neck filler missing, otherwise sound, RWO 7/04/87 525
Brant, Challenge Grade, branded Barron Hunt Club, NM condition, RB 2/10/85, 125% 2250
Brant, Challenge Grade, EX orig pnt, minor wear, bears 2 Barron brands, 2 checks on bk/sm dents in tail, RWO 7/05/86 2750
Brant, Challenge Grade, EX orig pnt, minor wear, bears 2 Barron brands, thin neck checks, otherwise EX, 193, RWO 7/02/88 3000
Brant, Challenge Grade, hollow, old working rpt, slight wear, putty has been applied at base of neck, RWO 7/05/85 435
Brant, Challenge Grade, NM orig pnt w/EX patina, tight age split on body, tight check on neck, rare, J/G 9/20/86 2250
Brant, Challenge Grade, NM orig pnt w/thin wash of overpnt on neck/under tail, 5" hairline crack in bk, J/G 9/20/86 1000
Brant, Challenge Grade, old rpt w/heavy wear, bill is a replacement, age split in bottom, RB 7/09/85 200
Brant, Challenge Grade, old working rpt, tight check in bk/underside of bodyblock, very sm chip in bill, J/G 9/20/86 300
Brant, Challenge Grade, orig pnt, average wear, sm check on side of body, thin coat of shellac applied, RWO 7/05/86, 70% 700
Brant, Challenge Grade, orig pnt, minor wear, prof rstr to part of bill/base of neck, several age lines, J/G 9/19/87 350
Brant, Challenge Grade, orig pnt, minor wear, tight check part way under tail/in neck, ls, extra fine, J/G 4/23/87 2050

Brant, Challenge Grade, orig pnt w/working rpt on lower sides, moderate wear, minor age split on 1 side, J/G 9/19/87 .... **450**
Bufflehead drake, Challenge Grade, snaky head, EX orig pnt, minor flaking, structurally EX, RWO 11/11/87 .... **5000**
Bufflehead drake, Standard Grade, glass eyes, G orig pnt, narrow crack/neck filler missing, rare, 193, RWO 7/02/88, 78% **700**
Bufflehead drake, Standard Grade, glass eyes, NM condition, filled age split in bk, 36, RB 2/01/85, 180% **1800**
Bufflehead drake, Standard Grade, glass eyes, NM orig pnt w/varnish, few chips in neck filler/rough area, J/G 9/20/86 .... **650**
Bufflehead drake, Standard Grade, tack eyes, G orig pnt w/some overpnt, rare, RB 7/07/87 .... **300**
Bufflehead hen, Standard Grade, glass eyes, weathered/worn, eyes are replacements, rare, RB 12/06/85 .... **275**
Bufflehead hen, Standard Grade, tack eyes, worn orig pnt, head broken & reglued/old neck repair, 3/36, RB 2/01/85 .... **375**
Bufflehead pr, Standard Grade, glass eyes, EX orig pnt, minor wear, 36/86, RB 2/01/85 .... **1400**
Bufflehead pr, Standard Grade, glass eyes, EX orig pnt, minor wear, hen has sm chips in neck filler, rare, J/G 4/23/87 .... **1600**
Bufflehead pr, Standard Grade, glass eyes, hen has M pnt w/minor flaking; drake G w/flaking on bk of body, RB 7/09/85 .... **600**
Canada Goose, Premier Grade, body taken down to orig pnt w/some wear, head is a replacement, 36, RB 2/01/85 .... **900**
Canada Goose, Premier Grade, EX feather pnt, minor crazing/wear, few tight checks, early, rare, J/G 4/24/86, 65% **1595**
Canada Goose, Premier Grade, EX orig pnt, minor wear, prof rstr to crack in bk/neck cracks/part of bill, J/G 9/19/87 .... **1300**
Canada Goose, Premier Grade, EX orig pnt, minor wear, sm check on underside/top of tail, 193, RWO 7/02/88, 138% **7000**
Canada Goose, Premier Grade, EX prof rpt in Mason style, minor wear, hairline crack on underside, J/G 9/19/87 .... **1100**
Canada Goose, Premier Grade, old working rpt in Mason style, age split in underside, J/G 4/23/87 .... **800**

Mason Factory
Canada Goose, Premier Grade, orig worn pnt, replaced bill, age split on bodyblock, rare, RB 2/01/85, $1,000.00.

Canada Goose, Premier Grade, overpnt w/evidence of orig underneath, bill is a replacement, RB 7/09/85 .... **350**
Canvasback drake, Challenge Grade, entire rpt, structurally sound, RWO 7/06/85 .... **80**
Canvasback drake, Challenge Grade, EX orig pnt, minor wear, some neck filler missing, early, RWO 7/02/88, 50% **375**
Canvasback drake, Challenge Grade, fine orig pnt, average flaking/wear, early, 39, RB 7/08/86 .... **350**
Canvasback drake, Challenge Grade, flat bottom, orig pnt, branded DWH, minor age split in bottom, RB 6/28/88, 75% **300**
Canvasback drake, Challenge Grade, G orig pnt, in-use wear, although patterns are bold, structurally EX, RWO 7/05/86 .... **275**
Canvasback drake, Challenge Grade, G orig pnt w/wear to bare wood in white areas, check running down bottom, RWO 7/05/85 .... **330**
Canvasback drake, Challenge Grade, hollow, G orig pnt, average in-use wear, ls, rare, RB 7/09/85 .... **550**
Canvasback drake, Challenge Grade, NM pnt, some sm age splits in neck/bill, 36, RB 2/01/85 .... **600**
Canvasback drake, Challenge Grade, orig pnt, heavy wear, head is possibly old working rpt, RWO 7/05/86 .... **140**
Canvasback drake, Challenge Grade, prof rstr by Ray Schalk, eyes replaced/crack in neck, RWO 11/06/85 .... **105**
Canvasback drake, Challenge Grade, snaky head, orig pnt, average wear w/rubs mostly on head, EX condition, RWO 2/12/88 .... **575**
Canvasback drake, Premier Grade, Chesapeake Bay model, orig pnt, minor wear, structurally EX, rare, J/G 4/23/87 .... **500**
Canvasback drake, Premier Grade, EX orig pnt, minor wear, ms, RB 7/09/85 .... **575**
Canvasback drake, Premier Grade, EX rpt in Mason style, sm tail chip, J/G 4/24/86 .... **192**
Canvasback drake, Premier Grade, NM orig pnt, minor wear, ls, 36, RB 2/01/85 .... **1200**
Canvasback drake, Premier Grade, NM pnt, minor wear, branded HHB, ls, 3, RB 6/28/88 .... **800**
Canvasback drake, Premier Grade, old working rpt, check in underside, ls, branded Barron, J/G 4/23/87 .... **275**
Canvasback drake, Premier Grade, orig pnt, average wear on bk/sides, tight check in neck/ls, J/G 4/24/86 .... **357**
Canvasback drake, Premier Grade, orig pnt, heavy in-use wear, RB 7/09/85 .... **300**
Canvasback drake, Premier Grade, overpnt taken down to orig w/black showing in some parts, filler in neck, RWO 11/06/85 .... **240**
Canvasback drake, Premier Grade, rpt w/average wear, both eyes missing, oversize, RB 7/09/85 .... **90**
Canvasback drake, Premier Grade, Seneca Lake model, EX orig pnt, minor wear, tiny age split in neck, RB 7/07/87 .... **750**
Canvasback drake, Premier Grade, Seneca Lake model, extra fine head cvg, orig pnt, minor wear/chips, ms, J/G 9/20/86 .... **650**
Canvasback drake, Premier Grade, Seneca Lake model, G orig pnt, average wear, sm age split in bottom, ls, RB 12/06/85 .... **400**
Canvasback drake, Premier Grade, Seneca Lake model, G orig pnt, average wear, thin crack in neck, RWO 11/06/85 .... **290**

Canvasback drake, Premier Grade, Seneca Lake model, G orig pnt, minor wear, structurally sound, 36, RB 2/01/85 600
Canvasback drake, Premier Grade, slightly turned head, slope-breast, EX prof pnt rstr/ls, Eaton brand, rare, J/G 4/23/87 500
Canvasback drake, Premier Grade, snaky head, hollow, orig pnt, branded BL, bk cracks/check on head/neck, RWO 7/02/88 400
Canvasback drake, Premier Grade, snaky head, orig pnt, in-use wear, check on 1 side of bk, early, RWO 7/02/88, 50% 450
Canvasback drake, Premier Grade/Seneca Lake model, pnt worn to wood in lg areas, body/neck cracks, RWO 7/02/88 135
Canvasback drake, Standard Grade, glass eyes, EX orig pnt, minor wear, several chips in neck filler, rare, J/G 9/20/86 400
Canvasback drake, Standard Grade, glass eyes, old rpt taken down to some orig w/heavy wear, early, RB 7/08/86 160
Canvasback drake, Standard Grade, glass eyes, orig pnt, minor wear, several sm dents in bk, J/G 9/20/86 325
Canvasback drake, Standard Grade, glass eyes, orig pnt, minor wear, age split on underside of bodyblock, J/G 9/20/86 175
Canvasback drake, Standard Grade, glass eyes, orig pnt on white areas, sm filled crack on underside of body, J/G 9/20/86 160
Canvasback drake, Standard Grade, glass eyes, orig pnt w/some overpnt on breast, 1 eye replaced, RWO 7/06/85 220
Canvasback drake, Standard Grade, glass eyes, overpnt, moderate wear, sm age split in bottom, RB 7/08/87 90
Canvasback drake, Standard Grade, glass eyes, working rpt, worn/flaking, neck filler missing/checks in bk, RWO 2/12/88 85
Canvasback drake, Standard Grade, pnt eye model w/glass eyes, EX orig pnt, ls, minor age split in bk, RB 7/09/85 175
Canvasback drake, Standard Grade, pnt eye model w/glass eyes, EX orig pnt, crack in underside of bodyblock, J/G 4/24/86 247
Canvasback drake, Standard Grade, pnt eyes, EX orig pnt, 1 side has several lg rubs/dents, J/G 4/24/86 165
Canvasback drake, Standard Grade, pnt eyes, NM orig pnt, hairline crack in neck, rare, J/G 9/20/86 160
Canvasback hen, Challenge Grade, old working rpt, minor wear, ls, early, J/G 4/23/87 500
Canvasback hen, Challenge Grade, orig pnt, heavy wear, branded, age check on side, RWO 11/06/85 190
Canvasback hen, Challenge Grade, snaky head, VG orig pnt, average wear, ls, otherwise EX, early, 193, RWO 7/02/88, 40% 400
Canvasback hen, Premier Grade, G orig pnt, minor wear, some sm age splits, 36, RB 2/01/85 700
Canvasback hen, Premier Grade, orig pnt, minor wear, head has been broken off & reglued, J/G 4/23/87 450
Canvasback hen, Premier Grade, rpt in Mason style, structurally sound, RWO 7/02/88 130
Canvasback hen, Premier Grade, Seneca Lake model, EX orig pnt w/average wear, age splits, eye missing, RB 3/06/87 425
Canvasback hen, Premier Grade, Seneca Lake model, EX orig pnt, minor wear, ls, RB 8/21/86 750
Canvasback hen, Premier Grade, Seneca Lake model, orig pnt, worn/weathered, thin crack in neck, hs, RWO 7/04/87 200
Canvasback hen, Premier Grade, worn orig pnt w/some traces of feather pnt, crack on bk/ding on head & bk, RWO 7/02/88 200
Canvasback hen, Standard Grade, G orig pnt, average wear, much of the neck filler missing/wear on bill, RWO 7/02/88 225
Canvasback hen, Standard Grade, glass eyes, EX orig pnt, minor flaking/wear, age split in bottom/ls, RB 6/28/88, 37% 150
Canvasback hen, Standard Grade, glass eyes, fine orig pnt, average wear, ls, 36, RB 2/01/85 300
Canvasback hen, Standard Grade, pnt eyes, minor wear on bill, tight check on underside of bodyblock, rare, J/G 4/24/86 247
Canvasback hen, Standard Grade, tack eyes, G orig pnt, average wear, slight age split in bottom, RB 8/21/86 175
Canvasback pr, Challenge Grade, orig pnt, minor wear, drake has age line on bk & underside, both are ls, J/G 9/19/87 800
Canvasback pr, Premier Grade, EX orig pnt, average wear, drake's bill chewed/tight checks on bk, hen is EX, RWO 7/05/86 2000
Canvasback pr, Premier Grade, EX orig pnt, minor wear, branded HED, hen has separated & been filled, J/G 9/19/87 850
Canvasback pr, Premier Grade, G orig pnt, hen has sm sliver missing under bill, otherwise structurally EX, RWO 11/06/85 1000

Mason Factory Canvasback pr, Premier Grade, NM orig pnt, minor wear, drake is ls; hen has prof rstr bill/shot holes, J/G 4/23/87, $2,100.00.

Canvasback pr, Premier Grade, NM orig pnt w/bold feather pnt, factory brand, drake has sm chip out of bill, J/G 4/24/86 3300
Canvasback pr, Premier Grade, Seneca Lake model, EX orig pnt, both have tight checks, otherwise sound, RWO 7/02/88, 57% 850
Canvasback pr, Premier Grade, Seneca Lake model, G orig pnt, drake is ls; hen has bill crack/ls, 193, RWO 7/02/88, 55% 1000
Canvasback pr, Premier Grade, Seneca Lake model, NM orig pnt, factory brand, structurally EX, J/G 4/24/86 1870
Canvasback pr, Premier Grade, Seneca Lake model, orig pnt, average wear, structurally sound, RB 8/27/87 800
Canvasback pr, Premier Grade, Seneca Lake model, orig pnt, minor wear, age splits on undersides, branded, J/G 4/23/87 1900
Canvasback pr, Premier Grade, Seneca Lake model, orig pnt w/working overpnt, drake has minor bill damage, RWO 7/05/86 350
Canvasback pr, Premier Grade, snaky head, orig pnt, minor wear, hen has hairline crack in bk, ls, 99, J/G 9/19/87 1550
Canvasback pr, Premier Grade, snaky heads, EX orig pnt, tight checks on bk/ls, otherwise EX, early, RWO 7/02/88 2500
Canvasback pr, Seneca Lake model, EX orig pnt, drake has sliver of wood missing from neck, otherwise EX, RWO 7/02/88 1800

Canvasback pr, Seneca Lake model, orig pnt, drake has tail chip/bill rpr; hen has eye missing/hs, RWO 7/02/88 .... **900**
Canvasback pr, Standard Grade, glass eyes, EX orig pnt, branded Barron, 30% neck filler missing, J/G 9/19/87 .... **500**
Canvasback pr, Standard Grade, glass eyes, hen has orig pnt w/minor wear; drake has average wear, EX, J/G 4/23/87 .... **400**
Canvasback pr, Standard Grade, glass eyes, orig pnt, average wear, structurally sound, RWO 7/05/86 .... **375**
Canvasback pr, Standard Grade, glass eyes, orig pnt, average wear, hen has bare spots/thin check, RWO 7/06/85 .... **300**
Canvasback pr, Standard Grade, pnt eyes, drake has NM orig pnt; hen has wear on bill/roughness to tail, J/G 9/19/87 .... **450**
Coot, Challenge Grade, EX orig pnt, minor wear, slight age split in bottom, 20, RB 12/06/85 .... **2750**
Coot, Challenge Grade, high-head style, EX orig pnt/lt varnish, eye/filler missing, ls, 1910, rare, J/G 9/19/87, 65% **1300**
Coot, Challenge Grade, NM pnt, chip at top of tail, rare, 36, RB 2/01/85 .... **1750**
Coot, old overpnt taken down to mostly orig pnt, average wear, rare, RB 7/08/87 .... **800**
Coot or Mudhen, Challenge Grade, outstanding orig pnt w/exceptional feather pnt, M condition, 193, RWO 7/02/88, 285% **10000**
Crow, EX orig pnt, average wear, tail chip/hairline crack running part way down underside, 193, RWO 7/02/88 .... **425**
Crow, glass eyes, G orig pnt, old repair to bill, rare, 36/86, RB 2/01/85 .... **900**

Mason Factory
Curlew, cvd raised wings, in the Bowman style, EX orig pnt, average wear, prof rpl bill, early, RWO 7/05/86, 80%, $12,000.00.

Curlew, G orig pnt, average wear, sm chip in tail/1 glass eye missing, otherwise structurally sound, RWO 7/05/86, 80% **1900**
Curlew, glass eyes, orig pnt, minor wear, sm hairline crack in bk of neck/side, rare, J/G 4/23/87 .... **3750**
Curlew, low-head style, glass eyes, spike bill, fine orig pnt, minor wear, rare, 36, RB 2/01/85 .... **7000**
Curlew, rpt in Mason style, minor age lines, ls, early, J/G 4/23/87 .... **700**
Curlew, sickle bill, EX orig pnt, average wear, slight age split in bottom of body, rare, 3, RB 3/06/87, 65% **3250**
Curlew, sickle bill, EX orig pnt, minor flaking/wear, slight age split in side/rpl eye, rare, 22, RB 5/02/86 .... **5250**
Curlew, sickle bill, G orig pnt, average wear, minor bill rstr, RB 12/06/85 .... **2000**
Curlew, sickle bill, high-neck style, orig pnt, very worn, age splits in body, rare, RB 12/06/85 .... **1000**
Curlew, sm crack where bill joins head, otherwise M, oversize, 18", J/G 4/24/86 .... **9350**
Curlew, spike bill, old coat of varnish is yellowed & faded, otherwise M, RB 3/06/87, 57% **4000**
Dove, glass eyes, NM detailed feather pnt, structurally perfect, 1 of 3 existent in this pnt style, J/G 4/24/86 .... **3025**
Dove, glass eyes, NM orig pnt w/highly detailed pnt pattern, ls, J/G 9/20/86, 50% **1000**
Dove, glass eyes, spike bill, fine orig pnt, ls, rare, 36, RB 2/01/85, 75% **1300**
Dove, orig pnt, average wear, gouge near tail, wooden bill may be an early replacement, early, 45, RWO 7/06/85 .... **550**
Dove, orig pnt, average wear w/area to bare wood on belly/bk, structurally sound, 193, RWO 7/02/88, 33% **500**
Dowitcher, EX orig pnt, minor wear, thin tight crack in breast running down to middle of underside, 193, RWO 7/02/88 .... **1400**
Dowitcher, glass eyes, spike bill, NM orig pnt, tight check in breast/tail chip has been prof rstr, ls, J/G 4/24/86, 70% **770**
Dowitcher, glass eyes, spike bill, orig pnt intact on bill, NM condition, 39, RB 7/08/86 .... **1500**
Dowitcher, tack eyes, EX orig condition, 39, RB 7/08/86 .... **700**
Dowitcher, tack eyes, orig pnt, average wear, no structural flaws, J/G 4/24/86 .... **385**
Dowitcher, tack eyes, split tail, orig pnt, slight wear, sm chip on underside of tail, early, J/G 9/20/86 .... **400**
Dunlin, glass eyes, orig pnt, minor wear, pc between 2 tight checks has been reglued, ms, very rare, J/G 9/19/87 .... **750**
Golden Plover, glass eyes, EX orig pnt w/highly detailed wing tips, extremely rare/collectible, J/G 4/24/86 .... **3190**
Golden Plover, glass eyes, EX orig swirled pnt, average wear, ls, early, RB 6/28/88, 58% **700**
Golden Plover, glass eyes, orig pnt, minor wear, minor age line on lower breast/underside, J/G 9/19/87 .... **750**
Golden Plover, split tail, orig pnt, structurally EX, very rare, 3/13, RWO 7/06/85 .... **425**
Golden Plover, tack eyes, fine orig pnt, Fall plumage, average wear, rare, 39, RB 7/08/86 .... **600**
Golden Plover, VG orig pnt, minimal wear, sm check running along 1 side, otherwise structurally EX, RWO 7/06/85 .... **750**
Goldeneye drake, Challenge Grade, mostly orig pnt, moderate wear, crack in underside/1 eye replaced, ls, J/G 9/20/86 .... **200**
Goldeneye drake, Challenge Grade, orig pnt, average wear w/some rubs to primer on head, EX condition, RWO 7/02/88 .... **400**
Goldeneye drake, Challenge Grade, orig pnt, moderate flaking/wear, RB 8/21/86 .... **225**

Goldeneye drake, Challenge Grade, orig pnt, roughness to edges of bill, age split in bottom, RB 7/07/87 300
Goldeneye drake, Challenge Grade, pnt prof taken down to orig w/minor wear, hairline crack, J/G 4/23/87 725
Goldeneye drake, Premier Grade, G orig pnt, average wear, old break in tail has been repaired, RB 8/21/86 525
Goldeneye drake, Premier Grade, G orig pnt, in-use flaking, 36, RB 2/01/85 350
Goldeneye drake, Premier Grade, old working rpt w/some orig, 1 glass eye missing, loose piece at neck, RWO 7/06/85 220
Goldeneye drake, special order model, working rpt w/traces of orig, structurally sound, RWO 7/06/85 170
Goldeneye drake, Standard Grade, glass eyes, EX orig pnt, hairline crack on underside of bodyblock, J/G 4/24/86 605
Goldeneye drake, Standard Grade, glass eyes, orig pnt, right eye missing/left eye damaged, age split in body, RB 3/11/88 160
Goldeneye drake, Standard Grade, tack eyes, EX orig pnt, minor wear, 36, RB 2/01/85 450
Goldeneye drake, Standard Grade, tack eyes, EX orig pnt, minor wear, age splits in bottom, otherwise EX/NM, RB 8/21/86 275
Goldeneye drake, Standard Grade, tack eyes, EX orig pnt, sm chunk missing from bk of head, otherwise EX, RWO 7/05/86 325
Goldeneye drake, Standard Grade, tack eyes, G orig pnt w/average flaking/wear, neck filler missing, rare, RWO 7/05/86 200
Goldeneye drake, Standard Grade, tack eyes, NM orig pnt, tight crack on underside of bodyblock, J/G 4/24/86 440
Goldeneye hen, Challenge Grade, orig pnt, average wear, 1 eye missing, ls, rare, J/G 4/24/86 247
Goldeneye hen, Premier Grade, hollow, fine orig pnt, minor wear, structurally EX, rare, RWO 11/06/85 1200
Goldeneye hen, Standard Grade, glass eyes, EX orig pnt, minor wear, age line in 1 side of body, 3/36, RB 2/01/85 400
Goldeneye hen, Standard Grade, glass eyes, EX orig pnt, neck filler missing, otherwise EX, early, rare, RWO 7/05/86 190
Goldeneye hen, Standard Grade, tack eyes, orig pnt, average wear, tight checks on bk of bodyblock, rare, J/G 4/24/86 330

Mason Factory
Goldeneye pr, Challenge Grade, hen has EX orig pnt w/minor wear; drake has fine orig pnt w/minor wear, 36, RB 2/01/85, $2,750.00.

Goldeneye pr, Premier Grade, fine orig pnt, average wear, 21, RB 7/08/85 3100
Goldeneye pr, Premier Grade, orig pnt, average wear, sm scuff/chip on lower breast of hen, rare, J/G 4/24/86 2255
Goldeneye pr, Standard Grade, G orig pnt, average wear, both have hairline cracks, RWO 7/02/88, 68% 800
Goose, Premier Grade, EX orig pnt, average wear w/feather pnt on bk & speculum, thin crack in neck, RWO 7/05/86, 60% 1800
Greenwinged Teal drake, Challenge Grade, EX orig pnt, slight wear, prof bill rstr, ms, very rare, 13, J/G 9/20/86 2100
Greenwinged Teal drake, Challenge Grade, G orig pnt, average wear, rare, RB 7/09/85 1000
Greenwinged Teal drake, Challenge Grade, snaky head, EX orig pnt, minor wear, rare, 36, RB 2/01/85, 125% 3800
Greenwinged Teal drake, Premier Grade, G orig pnt, a coat of varnish has been prof removed, ls, very rare, J/G 4/24/86 1650
Greenwinged Teal drake, Standard Grade, glass eyes, EX orig pnt, Mackey stamp, neck filler missing/bk rstr, RWO 2/12/88 575
Greenwinged Teal drake, Standard Grade, glass eyes, fine orig pnt, minor wear, lg age split on body, 36, RB 2/01/85 600
Greenwinged Teal drake, Standard Grade, glass eyes, fine orig pnt, minor wear, minor age split, 36, RB 2/01/85 750
Greenwinged Teal drake, Standard Grade, glass eyes, G orig pnt, average wear, age split in bottom, ls, RB 3/06/87 350
Greenwinged Teal drake, Standard Grade, glass eyes, G orig pnt, moderate flaking, ls, rare, RB 7/08/86 650
Greenwinged Teal drake, Standard Grade, glass eyes, orig pnt, sm bk chip/bill has touchup, rare, 193, RWO 7/02/88, 155% 950
Greenwinged Teal drake, Standard Grade, pnt eyes, most neck filler missing, otherwise M, extremely rare, RB 7/08/87, 50% 1750
Greenwinged Teal drake, Standard Grade, pnt eyes, NM orig pnt w/several sm rubs, extremely rare, J/G 4/23/87 1900
Greenwinged Teal drake pr, Premier Grade, G orig pnt, in-use wear, ls, 36, RB 2/01/85 3750
Greenwinged Teal hen, Challenge Grade, EX form w/snaky head, orig pnt, heavy wear to natural wood in areas, RB 8/21/86 375
Greenwinged Teal hen, Challenge Grade, fine orig pnt, minor wear to end of bill, glued repair, rare, RB 7/09/85 1350
Greenwinged Teal hen, Challenge Grade, fine orig pnt, minor wear, ls, rare, J/G 4/23/87 1500
Greenwinged Teal hen, Challenge Grade, orig pnt w/varnish, hairlines, half of bill rstr/sm hole in bk, rare, J/G 4/23/87 1650
Greenwinged Teal hen, Premier Grade, EX orig pnt, average wear, well preserved, RB 8/21/86, 50% 1000
Greenwinged Teal hen, Premier Grade, EX orig pnt, slight wear, 3 string marks/scratches on bill, 176, J/G 9/20/86, 75% 1900
Greenwinged Teal hen, Premier Grade, hollow, EX orig pnt, separation to body halves, EX, rare, 193/198, RWO 7/02/88, 45% 900
Greenwinged Teal hen, Premier Grade, NM orig pnt, slight separation where neck joins bodyblock, ls, branded, J/G 4/23/87 3300
Greenwinged Teal hen, Premier Grade, NM orig pnt, sm crack part way down bk, structurally outstanding, J/G 4/24/86 2475
Greenwinged Teal hen, Premier Grade, orig pnt, minor wear, sm tail chips, head has been reset, ls, 7, J/G 9/19/87 800
Greenwinged Teal hen, Standard Grade, glass eyes, fine orig pnt, minor wear, 36, RB 2/01/85 550
Greenwinged Teal hen, Standard Grade, glass eyes, orig pnt, minor wear, several sm age splits on body, J/G 9/20/86 690

Greenwinged Teal hen, Standard Grade, glass eyes, orig pnt, heavy wear, RB 3/06/87 .... **350**
Greenwinged Teal hen, Standard Grade, pnt eye model w/glass eyes, EX orig pnt, RB 8/27/87 .... **500**
Greenwinged Teal hen, Standard Grade, tack eyes, rpt in Mason style, RB 8/21/86 .... **175**
Grey Coot, Challenge Grade, EX orig pnt, average wear, check on underside, otherwise EX, rare, 193, RWO 7/02/88, 48% **1200**
Grey Coot, Challenge Grade, EX orig pnt, minor flaking/hairline, branded WB for Wm Barbour, Detroit MI, J/G 4/24/86 .... **2475**
Labrador Duck, slightly turned head, hollow, old pnt, moderate wear, early, very rare, J/G 9/20/86 .... **2500**
Mallard drake, Challenge Grade, EX orig pnt, average wear, sm tail chips, RWO 11/06/85 .... **375**
Mallard drake, Challenge Grade, EX orig pnt, average wear, sm tail chip/check near breast, otherwise sound, RWO 7/04/87 .... **350**
Mallard drake, Challenge Grade, EX orig pnt, bears Mackey stamp, sm tail chip, otherwise M, RWO 7/02/88, 140% **2500**
Mallard drake, Challenge Grade, EX orig pnt, minimal wear, sm chips at top of tail, RB 7/09/85 .... **650**
Mallard drake, Challenge Grade, EX orig pnt, minor wear, chip at top of tail, RB 12/06/85 .... **750**
Mallard drake, Challenge Grade, EX orig pnt, minor wear, thin crack down bk/sm chip at tail, RWO 11/06/85 .... **425**
Mallard drake, Challenge Grade, G orig pnt, strip on side where pnt is off, cracks in bk/checks/tail chip, RWO 7/02/88 .... **300**
Mallard drake, Challenge Grade, hollow, outstanding orig pnt, cracked eye, FDW/TC stencil, rare, J/G 4/24/86, 145% **1732**
Mallard drake, Challenge Grade, orig pnt, minor wear, slight age split in bottom, otherwise NM, RB 6/28/88 .... **800**
Mallard drake, Challenge Grade, orig pnt, moderate wear, old in-use repair to neck filler/bodyblock, J/G 9/20/86 .... **450**
Mallard drake, Challenge Grade, orig pnt w/overpnt on head/bill, age split on side of body, RB 12/06/85 .... **150**
Mallard drake, Challenge Grade, overpnt taken down to G orig pnt, lg tail chip, structurally sound, RWO 7/05/85 .... **200**
Mallard drake, Challenge Grade, rpt, average wear, RB 7/08/87 .... **100**
Mallard drake, Premier Grade, EX orig pnt, average wear w/some rubs around tail, NM condition, RWO 2/12/88 .... **1400**
Mallard drake, Premier Grade, extra fine pnt pattern, minor wear, tiny chip on tail, ls, J/G 4/23/87 .... **950**
Mallard drake, Premier Grade, fine orig pnt, average wear, chip at end of tail has been reglued, ms, RB 7/09/85 .... **550**
Mallard drake, Premier Grade, fine orig pnt, minor wear, hairline crack in bk, ls, early, J/G 9/19/87 .... **900**
Mallard drake, Premier Grade, fine orig pnt, minor wear, sm rough area on lower sides, J/G 4/23/87 .... **700**
Mallard drake, Premier Grade, orig pnt, average wear, chip at end of tail, RB 8/21/86 .... **375**
Mallard drake, Premier Grade, orig pnt, average wear, flaking/age split on breast, RWO 7/05/86, 70% **425**
Mallard drake, Premier Grade, orig pnt, heavy wear, lg chip out of tail/head has been reglued, RWO 7/06/85 .... **190**
Mallard drake, Premier Grade, orig pnt, minor wear, 2 hairline cracks in body, ls, early, J/G 4/23/87 .... **450**
Mallard drake, Premier Grade, orig pnt, minor wear w/old working rpt on head, tail chip, crack in bk/neck, J/G 9/19/87 .... **225**
Mallard drake, Premier Grade, prof rpt, sm chip in tail has been repaired, otherwise structurally sound, RWO 7/05/86 .... **140**
Mallard drake, Premier Grade, rpt in Mason style, tight check on underside/hairline in tail, oversize, rare, J/G 4/23/87 .... **175**
Mallard drake, Premier Grade, snaky head, orig pnt, minor wear, several sm tail chips, early, J/G 4/23/87 .... **625**
Mallard drake, Standard Grade, fine orig pnt, putty missing from neck, otherwise EX, salesman's sample, RWO 7/06/85 .... **600**
Mallard drake, Standard Grade, G orig pnt, average wear, sm tail chip, tight cracks on bottom/side, RWO 7/02/88 .... **225**
Mallard drake, Standard Grade, glass eyes, EX orig pnt, structurally EX, RWO 11/06/85 .... **450**
Mallard drake, Standard Grade, glass eyes, EX orig pnt w/signs of wear, some neck filler missing, RWO 7/05/86 .... **290**
Mallard drake, Standard Grade, glass eyes, G orig pnt, average in-use wear, neck filler missing, RWO 7/05/86 .... **150**
Mallard drake, Standard Grade, glass eyes, G orig pnt, average wear, slight age split in bottom, RB 3/06/87 .... **250**
Mallard drake, Standard Grade, glass eyes, NM condition, RB 7/07/87 .... **600**
Mallard drake, Standard Grade, glass eyes, NM orig pnt, slight wear, 21, RB 7/09/85 .... **400**
Mallard drake, Standard Grade, glass eyes, NM orig pnt, 25% neck filler missing, J/G 9/20/86 .... **300**
Mallard drake, Standard Grade, glass eyes, rpt, average wear, RB 6/28/88 .... **80**
Mallard drake, Standard Grade, pnt eyes, G orig pnt, average wear, neck filler missing/chips in tail/bill, RWO 7/05/86 .... **140**
Mallard drake, Standard Grade, pnt eyes, orig pnt, minor wear, head reglued, some neck filler missing, J/G 9/20/86 .... **125**
Mallard drake, Standard Grade, tack eyes, orig pnt, minor wear, 36, RB 2/01/85 .... **200**
Mallard drake, Standard Grade, tack eyes, orig pnt worn to wood in areas, bill damage/neck filler missing, RWO 2/12/88 .... **100**
Mallard drake, Standard Grade, tack eyes, rpt w/minor flaking, well preserved, RB 7/07/87 .... **500**
Mallard hen, Challenge Grade, EX orig pnt, average wear, thin check in bottom, minor repair, early, RWO 7/04/87 .... **300**
Mallard hen, Challenge Grade, EX orig pnt, minor wear, lg tail chip/sm ding on bottom of bill, otherwise NM, RWO 7/04/87 .... **575**
Mallard hen, Challenge Grade, EX orig pnt, thin crack on bk/hole on top of head has been filled, RWO 7/02/88 .... **950**
Mallard hen, Challenge Grade, hollow, fine orig pnt, minor flaking, minor age splits/tail chip, rare, RB 2/01/85 .... **450**
Mallard hen, Challenge Grade, hollow, orig pnt, average wear/touchup, nail holes in neck area, rare, J/G 9/19/87 .... **325**
Mallard hen, Challenge Grade, hollow, orig pnt, minor wear, several sm holes in underside, rare, J/G 9/19/87 .... **750**
Mallard hen, Premier Grade, EX orig pnt, average wear, fine dry patina, ls, RB 3/06/87 .... **650**
Mallard hen, Premier Grade, EX orig pnt, minor flaking/wear, superb swirling, 39, RB 7/08/86 .... **1000**
Mallard hen, Premier Grade, EX orig pnt, minor wear, NM condition, 40, RB 7/08/86, 133% **1600**
Mallard hen, Premier Grade, EX swirled feather pnt, branded Fuller, minor age splits on bk, otherwise NM, RB 3/11/88 .... **850**
Mallard hen, Premier Grade, fine orig pnt, minor wear, ls, RB 6/28/88 .... **700**
Mallard hen, Premier Grade, G orig pnt, average wear w/flaking on left side, well preserved, RB 3/06/87 .... **750**
Mallard hen, Premier Grade, Mamouth model, worn orig pnt w/areas to bare wood, tail chip/check in bottom, RWO 2/12/88 .... **200**
Mallard hen, Premier Grade, NM condition/unused, RB 7/09/85 .... **2500**

Mallard hen, Premier Grade, orig pnt, heavy wear, bill has been chewed/lg tail chip/head reglued, RWO 2/12/88 190
Mallard hen, Premier Grade, orig pnt, minor wear, sm tail chip/tight check in bk/upper breast, J/G 4/23/87 475
Mallard hen, Premier Grade, snaky head, EX orig pnt, tight checks/tail chip, otherwise EX, early, 193, RWO 7/02/88, 50% 600
Mallard hen, Premier Grade, snaky head, orig pnt, minor wear, rstr tail chip, ls, early, from DB Day rig, J/G 9/19/87 1500
Mallard hen, Standard Grade, glass eyes, EX orig pnt, minor wear, RB 7/09/85 300
Mallard hen, Standard Grade, glass eyes, NM orig pnt, circular weight set into underside, J/G 9/20/86 425
Mallard hen, Standard Grade, glass eyes, NM pnt, slight age split in bottom, 39, RB 7/08/86 475
Mallard hen, Standard Grade, orig & overpnt, moderate crazing/flaking, RB 8/25/88 100
Mallard hen, Standard Grade, pnt eyes, NM orig pnt, some neck filler missing, added weight, J/G 9/20/86 210
Mallard hen, Standard Grade, pnt eyes, orig pnt, heavy wear w/areas to bare wood, neck filler missing/ms, RWO 2/12/88 110
Mallard hen, Standard Grade, pnt eyes, overpnt on bill, several sm chips out of neck filler, otherwise M, J/G 4/24/86 385
Mallard hen, Standard Grade, rpl glass eyes, orig pnt, tight check on bk, chips out of neck filler, RWO 7/04/87 220
Mallard hen, Standard Grade, tack eyes, NM orig pnt, sm chip on tip of bill/tight age split in bk, J/G 4/24/86 330

Mason Factory
Mallard pr, Challenge Grade, hollow, NM pnt, minor flaking, rare, RB 2/01/85, 175%, $4,400.00.

Mallard pr, Challenge Grade, orig pnt, heavy flaking/wear, chips to tail, hen has check down bottom, RWO 11/06/85 200
Mallard pr, Challenge Grade, orig pnt, heavy in-use wear, 36, RB 7/09/85 550
Mallard pr, Challenge Grade, orig pnt, moderate wear, some age splitting, hen's bill has been chewed, RB 8/21/86 325
Mallard pr, Premier Grade, drake is NM w/EX swirling; hen has orig pnt w/flaking/wear, well preserved, RB 12/06/85 3500
Mallard pr, Premier Grade, EX orig pnt, average wear, 40, RB 7/08/86 1100
Mallard pr, Premier Grade, EX orig pnt, minor wear, both are are structurally EX, RWO 7/05/85 1500
Mallard pr, Premier Grade, EX orig pnt, minor wear, drake is ls; hen has rpl filler in seam, planed area, J/G 9/19/87 1400
Mallard pr, Premier Grade, EX orig pnt, minor wear, 21, RB 7/09/85 1600
Mallard pr, Premier Grade, G orig pnt, average in-use wear, sm tail chips/hen has neck repair, RB 7/09/85 900
Mallard pr, Premier Grade, G orig pnt, average wear, drake has sm check on bk; hen has lg base check, RWO 7/05/86, 45% 650
Mallard pr, Premier Grade, G orig pnt, average wear, factory stamp, hen has tail chip, both ls, 36, RB 2/01/85 800
Mallard pr, Premier Grade, G orig pnt, average wear, repair to hen's neck; lg chip on drake's tail, ms, RB 12/06/85 550
Mallard pr, Premier Grade, hen has EX pnt; drake shows average wear, 36, RB 2/01/85 1000
Mallard pr, Premier Grade, snaky heads, EX orig pnt, drake has rubs to bare wood on head, otherwise EX, 193, RWO 7/02/88 3700
Mallard pr, Standard Grade, drake has glass eyes; hen has tack eyes, orig pnt, average wear, age splits, 3/11/88 200
Mallard pr, Standard Grade, glass eyes, EX orig pnt, average wear, RWO 11/11/87, 160% 725
Mallard pr, Standard Grade, glass eyes, EX orig pnt, minor wear, both have 1 eye missing, RB 7/09/85 550
Mallard pr, Standard Grade, glass eyes, EX orig pnt, some neck filler missing on both decoys, J/G 4/24/86 577
Mallard pr, Standard Grade, glass eyes, hen has orig pnt; drake has working rpt, tight checks in bodyblocks, J/G 4/23/87 250
Mallard pr, Standard Grade, glass eyes, NM condition, 36, RB 2/01/85 900
Mallard pr, Standard Grade, glass eyes, orig pnt, average wear, some neck filler missing, J/G 9/20/86 300
Mallard pr, Standard Grade, glass eyes, orig pnt, hen w/minor wear; drake w/average wear, both w/age splits, J/G 4/23/87 425
Mallard pr, Standard Grade, glass eyes, rpt, structurally sound, RWO 11/06/85 130
Mallard pr, Standard Grade, pnt eyes, EX orig pnt, heavy varnish, average wear, RB 7/08/86 200
Mallard pr, Standard Grade, pnt eyes, EX orig pnt, minor wear, 36, RB 2/01/85 350
Mallard pr, Standard Grade, pnt eyes, EX orig pnt, minor wear, drake has several age checks in bodyblock, J/G 4/23/87 325
Mallard pr, Standard Grade, pnt eyes, G orig pnt, average wear, neck filler missing, head reattached, RWO 7/04/87 375
Mallard pr, Standard Grade, pnt eyes, G orig pnt, average wear, hen has gouge on right side of body, RB 7/09/85 250
Mallard pr, Standard Grade, tack eyes, orig pnt, average wear w/dings/wear marks, structurally sound, RWO 7/05/86 375
Mallard pr, Standard Grade, tack eyes, orig pnt, average wear on drake; moderate on hen, several age splits, RB 6/28/88 275
Mallard pr, Standard Grade, tack eyes, orig pnt, in-use wear, drake has thin check along side, RWO 7/05/85 350
Merganser drake, American; Premier Grade, G orig pnt, crack has been filled w/glue, otherwise sound, RWO 7/02/88, 70% 1400
Merganser drake, Challenge Grade, EX orig pnt, factory brand, sm dabs of red paint on bk, otherwise NM, RB 3/06/87 2600
Merganser drake, Challenge Grade, EX orig pnt, light wear, ms, 36, RB 2/01/85 3000
Merganser drake, Challenge Grade, EX orig pnt, minor wear, structurally EX, J/G 4/24/86 1870
Merganser drake, Challenge Grade, orig pnt, minor wear, prof removed overpnt, ls, tight split, J/G 9/20/86 1300
Merganser drake, Challenge Grade, prof rpt taken down to orig by DeLong, moderate wear, chipped tail, RB 3/06/87 450
Merganser drake, Challenge Grade, rpt w/traces of orig, bill is a replacement/some age splits in bottom, RB 7/09/85 470

Merganser drake, Premier Grade, G prof pnt rstr, no structural flaws, J/G 4/23/87 350
Merganser drake, Premier Grade, orig pnt, moderate wear, possible rstr to underside of bill, RB 8/21/86 650
Merganser drake, Premier Grade, orig pnt w/some rpt, orig shows minor wear, Serges brand on bottom, ls, J/G 9/20/86 450
Merganser drake, Premier Grade, prof rpt, RB 7/07/87 225
Merganser drake, Standard Grade, glass eyes, EX orig pnt w/several sm rubs, sm crack in bill, very rare, J/G 4/24/86 935
Merganser drake, Standard Grade, glass eyes, NM pnt, slight age split in bottom, otherwise NM, 36, RB 2/01/85 750
Merganser drake, Standard Grade, glass eyes, working rpt worn to orig, 2 cracks/rpl neck filler, early, 33, J/G 9/19/87 160
Merganser drake, Standard Grade, tack eyes, orig pnt, tight check down bk/neck filler missing, RWO 7/06/85 360
Merganser hen, Challenge Grade, EX orig pnt, very minor wear, end of bill/base of neck have been prof rstr, J/G 4/24/86 1375
Merganser hen, Challenge Grade, G orig pnt, average wear, sm tail chip/age line in bill rstr by DeLong, 36, RB 2/01/85 1000
Merganser hen, Challenge Grade, orig pnt, average wear, tiny nick at end of comb, age split in bottom, RB 7/07/87 450
Merganser hen, Challenge Grade, orig pnt, minor wear, 2 chips in neck filler, well preserved, 1905, J/G 4/23/87, 85% 3000
Merganser hen, Challenge Grade, orig pnt w/some old working rpt on neck/breast, hairline crack in bk, J/G 4/24/86 660
Merganser hen, Challenge Grade, prof rpt taken down to orig by DeLong, minor wear, ls, rare, RB 3/06/87, 45% 900
Merganser hen, Challenge Grade, rpt as a Redbreasted Merganser drake w/EX orig underneath, ls, 39, RB 7/08/86, 48% 950
Merganser hen, Premier Grade, early head style, NM orig pnt, factory brand, ms, 154, J/G 9/19/87, 75% 4500
Merganser hen, Premier Grade, 50% orig pnt/50% rpt, average wear, 36, RB 2/01/85, 50% 700
Merganser hen, Standard Grade, glass eyes, NM condition, 36, RB 2/01/85 750
Merganser hen, Standard Grade, tack eyes, orig pnt, minor wear, tight check in underside, rare, J/G 4/23/87, 70% 700
Merganser pr, Challenge Grade, EX orig pnt, hen shows flaking/1 glass eye missing, 47, RWO 7/04/87, 65% 4000

Mason Factory
Merganser pr, Challenge Grade, orig pnt w/minor wear, rare, NM condition, RB 12/06/85, $7,000.00.

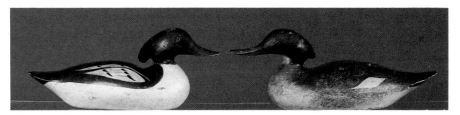

Merganser pr, Challenge Grade, outstanding orig pnt w/no flaws, sm area on bill w/pnt rubbed off, 113, RWO 7/05/85 8000
Merganser pr, Standard Grade, glass eyes, orig pnt, minor wear, drake: age line; hen: rstr bill, rare, J/G 9/19/87 700
Old Squaw drake, Standard Grade, glass eyes, orig pnt w/some overpnt, minor wear, rare, 36/86, RB 2/01/85 1800
Pectoral Sandpiper, tack eyes/split tail/wooden bill, EX orig pnt, in-use wear, chip/rpl bill, 3/36, RB 2/01/85, 60% 1750
Pintail drake, Premier Grade, EX orig pnt, minor wear, structurally EX, never weighted, RWO 2/13/87 1650
Pintail drake, Premier Grade, EX orig pnt, seam between body block has been prof rstr, very rare, J/G 4/24/86 3300
Pintail drake, Premier Grade, EX orig pnt w/prof touchup, EX condition, branded Vone Leingerke/Antone, 1900, J/G 4/23/87 2500
Pintail drake, Premier Grade, old rpt w/average wear, ms, RB 3/06/87 450
Pintail drake, Premier Grade, orig pnt, average wear, old rstr to crack in neck/sm chip under tail, early, J/G 4/23/87 300
Pintail drake, Premier Grade, orig pnt, average wear, very well preserved, RB 12/06/85 800
Pintail drake, Premier Grade, orig pnt, in-use wear, factory stamp, 42, RB 2/01/85, 50% 500
Pintail drake, Premier Grade, orig pnt, moderate wear, ms, rare, RB 8/21/86 700
Pintail drake, Premier Grade, orig pnt, worn to bare wood on body/head, 1 glass eye missing, 210, RWO 2/12/88, 230% 400
Pintail drake, Premier Grade, pnt worn to bare wood, crack in bk/tail rpr/head is loose, early, RWO 7/02/88 125
Pintail drake, Premier Grade, snaky head, hollow, EX orig pnt/varnish, minor wear on tail, EX, RWO 7/02/88, 40% 1000
Pintail drake, Standard Grade, glass eyes, EX orig pnt, average wear, neck filler missing, otherwise EX, RWO 7/02/88 600
Pintail drake, Standard Grade, glass eyes, EX orig pnt, minor wear, age split on right side of body, rare, RB 7/09/85 500
Pintail drake, Standard Grade, glass eyes, G orig pnt, age split on underside of bodyblock, 1 eye missing, J/G 9/20/86 200
Pintail drake, Standard Grade, glass eyes, G orig pnt, average wear, sm age split in bottom, rare, RB 12/06/85 375
Pintail drake, Standard Grade, glass eyes, G orig pnt, average wear, well preserved, RB 3/06/87 410
Pintail drake, Standard Grade, glass eyes, G orig pnt, Mackey stamp, neck filler missing/chew marks on tail, RWO 2/12/88 450
Pintail drake, Standard Grade, glass eyes, G orig pnt, tight checks on bodyblock/head, 1 eye missing, J/G 9/20/86 200
Pintail drake, Standard Grade, glass eyes, M condition, 36, RB 2/01/85, 200% 1600
Pintail drake, Standard Grade, glass eyes, old working rpt, sm crack in bk/some neck filler missing, J/G 4/23/87 200
Pintail drake, Standard Grade, glass eyes, orig pnt, 1 eye missing, most of the neck filler missing, RWO 7/02/88 325
Pintail drake, Standard Grade, orig pnt, in-use flaking/wear, both glass eyes missing/head is reglued, RWO 7/02/88 250
Pintail drake, Standard Grade, tack eyes, orig pnt, average wear, some repair work done at base of neck, RWO 7/06/85 225
Pintail hen, Premier Grade, G orig pnt, minor flaking/wear, 36, RB 2/01/85 1300
Pintail hen, Premier Grade, hollow, G orig pnt w/some wear, otherwise sound, early, 197, RWO 7/02/88, 50% 750
Pintail hen, Premier Grade, slope-breast, VG orig pnt, worn to bare wood on bk, otherwise EX, early, 193, RWO 7/02/88 1250
Pintail hen, Premier Grade, snaky head, orig pnt, heavy wear, EX condition, early, RWO 2/12/88 550

Pintail hen, Standard Grade, pnt eyes, M condition, J/G 4/23/87 1000
Pintail pr, Challenge Grade, hollow, NM orig pnt, drake has roughness to end of bill/ls, rare, 36/86, RB 2/01/85 5000
Pintail pr, Challenge Grade, orig pnt, minor wear, prof pnt rstr to parts of bks/tails/bills, rare, J/G 9/19/87 1850
Pintail pr, Challenge Grade, snaky heads, G orig pnt, average flaking/wear, 36, RB 2/01/85 3250
Pintail pr, Challenge Grade, snaky heads, VG orig pnt, average flaking/wear, thin pnt wash on bottom, rare, J/G 4/23/87 2200
Pintail pr, Premier Grade, EX orig pnt, minor wear, chip at end of hen's tail was prof rstr by DeLong, RB 12/06/85 4500
Pintail pr, Premier Grade, orig pnt, average wear, Premier stamp, drake has short tight check on bk, rare, J/G 4/24/86 2475
Pintail pr, Premier Grade, orig pnt, in-use wear, 36, RB 2/01/85, 75% 1500
Pintail pr, Standard Grade, glass eyes, M condition, 36, RB 2/01/85, 233% 3500
Pintail pr, Standard Grade, glass eyes, orig pnt, heavy wear, structurally poor to fair, RWO 11/11/87 280
Plover, glass eyes, orig pnt, minor wear, age split in bottom, bill prof rpl by DeLong, well preserved, RB 3/06/87 500
Plover, glass eyes, spike bill, EX orig pnt, ls, eyes may be a replacement, 36, RB 2/01/85, 40% 1000
Plover, special order model, minor flaking on bill, NM condition, RWO 2/12/88 2600
Plover, split tail, EX orig pnt, Winter plumage, some flaking on bk/head, structurally EX, 193, RWO 7/02/88, 70% 700
Plover, tack eyes, orig pnt, in-use wear, structurally EX, RWO 2/12/88 380
Plover, tack eyes, pnt taken down to orig w/some overpnt, sm dents in tail, J/G 4/23/87 250
Plover, tack eyes, spike bill, G orig pnt, average wear, heavy wear to right side, ls, RB 8/21/86 500

Mason Factory
Merganser drake, Challenge Grade, G orig pnt, in-use flaking/wear, extremely rare, RWO 7/05/86, $4,500.00.

Redbreasted Merganser drake, Challenge Grade, orig pnt, heavy weathering/wear, tail chip, RB 7/09/85 550
Redbreasted Merganser drake, Premier Grade, pnt taken down to mostly orig, bill has a prof repair, RB 7/09/85, 60% 600
Redbreasted Merganser pr, Premier bodies/Challenge heads, orig pnt, heavy in-use wear, RB 7/09/85 800
Redhead drake, Challenge Grade, EX orig pnt, minor wear, tight check on underside of bodyblock, ls, J/G 9/20/86 475
Redhead drake, Challenge Grade, orig pnt, average wear, head has been reglued, otherwise sound, RWO 7/06/85 225
Redhead drake, Challenge Grade, orig pnt w/some possible overpnt on head, average wear, structurally sound, RWO 2/12/88 375
Redhead drake, Challenge Grade, snaky head, orig pnt, average wear, sm dings on head, otherwise sound, RWO 11/11/87 475
Redhead drake, Premier Grade, EX orig pnt, average wear, possible touchup to head, EX condition, early, RWO 7/02/88 850
Redhead drake, Premier Grade, EX orig pnt, average wear, well preserved, rare, oversize, RB 12/06/85 700
Redhead drake, Premier Grade, EX orig pnt, tiny flaking areas, minor separation to body halves, RB 7/07/87 850
Redhead drake, Premier Grade, EX orig swirled pnt, shows minor pnt rubs, otherwise NM, rare, RB 3/06/87 900
Redhead drake, Premier Grade, fine orig pnt, minor wear, 36, RB 2/01/85 450
Redhead drake, Premier Grade, G orig pnt, average wear w/1 lg worn area on left side of body, RB 8/21/86 300
Redhead drake, Premier Grade, G orig pnt, minor wear, ls, J/G 4/24/86 605
Redhead drake, Premier Grade, G orig pnt, minor wear, sm crack in tail/slight seam separation, J/G 9/20/86 550
Redhead drake, Premier Grade, heavy wear to natural wood w/traces of orig pnt, RB 3/06/87 200
Redhead drake, Premier Grade, hollow, orig pnt, average wear, few nicks/dings, otherwise sound, RWO 11/11/87 450
Redhead drake, Premier Grade, hollow, orig pnt, heavy wear, branded BL, 2 thin body cracks/ms, RWO 7/02/88 275
Redhead drake, Premier Grade, low-head style, orig pnt, heavy wear, slight age split in bk, rare, 36, RB 2/01/85 700
Redhead drake, Premier Grade, root-head, orig pnt, average wear w/some flaking, age splits/lg chip gone, RB 3/11/88 500
Redhead drake, Premier Grade, rpt, minor wear, prof rstr to chip in the bill, J/G 9/20/86 90
Redhead drake, Premier Grade, several tiny flakes of pnt misssing, otherwise M, J/G 4/23/87 1250
Redhead drake, Premier Grade, slightly turned head, pnt rstr in Mason style, ls, rare, 68, J/G 9/19/87 350
Redhead drake, special order, G orig pnt, wear at tip of bill/tail, otherwise EX, 193/197, RWO 7/02/88 1500
Redhead drake, Standard Grade, glass eyes, EX rpt, RB 7/08/87 140
Redhead drake, Standard Grade, glass eyes, fine orig pnt, average wear, age split in bottom/ls, rare sm size, RB 7/09/85 450
Redhead drake, Standard Grade, glass eyes, fine orig pnt, average wear, RB 7/09/85 190

Redhead drake, Standard Grade, glass eyes, orig & overpnt, moderate wear, some age splitting to body, RB 6/28/88 .... **110**
Redhead drake, Standard Grade, glass eyes, orig pnt, average wear, minor age splitting, RB 7/07/87 .... **120**
Redhead drake, Standard Grade, glass eyes, orig pnt, minor wear, several chips in neck filler, J/G 9/20/86 .... **300**
Redhead drake, Standard Grade, glass eyes, orig pnt shows some wear, right eye broken, RB 8/25/88 .... **90**
Redhead drake, Standard Grade, glass eyes, rpt, RB 7/08/87 .... **110**
Redhead drake, Standard Grade, pnt eyes, NM orig pnt, slight discoloration, sm chips in neck filler, rare, J/G 4/23/87 .... **200**
Redhead drake, Standard Grade, pnt eyes, NM orig pnt, structurally EX, J/G 4/24/86 .... **467**
Redhead drake, Standard Grade, pnt eyes, NM orig pnt, tight crack in neck filler, rare, J/G 4/24/86 .... **275**
Redhead drake, Standard Grade, pnt eyes, orig pnt w/minor wear, slight mar at end of tail, RB 7/07/87 .... **150**
Redhead drake, Standard Grade, tack eyes, EX orig pnt, minor wear, structurally EX, RWO 7/04/87 .... **300**
Redhead hen, Challenge Grade, G orig pnt, average wear, slight age split in right side of body, ls, 36, RB 2/01/85 .... **300**
Redhead hen, Challenge Grade, snaky head, EX orig pnt, minor wear, slight age splits, 36, RB 2/01/85 .... **650**
Redhead hen, Premier Grade, early head style, orig pnt, minor wear, neck filler missing, ls, very rare, J/G 9/19/87 .... **800**
Redhead hen, Premier Grade, NM orig pnt w/great patina, factory hairline crack in bk, from the Gavit rig, J/G 4/24/86 .... **1155**
Redhead hen, Premier Grade, orig pnt, average flaking/wear, several sm age splits, RB 7/09/85 .... **350**
Redhead hen, Standard Grade, glass eyes, NM orig pnt, factory brand, age split on underside of bodyblock, J/G 9/20/86 .... **450**
Redhead pr, Premier Grade, fine orig pnt, flaking/wear, ls, otherwise well preserved, RB 7/09/85 .... **1200**
Redhead pr, Premier Grade, NM orig pnt, minor flaking/wear, well preserved, rare, 86, RB 8/21/86, 50% **1300**

Mason Factory
Redhead pr, Premier Grade, NM orig pnt, minor wear, structurally EX, used little if any, RWO 2/13/87, $2,300.00.

Redhead pr, Premier Grade, snaky heads, orig pnt, minor wear/chips, ms, rare, 131, J/G 9/19/87, 55% **850**
Redhead pr, Standard Grade, glass eyes, EX orig pnt, average wear, some slight age splits, 36, RB 2/01/85 .... **450**
Redhead pr, Standard Grade, glass eyes, EX orig pnt, minor wear, some neck filler missing, cracked eyes, J/G 9/19/87 .... **450**
Redhead pr, Standard Grade, pnt eyes, EX orig pnt, minor wear/1 chip, structurally sound, RWO 7/06/85 .... **350**
Redhead pr, Standard Grade, pnt eyes, G orig pnt, average wear, age split in bottom of hen, 36, RB 2/01/85 .... **325**
Redhead pr, Standard Grade, working rpt taken down to orig w/heavy wear, neck filler not orig, RWO 7/04/87 .... **275**
Ringbill drake, Challenge Grade, orig pnt, in-use wear, very sm splits on bk, otherwise sound, RWO 7/05/86 .... **300**
Ringbill pr, Challenge Grade, G orig pnt, in-use wear, ls, roughness at edges of bills, very rare, 36, RB 2/01/85, 55% **1100**
Ringbill pr, Challenge Grade, orig pnt, average wear, tight cracks on undersides, very rare, J/G 4/24/86, 68% **1375**
Robin Snipe, EX orig condition, 193, RWO 7/02/88 .... **3750**
Robin Snipe, glass eyes, EX orig pnt, minimal wear, tight factory check in 1 side, ls, 86/157, J/G 4/24/86 .... **1870**
Robin Snipe, glass eyes, spike bill, fine orig pnt, sm age split on left side of body, rare, 36, RB 2/01/85, 48% **1200**
Robin Snipe, tack eyes, EX orig pnt, little wear, rare, RB 7/09/85 .... **1100**
Robin Snipe, tack eyes, EX orig pnt, minor wear, slight separation at edges of a knot, J/G 4/23/87 .... **1500**
Robin Snipe, tack eyes, fine orig pnt, minor wear, 39, RB 7/08/86 .... **750**
Robin Snipe, tack eyes, NM pnt, ms, 39, RB 7/08/86, 80% **800**
Ruddy Turnstone, EX swirl/feather pnt, M condition, rare, 193, RWO 7/02/88, 130% **3250**
Scoter drake, Standard Grade, rpt in Mason style, structurally sound, rare, RWO 7/05/86 .... **120**
Snipe, tack eyes, outstanding orig condition, 3, RWO 5/07/85 .... **1100**
Snipe, tack eyes, pnt taken down to orig w/average wear, ls, J/G 4/23/87 .... **525**
Snipe, tack eyes, spike bill, orig pnt, moderate wear, ls, rare, 36, RB 2/01/85, 45% **900**
Surf Scoter, Standard Grade, glass eyes, orig pnt w/areas of rpt, minor wear, rare, 36, RB 2/01/85 .... **400**
Whitewinged Scoter, Standard Grade, tack eyes, EX orig pnt, minor flaking, rare, 36, RB 2/01/85, 130% **2000**
Whitewinged Scoter, Standard Grade, tack eyes, EX orig pnt, crack in 1 side, extremely rare, J/G 9/20/86 .... **1450**
Widgeon drake, Challenge Grade, G orig pnt, in-use wear, age split in bottom, ls, 36, RB 2/01/85 .... **850**
Widgeon drake, Challenge Grade, G orig pnt, moderate in-use wear, sm age split in side/rough area, rare, RB 12/06/85 .... **500**
Widgeon drake, Challenge Grade, snaky head, orig pnt, check down each side, otherwise sound, rare, RWO 7/06/85 .... **475**
Widgeon drake, Premier Grade, G orig pnt w/wear to bare wood in several areas, 36, RB 2/01/85, 160% **1900**
Widgeon drake, Premier Grade, orig pnt w/some working touchup, prof rstr to chip on 1 side of tail, rare, J/G 4/24/86 .... **825**

Widgeon drake, Premier Grade, worn orig pnt, structurally EX, early, RWO 7/06/85 215
Widgeon drake, Standard Grade, glass eyes, fine orig pnt, minor wear, old filler on breast, rare, 36, RB 7/09/85 500
Widgeon drake, Standard Grade, glass eyes, G orig pnt, minor wear, ms, RB 7/09/85 500
Widgeon drake, Standard Grade, glass eyes, orig pnt, moderate wear, split on bodyblock/1 eye missing, J/G 9/20/86 290
Widgeon drake, Standard Grade, glass eyes, rpt by Ray Schalk, 3 minor age lines, J/G 4/23/87 125
Widgeon drake, Standard Grade, tack eyes, NM orig pnt, 2 tiny surface chips in neck filler, never used, J/G 9/19/87 2900
Widgeon drake, Standard Grade, tack eyes, orig pnt, heavy wear, 36, RB 2/01/85 250
Widgeon hen, Challenge Grade, orig pnt, in-use flaking, slight age split in bk, 36, RB 2/01/85 850
Widgeon hen, Premier Grade, G orig pnt, average wear, repair to chip in tail, rare, RB 7/09/85 600
Widgeon hen, Standard Grade, glass eyes, orig pnt, minor wear, punched initials: FL, rare, J/G 4/23/87 450

Mason Factory
Widgeon pr, Premier Grade, NM orig pnt on drake; hen has minor wear, JB Semple Brand, very rare, J/G 9/20/86, $7,000.00.

Widgeon pr, Standard Grade, glass eyes, G orig pnt, in-use wear, ls, 36, RB 2/01/85 900
Widgeon pr, Standard Grade, glass eyes, orig pnt, minor wear, both have minor cracks, rare, J/G 4/24/86 715
Willet, exceptional pnt pattern w/minor wear, ls, RB 7/09/85 2300
Willet, glass eyes, NM orig pnt w/detailed feathering/wing tips, ls, rare, J/G 4/24/86 1760
Willet, tack eyes, EX orig pnt, average wear, narrow check running part way up breast, ms, RWO 7/04/87 475
Willet, tack eyes, spike bill, G orig pnt, minor wear, ls, RB 2/01/85 800
Wood Duck drake, Standard Grade, glass eyes, rpt in Mason's style, slight age splitting, RB 8/25/88, 160% 400
Wood Duck drake, Standard Grade, tack eyes, EX orig pnt, minor flaking/wear, well preserved, RB 12/06/85 7000
Yellowlegs, EX orig pnt, body check has been filled, thin tight check on 1 side/sm tail chip, 193, RWO 7/02/88 900
Yellowlegs, glass eyes, cvd split tail, NM orig pnt, minor flaking, sm tail chip, rare, J/G 4/23/87 1650
Yellowlegs, glass eyes, NM orig pnt, highly detailed wing/tail feathers, ls, J/G 9/20/86 2250
Yellowlegs, tack eyes, EX orig pnt, minor wear, ls, 39, RB 7/08/86 600
Yellowlegs, tack eyes, G orig pnt, average wear, sm chip on underside of bill, 3, RB 3/06/87 650
Yellowlegs, tack eyes, NM condition, 39, RB 7/08/86 1000
Yellowlegs, tack eyes, NM pnt shows little or no wear, structurally NM, RWO 7/06/85 900
Yellowlegs, tack eyes, orig pnt, in-use wear w/few areas to bare wood, narrow crack in head, RWO 11/11/87 325
Yellowlegs, tack eyes, orig pnt, minor wear mostly on sides, ls, J/G 9/20/86 425
Yellowlegs, tack eyes, overpnt w/signs of G orig pnt underneath, bill is slightly loose, 3, RB 3/06/87 250
Yellowlegs, tack eyes, spike bill, outstanding/NM condition, 36, RB 2/01/85 2500
Yellowlegs or Dowitcher, orig pnt, average wear, 1 glass eye missing, otherwise structurally EX, 193, RWO 7/02/88 325
Outing Mfg. Company
Owl, folding tin, orig pnt shows minor flaking, surface rusting, RB 7/08/86, 360% 900

Owl, folding tin, orig pnt w/few old scratches, otherwise M, J/G 9/19/87 .... **225**
Paw Paw Decoy Factory
Mallard drake, G orig pnt, average wear, RB 2/01/85 .... **50**
Pintail pr, full wood bodies, G orig pnt, average wear, hen has factory brand, RB 2/01/85 .... **90**
Peterson Decoy Factory
Bluebill drake, orig pnt, minor wear, chip missing/neck filler replaced, ca 1880, J/G 4/23/87 .... **500**
Bluebill drake, slope-breast model, hollow, G orig pnt, average wear, well preserved, ca 1870's, 193, RWO 7/02/88 .... **900**
Bluewinged Teal hen, hollow, orig pnt, average wear, head damage reinforced w/a nail, rare, early, 193, RWO 7/02/88 ...... **400**
Canvasback drake, early, fine orig pnt, average wear, well preserved, RB 12/06/85 .... **550**

Peterson Decoy Factory
**Goldeneye drake, orig pnt, in-use wear, minor damage to end of
bill/check in bottom, neck filler missing, RWO 7/04/87, $375.00.**

Mallard drake, G orig pnt, average wear, thin crack on side, sm chip out of bill, otherwise G, RWO 7/05/85 .... **650**
Pratt Mfg. Co.
Black Duck, fine orig pnt shows little wear, RB 7/08/86 .... **150**
Black Duck, orig pnt, slight wear, sm pnt drips, worn factory label, no structural flaws, J/G 4/23/87 .... **150**
Bluebill hen, balsa body, orig pnt, minor wear, sm rough area on top of tail/lower side, J/G 4/23/87 .... **100**
Bluewinged Teal drake, Premier Grade, EX orig pnt, branded Hayhoe #7, ca 1930, J/G 4/23/87 .... **250**
Bluewinged Teal hen, orig pnt, flaking to primer on bk/head, sm chunk missing from tail/head crack, rare, RWO 7/02/88 .... **250**
Coot, orig pnt, heavy flaking on head/neck, 1 glass eye missing, RWO 7/02/88 .... **55**
Coot, orig pnt, heavy wear, chip to the tail, otherwise structurally sound, RWO 7/05/85 .... **50**
Crow, early gunning decoy, orig pnt, worn/flaking, chip at tip of bill, sm gouge gone from side of head, RWO 11/11/87 ...... **425**
Crow, old working rpt, average wear, in-use bill rpr, tight age splits in bottom, RWO 7/02/88 .... **150**
Goldeneye pr, orig pnt, minor wear, age split on underside of drake/chip in side of head, rare, J/G 9/19/87 .... **395**
Greenwinged Teal drake, fine old pnt, some orig, much wear on 1 side, 36, RB 2/01/85 .... **300**
Mallard pr, orig pnt, in-use wear, drake has a crack in the neck/age split on bottom, RWO 7/05/85 .... **130**
Redbreasted Merganser pr, orig pnt, average wear, drake's bill has been chewed, otherwise sound, rare, RWO 2/12/88 .... **275**
Redhead drake, orig pnt, minor wear, tiny chip gone from base of neck, J/G 4/23/87 .... **125**
Sport Craft Company
Black Duck, swimming, orig pnt, minimal wear, factory stamp, thin crack in neck/check in bottom, ca 1945, RWO 7/04/87 ...... **250**
Stevens Company
Black Duck, EX orig pnt, average wear, well preserved, rare, RB 7/09/85, 66% **1000**
Black Duck, old working rpt, sm rough area on 1 side, early, J/G 4/23/87 .... **425**
Black Duck, orig pnt, average wear, branded, several mars on right side, RB 3/06/87 .... **900**
Bluebill drake, complete pnt rstr, prof rstr at base of neck, RWO 11/06/85 .... **375**
Bluebill drake, EX orig pnt, flaw in bk was plugged/pnt, pc of wood gone from bill, otherwise EX, 196, RWO 7/02/88, 55% ... **1300**
Bluebill drake, humpback, G orig scratch feather pnt, average wear, ls, RB 12/06/85 .... **275**
Bluebill drake, old working rpt w/comb pnt on bk, hairline crack in neck/sm chip under bill, J/G 4/23/87 .... **250**
Bluebill drake, orig pnt, average wear, factory brand, eyes are replacements, age split in neck, rare, RB 3/11/88 .... **1200**
Bluebill drake, orig pnt, moderate flaking/wear, bill is a replacement, ls, RB 3/11/88 .... **300**
Bluebill drake, pnt completely rstr, rstr at base of neck, factory stencil may also be rstr, RWO 11/06/85 .... **375**
Bluebill drake, pnt taken down to orig w/heavy wear, factory brand, old rstr to lower portion of neck, RB 8/21/86 .... **400**
Bluebill hen, orig pnt, heavy in-use wear, 6, RB 6/28/88 .... **200**
Bluebill hen, working rpt, minor wear, no structural flaws, J/G 9/20/86 .... **350**
Bluewinged Teal drake, old rpt in orig Stevens pnt style, no structural flaws, J/G 9/19/87 .... **350**
Bufflehead drake, G orig pnt, flaking to bare wood on bk, branded GW Stevens, Weedsport NY, rare, 193, RWO 7/02/88 ...... **3400**
Bufflehead drake, old working rpt, minor wear, old tail chip repair, several age lines in side, early, J/G 9/19/87 .... **700**
Bufflehead drake, orig pnt, minor wear, sm chip under tail/sm crack in bill, ls, very rare, J/G 4/24/86 .... **1980**
Canvasback drake, hollow, orig pnt, average wear, ms/crack running through neck, rare, 193, RWO 7/02/88 .... **1300**
Canvasback drake, NM pnt w/minor flaking from wood shrinkage, factory stamp, age split in neck, rare, RB 7/09/85, 62% **2500**
Canvasback drake, old working rpt, prof rstr to half of bill, tight check in neck/top of head, rare, J/G 9/19/87 .... **300**
Goldeneye drake, goiter neck, rpt w/evidence of orig pnt, sm age split to body, roughness to edges of bill, RB 12/06/85 ...... **325**

Goldeneye drake, humpback, old rpt, shallow chip on underside of bill, otherwise well preserved, RB 7/09/85 350
Goldeneye drake, humpback, old working rpt, average wear, structurally sound, RWO 7/06/85 190
Goldeneye drake, old working rpt, heavy flaking/wear, RB 7/09/85 150
Goldeneye drake, rpt by Kenneth DeLong, structurally EX, RWO 7/06/85 250
Goldeneye drake, rpt w/heavy wear, factory stamp, RB 7/09/85 225
Mallard drake, goiter neck, unusual cvd shoulder groove in bk, EX orig pnt, minor wear, well preserved, RB 7/09/85, 70% 1750
Mallard drake, retains orig label reading HA Stevens, Manufacturer of Decoy Ducks, Weedsport MA, EX, 193, RWO 7/02/88 4250
Mallard drake, rpt, poor bill repair/structural damage at base of neck, RWO 11/11/87 80
Mallard hen, EX orig pnt, average wear, flaked areas on body, worn area on top of head, rare, RB 7/07/87 3300

Stevens Company
Mallard hen, orig pnt, minor wear, hairline crack in bk of neck, branded CW Whittier, extremely rare, 3, J/G 4/23/87, $7,250.00.

Redhead drake, EX comb feather detail, hit twice by shot, EX classic form, NM condition, RB 7/07/87, 75% 2300
Redhead drake, G orig pnt, average wear w/some rubs to primer on bk, structurally EX, RWO 7/02/88, 55% 800
Redhead drake, old rpt w/traces of orig underneath, chip in right side of neck, RB 7/09/85 750
Redhead drake, orig pnt, in-use flaking & wear, prof head replacement, RB 3/06/87 275
Redhead hen, goiter neck, old working rpt, no structural flaws, J/G 9/20/86 105
Redhead hen, VG orig pnt, average wear w/flaking around a knot on breast, structurally EX, rare, RWO 7/02/88 2500
Redhead pr, fine orig pnt, slightly worn, sm chip at end of drake's tail, early, RB 7/09/85, 70% 1400
Widgeon drake, factory stamp, NM orig condition/unused, this specie is 1 of the rarest made by Stevens, RB 7/09/85 6500
Widgeon drake, old working rpt removed to reveal traces of orig, much taken down to bare wood, VG condition, RWO 2/12/88 625
Widgeon drake, outstanding orig pnt, factory brand, structurally sound, ca 1870-1902, extremely rare, RWO 7/05/86, 80% 4750
Strater and Sohier
Blackbellied Plover, folding tin, EX & orig condition, RWO 2/12/88 110
Dowitcher, folding tin, G orig pnt, average wear w/some rusting, 1 side has part of bill missing, RWO 11/11/87 70
Dowitcher, folding tin, orig pnt, average wear w/minor rusting, hs, otherwise structurally sound, RWO 11/11/87 140
Golden Plover, folding tin, minor rust near tail, otherwise EX & orig condition, RWO 2/12/88 120
Golden Plover, folding tin, orig pnt, in-use wear w/areas of flaking to bare metal, RWO 11/11/87 70
Peep, folding tin, October patent date, fine orig pnt, average wear, rare, RB 12/06/85 450
Peep, folding tin, orig pnt, minor wear, sm dent in side, J/G 4/23/87 .... 205 Yel-
lowlegs, folding tin, orig pnt, several areas worn to bare metal, structurally sound, RWO 11/11/87 40
Yellowlegs, folding tin, set of 12, NM orig pnt, few have slight surface rust, w/orig sticks & tin box, J/G 4/23/87 800
Swisher and Soules Decoy Company
Owl, flapping-wings model, traces of flock pnt remain, factory brand/patent date, ca 1930's, RWO 4/07/87 400
Owl, metal, orig flock pnt, minor wear/flaking, structurally EX, ca 1930's, RWO 7/04/87 300
Tuveson Mfg. Company
Mallard drake, flying, factory paper label, M condition, rare, RB 7/08/86 500
Victor Animal Trap Company
Canvasback drake, G orig pnt, average flaking/wear, factory stamp, RB 3/06/87 90
Mallard drake, orig pnt, moderate in-use flaking/wear, shallow chip on right side of bill, age split in neck, RB 3/06/87 35
Mallard pr, celluloid factory heads, both retain stamps on bottom, M condition, RB 8/25/88 110
Pintail drake, orig pnt, right eye missing/left eye is damaged, otherwise structurally NM, RB 3/11/88 100
Wales and Snow
Blackbellied Plover, wood w/flappable canvas & cardboard wings, EX pnt & condition, ls, 87, J/G 9/19/87 550
Wildfowler Decoy Company
Black Duck, Atlantic Coast model, cork/pine, signed Richard & Marion Harris, M condition, 144, J/G 9/19/87 280
Black Duck, Atlantic Coast model, rpt, minor wear, oversize, 144, RB 8/25/88 80
Black Duck, balsa body, fine orig pnt, minor wear on body, heavier wear on head, unbranded, RB 8/25/88 120
Black Duck, balsa body, NM condition, RB 12/06/85 160
Black Duck, balsa body, NM orig pnt, factory brand, structurally EX, 144, RB 12/06/85 125

Black Duck, balsa body, orig pnt, average flaking/wear, unbranded, oversize, RB 8/25/88 70
Black Duck, balsa body, orig pnt, average wear, structurally EX, RWO 7/06/85 65
Black Duck, balsa body, orig pnt, heavy wear, few dings, otherwise structurally sound, RWO 2/12/88 70
Black Duck, balsa body, orig pnt, heavy wear, structurally sound, 39, RB 7/08/86 90
Black Duck, balsa body, orig pnt, moderate flaking/wear, structurally sound, RB 7/08/87 100
Black Duck, balsa body, rpt, probably by Bill Cranmer, average flaking/wear, unbranded, RB 8/25/88 90
Black Duck, diver, balsa body, EX orig pnt, minor wear, RB 7/08/87 75
Black Duck, diver, balsa body, EX orig pnt, minor wear, well preserved, 144, RB 7/08/87 225
Black Duck, EX orig pnt, factory brand, 145, RWO 11/11/87 75
Black Duck, EX orig pnt, minor wear, factory brand, oversize, 145, RB 7/08/87 150
Black Duck, head tucked down, balsa body, orig pnt, average wear, structurally sound, RB 2/01/85 100
Black Duck, hollow, cvd by Charles Birdsall, signed/branded CRB, RB 12/06/85 150
Black Duck, hollow, EX orig pnt, minor wear, factory bra nd, 144, RB 7/08/87 375
Black Duck, hollow, orig pnt, average wear, age split in neck, 144, RB 7/08/87 175
Black Duck, hollow, orig pnt, in-use flaking/wear, structurally sound, 144, RB 7/09/85 140
Black Duck, hollow, pine body, fine orig pnt, average wear w/minor flaking, well preserved, early, RB 3/06/87 450
Black Duck, inlet head, orig pnt, minor wear, slight rough area on bottom edge of bodyblock, 144, J/G 9/20/86 115
Black Duck, low-head style, balsa body, G orig pnt, RWO 7/06/85 50
Black Duck, NM condition, oversize, 144, RWO 7/06/86 140
Black Duck, NM orig pnt, factory stamp, EX condition, 144, J/G 9/20/86 165
Black Duck, NM orig pnt, factory stamp, several sm dents along bottom edge, otherwise structurally EX, 144, J/G 9/20/86 300
Black Duck, orig pnt, factory brand, structurally outstanding, 144, RWO 7/06/86 140
Black Duck, pine body, EX orig pnt, minor wear, factory brand, 144, RB 3/06/87 275
Black Duck, pine body, NM orig pnt, factory stamp, 2 short hairline cracks in body, 144, J/G 9/19/87 300
Black Duck, sleeper, balsa body, factory brand, M condition, oversize, 145, J/G 9/19/87 250
Black Duck, sleeper, balsa body, factory brand, NM condition, 144, RB 12/06/85 375
Black Duck, sleeper, balsa body, rpt, average wear, right eye missing, rare, RB 8/27/87 110
Black Duck, sleeper, NM orig pnt, structurally EX, rare, 145, J/G 9/20/86 350
Bluebill drake, Atlantic Coast model, balsa body, orig pnt, minor wear, factory stamp, 144, J/G 9/20/86 70
Bluebill drake, balsa body, EX orig pnt, minor wear, RB 8/21/86 100
Bluebill drake, balsa body, orig pnt, moderate wear, minor age splitting to head, 22/144, RB 8/25/88 70
Bluebill drake, G orig pnt, both glass eyes missing, RWO 7/02/88 120
Bluebill drake, Harry Shourds model, hollow, NM orig pnt, no flaws, inset rectangular weight, 145, J/G 4/23/87 150
Bluebill drake, hollow, NM condition, 144, RB 7/08/87 275
Bluebill drake, hollow, working rpt, in-use flaking/wear, crack running through neck/head is loose, RWO 11/11/87 55
Bluebill drake, orig pnt, in-use wear, factory stamp, 144, RWO 7/06/86 100
Bluebill hen, factory brand, signed Charlie Birdsall, dated 1965, EX & orig, 145, RB 8/27/87 130
Bluebill pr, balsa bodies, EX orig pnt, average wear, structurally EX, RWO 11/11/87 150
Bluebill pr, balsa bodies, fine orig pnt, average wear, factory brand, 144, RB 7/09/85 225
Bluebill pr, balsa bodies w/pine heads/keels, orig pnt, minor wear, several sm cracks in bodyblock, J/G 9/20/86 140
Bluebill pr, G orig pnt, slight split in drake's bill, 145, RB 7/08/86 150

Wildfowler Decoy Company
Bluebill pr, hollow, drake has Old Saybrook brand, EX orig pnt, minor wear, RB 7/07/87, $550.00.

Bluebill pr, orig pnt, minor wear, factory stamp, branded CHM, 145, J/G 9/19/87 250
Bluewinged Teal drake, EX orig pnt, average wear, structurally EX, RWO 7/02/88 375

Bluewinged Teal drake, pine, EX orig pnt, NM condition, rare, RB 3/06/87, 170% 850
Bluewinged Teal drake, pine body, EX orig pnt, unbranded, end-of-tail chip/left eye missing, rare, RB 8/25/88 450
Bluewinged Teal hen, pine body, EX orig pnt, rare, 144, RB 12/06/85 325
Brant, balsa body, NM condition, 39, RB 7/08/86 400
Brant, balsa body, signed by Charles Birdsall on bottom, EX condition, RB 7/08/86 200
Brant, factory mark, signed Charles R Birdsall/dated 1972, M condition, 145, RWO 7/04/87 170
Brant, Harry Shourds model, hollow, G orig pnt, average wear, 145, RB 3/06/87 200
Brant, hollow, pnt shows average wear, signed by Charles Birdsall, RB 8/25/88 225
Brant, orig pnt, average wear, signed CR Birdsall/dated 1965, structurally EX, 145, RWO 11/11/87 135
Brant, signed by Charles Birdsall, dated 1972, NM condition, 145, RB 8/25/88 150
Brant, special order, Coastal model, orig pnt, structurally outstanding, 144, RWO 7/06/86 210
Brant, swimming, Harry Shourds model, Charles Birdsall brand & signature, M condition, J/G 9/19/87 350
Brant pr, rpt (probably by factory) w/average wear, 145, RB 8/21/86 175
Bufflehead drake, factory stamp, also signed Charles R Birdsall, M condition, 145, RWO 7/06/85 120
Bufflehead drake, rpt w/average wear, well preserved, 145, RB 7/08/86 275
Bufflehead pr, factory stamp, EX condition, 145, RB 3/06/87, 180% 700
Bufflehead pr, factory stamp, M condition, ca 1966, 145, RWO 7/06/85 220
Canada Goose, balsa body, fine orig pnt, minor wear, factory brand, well preserved, 145, RB 12/06/85 250
Canada Goose, balsa body, rpt by Milliken, minor wear, well preserved, RB 2/01/85 100

Wildfowler Decoy Company
Canada Goose, EX orig pnt, average wear, factory brand, break in neck has been reglued, 145, RB 7/08/87, $225.00.

Canada Goose, hollow, orig pnt covered w/a coat of wax, structurally sound, RWO 7/04/87 280
Canada Goose, tip-up, balsa body, orig pnt w/areas flaking to wood, factory brand, several body checks, 146, RWO 7/02/88 150
Canvasback drake, Atlantic Coast model, balsa body, NM orig pnt, varnished, factory stamp, 144, J/G 9/20/86 175
Canvasback drake, factory brand, M condition, 144, RWO 7/06/86 200
Canvasback drake, hollow, EX orig pnt, cvd by Charles Birdsall, signed/branded CRB, structurally EX, RB 12/06/85 150
Canvasback drake, hollow, orig pnt, average wear, Glen L Martin brand, RWO 11/11/87 165
Canvasback drake, hollow, orig pnt, minor wear, 145, RB 8/25/88 220
Canvasback drake, inlet head, hollow, orig pnt, minor wear, working touchup to bill/breast, 144, J/G 9/20/86 160
Canvasback drake, orig pnt, average wear, factory brand, 1 eye missing, oversize, 144, RWO 7/05/86 90
Canvasback drake, 2-pc balsa body, G orig pnt, average wear, RWO 7/02/88 125
Canvasback hen, orig pnt, average wear, structurally EX, 144, RWO 11/06/85 60
Canvasback pr, balsa bodies, drake is rpt; hen is orig pnt, minor wear, RB 2/01/85 125
Canvasback pr, factory brand, hen has few minor dents, otherwise both are M condition, oversize, 144, RWO 7/02/88 400
Coot, balsa body, rpt, moderate wear, 144, RB 7/08/87 110
Coot, NM orig pnt, factory stamp, structurally EX, rare, 145, J/G 9/20/86 180
Eider drake, hollow, pine body, G orig pnt, in-use wear, slight age split in neck, 39, RB 7/08/86 500
Eider hen, balsa body, fine orig pnt, average wear, rare, 39, RB 7/08/86 300
Eider pr, pine body, hollow, EX & orig condition, rare, 144, RB 12/06/85 950
Goldeneye drake, EX orig pnt, has had a thin coat of shellac applied, signed, rare, 145, RWO 7/06/86 70
Goldeneye hen, balsa body, fine orig pnt, minor flaking/wear, structurally sound, 144, RB 7/08/87 275
Greenwinged Teal drake, balsa body, EX orig pnt, average wear w/few nicks/dings, structurally sound, RWO 2/12/88 290
Greenwinged Teal drake, NM orig pnt, hairline crack in neck, ca 1970, 145, J/G 9/20/86 95
Greenwinged Teal drake, NM orig pnt, several tiny dents at waterline, early, J/G 9/19/87, 137% 700
Greenwinged Teal drake, pine body, NM pnt, unbranded, rare, RB 8/21/86 325
Greenwinged Teal hen, balsa body, G orig pnt, average wear, well preserved, RB 3/11/88 300
Greenwinged Teal pr, balsa bodies, G orig pnt, average wear, factory brand, chip on end of bill, 146, RWO 11/11/87 350

Greenwinged Teal pr, G orig pnt, average wear, factory brand, EX condition, 146, RWO 7/06/86 210
Greenwinged Teal pr, NM pnt, factory brand, hen's bill broken & reglued, otherwise structurally EX, 145, RB 7/09/85 200
Greenwinged Teal pr, turned heads, orig pnt, some wear, orig from Ted Mulliken's personal rig, 22/44, RB 5/02/86 1500
Grey Coot, orig pnt, minor wear, factory stamp, no structural flaws, rare, 144, J/G 9/19/87 300
Mallard drake, balsa body, G orig pnt, several sm dents & scrapes on body, 144, J/G 4/24/86 137
Mallard drake, balsa body, orig pnt, average wear, structurally sound, RWO 7/05/85 60
Mallard drake, balsa body w/pine head, orig pnt, minor wear, factory stamp, keel is gone/sm dents, 146, J/G 9/20/86 125
Mallard drake, G orig pnt, minor wear, upper tail has semi-transparent blue overpnt, RB 3/11/88 150
Mallard drake, hollow, old working rpt, heavy wear, structurally fair, RWO 2/12/88 50
Mallard drake, hollow pine body, EX orig pnt, minor wear, orig bill broken & reglued, 144, RB 12/06/85 200
Mallard drake, sleeper, balsa body, fine orig pnt, minor wear, factory brand, well preserved, RB 7/08/87 275
Mallard hen, balsa body, factory brand, EX & orig, oversize, 145, RB 12/06/85 100
Mallard hen, G orig pnt, minor flaking, factory brand, ca 1939, oversize, 1/144, RB 12/06/85 100
Mallard hen, orig pnt, minor wear, branded PPB, no structural flaws, 144, J/G 9/19/87 250
Mallard hen, sleeping, balsa body, G orig pnt, minor flaking/wear, 144, RB 7/09/85 375
Mallard pr, balsa bodies, G orig pnt, average wear, drake has wear to bare wood on sides, otherwise sound, RWO 11/11/87 140
Mallard pr, EX orig pnt, factory brand, signed by Charles Birdsall, oversize, 145, RB 7/09/85 350
Mallard pr, hollow, old working rpt, minor wear, factory stamp, drake has a crack in neck, 144, J/G 9/20/86 250
Mallard pr, NM orig pnt, factory brand, structurally EX, dated 1971, magnum, rare, 4/145, J/G 9/19/87 550
Old Squaw drake, slightly turned head, iron tail sprig, factory stamp, M condition, very rare, 145, J/G 9/19/87 450
Old Squaw hen, factory brand, M condition, very rare, 145, J/G 9/19/87 450
Old Squaw pr, Chesapeake Bay style, hollow, EX orig pnt, average wear, rare, 94/145, RWO 7/04/87 380
Old Squaw pr, hen has some damage around tail, otherwise NM, ca 1965, 94, RWO 7/04/87 260
Pintail drake, balsa body, EX orig pnt, RB 12/06/85 150
Pintail drake, balsa body, half orig/half rpt, moderate wear, 1 eye missing, RB 3/11/88 75
Pintail drake, EX orig pnt, minor wear, factory brand, 145, RB 3/06/87 300
Pintail drake, hollow, orig pnt, flaking/wear to bare wood in many areas, several age splits in head, 144, RB 11/11/87 85
Pintail drake, hollow cedar body, G orig pnt, slight age split in bk, RB 3/11/88 275
Pintail drake, orig pnt, factory brand, structurally EX, 145, RWO 7/05/85 105
Pintail hen, balsa body, NM condition, rare, RB 3/06/87 300
Pintail hen, EX pnt, factory brand, 145, RB 7/08/86 150
Pintail hen, G orig pnt, average wear, structurally sound, RWO 7/02/88 190
Pintail pr, balsa bodies, G orig pnt, average wear, possibly from Old Saybrook, RB 3/11/88 325

Wildfowler Decoy Company
Redbreasted Merganser pr, balsa bodies, EX orig pnt, minor wear, factory brand, well preserved, 146, RB 3/06/87, 235%, $1,200.00.

Redhead hen, factory brand, M condition, 144, RWO 11/11/87 225
Redhead hen, great patina, factory brand, M condition, 144, RWO 7/06/86 300
Redhead hen, orig pnt, worn to bare wood on head/bill/along 1 side, structurally EX, RWO 7/02/88 200
Scoter, NM orig pnt, several sm dents in 1 side, rare, J/G 9/19/87 450
Scoter pr, orig pnt, minor wear, no structural flaws, J/G 9/19/87 550
Sea Gull, balsa body, G orig pnt, average wear, factory brand, few dents, otherwise sound, 146, RWO 7/02/88 250
Sea Gull, hollow pine body, orig pnt, factory brand, signed, EX & orig, 145, RWO 7/06/86 200
Shoveler drake, NM orig pnt, stamped/signed by Charles Birdsall on underside, structurally EX, rare, 145, J/G 4/23/87 400
Shoveler hen, M pnt, signed/stamped by Charles Birdsall on underside, rare, 145, J/G 4/23/87 350
Surf Scoter, balsa body, fine orig pnt, average wear, rare, 39, RB 7/08/86 550
Widgeon drake, balsa body, factory brand, EX condition, 144, RB 7/09/85 175

Widgeon drake, balsa body, rpt w/minor wear, 21, RB 2/10/85 .... **45**
Widgeon drake, hollow pine body, orig pnt w/some minor areas of overpnt, moderate wear, left eye missing, RB 8/25/88 .... **225**
Widgeon drake, NM orig pnt, structurally EX, rare, ca 1970, 145, J/G 9/20/86 .... **235**
Widgeon hen, NM orig pnt, structurally EX, ca 1970, rare, 145, J/G 9/20/86 .... **150**
Widgeon pr, balsa bodies, EX pnt, factory brand, NM condition, 45, RB 8/25/88 .... **400**
Widgeon pr, balsa bodies, fine orig pnt, minor wear, well preserved, 144, RB 7/09/85 .... **325**
Widgeon pr, balsa bodies, G orig pnt, average wear, RB 3/11/88, 128% **450**

Wildfowler Decoy Company
Wideon pr, balsa bodies, orig pnt, average wear, structurally EX, 144, RWO 11/11/87, $275.00.

Wood Duck drake, detailed cvg, factory brand, M condition, rare, 145, RWO 7/06/86 .... **375**

Miniatures

Adams, Frank (West Tisbury, MA)
Bluebill drake, slight wear on tip of tail, otherwise M, J/G 9/20/86 75
Allen, Courtney
Canada Geese pr, mounted on driftwood, EX condition, RB 7/08/86, 50% 200
Merganser hen, head is slightly loose, 22, RB 5/02/86 125
Anger, Ken (Dunnville, Ont)
Black Duck, hollow, orig pnt, average wear, structurally EX, RWO 11/11/87 575
Bach, Ferdinand; att (Detroit, MI)
Canvasback drake, cvd wings & feather detail on bk, EX orig pnt, RB 7/07/87 200
Baldwin, John Lee (Babylon, LI)
Mallard drake, fine orig pnt, sm chip on end of tail, RB 7/09/85 50
Merganser hen, head has been reglued, otherwise structurally EX, RB 7/09/85 50
Barber, Joel (Long Island, NY)
Canvasback, cast aluminum on oval stepped base, structurally EX, 22, RB 5/02/86 200
Mallard drake, G orig pnt, bill is a replacement, 22, RB 5/02/86 150
Redhead drake, EX condition, 22, RB 5/02/86 225
Berry, Charles R.
Wood Duck pr, mounted on driftwood, EX pnt, signed/dated on bottom, RB 7/09/85 325
Blair, John (Philadelphia, PA)
Mallard hen, superb feather pnt, classic style, sm chip at base of neck, otherwise EX, very rare, RWO 7/04/87, 35% 850
Bodley, C. (Toronto, Canada)
Loon, EX condition, RB 8/25/88 55
Boyd, George (Seabrook, NH)
Goldeneye pr, EX orig pnt, RB 7/09/85 1200
Labrador Duck drake, pnt shrinkage on part of head/body, otherwise M, rare, J/G 9/20/86 400
Labrador Duck hen, pnt shrinkage, sm chips & pnt missing from bill, rare, J/G 9/20/86 225

Boyd, George
Loon, fine orig pnt, slight crazing, identified in artist's handwriting, EX condition, rare, RB 7/07/87, $2,700.00.

Merganser pr, American; EX orig pnt, minor crazing on drake, RB 7/09/85, 240% 2900
Pintail drake, 1 side of tail is missing, EX condition, rare, RB 12/06/85 350
Piping Plover, M condition, RWO 7/02/88 800
Ruffed Grouse, EX condition, RB 12/06/85 700
Swan, NM condition, rare, RB 12/06/85 600
Turkey, EX orig pnt w/several areas of heavy crazing, EX condition, rare, RB 12/06/85 550
Wood Duck pr, EX pnt, rare, RB 7/09/85 1700
Yellowlegs, fine orig pnt, average wear, EX patina, slight age split at neck, rare, RB 3/06/87, 80% 2000
Bull, Roy (Chesapeake Bay)
Yellowlegs, running, orig pnt, EX condition, 22, RB 5/02/86 175
Burr, Russ (Hingham, MA)
Black Duck pr, artist stamp, EX condition, RB 8/25/88 230
Bluebill pr, flying, artist stamp, EX condition, RB 7/08/86 150
Canada Goose pr, artist stamp, EX condition, RB 7/08/86 200
Goldeneye pr, flying, artist stamp, EX condition, RB 7/08/86 200
Gull, flying, artist stamp, EX condition, RB 8/27/87 50
Hooded Merganser pr, artist stamp, EX condition, RB 7/08/86 150
Mallard pr, feeding, mounted on piece of burled wood, artist stamp, EX condition, RB 9/27/87 150

Old Squaw pr, artist stamp, EX & orig condition, RB 7/09/85 525
Pintail drake, artist stamp, tiny nick at underside of bill, otherwise EX, RB 8/27/87 225
Pintail pr, artist stamp, EX condition, RB 7/08/86 100
Redhead drake, detailed wing/tail cvg, EX & orig condition, 193, RWO 7/02/88 150
Ruffed Grouse, artist stamp, EX condition, RB 7/07/87 275
Woodcock, artist stamp, EX condition, RB 7/09/85 175
Woodcock, artist stamp, EX condition, RB 9/27/87 150
Yellowlegs pr, artist stamp, EX condition, RB 7/08/86 150

Bush, Walter (Newark, NJ)
Bluebill pr, signed on bottom, EX condition, RB 7/09/85 100
Greenwinged Teal pr, signed on bottom, EX condition, RB 7 /09/85 85
Hooded Merganser pr, signed/dated 1985 on bottom, EX condition, RB 7/08/86 75
Mallard pr, signed on bottom, EX condition, RB 7/09/85 100

Bush, Wilfred (Pekin, IL)
Canada Goose, signed, crack in bill has been reglued, otherwise M, J/G 9/19/87 55
Hooded Merganser pr, signed on underside, M condition, J/G 9/20/86 85
Ruddy Duck pr, signed, M condition, J/G 4/23/87 95

Buzzanco, Eileen (Mt. Kisco, NY)
Canada Goose, cvd primaries/secondaries, highly detailed pnt, M condition, J/G 4/24/86 137
Loon, fine cvg & pnt detail, M condition, ca 1972, J/G 4/23/87 75
Redhead drake, standing, fine cvg & pnt detail, M condition, ca 1977, J/G 4/23/87 100

Carlock, Thomas
Eider drake, signed/dated 1967, EX & orig condition, RB 3/11/88 110

Chase, F.M. (Vinalhaven, ME)
Mallard drake, flying, 1 foot missing, 22, RB 5/02/86 25

Cheezum, Eddie
Bufflehead pr, cvd tail feathers/raised wing tips, EX pnt, signed/dated on bottom, RB 8/21/86 150

Clifford, Bob
Sandpiper, cvd wing tips, EX condition, 22, RB 5/02/86 150

Coleman, Frank (Hennepin, IL)
Spoonbill pr, cvd wing tips, EX pnt, artist stamp, ca 1940, RB 7/09/85 125

Coykendall, Ralf
Black Duck, preening, EX condition, RB 7/09/85 150
Black Duck, signed/dated on bottom, EX condition, RB 7/08/86 30
Canada Goose, preening, EX condition, RB 7/09/85 175
Canada Goose, preening, signed on bottom, EX condition, RB 8/21/86 100
Redbreasted Merganser pr, EX condition, RB 7/09/85 225
Swan, hollow, EX condition, RB 7/09/85 250

Crowell, A. Elmer (East Harwich, MA)
Baltimore Oriole, rectangular brand, some pnt bubbling on right side, otherwise EX, RB 6/28/88 450
Barrow's Goldeneye, paper label on bottom, EX condition, rare, RB 6/28/88 1000
Bettlehead Plover, M condition, rare, 57/104, J/G 9/20/86 1700
Black Duck, head slightly extended, retains rectangular brand, M condition, RWO 11/11/87 1150
Black Duck, minor crazing to pnt, rectangular brand, NM condition, RB 6/28/88 500
Black Duck, rectangular brand, EX condition, RB 6/28/88 800
Black Duck, running, artist label, M except for minor wear on tail, 57/104, J/G 4/23/87 1450
Black Duck, running, EX feather details, stamped, NM condition, larger than normal size, RB 3/06/87 2750
Black Duck, running, rubber stamp on bottom, early, EX condition, RB 7/08/86, 165% 2500
Black Duck, superb pnt pattern, rubber stamp on bottom, M condition, RB 12/08/85, 260% 1800
Black Duck, upright, bears rectangular stamp, M condition, RWO 11/06/85 650
Black Duck, upright, EX orig pnt w/fine patina, artist brand, rare, RB 7/07/87 1150
Blue Jay, M condition, 57/104, J/G 4/23/87 500
Blue Jay, minor nick at crest, otherwise EX, RB 6/28/88 250
Bluebill drake, artist brand, mounted on oval base, M condition, RWO 7/04/87 900
Bluebill drake, EX feather cvg, NM condition, half again as large as normal size, RB 3/06/87 1600
Bluebill drake, EX pnt, artist brand, NM condition, RB 7/07/87 750
Bluebill drake, M condition, 57/104, J/G 9/20/86 575
Bluebill drake, made in form of a decoy, handwritten signature, EX condition, RB 8/27/87 650
Bluebill drake, mounted on an oval base w/traces of circular rubber stamp, M condition, RWO 7/06/86, 125% ... 1250
Bluebill drake, paper label/artist stamp, M condition, RWO 11/11/87, 75% 750
Bluebill drake, rectangular brand, EX condition, RB 6/28/88 600

Bluebill drake, rectangular brand, EX condition, RB 6/28/88 750
Bluebill drake, rubber stamp on bottom, M condition, RB 12/06/85, 140% 1000
Bluebill hen, artist brand, EX condition, RB 7/07/87 550
Bluebill hen, artist label, M condition, 57/104, J/G 4/23/87 500
Bluebill hen, EX feather details, early stamp, NM condition, half again as large as normal size, RB 3/06/87 1150
Bluebill hen, fuller body than next example, rectangular brand, EX condition, RB 6/28/88 750
Bluebill hen, rectangular brand, EX condition, RB 6/28/88 600
Bluewinged Teal drake, artist label, M condition, 57/104, J/G 9/20/86, 50% 450
Bluewinged Teal drake, artist stamp, M condition, lg, J/G 4/23/87 1000
Bluewinged Teal drake, EX feather details, stamped, NM condition, larger than normal size, RB 3/06/87 1600

Crowell, A. Elmer
Bluewinged Teal drake, EX orig pnt pattern, artist brand, M condition, rare, RB 8/21/86, $1,000.00.

Bluewinged Teal drake, rectangular brand, break in neck has been reglued, RB 6/28/88 550
Bluewinged Teal drake, rubber stamp, M condition, RB 12/06/85 750
Bluewinged Teal drake, running, EX feather details, stamped, NM condition, larger than normal size, RB 3/06/87 3100
Bluewinged Teal hen, Crowell paper label on underside, M condition, 57/104, J/G 9/20/86 1050
Bobolink, M condition, 57/104, J/G 9/20/86 350
Brant, cvd 'V' wing tips, EX pnt pattern, rectangular brand, prof cleaned by K DeLong, oversize, RB 6/28/88 1400
Brant, early, swimming, minor retouching, otherwise EX, RB 7/08/86, 150% 2250
Brant, EX orig condition, rare, RB 8/21/86 1650
Brant, feeding, Crowell paper label on underside, M condition, 57/104, J/G 9/20/86 1300
Brant, hissing, artist brand, M condition, RWO 11/11/87 1000
Brant, identified in pencil, artist brand, M condition, RWO 7/04/87 1200
Brant, rectangular brand, EX condition, RB, 6/28/88 1200
Brant, running, EX feather details, stamped, NM condition, larger than normal size, RB 3/06/87 3500
Brant, swimming, EX feather pnt/patina, artist brand, structurally NM, RB 7/07/87 1350
Brant, swimming, EX pnt, artist brand, RB 7/07/87 650
Brant, swimming, EX pnt, rectangular brand, RB 7/08/86 1750
Bufflehead drake, artist brand, EX condition, RB 7/07/87 600
Bufflehead drake, artist stamp on bottom, M condition, RB 12/06/85, 135% 800
Bufflehead drake, EX feather details, stamped, NM condition, larger than normal size, RB 3/06/87 1300
Bufflehead drake, paper label/artist stamp, M condition, RWO 11/11/87 900
Bufflehead drake, rectangular brand, EX condition, RB 6/28/88 1000
Bufflehead hen, EX feather details, stamped, NM condition, larger than normal size, RB 3/06/87 1500
Bufflehead hen, M condition, 57/104, J/G 9/20/86 850
Bufflehead pr, mounted on oval bases w/traces of circular rubber stamp, M condition, RWO 7/06/86 2250
Canada Goose, artist stamp, EX condition, RB 12/06/85 1600
Canada Goose, early, mounted on oval base, M condition, RWO 7/04/87 1800
Canada Goose, early, rubber stamp on bottom, break in neck, otherwise EX condition, rare, RB 6/28/88 1400
Canada Goose, EX feather details, stamped, NM condition, larger than normal size, RB 3/06/87 3000
Canada Goose, EX pnt, artist brand, structurally NM, RB 8/27/87 1100
Canada Goose, head stretched out, cvd split tail, NM pnt, artist brand, rare, RB 8/21/86, 140% 3100
Canada Goose, M pnt, slight wear on beak, artist label, 57/104, J/G 4/23/87, 80% 1200
Canada Goose, minor pnt crazing, otherwise NM, RB 6/28/88, 127% 2300
Canada Goose, mounted on a curly maple box, EX orig pnt, RB 8/21/86 850

Canada Goose, rectangular brand, M condition, RWO 7/02/88 1200
Canada Goose, slightly turned head, superb orig pnt w/minor touchup, artist brand on mounded base, oversize, RB 7/07/87 2750
Canada Goose head, brass tack eyes, bill is cvd w/exceptional detail, showing the tongue, EX condition, RB 6/28/88, 160% 1600
Canvasback drake, exceptional pnt pattern, rectangular brand, minor crazing to head, otherwise NM, RB 6/28/88 1400
Canvasback drake, feeding, EX & orig, RB 12/06/85, 145% 1450

Crowell, A. Elmer
**Canvasback drake, feeding, EX feather details, early
stamp, sm chip on wing tip, larger than normal, RB
3/06/87, 75%, $1,550.00.**

Canvasback drake, feeding, paper label, M condition, exceptional, 132, J/G 9/19/87 1050
Canvasback drake, oval rubber stamp on bottom, EX condition, extremely rare, RB 6/28/88 1150
Canvasback hen, Crowell paper label on underside, tiny pnt flake from tip of bill, 57/104, J/G 9/20/86, 55% 500
Canvasback hen, EX feather details, early stamp, NM condition, larger than normal size, rare, RB 3/06/87, 55% 1150
Canvasback hen, paper label/artist stamp, M condition, RWO 11/11/87, 60% 600
Canvasback hen, rectangular brand, EX condition, RB 6/28/88 700
Canvasback hen, rectangular brand, EX condition, RB 6/28/88 1000
Canvasback hen, rubber stamp on bottom, M condition, RB 12/06/85, 135% 1100
Cardinal, M condition, 57/104, J/G 4/23/87 650
Cedar Waxing, rectangular brand, EX condition, RB 6/28/88 300
Cedar Waxing, unmarked, EX condition, RB 6/28/88 500
Dowitcher, M condition, rare, 57/104, J/G 9/20/86 1450
Eastern Kingbird, rectangular brand, EX condition, RB 6/28/88 300
Eider drake, EX feather details, early stamp, NM condition, larger than normal size, rare, RB 3/06/87 3200
Eider hen, EX feather details, early stamp, NM condition, larger than normal size, rare, RB 3/06/87, 70% 1700
Flicker, G orig pnt, artist stamp, possible bill repair, RB 7/08/86 400
Flicker, M condition, 57/104, J/G 9/20/86 325
Gadwall hen, EX feathering, early stamp, NM condition, half again as lg as standard sz, RB 3/06/87, 130% 2600
Gold Finch, M condition, 57/104, J/G 9/20/86 300
Golden Plover, EX orig pnt, artist brand, RB 2/01/85 925
Golden Plover, M condition, 57/104, J/G 9/20/86 1300
Goldeneye drake, artist brand, EX condition, RB 7/07/87 650
Goldeneye drake, artist brand, M condition, J/G 9/20/86 650
Goldeneye drake, artist stamp, EX condition, RB 12/06/85, 140% 850
Coldonoyo drake, early, preening, EX orig pnt, hairline crack in base of neck, RWO 7/04/87, 30% 450
Goldeneye drake, EX feather details, stamped, NM condition, larger than normal size, RB 3/06/87, 70% 1100
Goldeneye drake, M pnt w/G patina, paper label on underside, J/G 4/23/87 800
Goldeneye drake, mounted on oval base, identified/artist brand, M condition, RWO 7/04/87 1200
Goldeneye drake, orig pnt, paper label, structurally EX, RB 8/27/87 475
Goldeneye drake, rectangular brand, EX condition, RB 6/28/88 850
Goldeneye drake, superb feather pnt, rectangular brand, NM condition, RB 6/28/88 900
Goldeneye hen, EX feather detail, NM condition, half again as large as normal size, RB 3/06/87 1700
Goldeneye hen, M pnt w/EX patina, highly detailed feather pnt, paper label on bottom, J/G 4/24/86 825
Goldeneye hen, sm pnt rub on top of head, otherwise M, J/G 9/20/86 600
Green Heron, artist stamp, M condition, RB 12/06/85 850
Green Heron, rectangular brand on bottom, sm chip at end of bill/tail, otherwise EX, RB 3/06/87, 210% 1050
Greenwinged Teal drake, artist brand, EX condition, RB 7/07/87 750
Greenwinged Teal drake, EX & orig, RB 12/06/85 750
Greenwinged Teal drake, rectangular brand, minor crazing, otherwise EX, RB 6/28/88 800
Greenwinged Teal drake, rectangular brand on base, EX condition, RB 6/28/88 800
Greenwinged Teal drake, tiny pnt flake missing from tip of bill, 57/104, J/G 9/20/86 1100
Greenwinged Teal hen, artist label, M condition, 57/104, J/G 9/20/86 850
Greenwinged Teal hen, EX feather details, stamped, NM condition, larger than normal size, RB 3/06/87, 70% 1100
Greenwinged Teal pr, flying, EX orig pnt w/detailed pnt on upper/lower portions of wings, RB 8/21/86 1300

Greenwinged Teal pr, retain traces of circular rubber stamp, M condition, RWO 7/06/86 .... **2000**
Grosbeak, M condition, 57/104, J/G 9/20/86 .... **300**
Herring Gull, rectangular brand, minor rstr to tip of bill by GiGi Hopkins, otherwise EX & orig, rare, RWO 7/02/88 .... **900**
Hooded Merganser drake, EX feather details, early stamp, NM condition, larger than normal size, rare, RB 3/06/87 .... **1600**
Hooded Merganser drake, EX orig pnt, artist brand, RB 7/07/87 .... **1000**
Hooded Merganser drake, rectangular brand, EX condition, RB 6/28/88 .... **1000**
Hooded Merganser hen, EX feather details, early stamp, NM condition, larger than normal size, rare, RB 3/06/87 .... **2000**
Jack Curlew, rubber stamp, NM condition, rare, RB 12/06/85, 133% **1600**
Jack Snipe, M condition, very rare, 57/104, J/G 4/23/87 .... **1450**
Kildeer Plover, NM condition, RB 12/06/85 .... **650**
Kingfisher, M condition, 57/104, J/G 9/20/86 .... **300**
Kingfisher, paper label, M condition, RB 12/06/85 .... **600**
Mallard drake, EX pnt pattern, artist brand, bill has been prof rstr by DeLong, otherwise NM, RB 8/27/87 .... **575**
Mallard drake, head cocked & slightly turned, cvg has raised gesso feet on base, EX pnt, artist brand, rare, RB 3/06/87 .... **1100**
Mallard drake, minor pnt flaking on 1 side of head, artist brand, EX condition, RWO 11/11/87 .... **800**
Mallard drake, nice patina, rectangular brand, M condition, RWO 7/02/88, 60% **450**
Mallard drake, orig pnt, artist brand, some crazing to breast, otherwise EX, RB 8/27/87 .... **375**
Mallard drake, paper label, M condition, 132, J/G 9/19/87 .... **750**
Mallard drake, rectangular brand, fine hairline crack in bill, otherwise EX & orig condition, RWO 7/02/88 .... **475**
Mallard drake, rectangular brand, M condition, larger than average, RB 7/07/87, 70% **700**
Mallard drake, rectangular brand, minor crazing, otherwise EX condition, RB 6/28/88 .... **800**
Mallard drake, rectangular brand, slight crazing, otherwise NM, RB 6/28/88 .... **900**
Mallard drake, slightly turned head, EX feather details, stamped, NM condition, larger than normal size, RB 3/06/87, 75% **1600**
Mallard hen, artist brand, NM condition, RB 8/27/87 .... **600**
Mallard hen, EX feather details, stamped, NM condition, larger than normal size, RB 3/06/87 .... **1800**
Mallard hen, M pnt, G patina, artist brand, J/G 9/20/86 .... **575**
Mallard hen, rectangular brand, minor crazing, slight chip on underside of bill, otherwise EX, RB 6/28/88 .... **900**
Mallard pr, artist stamp, M condition, RB 12/06/85 .... **2000**
Mallard pr, mounted on wooden base, rectangular brand/signed, outstanding orig condition, exceptional, RWO 7/05/85 .... **2050**

Crowell, A. Elmer
Mallard pr, mounted on wooden base, signed/inscribed, M
condition, RWO 7/04/87, $2,800.00.

Mallard pr, paper label on underside, M condition, 57/014, J/G 4/23/87 .... **1400**
Marsh Wren, M condition, 57/104, J/G 9/20/86 .... **390**
Merganser drake, American; artist brand, EX condition, RB 7/07/87 .... **650**
Merganser drake, American; artist label, tiny pnt flake from tip of bill, 57/104, J/G 9/20/86 .... **1200**
Merganser drake, American; artist stamp, M condition, RWO 11/11/87 .... **900**
Merganser drake, American; detailed feathering, M pnt, artist stamp, M condition, J/G 4/23/87 .... **750**
Merganser drake, American; EX feather details, early stamp, NM condition, larger than normal size, rare, RB 3/06/87, 72% **1600**
Merganser drake, American; M pnt, mounted on oval base, identified on bottom, rare, RWO 7/04/87 .... **1200**
Merganser drake, American; rectangular brand, EX condition, RB 6/28/88 .... **800**
Merganser drake, running, paper label on underside, M condition, 57/104, RB 4/23/87 .... **800**

Merganser hen, running, orig pnt, paper label on underside, 57/104, J/G 4/23/87 650
Merganser pr, American; M pnt, rubber stamp on bottom, rare, RB 12/06/85 1750
Old Squaw drake, artist brand, EX orig condition, RB 7/07/87 550
Old Squaw drake, paper label on bottom, EX condition, RB 7/09/85 675
Old Squaw drake, paper label/artist stamp, M condition, RWO 11/11/87 900
Old Squaw drake, rectangular brand, EX condition, RB 6/28/88 850
Old Squaw drake, rubber stamp, M condition, RB 12/06/85 650
Old Squaw drake, slightly turned head, EX feather details, stamped, NM, larger than normal size, RB 3/06/87, 125% 2500
Ovenbird, rectangular brand, bill has been chipped, but orig pc has been reglued by Kenneth DeLong, RB 6/28/88 325
Owl, EX orig pnt, left ear is prof rstr by Kenneth Delong, tiny nick to end of foot, rare, 6, RB 7/07/87 1400
Pheasant, mounted on oval base w/traces of circular brand, tip of tail broken off, otherwise NM, RWO 7/06/86 750
Pheasant, rectangular brand on bottom, EX & orig, RB 3/06/87 1000
Pintail drake, artist stamp, EX & orig, RB 12/06/85 700
Pintail drake, artist stamp, EX condition, RB 7/07/87 950
Pintail drake, early, alert high-head style, EX orig pnt, minor flaking, 40, RB 7/08/86, 125% 1750
Pintail drake, early, fine orig pnt, tips of wings are broken/tip of tail is missing, head reglued, RWO 7/04/87 550
Pintail drake, EX feather details, stamped, NM condition, larger than normal size, RB 3/06/87 2500
Pintail drake, EX orig pnt, artist brand, minor rstr to neck by Kenneth DeLong, RB 2/01/85 675
Pintail drake, fine orig pnt, artist brand, age split at neck, RB 8/27/87 575
Pintail drake, preening, EX pnt, artist stamp, on chip-cvd base, rare, RB 7/07/87 2500
Pintail drake, rectangular brand, minor crazing to head, otherwise EX, RB 6/28/88 800
Pintail drake, rectangular brand, tiny nick at end of tail, RB 6/28/88 475
Pintail hen, EX orig pnt, artist brand, old break at neck has been reglued, RB 8/27/87 450
Pintail hen, orig pnt w/some surface flaking, artist brand, structurally sound, RB 3/06/87 375
Pintail hen, paper label, artist stamp, M condition, RWO 11/11/87, 55% 550
Pintail hen, rectangular brand, EX condition, RB 6/28/88 950
Pintail hen, rubber stamp, M condition, RB 12/06/85 400
Piping Plover, NM condition, RB 12/06/85 600
Quail, artist stamp, M condition, RB 12/06/85 500
Quail, early, EX feather pattern, base has minor pnt flaking, otherwise NM, RB 6/28/88 450
Quail, rectangular brand on bottom, EX & orig, RB 3/06/87 800
Red-Eyed Towhee, rectangular brand, EX condition, RB 6/28/88 300

Crowell, A. Elmer
Redbreasted Merganser drake, artist brand, EX condition, RB 7/07/87, $1,000.00.

Redbreasted Merganser drake, artist stamp, EX condition, RB 12/06/85, 140% 1100
Redbreasted Merganser drake, artist stamp on bottom, EX condition, RB 7/09/85 775
Redbreasted Merganser drake, early, artist signed, NM condition, RB 6/28/88, 120% 1200
Redbreasted Merganser drake, fine orig pnt, artist brand, chip on underside of bill, 36, RB 2/01/85 500
Redbreasted Merganser drake, orig pnt, artist stamp, M condition, RWO 7/04/87 1300
Redbreasted Merganser drake, rectangular brand, NM condition, RB 6/28/88 700
Redbreasted Merganser drake, running, EX feather details, early stamp, NM condition, larger than normal size, RB 3/06/87 ... 2000
Redbreasted Merganser hen, artist brand, EX condition, RB 7/07/87 550
Redbreasted Merganser hen, EX feather pnt/patina, artist brand, structurally NM, RB 7/07/87 800
Redbreasted Merganser hen, rectangular brand, artist signed, NM condition, RB 6/28/88 750
Redbreasted Merganser hen, rectangular brand, NM condition, RB 6/28/88 650
Redfaced Warbler, tiny flake of pnt is missing from tip of beak, otherwise M, J/G 4/23/87 350
Redhead drake, artist brand, EX & orig, RB 7/07/87 900
Redhead drake, artist brand, slight age check in bill, otherwise EX condition, RB 7/07/87 850
Redhead drake, EX feather details, early stamp, NM condition, larger than normal size, rare, RB 3/06/87 2000
Redhead drake, full body, tiny pnt fleck retouched by DeLong, artist stamp, 6, RB 9/27/87 600
Redhead drake, mounted on oval base, identified/artist brand, M condition, RWO 7/04/87 1200

Redhead drake, paper label, slight pnt crazing on breast, 57/104, J/G 9/20/86 900
Redhead drake, rectangular brand, minor crazing to head, otherwise EX, RB 6/28/88 1300
Redhead drake, rectangular stamp, outstanding orig condition, superb, RWO 7/05/85 675
Redhead drake, several sm flaked areas to body in need of rpt, artist stamp, RB 12/06/85, 170% 1050
Redhead hen, artist brand, EX condition, RB 7/07/87 650
Redhead hen, paper label, M condition, 57/104, J/G 9/20/86 57/104, J/G 9/20/86 850
Redhead hen, rectangular brand, EX condition, RB 6/28/88 900
Redhead hen, sm amount of pnt shrinkage on neck, otherwise M, rectangular stamp, J/G 9/19/87 400
Redheaded Woodpecker, artist stamp, EX condition, RB 2/01/85 250
Redheaded Woodpecker, M condition, 57/104, J/G 9/20/86 425
Ringneck, M condition, 57/104, J/G 9/20/86 900
Robin, artist brand, M condition, RB 12/06/85 800
Robin, rectangular brand, EX condition, RB 6/28/88 450
Robin, Redbreasted; M condition, 57/104, J/G 9/20/86 350
Ruddy Duck, artist brand, sm amount of crazing to breast, otherwise EX condition, RB 7/07/87 600
Ruddy Duck, artist stamp, M condition, RWO 7/04/87 1300
Ruddy Duck, mounted on oval base w/traces of circular rubberstamp, M condition, RWO 7/06/86 1000
Ruddy Duck, rectangular brand, EX condition, RB 6/28/88, 122% 1100
Ruddy Duck pr, paper label on underside, M condition, 57/104, J/G 4/23/87, 70% 950
Ruddy Duck pr, rubber stamp on bottom, M condition, RB 12/06/85 1500
Ruddy Turnstone, artist stamp, NM condition, RB 12/06/85 700
Ruddy Turnstone, running, M condition, rare, J/G 4/23/87, 130% 1550
Ruffed Grouse, paper label, M condition, 132, J/G 9/19/87 900
Sanderling, tiny tail chip, 57/104, J/G 9/20/86 1250
Scarlet Tanager, rectangular brand, tiny bill chip, otherwise EX, RB 6/28/88 400
Scoter, paper label, M condition, very rare, 57/104, J/G 9/20/86, 123% 1850
Scoter hen, slightly turned head, M pnt, artist label, extremely rare, 57/104, J/G 4/23/87 750
Shoveler drake, artist label, sm dent on side of bill/sm pnt flakes missing from top of head, rare, J/G 4/23/87 ... 750
Shoveler drake, artist stamp, NM condition, rare, RB 12/06/85 500
Shoveler drake, EX feather details, early stamp, NM condition, larger than normal size, rare, RB 3/06/87 3100
Shoveler drake, orig pnt, retains circular rubber stamp, M condition, RWO 7/06/86, 160% 650
Shoveler hen, M condition, rare, 57/104, J/G 4/23/87 500
Shoveller drake, paper label on bottom, EX condition, rare, RB 6/28/88 1100
Solitary Sandpiper, artist stamp, M condition, RB 12/05/85, 160% 800

Crowell, A. Elmer
Spotted Sandpiper, early, raised cvd wings/flipped up tail, M condition, J/G 4/24/86, $770.00.

Spotted Sandpiper, M pnt, slight wear on tip of bill, otherwise M, rare, 57/104, J/G 4/23/87, 130% 1550
Stilt, minnow-in-throat neck form, sm flake of pnt missing from tip of bill, otherwise M, very rare, 57/104, J/G 4/23/87 1800
Surf Scoter drake, EX feather detail, rubber stamp, NM condition, larger than normal size, RB 3/06/87 2500
Surf Scoter hen, artist stamp, M condition, RB 12/06/85 500
Surf Scoter hen, EX feather details, early stamp, NM condition, larger than normal, RB 3/06/87 3000
Thrush, rectangular brand, EX condition, RB 6/28/88 250
Towhee, rectangular brand, signed, EX condition, RB 6/28/88 375
Tufted Titmouse, very slight wear on tip of beak & tip of crest, otherwise M, 57/104, J/G 4/23/87 450
Widgeon drake, artist brand, EX condition, RB 7/07/87 750
Widgeon drake, artist stamp, M condition, RB 12/06/85 850
Widgeon drake, EX feather details, early stamp, NM condition, larger than normal, rare, RB 3/06/87, 80% 1600
Widgeon drake, EX orig pnt, sm nick at end of tail, rare, RB 7/08/86 700
Widgeon drake, M condition, 57/104, J/G 9/20/86, 75% 600

Widgeon drake, mounted on oval base w/traces of circular rubber stamp, M condition, RWO 7/06/86 1000
Widgeon drake, paper label/artist stamp, M condition, RWO 11/11/87, 65% 650
Widgeon drake, rectangular brand, EX condition, RB 6/28/88 900
Widgeon hen, EX feather details, early stamp, NM condition, larger than normal, rare, RB 3/06/87, 50% 1000
Widgeon hen, M condition, 57/104, J/G 9/20/86 850
Wood Duck drake, artist brand, EX & orig, rare, RB 3/06/87 1100
Wood Duck drake, artist brand, EX & orig, RB 7/07/87 850
Wood Duck drake, artist stamp, EX & orig, RB 12/06/85, 180% 1300
Wood Duck drake, EX feather details, early stamp, NM condition, larger than normal size, rare, RB 3/06/87 1900

Crowell, A. Elmer
Wood Duck drake, head tucked down, EX detailed pnt/ patina, artist brand, NM condition, RB 7/07/87, $1,300.00.

Wood Duck drake, head tucked into content position, EX pnt, rectangular brand, NM condition, RB 6/28/88, 140% 1700
Wood Duck drake, M pnt, slight crazing on upper edge of breast, paper label, 57/104, J/G 4/23/87 600
Wood Duck drake, mounted on oval base, bears rectangular brand, M condition, RWO 7/04/87 1400
Wood Duck drake, paper label, EX condition, RB 12/06/85 700
Wood Thrush, rectangular brand, EX condition, RB 6/28/88 250
Woodcock, artist stamp, M condition, RB 12/06/85 700
Woodpecker, preening, mounted on bark, rectangular brand on bark, EX condition, life-size, rare, RB 12/06/85 1700
Yellow-Bellied Sapsucker, unmarked, bill is chipped & pc missing, otherwise EX & orig condition, RB 6/28/88 200
Yellow-Throated Vireo, slight wear on tip of beak, otherise M, J/G 4/23/87 350
Yellowlegs, EX orig pnt, artist brand, bill has been prof rstr by Kenneth DeLong, 40, RB 7/08/86, 200% 2000
Yellowlegs, preening, mounted on a clam shell, rectangular brand, NM condition, 6" tall, RB 7/07/87, 215% 6500
Yellowlegs, preening, mounted on clam shell, rectangular brand, rstr wing tip/feet, EX, rare, RWO 7/02/88, 140% 3400
Yellowlegs, preening, mounted on cvd wooden clam shell, rectangular brand, rstr wing tip, otherwise NM, RB 8/25/88 3500
Yellowlegs, rectangular brand, bill rstr by GiGi Hopkins, otherwise M, RWO 7/02/88 1600
Yellowlegs, running, NM condition, rare, RB 12/06/85 550
Yellowlegs, running, Winter plumage, M condition, 57/104, J /G 4/23/87 1450
Yellowlegs, Summer plumage, M condition, 57/104, J/G 4/23/87, 150% 1350

Crowell, Cleon
Wood Duck drake, rectangular brand on bottom, EX condition, 22, RB 5/02/86 600

Dettman, F.A. (Connecticut)
Canada Goose, crack running through neck, otherwise EX & orig condition, 193, RWO 7/02/88 150
Grouse, sm chips in tail/end of bill, otherwise EX & orig condition, 193, RWO 7/02/88 150
Redbreasted Merganser drake, similar to the work of Elmer Crowell, fine orig condition, 193, RWO 7/02/88 125
Semi-Palmated Plover, part of the bill is missing/sm tail chips, otherwise EX, 193, RWO 7/02/88 150

Dunn, Noel L.
Mallard drake, hollow, cvg/pnt in style of Premier grade Mason, M condition, J/G 4/24/86 88
Mallard hen, hollow, cvg/pnt in style of Premier grade Mason, M condition, J/G 4/24/86 88

Elliot Brothers (Easton, MD)
Canada Geese, thin cracks in neck, otherwise structurally EX, ca 1940's, RWO 11/11/87 140
Canvasback pr, minor repairs to cracks in necks, otherwise structurally EX, ca 1940's, RWO 11/11/87 100

Ernst, Clarence; att (Indian Point, NS)
Eider pr, M condition, ca 1940's, RWO 7/04/87 50
Goldeneye pr, M condition, ca 1940's, RWO 7/04/87 100

Ewell, M.B.
Canada Goose, EX condition, RB 3/11/88 25

Feasel, Michelle
Redbreasted Merganser pr, EX condition, RB 6/28/88 70

Finney, Frank (Detroit, MI)

Mallard pr, cvd in the style of the Caines Brothers, made to look old, RWO 7/02/88 .... **200**

Merganser hen, inlet head, cvd in style of Gus Wilson, RWO 7/02/88 .... **150**

Ruddy Duck, cvd in the style of Lem Dudley, made to look old, RWO 7/02/88 .... **325**

Ruddy Duck, made in the style of Alvirah Wright, made to look old, RWO 7/02/88 .... **140**

Fleck, Henry

Black Duck, initialed/dated 1962, EX condition, RB 7/07/87 .... **60**

Franco, Jack (Massachusetts)

Avocet, cvd primaries/crossed wing tips, signed/dated 1975 on bottom, EX condition, RB 7/08/86 .... **225**

Canada Goose, raised wing tips, signed/dated 1973, EX condition, RB 8/27/87 .... **150**

Curlew, cvd primaries/crossed wing tips, signed/dated 1974 on bottom, EX condition, RB 7/08/86 .... **200**

Mallard, signed/dated 1974, EX condition, RB 8/27/87 .... **50**

Ruffed Grouse, EX pnt, signed/dated 1973 on bottom, RB 7/08/86 .... **225**

Yellowlegs, cvd primary feathers/crossed wing tips, EX pnt, signed/dated 1973 on bottom, RB 7/08/86 .... **150**

Freeman, Russell

Bufflehead, flying, sm chip on bottom of wing tip/sm chip on underside of tail has been reglued, 22, RB 5/02/86 .... **150**

Canada Goose, EX condition, RB 5/02/86 .... **75**

Garren, Otto (Canton, IL)

Mallard hen, EX orig pnt w/nice patina, 193, RWO 7/02/88 .... **200**

Garton, George

Coot, EX orig pnt, neck is whimsically tied in a knot, signed/dated 1976, VG condition, 22, RB 5/02/86 .... **225**

Garton, John B. (Smith's Falls, Ont)

Black Duck, EX condition, RB 8/27/87 .... **80**

Bluewinged Teal drake, EX condition, RB 7/08/86 .... **60**

Bufflehead, EX condition, RB 8/27/87 .... **110**

Canada Goose, EX condition, RB 8/27/87 .... **90**

Goldeneye drake, EX condition, RB 8/27/87 .... **50**

Greenwinged Teal drake, EX condition, RB 8/27/87 .... **65**

Hooded Merganser, EX condition, RB 8/27/87 .... **85**

Pintail drake, EX condition, RB 7/08/86 .... **75**

Ringbill drake, EX condition, RB 7/08/86 .... **80**

Widgeon, EX condition, RB 8/27/87 .... **75**

Gibbs, Harold

Bald Eagle, initialed/dated 1960, EX condition, RB 6/28/88 .... **140**

Brown Thrasher, initialed on bottom, EX condition, RB 6/28/88 .... **150**

Canada Goose, artist signed/dated 1968, EX condition, RB 6/28/88 .... **170**

Comorant, initialed/dated 1946, EX condition, RB 6/28/88 .... **100**

Golden Pheasant, initialed/dated 1942, RB 6/28/88 .... **150**

Harlequin Duck, initialed/dated 1948, EX condition, RB 6/28/88 .... **150**

Osprey, unsigned, EX condition, RB 6/28/88 .... **200**

Ruffed Grouse, initialed/dated 1960, EX condition, RB 6/28/88 .... **150**

Sharp-Tailed Grouse, initialed/dated 1958, EX condition, RB 6/28/88 .... **140**

Towhee, initialed on bottom, EX condition, RB 6/28/88 .... **100**

Gilley, Wendell (Southwest Harbor, ME)

Black Duck, signed on bottom, break in neck has been reglued, otherwise EX condition, RB 7/08/86 .... **300**

Bluebill drake, signed on bottom, EX condition, RB 7/08/86 .... **400**

Canada Goose, signed on bottom, EX condition, RB 7/08/86 .... **500**

Mallard drake, signed on bottom, EX condition, RB 3/06/87, 140% **700**

Mallard drake, signed on bottom, EX condition, RB 7/08/86 .... **450**

Pintail drake, signed, EX condition, RB 3/11/88, 142% **850**

Gilley, Wendell
Pintail pr, mounted on driftwood, signed/dated 1959,
EX condition, RB 7/08/86, 150%, $1,500.00.

195

Redhead drake, EX condition, RB 7/08/86	300
Spotted Sandpiper, signed on bottom, EX condition, RB 7/08/ 86	550
Widgeon drake, signed on bottom, EX condition, RB 7/08/86	400
Wood Duck drake, signed on bottom, EX & orig, rare, RB 7/07/87	500
Wood Duck drake, signed on bottom, EX orig condition, RB 3/06/87, 140%	700
Woodcock, signed/dated 1969 on bottom, M condition, J/G 4/24/86	220

Glassford, Al
Pintail pr, cvd wing tips, highly detailed pnt, sm flake missing from drake, otherwise M, one quarter-size, J/G 4/23/87	300

Glenn, Capt. John (Rock Hall, MD)
Canvasback pr, flying, EX orig pnt shows soft patina, minor chipping on bk/wings, one third-size, RWO 11/11/87	900

Haertel, Harold (Dundee, IL)
Canada Goose, raised cvd wing tips, signed/dated, 1 of 4 existent, M condition, one quarter-size, J/G 4/23/87	800
Dove, orig pnt, cvd HH in bottom, EX condition, 22, RB 5/02/86	850
Pied-Bill Grebe, signed/dated 1968 on bottom, orig pnt, EX condition, rare, 22, RB 5/02/86	700

Haertel, Howard (Dundee, IL)
Spotted Sandpiper, orig pnt, cvd wings/primary feathers, cvd HH in bottom, EX condition, 22, RB 5/02/86	900

Hancock, Miles (Chincoteague, VA)
Bluebill drake, signed/dated 1968, M condition, RWO 11/06/85	40
Canada Goose, artist signed, EX & orig condition, RWO 2/12/88	80
Canada Goose, EX orig pnt, fine crack in head, signed/dated 1968, RWO 11/06/85	45
Greenwinged Teal drake, signed/dated 1968, M condition, RWO 11/06/85	50
Mallard drake, EX & orig, RB 7/07/87	10
Pintail pr, M condition, RWO 11/06/85	230
Redbreasted Merganser drake, EX & orig, RB 7/09/85	180
Redhead drake, EX & orig, RB 7/09/85	110
Redhead drake, stamped w/location, EX condition, RB 7/07/87	130

Harrington, David
Redhead drake, signed/dated 1973 on bottom, EX condition, RB 7/08/86	50

Harris, Ken (Woodville, NY)
Mallard pr, artist stamp, EX condition, RB 8/27/87	150
Wood Duck Hen, EX condition, RB 3/11/88	170
Wood Duck hen, EX pnt, artist stamp, RB 7/07/87	190

Havens, Lloyd E.
Canada Goose, signed, EX & orig, one third-size, 22, RB 5/02/86	275
Canada Goose, standing, outstanding workmanship, stamped Hand cvd & pnt, signed, EX condition, RWO 2/13/87	290

Hawthorne, Davison B.
Semipalmated Sandpiper pr, signed/dated 1967 on bottom, EX condition, RB 8/07/87	375
Spotted Sandpiper, orig pnt, detailed head & cvd primary feathers, EX condition, 22, RB 5/02/86	400

Hill, Dr. Lewis Webb (Chatham, MA)
Canvasback drake, cvd crossed wing tips, EX orig feather pnt, 1 sm mark on breast, otherwise EX, RB 7/08/86	200

Hiltz, Oran; att (Indian Point, NS)
Redbreasted Merganser pr, orig pnt, drake has chip in tail/hen has crack in neck, otherwise sound, RWO 7/04/87	45

Hinck, Bud
Mallard pr, both signed/dated, EX condition, RB 6/28/88	25

Holland, Mark (Cape Cod, MA)
Black Ducks, both signed on bottom, EX conditon, RB 7/07/87	275

Holland, Mark
Quail hen & 6 chicks, signed/dated 1973 on bottom, EX condition, RB 3/06/87, $275.00.

Spotted Sandpiper, preening, structurally EX, RB 7/09/85	250

Holly Family (Havre de Grace, MD)
Canvasback drake, EX & orig, RB 7/09/85 950
Holtz, Ken
Surf Scoter, cork body, EX pnt, signed/dated 1979 on bottom, RB 7/08/86 35
Jenkins, Bradford and Virginia (Duxbury, MA)
Canada Goose, copied from Joe Lincoln, orig pnt, EX condition, dated 1983, 22, RB 5/02/86 50
Jester, Doug (Chincoteague, VA)
Canada Goose, EX orig condition w/light coat of varnish, RWO 11/06/85 125
Pintail pr, hairline cracks running through necks, otherwise M condition, RWO 11/06/85 250
Jester, Sam
Canada Goose, old break in neck has been reglued, otherwise structurally EX, 22, RB 5/02/86 120
Hooded Merganser pr, structurally EX, 22, RB 5/02/86 175
Merganser pr, structurally EX, 22, RB 5/02/86 175
Redbreasted Merganser drake, EX condition, 22, RB 5/02/86 125
Jobes, Capt. Harry (Havre de Grace, MD)
Swan, split in neck has been reglued, otherwise structurally sound, 22, RB 5/02/86 175
Joeckel, Bill (Long Island, NY)
Brant, raised wing tips, signed/dated 1974, tiny rub at top of head & end of bill, otherwise EX, RB 8/27/87 130
Johnson, George
Semipalmated Sandpiper, cvd primary feathers, signed/dated 1963, structurally EX, 22, RB 5/02/86 250
Kerr, Bob (Smith's Falls, Ont)
Mallard drake, relief cvg, G scratch pnt, signed/dated 1972, M condition, RWO 11/06/85 390
King, A.J.
Redhead pr, detailed cvd wing tips, M condition, J/G 4/23/87 950
Swan pr, cvd feather detail w/raised wing tips, artist signed, EX condition, RB 7/08/86, 65% 650
Lapham, James (Dennisport, MA)
Black Duck, raised wing tips, signed on bottom, EX condition, RB 8/27/87 175
Black Turnstone, EX condition, half-size, RB 8/21/86 75
Canvasback, feeding, EX condition, RB 8/25/88 90
Curlew, cvd w/spread wings, signed on bottom, EX condition, half-size, RB 7/08/86 175
Loon, signed/identified on bottom, EX condition, rare, RB 7/09/85 200
Piping Plover, EX condition, half-size, RB 8/21/86 50
Redbreasted Merganser drake, raised wings/wing tips, EX pnt, RB 7/07/87 275
Redbreasted Merganser pr, EX pnt, signed on bottom, RB 7/08/86 150
Ringneck Plover, signed/identified on bottom, EX condition, RB 7/09/85 125
Sanderling, EX pnt, signed on bottom, RB 7/08/86 120
Laurie, R.D. (Hingham, MA)
Bufflehead drake, EX pnt, stamped on bottom, RB 7/08/86 100
Canada Goose, artist stamp, EX condition, 22, RB 5/02/86 150
Goldeneye hen, artist stamp, EX condition, RB 7/08/86 140
Mallard hen, artist stamp, EX & orig, RB 7/08/86 100
Old Squaw drake, artist stamp, EX condition, RB 7/08/86 170
Sea Gull, artist stamp, EX condition, RB 7/08/86 130
Sea Gull, heavy varnish, artist stamp, EX orig condition, RB 9/27/87 175
Wood Duck drake, artist stamp, EX condition, RB 7/08/86 125
Laurie, R.D.; att (Hingham, MA)
Canada Goose, old break in neck has been reglued, otherwise EX & orig, RB 7/08/86 200

Lawrence, Homer
Woodcock, pnt by S Riffe, EX condition, RB
7/09/85, $200.00.

Lawson, Oliver (Crisfield, MD)

Greenwinged Teal hen, cvg/pnt resemble work of the Ward Brothers, M condition, RWO 7/06/86 70

Lincoln, Joe (Accord, MA)

Black Duck, EX feather pnt, structurally M, RB 7/09/85 800

Bluewinged Teal pr, artist stamp, EX & orig, 40, RB 7/08/8 6 2000

Brant, superb pnt, EX condition, rare, 40, RB 7/08/86, 165% 2500

Canada Goose, EX pnt pattern, artist stamp, break in neck has been rstr by KE DeLong, 40, RB 7/08/86 1800

Canada Goose, hissing, M condition, approximately 7" long, RWO 7/04/87 950

Canada Goose, hissing, outstanding orig condition, RWO 7/02/88, 40% 800

Canada Goose, M condition, J/G 4/23/87 800

Canada Goose, sleeping, M condition, very rare, J/G 4/23/87 1150

Canada Goose, swimming, EX feathering, several sm pnt flecks missing, otherwise M, J/G 9/19/87 750

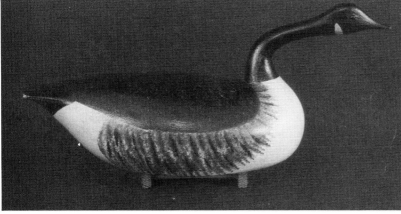

Lincoln, Joe
Canada Goose, swimming, feather pnt on sides & bk, one quarter-size, M condition, RB 12/06/85, $2,750.00.

Canada Goose, swimming, fine feather detail, pnt eye, slight wear to bill & tail, otherwise M, J/G 9/19/87, 60% 650

Canada Goose, swimming, M condition, rare, J/G 4/23/87 1050

Hooded Merganser drake, extremely slight wear on extremities, otherwise M, artist stamp, rare, J/G 9/19/87 600

Loon, M condition, J/G 4/23/87 650

Mallard, exceptional feather pnt pattern, NM condition, rare, RB 6/28/88 800

Mallard drake, thin neck crack, otherwise M, rubber stamp on bottom reads, Joe Lincoln, Accord MA, 193, RWO 7/02/88 500

Redhead hen, outstanding orig pnt, structurally EX, rare, RWO 7/04/87 750

Wood Duck drake, EX condition, RB 7/09/85 950

Wood Duck drake, EX form, artist stamp, age check in bill, otherwise EX, used as a sm paperweight, rare, RB 7/07/87 1800

Lovell, Wallace

Hooded Merganser pr, signed/dated 1975, M condition, J/G 9/20/86 70

Redbreasted Merganser drake, signed/dated 1975, M condition, J/G 9/20/86 175

Malmstrom, Carl

Mallard drake pr, structurally EX, 22, RB 5/02/86 80

McGaw, Bob (Havre de Grace, MD)

Bluebill drake, artist stamp, chip on underside of bill, otherwise EX, RB 7/09/85 300

Canada Goose, sm dent on top of tail, otherwise M, J/G 9/19/87 450

Pintail hen, artist stamp, EX condition, RB 7/09/85 200

Redhead drake, artist stamp, M condition, RB 7/09/85 600

McNair, Mark (Old Lyme, CT)

Black Duck, signed, EX orig condition, RWO 2/13/87 375

Goose, early, hollow, Brady style, EX orig pnt, artist initialed, 3 sm tight checks in body, J/G 9/19/87 500

Goose, swimming, orig pnt, minor wear, structurally EX, J/G 9/19/87 500

Mallard drake, slightly turned head, raised cvd wing tips, M condition, rare, J/G 4/23/87 250

Miller, Bob

Canvasback pr, cvd tail feathers/raised wing tips, EX pnt, signed on bottom, RB 8/21/86 100

Morse, Robert (Churches Island, NC)

Greenwinged Teal drake, mounted on wood, EX condition, RB 8/21/86 150

Muellermatt, E.F.

Canada Goose, cvd raised wing tips, highly detailed feather pnt, signed, EX condition, RB 3/11/88 275

Munro, Alan (Shelburne, VT)

Bufflehead drake, age split in neck, otherwise structurally EX, 22, RB 5/02/86 80

Redhead pr, orig pnt, minor flaking, structurally EX, 22, RB5/02/86 225

Pascoe, Robert

Canvasback drake, signed on bottom, EX condition, RB 8/27/87 65

Perdew, Charles (Henry, IL)

Hooded Merganser pr, glass eyes, raised wings, burl base, EX orig pnt w/coat of varnish, rare, 193, RWO 7/02/88 2000

Mallard pr, cvd raised wings, drake has neck crack w/minor flaking, otherwise M, one third-size, 193, RWO 7/02/88, 55% 800

Mallard pr, cvd raised wings, mellow patina, M condition, RWO 7/02/88 1200

Mallard pr, EX & orig, ca 1925, rare, RB 7/09/85 600

Mallard pr, hen is a sleeper, both have cvd raised wings, M & orig condition, RWO 7/02/88 1700

Perdew, Charles
Mallard pr, raised wings, mounted on burl base, varnished by Charles, EX & orig condition, 193, RWO 7/02/88, 65%, $1,600.00.

Pintail pr, flying, detailed feather pnt, M condition, RWO 7/02/88 300

Wood Duck drake, standing, raised primaries, EX pnt by Edna, glued rpr on bill, losses, quarter-size, J/G 4/24/86 1100

Wood Duck pr, cvd raised wings, M condition, both bear brass tags reading Chas H Perdew, Henry IL, 193, RWO 7/02/88 1250

Phillips, Ed

Canada Goose, EX & orig, RB 7/07/87 25

Powers, Cris (Peru, IL)

Mallard pr, EX patina, M condition, ca 1930's, 193, RWO 7/02/88 800

Ramsay, John (Summerside, PEI)

Canada Goose, slightly turned head, feeding, hollow, fine orig pnt, average wear, well preserved, RB 3/06/87 1600

Reed, J. Corbin (Chincoteague, VA)

Black Duck, EX condition, RB 7/07/87 150

Reingold

Canada Goose, raised cvd wing tips, EX condition, RB 7/08/86 60

Greenwinged Teal drake, raised cvd wing tips, EX condition, RB 7/08/86 40

Grouse, flying, some chips at end of cvd feathers on upper wing/rub at end of bill, otherwise EX, RB 8/25/88 175

Mallard drake, raised wing tips, EX condition, RB 7/08/86 25

Quail, flying, minor rub at end of bill, otherwise EX, RB 8/25/88 170

Wood Duck drake, raised cvd wing tips, EX condition, RB 7/08/86 70

Reisinger, J.

Black Duck, preening, EX condition, RB 8/25/88 45

Ries, Al (Chicago, IL)

Mallard pr, copies of his life-size decoys, M condition, both were used as paperweights, 193, RWO 7/02/88 325

Ross, Willie (Chebeague Island, ME)

Redbreasted Merganser drake, EX & orig, rare, RB 7/07/87 100

Redbreasted Merganser pr, G orig pnt, feather combs are somewhat deteriorated/drake has several age splits, RB 3/06/87 3400

Rue, Ron (Cambridge, MD)

Canada Goose, flying, EX form, minor roughage to end of bill, RB 3/11/88 140

Schalk, Ray

Black Duck, signed, sm flake of pnt missing from tip of bill, otherwise M, J/G 9/19/87 70

Black Duck, signed/dated '78, EX condition, RB 6/28/88 .... **50**
Bluebill pr, signed/dated 1976, M condition, J/G 9/19/87 .... **130**
Bluewinged Teal drake, Mason style, signed, M condition, J/G 4/23/87 .... **50**
Bluewinged Teal pr, signed/dated '79, M condition, RB 6/28/88 .... **70**
Canvasback pr, signed, EX condition, RB 6/28/88 .... **75**
Goldeneye drake, Mason style, structurally M, J/G 4/23/87 .... **70**
Greenwinged Teal pr, signed/dated 1979, M condition, RB 6/28/88 .... **70**
Mallard drake, Mason style, M condition, J/G 4/23/87 .... **50**
Mallard pr, cvd in the style of a Mason Premier Grade, M condition, 193, RWO 7/02/88 .... **160**
Mallard pr, signed/dated 1976, EX condition, RB 6/28/88 .... **160**
Pintail pr, signed/dated '77, EX condition, RB 6/28/88 .... **50**
Swan, signed, M condition, J/G 4/23/87 .... **50**
Swan, signed/dated '81, EX condition, RB 6/28/88 .... **65**

Schalk, Roy
Swan, cvd in the style of a Mason Premier Grade, signed/ dated, EX condition, 22, RB 5/02/86, $400.00.

Schmidt, Ben (Detroit, MI)
Bluebill hen, detailed wing/tail cvg, M condition, J/G 4/23/87 .... **150**
Widgeon drake, detailed wing/tail cvg, M condition, quarter-size, J/G 4/23/87 .... **150**
Schroeder, Tom
Widgeon drake, cvd wing tips/primary feathers, EX pnt, ca 1945, RB 7/09/85 .... **250**
Seme, Joe
Bluebill drake, copy of an Ira Hudson, orig pnt, EX condition, 22, RB 5/02/86 .... **50**
Shourds, Harry V. (Tuckerton, NJ)
Black Duck, old pnt, minor wear, well preserved, rare, RB 7/07/87 .... **550**
Mallard pr, signed/dated 1973, EX condition, RB 3/11/88 .... **175**
Skeete, G.
Hudsonian Curlew, allover feather cvg, made in Barbados, dated 1983, EX condition, 22, RB 5/02/86 .... **150**
Smith, Del (Canby, OR)
Goose, slat-body, EX pnt, 36, copy of a Joe Lincoln, RB 2/01/85 .... **250**
Sparre, Stan
Canada Goose, signed, EX condition, RB 9/27/87 .... **45**
Sicklebill Curlew, allover feather cvg, signed/dated, sm chip at end of bill, otherwise EX, half-size, 22, RB 5/02/86 .... **175**
Skimmer pr, signed/dated on bottom, under glass dome, EX condition, 22, RB 5/02/86 .... **125**
Starr, George Ross (Duxbury, MA)
Black Duck, cvd primary feathers, signed/dated 1958, several chips on tail, otherwise EX, one third-size, 22, RB 5/02/86 .... **600**
Black Duck, cvd primary feathers, structurally EX, one third-size, 22, RB 5/02/86 .... **500**
Black Duck, preening, 1 raised cvd wing, structurally EX, one third-size, 22, RB 5/02/86 .... **500**
Black Duck, preening, 1 raised wing, signed/1956, structurally EX, one third-size, 22, RB 5/02/86 .... **800**
Tooker, Jim
Canada Goose, cvd in the style of Ira Hudson, artist's initials in bottom, EX condition, RWO 7/02/88 .... **135**
Canvasback drake, reproduction of a Lem Dudley decoy, EX condition, RWO 7/02/88 .... **75**
Tyler, Lloyd (Crisfield, MD)
Quail, EX condition, RB 8/21/86 .... **75**
Yellowlegs, EX condition, RB 8/21/86 .... **100**
Urie, Capt. Jess (Rock Hall, MD)
Canada Goose, EX orig pnt, tiny nicks in pnt, signed on bottom, RB 7/07/87 .... **80**
Goldeneye pr, hen has minor flaking on breast, otherwise EX, signed on bottom, RB 7/07/87 .... **125**

Pintail pr, signed, EX condition, RB 7/07/87 .... **70**

Van Dyke, Harold

Dunlin, cvd primary feathers, structurally EX, 22, RB 5/02/86 .... **125**

Semipalmated Plover, cvd feather detail on bk of wings, structurally EX, 22, RB 5/02/86 .... **125**

Stilt Sandpiper, cvd primary feathers, minor lifting to pnt on breast, signed/dated, 22, RB 5/02/86 .... **125**

Waite, H.J.

Canada Goose, flying, sm nick on 1 wing, otherwise EX, RB 7/08/86 .... **70**

Walker, Charles (Princeton, IL)

Duckling, hollow, M condition, ca 1930's, rare, 193, RWO 7/02/88 .... **900**

Duckling, hollow, M condition, ca 1930's, RWO 7/02/88, 160% **1300**

Mallard pr, both have neck cracks, hen has pnt smudge on bk, otherwise EX & orig, ca 1930's, rare, 193, RWO 7/02/88 .... **4000**

Mallard pr, drake has minor pnt flaking near breast/sm tail chip/sm ding near tail, EX & orig, 193, RWO 7/02/88, 130% ... **4500**

Mallard pr, EX orig pnt/patina, varnished, checks in neck/hen has minor flaking on neck, 193/200, RWO 7/02/88, 130% **5250**

Pintail hen, preening, cvd raised wings, check in neck/dings on head, otherwise EX & orig, rare, 201, RWO 7/02/88, 175% ... **3500**

Walker, Charles; att (Princeton, IL)

Mallard drake, EX & orig condition, less than 3" in size, 193, RWO 7/02/88 .... **140**

Walker, George

Bluebill drake, EX orig pnt, signed/dated on bottom, EX condition, quarter-size, 22, RB 5/02/86 .... **300**

Canvasback drake, EX pnt, signed/dated on bottom, EX condition, quarter-size, 22, RB 5/02/86 .... **225**

Wallace, Amos (West Point, ME)

Redbreasted Merganser drake, EX & orig, rare, RB 7/07/87 .... **225**

Ward, David (Essex, CT)

Canada Goose, EX condition, RB 7/08/86 .... **40**

Canada Goose, signed/dated 1974, EX condition, RB 6/28/88 .... **65**

Canvasback drake, EX condition, RB 7/08/86 .... **35**

Ward Brothers (Crisfield, MD)

Goldeneye pr, EX orig pnt, quarter-size, RB 7/07/87 .... **650**

Mallard hen, balsa body, minor pnt flaking on top of head, signed/dated 1963, EX & orig condition, RWO 2/12/88 .... **325**

Pintail drake, EX condition, quarter-size, RB 7/07/87 .... **600**

Pintail pr, balsa bodies, raised cvd wing tips, drake's tail has sm chip, otherwise structurally EX, RB 7/08/86 .... **750**

Warfield, Robert and Virginia

Sew-Whet Owl, orig pnt, signed/dated, EX condition, 22, RB 5/02/86 .... **175**

Spotted Sandpiper, EX pnt, signed/dated 1972 on bottom, RB 7/08/86 .... **90**

Waterfield, Curtis

Blackneck Stilt, allover feather cvg, orig pnt, EX condition, 22, RB 5/02/86 .... **300**

Weaver, Janet (Towaco, NJ)

Avocet, preening a feather from its breast, mounted on driftwood, cvd mouth, signed/dated 1979, half-size, RB 9/27/87 .... **130**

Weaver, Janet
Greenwinged Teal drake, cvd featherwork/crossed wing tips, mounted on wood w/cvd frog, EX condition, RB 7/09/85, $550.00.

Wood Duck, preening, detailed cvg/pnt, mounted on driftwood w/sm cvd frog, signed/dated 1977, half-size, RWO 11/11/87 .... **110**

Wendth, Herman (Wisconsin)

Bluebill hen, EX condition, RB 7/09/85 .... **70**

Bufflehead drake, EX condition, RB 7/09/85 .... **100**

Canvasback drake, EX condition, RB 7/09/85 .... **100**

Canvasback drake, swimming, EX condition, RB 7/09/85 .... **125**

Hooded Merganser drake, EX condition, RB 7/09/85 .... **75**

Spoonbill drake, exaggerated bill cvg, structurally EX, RB 7/09/85 .... **75**

Wheeler, Charles (Stratford, CT)

Snipe, finely detailed raised opened wings w/extended tips, full round body, M condition, 4" long, 109, J/G 4/23/87, 65% **1300**

Snipe, raised joined wings, finely-blended pnt, M condition, 4" long, 109, J/G 4/23/87, 55% **1100**

Wheeler, Charles
Wood Thrush, well detailed cvd wings w/extended tips, M condition, 4" long, 109, J/G 4/23/87, $500.00.

Winters, George
Goldeneye drake, artist stamp, M condition, J/G 4/24/86 .... **220**
Redhead drake, M condition, stamped Made for Abercrombie & Fitch, ca 1935, J/G 4/23/87 .... **150**
Zachman, John F. (Michigan)
Canvasback drake, EX pnt & condition, quarter-size, 22, RB 5/02/86 .... **200**

Other Decorative Carvings

Adams, Frank (West Tisbury, MA)
Mallard drake paperweight, artist stamp, EX orig condition, 39, RB 7/08/86 80
Alsop, Chip
Canada Goose, stick-up, EX condition, a copy of the Sam Soper Watch Gander, RB 6/28/88 150
Anderlik, Joe
Blackbellied Plover, EX pnt & condition, 22, RB 5/02/86 150
Bieber, Bruce (Cape May, NJ)
Curlew, preening, EX orig pnt, artist brand, bill has been reglued, RB 8/25/88 100
Birchler
Black Duck, flying, individual feathers have sm chips & age splits, otherwise EX, 185, RB 3/06/87 1100
Birk, Will (Bridgeport, CT)
Canvasback pr, relief feather cvg, detailed pnt, ca 1962, RWO 7/04/87 1100

Birk, Will
Pintail pr, relief cvg, detailed pnt,
ca 1963, RWO 7/04/87, $1,100.00.

Black, Roy
Brant, hissing, Nathan Cobb style, RWB cvd in bottom, EX & orig condition, one third-size, RB 8/25/88 100
Brant, hissing, RWB cvd in bottom, EX & orig condition, quarter-size, RB 8/25/88, 25% 100
Curlew, feeding, cvd raised wings, RWB cvd in bottom, EX & orig condition, RB 8/25/88 125
Redbreasted Merganser drake, hollow w/raised wing detail, signed/dated 1976, EX & orig condition, RB 8/25/88, 30% 200
Snow Goose, stick-up, cvd feather detail on wing tips/tail, RWB cvd in bottom, EX condition, RB 8/25/88, 60% 300
Buchanan, Charles
Surf Scoter, EX cvg w/cvd primaries, EX condition, 39, RB 7/08/86 200
Burr, Elisha; att
Wood Duck drake, standing, cvd crossed wing tips/primaries, NM, life-size, acquired from Burr in 1970, 40, RB 8/21/86 2200
Carlock, Thomas W.
American Bittner, highly detailed cvg/pnt, bill has been reglued, RB 3/11/88 650
Clapper Rail, EX cvd feather detail, EX condition, RB 3/11/88, 80% 400
Greenwinged Teal pr, raised wing tips, highly detailed feather cvg/pnt, drake's bill reglued, otherwise EX, RB 3/11/88 600
Kingfisher, EX feather cvg, several sm nicks at crest, otherwise EX, RB 3/11/88 250
Wood Duck pr, exceptional feather cvg/pnt, drake's crest has been cleanly reglued; hen's legs are loose, RB 3/11/88, 33% 500
Carney, Armand (Tuckerton, NJ)
American Oyster Catcher, signed/dated 1971 on base, EX condition, RB 3/11/88 150
Curlew, preening, EX condition, RB 3/11/88 80
Carter, Paul
Redbreasted Merganser drake, artist signed/branded, EX condition, copy of a George Huey decoy, RB 6/28/88, 37% 150
Redbreasted Merganser pr, artist brand, EX condition, copies of Keyes Chadwick's work, RB 6/28/88, 35% 175
Wood Duck drake, artist brand, EX condition, copy of a Joe Lincoln decoy, RB 6/28/88, 62% 250
Chaido, Thomas (Spring Valley, IL)
Pintail drake, sleeping, signed on bottom, M condition, J/G 4/24/86 275
Chesser, Grayson (Chincoteague, VA)
Brant, hollow, EX & orig condition, RB 6/28/88 175
Collins, Martin (Bridgeport, MA)
Black Duck, preening, cvd primary feathers, branded, EX condition, copy of an Elmer Crowell decoy, RB 6/28/88 225
Redbreasted Merganser drake, cvd crossed primary feathers, EX condition, copy of an Elmer Crowell decoy, RB 6/28/88 175
Conklin, Hurley (Manahawkin, NJ)
Crow, artist brand, EX & orig condition, RB 8/25/88 110
Sanderling, EX orig pnt, made as a mantel bird, RWO 11/11/87 50

Yellowlegs, EX orig pnt, made as a mantel bird, RWO 11/11/87 .... **80**

Cranford, Ralph (Long Island)

Bluebill drake, flying, may have old touchup on head, otherwise EX, RWO 7/02/88 .... **450**

Crowell, A. Elmer (East Harwich, MA)

Bartailed Godwit or Western Willet, early, EX cvg & feather pnt, tack eyes, oval brand, mantel cvg, NM, RB 3/06/87 .... **9000**

Black Duck, early, preening, raised cvd wing tips, oval brand, NM condition, life-size mantel cvg, RB 7/07/87 .... **22000**

Black Duck, preening, cvd tail feathers/primaries, artist brand, minor rstr, life-size mantel cvg, RB 3/06/87, 58% **17500**

Black Duck ash tray, orig pnt, minor crazing, oval brand/paper label, EX condition, half-size, J/G 9/19/87 .... **1200**

Black Duck weathervane, early, flying, orig pnt, head broken off & reglued, 1 eye missing, rare, RWO 11/11/87 .... **3750**

Blackbellied Plover, running, clam shell base, cvd tail feathers, minor rstr, 39, RB 7/08/86 .... **9000**

Blackbellied Plover, slightly lifted wing tips, NM orig pnt, full-size, J/G 9/19/87 .... **7250**

Blackbellied Plover, varnish prof removed by K DeLong, touchup to bill/wing tips, oval brand, life-size, RB 6/28/88 .... **5750**

Crowell, A. Elmer

Blue Jay, early, NM orig well-blended pnt, reglued chip, tiny rstr on bill, well preserved, mantel size, J/G 9/19/87, $2,400.00.

Blue Jay, oak leaf/acorn relief cvd base, branded/artist signed, reglued tail chip, otherwise NM, life-size, RB 6/28/88 .... **2200**

Bluebill drake, full body, cvd crossed wing tips/primaries/tail feathers, EX orig pnt, NM condition, RB 3/06/87, 75% **15000**

Bluebill pr, EX feather pnt & cvg, weighted as bookends, NM condition, half-size, RB 3/06/87 .... **2000**

Bluebird, M condition, 57/104, J/G 4/23/87 .... **500**

Canada Goose, hissing, stretched-out wings, NM orig pnt, artist brand, sm rpr, life-size, ca 1915, 8, RWO 7/05/86, 200% **150000**

Canada Goose head, half-cvd, rectangular brand on bk, EX condition, RB 6/28/88 .... **300**

Canada Goose weathervane, flying, old pnt, weathered/worn w/traces of orig pnt, J/G 9/19/87 .... **1200**

Chickadee on branch, NM orig pnt, rectangular stamp/dated 1941, structurally EX, J/G 9/19/87 .... **2950**

Common Tern, cvd wings, artist signed, rectangular brand, sm flake on bk of head, otherwise EX, half-size, RB 6/28/88 .... **2500**

Common Tern, cvd wings w/4 extended tail & wing tips, base cvd as oyster shell, rectangular brand, NM, RB 7/07/87 .... **6250**

Curlew, early, cvd primary feathers, wire legs, EX orig pnt, oval brand, rstr wing tips/half-inch bill rpl, RB 3/11/88 .... **9000**

Goldeneye drake, early, EX orig pnt, tiny nick at end of tail, twice the size of a miniature, RB 7/09/85 .... **975**

Goose weathervane, flying, touchup to black areas/head/tail/breast, white is orig, structurally EX, rare, RWO 7/04/87 .... **7000**

Killdeer, standing, fine cvd detail, detailed pnt pattern, rectangular brand/signed, NM condition, J/G 9/20/86 .... **9000**

Least Sandpiper, artist signed/branded, left eye cracked, cleaned by K DeLong, EX & orig, life-size, RB 6/28/88, 70% **2500**

Lesser Yellowlegs, early, EX orig pnt, minor flaking on head, rectangular brand, bill rstr by DeLong, 39, RB 7/08/86 .... **5000**

Mallard bookends, cvd crossed wing tips/tail feathers, rectangular brand, EX condition, half-size, RB 7/08/86 .... **4500**

Mallard drake ash tray, fluted tail, unstamped, well cvd, NM condition, J/G 9/19/87 .... **1700**

Pine Sparrow, M condition, 57/104, J/G 4/23/87 .... **375**

Piping Plover, M pnt, oval brand, minor repair to gesso around feet, life-size, RB 7/07/87 .... **6000**

Piping Plover, signed/rectangular brand, EX condition, mantel cvg, 39, RB 7/08/86, 250% **5000**

Redbreasted Merganser weathervane, early, worn/weathered, 1 eye/parts of both feet missing, RWO 7/05/86 .... **20000**

Ringnecked Pheasant, head cocked/turned slightly, EX pnt, signed/dated 1932, NM condition, life-size, RB 7/07/87 .... **12000**

Rose Grosbeak, M condition, 57/104, J/G 4/23/87 .... **400**

Sandpiper, finely detailed pnt in NM condition, rectangular brand, structurally EX, mantel size, J/G 9/19/87, 75% 1900
Sandpiper, signed, EX condition, mantel cvg, 40, RB 7/08/86, 170% 4250

Crowell, A. Elmer
Tern, flying, fine dry orig pnt, structurally EX, rare, life-size, RWO 7/06/86, $3,750.00.

Tern, flying, fine orig pnt, bill/wing tips prof rstr by Kenneth DeLong, rare, life-size, RB 12/06/85 1350
Tern, NM orig pnt, artist brand, half of bill/wing tips broken off, gesso feet missing, mantel size, J/G 9/19/87, 137% 1250
Tern, raised cvd wings w/extended tips, artist brand, M condition, mantel size, J/G 9/19/87 4000
Vue, M condition, 57/104, J/G 4/23/87 350
Wilson Plover, cvd tail feathers, superb feathered pnt pattern, rectangular brand, life-size, RB 7/07/87 6500
Wood Duck drake, slightly turned head, cvd tail feathers/wing tips, rasped crest, NM pnt, artist brand, RB 3/06/87, 33% 6500
Woodcock, head tucked, pnt grass on base, artist signed, crazing on body/bill, otherwise NM, half-size, RB 6/28/88 2800
Yellowlegs, NM orig pnt, paper label, minor chips on feet & tip of bill, full-size mantel cvg, 131, J/G 9/19/87 5000
Yellowlegs, preening, mantel cvg, EX condition, RB 7/08/86 4000
Yellowlegs, preening, raised cvd wings, open bill w/feather in mouth, EX pnt, rectangular brand, RB 7/07/87 10500
Yellowlegs, running, EX feather detail & form, oval brand, NM condition, mantel cvg, RB 3/06/87 6000

Daisy, Delbert (Chincoteague, VA)
Greenwinged teal pr, hollow cvd hen; drake retains show label, both branded 'Cigar,' NM condition, RB 12/06/85 550
Redbreasted Merganser pr, hollow, drake: comb pnt/cvd crest; hen: EX feathering, signed/dated 1974, RWO 11/11/87, 140% 1400

Dobbins, Frank (Jonesport, ME)
Surf Scoter, preening, cvd wing tips, M condition, RB 8/27/87 100

Doviak, Gary (Amsterdam, NY)
Hooded Merganser pr, M condition, both have won several gunning class contests, RWO 2/12/88 375

Dudley, Lem or Lee (Knott's Island, NC)
Canvasback head, mounted on a hardwood block, crack running through neck, otherwise EX, ca 1890, RWO 7/05/85, 650% 2300

Eastland, Tim (Old Lyme, CT)
Sanderling, cvd crossed wing tips, signed on base, EX condition, RB 8/25/88 65

Finney, Frank (Pungo, VA; Virginia Beach, VA)
Canvasback drake, cvd in the style of Alvirah Wright, made to look old, RWO 7/02/88 175
Swan, contemporary copy of a North Carolina Swan, antiqued in every detail, M condition, RB 3/06/87 1500
Wood Duck pr, flying, outstanding/orig, 'FF' scratched into the glass eyes, RWO 7/05/85 2100

Franta, Robert (Amherst, OH)
Greenwinged Teal pr, hollow, superb detailed feather cvg/pnt, RWO 2/12/88, 53% 800

Pintail, hollow w/highly detailed feather cvg/pnt, cvd as a contest bird winning numerous championships, RWO 2/12/88 .... **1100**
Garton, John B. (Smith's Falls, Ont)
Black Duck, slightly turned head, hollow w/raised cvd primaries, M condition, 91, J/G 4/24/86 .... **1320**
Whimbrel, signed on bottom, EX condition, RB 8/25/88 .... **325**
Gibian, William (Accomac, VA)
Dove, cvd primary feathers, artist signed, EX condition, RB 6/28/88 .... **350**
Golden Plover, feeding, cvd primaries, signed, EX condition, RB 7/08/86 .... **250**
Heron, mounted on driftwood, EX condition, RB 8/21/86 .... **200**
Knot pr, mounted on driftwood, EX condition, RB 8/21/86 .... **300**
Passenger Pigeon, artist signed, EX condition, RB 6/28/88 .... **225**

Gibian, William
Pintail drake, preening, EX primary cvg/scratch feather pnt, signed, RB 8/21/86, $1,100.00.

Ruddy Turnstone, feeding, cvd primary feathers, signed on bottom, EX condition, RB 8/25/88 .... **200**
Ruddy Turnstone, flying, full body, feather detail on wings/tail, signed, EX condition, RB 8/21/86 .... **325**
Ruddy Turnstone, head extended & turned slightly left, artist signed, EX condition, RB 6/28/88, 50% **200**
Ruddy Turnstone, head slightly turned to the right, cvd wings, EX condition, RB 6/28/88 .... **350**
Wood Duck drake, turned head, cvd wing tips, signed, EX condition, RB 7/08/86 .... **450**
Wood Duck pr, raised cvd wing tips/tail feathers, signed, EX condition, RB 8/21/86 .... **1000**
Woodcock, running, cvd primary feathers, artist signed, EX condition, RB 6/28/88 .... **300**
Gleason, Ken
Whitewinged Scoter, hollow, cvd for competition, M condition, 211, RWO 2/12/88 .... **450**
Green, Richard
Yellowlegs, EX condition, RB 3/11/88 .... **75**
Haertel, Harold (Dundee, IL)
Horned Grebe, signed/dated 1968, EX & orig condition, 189, RB 6/28/88 .... **600**
Pied-Bill Grebe, signed/dated 1968, EX condition, 189, RB 6/28/88 .... **850**
Pied-Bill Grebe, swimming, signed/dated 1968, M condition, J/G 9/20/86 .... **700**
Western Grebe, preening, precise wing tip cvg, fine feather pnt, identified/signed/dated 1974, M, J/G 4/24/86, 145% **1320**
Hancock, Herb
Canada Goose, artist signed/branded, EX condition, RB 6/28/88, 50% **150**
Hand, Jamie (Cape May, NJ)
Blue Heron, EX condition, 189, RB 6/28/88 .... **50**
Swan, hollow, EX condition, RB 6/28/88 .... **700**
Harris, Ken (Woodville, NY)
Harlequin Duck, detailed cvg/pnt, artist brand, RWO 7/02/88 .... **450**
Hooded Merganser drake, detailed feather pnt/cvg, artist brand, M condition, RWO 7/02/88 .... **300**
Mallard hen bookends, EX condition, RB 8/21/86 .... **150**
Havel, Bob
Bufflehead drake, highly detailed feather cvg/pnt, M condition, RWO 2/12/88 .... **160**
Hawthorne, Davey (Salisbury, MD)
Kildeer, mounted on section of limb, signed/dated, EX condition, RB 8/21/86 .... **275**
Least Sandpiper, EX condition, near life-size, RB 7/07/87, 130% **400**
Ruddy Turnstone, mounted on driftwood chip, signed/dated, EX condition, RB 8/21/86 .... **300**
Woodcock, extremely fine cvg w/delicate pnt pattern, EX condition, RB 8/27/87 .... **175**
Hayden, Larry (Farmington, MI)
Wood Duck drake, hollow, signed/1st in World Championship Decoy Contest, 1971, Salisbury MD,' EX, RB 7/08/86, 140% **3500**
Higgins, Reid
Tern, feeding minnow in its bill to a nestling, cvd primaries, extended wings, signed, EX condition, RB 7/08/86 .... **300**

Holland, Mark (Cape Cod, MA)
Greater Yellowlegs, preening, feather in its bill, well executed, EX condition, RB 7/09/85, 70% 700
Pheasant pr w/7 chicks, mounted on driftwood, unsigned, EX condition, RB 12/06/85 400
Quail, signed on bottom, EX condition, RB 7/07/87 300
Quail pr, mounted on driftwood, signed/dated 1974, EX condition, RB 9/27/87 250
Ringnecked Plover pr, mounted on wood base, signed/dated, EX condition, RB 8/21/86 250
Ruffed Grouse, detailed cvg & pnt, mounted on driftwood, signed on bottom, EX condition, RB 12/06/85 600
Sandpiper pr, mounted on mounded base, signed/dated, EX condition, RB 8/21/86 175

Holland, Mark
Wood Duck pr, turned heads, open wings, fine pnt detail to feather/wing cvg, NM & orig, J/G 9/20/86, 25%, $600.00.

Hoppe, Frank (Lincoln, NE)
Ruddy Duck, cvd w/Ruddy chick on bk, M condition, this is the only Ruddy Duck made by Hoppe, RWO 2/12/88, 48% 190
Hudson, Ira (Chincoteague, VA)
Widgeon drake, flying, cvd feet, intricate scratch pnt, NM condition, three quarter-size, J/G 4/24/86 3025
Iski, Jules
Black Duck, hollow, EX orig pnt, inscribed on bottom: My First Decoy/1970, RB 7/07/87 100
Jester, Doug (Chincoteague, VA)
Mallard drake, flying, 1 wing cleanly broken off & reglued, otherwise EX, J/G 9/20/86 60
Redbreasted Merganser pr, flying, NM pnt, drake's foot has been broken off & reglued, RB 8/21/86 350
Johnson, Lloyd (Crisfield,NJ)
Sanderling pr, EX & orig condition, RWO 7/02/88 100
Johnson, Michael (Inman, SC)
Pintail drake, artist signed/dated 1988, M condition, RWO 7/02/88 80
Kean, Louis L. (Hopewell, VA)
Widgeon drake, hollow, highly detailed feather/relief cvg w/raised primaries, EX, 212, RWO 2/12/88, 70% 1050
Kerr, Bob (Smith's Falls, Ont)
Bufflehead pr, hen has minor repair to tip of bill, otherwise M, ca 1965, RWO 7/04/87 650
Mallard drake, detailed feather cvg/raised primaries, artist brand/dated 1972, M condition, RWO 7/04/87 475
Pintail drake, slightly turned head, detailed wing/tail cvg, raised crossed wing tips, EX comb pnt, 91, J/G 4/24/86 990
Wood Duck, detailed cvg of primaries/wings, artist brand, M condition, RWO 7/02/88 650
Knorr, Dick and Tallie
Avocet, signed/dated 1982, EX condition, RB 8/21/86 100
Langlais, Armand (St. Lawrence River area)
Rail, EX condition, RB 9/27/87 125

Woodcock, sm leaf has tiny nick, otherwise EX, life-size, RB 7/08/86 350
Lapham, James (Dennisport, MA)
Piping Plover, slight discoloration from varnish, otherwise EX, signed on bottom, half-size, RB 7/08/86 140
Libensperger, Robert (Levittown, PA)
Bluebill drake, EX orig condition, signed/dated 1968, inscribed: 2nd place LI Broadbill, RB 7/07/87 450
Bluebill drake, hollow, signed/dated 1970, EX & orig, RB 7/07/87 200
Bufflehead drake, head tucked, signed/inscribed: 3rd place NY 1967, EX & orig, RB 7/07/87 250
Canvasback drake, EX orig pnt, minor flaking on sides, signed/dated 1967, RB 7/07/87 225
Redhead drake, hollow, signed/dated on bottom, EX condition, RB 7/07/87 200
Malmstrom, Carl
Pintail drake, flying, wall mount, EX condition, 22, RB 5/02/86 375
Manning, Robert (Empire, MI)
Snow Goose, hollow, artist brand, M condition, RWO 2/12/88 190
Mason Factory
Yellowlegs or Willet, tack eyes, orig pnt, average wear, structurally sound, 193, RWO 7/02/88, 55% 450
McGloughlin, John (Bordentown, NJ)
Old Squaw drake, signed on bottom, EX & orig, RB 7/07/87 600
McNair, Mark (Old Lyme, CT)
Blackbellied Plover, signed, EX condition, RB 12/06/85 550
Bluewinged Teal drake, hollow, signed on bottom, EX condition, RB 12/06/85 750
Brant, hollow, signed on bottom, EX condition, cvd in manner of Nathan Cobb, rare, RB 12/06/85 750
Bufflehead drake, hollow, artist signed, EX condition, cvd in manner of Lee Dudley, RB 6/28/88, 62% 500
Curlew, Cobb Island style, cvd eyes/wings, signed M on bottom, age split in bottom, otherwise EX, RB 6/28/88 550
Curlew, cvd wings, artist signed, EX & orig condition, RB 6/28/88 550
Curlew, cvd wings, signed on bottom, EX condition, 22, RB 5/02/86 1050
Curlew, feeding, cvd wings, artist signed, EX condition, RB 6/28/88 700
Curlew, feeding, EX & orig, RWO 11/11/87 750
Curlew, running, natural wood, signed/dated 1973, chip on underside of bill, RB 12/06/85 350
Curlew, signed, EX condition, RB 12/06/85, 125% 1250
Dove, hollow, signed on bottom, EX condition, RB 12/06/85 500
Gadwall hen, hollow, signed on bottom, EX condition, RB 12/06/85 1200
Godwit, head & neck are extended outward & turned to right, cvd M on bottom, EX condition, 22, RB 5/02/86 700
Greenwinged Teal Drake, hollow, artist signed, EX condition, cvd in manner of John Blair, RB 6/28/88 750
Jack Snipe, artist signed, EX & orig condition, RB 6/28/88 600
Jack Snipe, signed on bottom, EX condition, RB 12/06/85 300
Knot, raised cvd wing tips, signed on bottom, EX & orig, RB 7/07/87 700

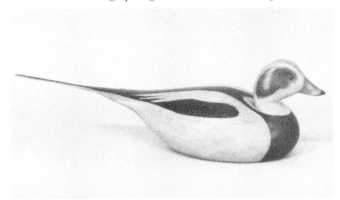

McNair, Mark
Old Squaw drake, signed on bottom, EX condition, 22, RB 5/02/86, 125%, $1,500.00.

Peep, signed on bottom, EX condition, RB 12/06/85 700
Pintail drake, hollow, signed on bottom, EX condition, RB 12/06/85, 145% 1450
Ruddy Duck, cvd in manner of Knots Island carvers, EX condition, RB 12/06/85 850
Ruddy Duck drake, artist signed, EX condition, done in the manner of John Williams, RB 6/28/88 1250
Ruddy Duck drake, signed, EX condition, copied from the work of Lee Dudley, RB 7/08/86 800
Tern, artist signed, EX & orig condition, RB 6/28/88 300
Tern, signed, EX condition, RB 12/06/85 450
Widgeon drake, hollow, superb comb feather pnt, marked McNair, EX & orig condition, RB 6/28/88 1050
Willet, artist signed, EX condition, RB 6/28/88 450
Wood Duck drake, signed on bottom, EX condition, RB 12/06/85 900

Yellowlegs, feeding, signed, EX condition, RB 12/06/85 .... **400**
Miller, Bob
   Bufflehead pr, orig pnt, signed & dated on bottom of each, EX condition, 22, RB 5/02/86 .... **650**
   Canada Geese pr encountering a skunk, inscribed/signed/dated, minor damage to legs, otherwise EX, 22, RB 5/02/22 .... **200**
   Hooded Merganser pr, orig pnt, signed on bottom, EX condition, 22, RB 5/02/86 .... **550**
   Old Squaw pr, beautifully cvd, signed/dated 1975, EX condition, 22, RB 5/02/86 .... **250**
Miller, Clarence (Brockville, Ont)
   Goldeneye pr, detailed relief cvg on bk/around bills, signed/dated 1970, M condition, RWO 7/02/88, 130% **1150**
Morse, Harold
   Mallard pr, orig pnt, signed/dated, EX condition, 22, RB 5/02/86 .... **350**
Murray, Dave (Salisbury, MD)
   Sanderling, EX feather cvg, mounted on driftwood, EX condition, RB 8/21/86 .... **200**
Newell, Tom (Gig Harbor, WA)
   Widgeon pr, hollow, drake was best species at Santa Ana Decoy show/hen was best at Michigan Decoy show, RWO 2/12/88, 78% . **1100**
Oler, William
   Curlew, cvd wings, branded on bottom, EX condition, 22, RB 5/02/86 .... **175**
Orcutt
   Curlew, feeding, exaggerated, fine orig pnt, minor flaking, artist stamp, 39, RB 7/08/86 .... **150**
   Curlew, head turned to left, artist stamp, EX condition, RB 7/08/86 .... **225**
Pittman, C.F.
   Pied-Bill Grebe, head has been broken off & reglued, RB 3/11/88 .... **175**
Polite, Jim
   Bluewinged Teal pr, superb feather detail, signed/dated 1974, EX condition, RB 3/11/88, 75% **300**
   Greenwinged Teal pr, EX feather detail, signed/dated 1974, lower half of hen's bill broken off, otherwise EX, RB 3/11/88 .... **200**
   Pied Bill Grebe, cvd w/minnow in the mouth, signed/dated 1974, EX condition, RB 3/11/88 .... **325**
Pratt, Norris (Kemblesville, PA)
   Sea Gull, raised cvd wing tips, signed/dated 1967, EX condition, RB 9/27/87 .... **225**
Reed, Corbin (Chincoteague, VA)
   Black Duck, relief cvg on tail/wings, EX & orig condition, RWO 2/12/88 .... **475**
   Canvasback pr, hollow w/feet cvd along side, detailed pnt, artist signed/branded, M condition, RWO 2/12/88, 167% **1250**
Rhodes, David (Absecon, NJ)
   Crow, minor check at tip of bill, otherwise EX, RB 3/11/88 .... **75**
   Curlew, signed on base, minor age split in neck, otherwise EX, RB 3/11/88 .... **120**
   Hudsonian Curlew, signed on underside of tail, EX condition, RB 3/11/88 .... **250**

Rhodes, David
Owl w/crow, EX condition, R/B
3/11/88, 75%, $900.00.

Semipalmated Plover, EX condition, RB 3/11/88 .... **80**
Semipalmated Sandpiper, EX condition, RB 3/11/88 .... **225**

Yellowlegs, EX condition, RB 3/11/88 150
Schaber, Bob
Bufflehead drake, EX condition, RB 3/11/88 200
Shoveller hen, EX condition, RB 3/11/88 275
Scheeler, Ken
Old Squaw drake, inserted tail feathers, hollow w/highly detailed featherwork, 213, RWO 2/12/88 900
Schifferl, Lou (Green Bay, WI)
Blackbellied Plover, EX condition, 39, RB 7/08/86 275
Redbreasted Merganser pr, cvd as exaggerated copies of the Lothrop Holmes Mergansers, EX condition, 39, RB 7/08/86 ... 900
Rock Ptarmigan, EX condition, 39, RB 7/08/86 300
Tern, EX condition, 39, 7/08/86 450
Schmiedlin, Jim (Bradford Woods, PA)
Bluewinged Teal drake, slightly turned head, hollow w/wing/tail cvg, NM orig pnt, structurally EX, rare, J/G 4/24/86 ... 385
Seme, Joe
Pintail drake, copy of an Ira Hudson, orig pnt, EX condition, 22, RB 5/02/86 60
Shourds, Harry V. (Tuckerton, NJ)
Curlew, signed/dated 1971 on base, EX condition, RB 3/11/88 160
Siloski, Jerry
Crow, cvd wings, head turned slightly to right, EX condition, 22, RB 5/02/86 425
Dove, hollow, removable dovetailed head, pin through the body, EX condition, 22, RB 5/02/86 250

Smart, Raymond E. (Peabody, MA)
Buffleheads, 3 flying, wing/tail feathers individually cvd/inserted, outstanding & orig, 137, RWO 7/05/86, 150%, $3,000.00.

Smith, Holger G. (Massachusetts)
Gadwall hen, signed/dated 1974, artist brand, EX condition, RB 6/28/88 100
Spiron, Charles (Goldsboro, NC)
Pintail pr, artist signed, EX condition, RB 6/28/88, 56% 225
Redbreasted Merganser hen, orig pnt, minor wear, artist brand, EX condition, J/G 9/20/86 195
Sprankle, Jim
Hooded Merganser drake, cvd feet, highly detailed featherwork, EX condition, 214, RWO 2/12/88 2950
Stanmire, E.C.
Black Duck, preening, cvd raised wings, end of 1 wing tip has been reglued, some fragments of black missing, RB 3/11/88 ... 200
Sterling, Lloyd (Crisfield, MD)
Godwit, balsa body, EX condition, made as a mantel bird, RWO 11/11/87 50
Yellowlegs, bill has been reglued, otherwise NM, ca 1940, rare, RB 8/25/88 150
Stump, George
Hooded Merganser, hollow, G Stump cvd in bottom, EX orig condition/nicely aged, in style of Harry Shourds, RWO 2/12/88 ... 175
Thornes, Ira
Hooded Merganser drake, orig pnt, EX condition, 22, RB 5/02/86 50
Tooker, Jim
Redbreasted Merganser, hollow, racy form, JET cvd in bottom, EX & orig condition, RWO 2/12/88 235
Tyler, Lloyd (Crisfield, MD)
Dove, early, G orig pnt, some putty flaked away where 1 leg meets body, otherwise structurally sound, RWO 11/06/85 ... 130

Wallace, Ed (Galena, MD)
Canvasback pr, highly detailed feather cvg, signed/dated 1984, M condition, RWO 2/12/88 .... **800**
Pintail pr, highly detailed cvg/pnt, artist signed/dated 1985, M condition, RWO 2/12/88, 60% **600**

Ward, David (Essex, CT)
Crow, artist brand/dated 1977, EX condition, RB 8/25/88 .... **80**
Curlew, cvd wings, signed/dated 1978, inscribed: To George Ross Starr, EX condition, 22, RB 5/02/86 .... **500**

Ward, Lem (Crisfield, MD)
Canada Goose head, superb cvg, EX orig pnt, minor flaking, sm nick on underside of bill/age split in neck, RB 8/21/86 .... **300**
Canvasback hen, hollow, head slightly turned right, cvd primaries, EX feather pnt, inscribed/dated 1973/poem, RB 3/06/87 .... **3500**
Mallard hen, early, raised wings/primaries, fine orig pnt, signed/dated 1930, leg missing, RWO 7/04/87 .... **4500**

Ward Brothers (Crisfield, MD)
American Eagle, head turned left, facial/feather details, on limb, rotating stand, NM, life-size, w/letter, RB 3/06/87 .... **16000**
Black Duck, standing, highly detailed wing/feather cvg, cvd webbed ft, NM orig pnt, glued crack in ft, J/G 9/20/86, 50% **4000**
Bluewinged Teal drake, EX wing/tail feather cvg, inscribed: Anis Discors SFD, nickel label/dated 1918, NM, RB 8/21/86 .... **2600**
Bufflehead pr, turned heads, signed/dated 1966, EX & orig, RB 3/06/87 .... **2250**
Canada Goose, hollow, content, full body/raised wing tips, EX feather pnt, inscribed: To Percell Jones/poem, RB 3/06/87 .... **6000**
Canvasback pr, flying, mounted on a wooden plaque, signed/dated 1952, EX orig condition, RWO 7/05/85 .... **8500**
Greenwinged Teal pr, standing, EX orig pnt shows signs of age, stamped/signed, structurally VG, RWO 7/05/86, 70% **1800**
Mallard drake, outstretched wings, mounted on a hardwood block, signed LT/dated 1936, superb & orig, RWO 7/05/85 .... **8000**

Wargas, Charles
Canvasback drake, cvd wing tips, EX condition, 189, RB 6/28/88 .... **75**

Weiler, Milton
Sanderling, EX pnt pattern, signed, fine structural condition, rare, RWO 7/05/85 .... **1000**

Wheeler, Charles (Stratford, CT)

Wheeler, Charles
Passenger Pigeon, raised wings, outstanding pnt w/EX patina, only 1 of specie existent, NM, 27, J/G 9/20/86, $15,000.00.

Rail, mounted on wood, fine orig pnt, defined feather pnt, some flakes missing from feet, rare, RB 7/09/85 .... **1500**

Wheeler, Chauncey (Alexandria Bay, NY)
Dove, inserted metal tail, detailed featherwork, M orig condition, rare, RWO 7/02/88, 155% **5500**
Mallard, flying, EX orig pnt, 1 side as a drake/1 as a hen, check on bottom, otherwise EX, rare, 193, RWO 7/02/88, 210% **9500**

White, Roy (Knott's Island, NC)
Mallard drake, orig pnt, structurally sound, RWO 2/12/88 .... **70**

Whittington, Hector (Oglesby, IL)
Bluebill drake, sleeping, M orig pnt w/rpt on white area on sides/bottom, dated 1969, structurally EX, J/G 4/24/86 495
Coot, artist stamp/signed/dated 1976 twice, M condition, J/G 4/24/86 440
Greenwinged Teal drake, highly detailed feather pnt, artist stamp/dated 1978, M condition, J/G 4/24/86 330
Pintail pr, slightly turned heads, highly detailed feather pnt, stamped/dated 1975, J/G 4/24/86 1320
Widgeon pr, slightly turned heads, dated 1975, M condition, rare, J/G 4/24/86 1430
Wilson, Gus (South Portland, ME)
Robin, EX orig pnt, pnt prof rstr by Wendell Gilley, ca 1932, RWO 7/05/85 600
Yardrau, J.J.
Canada Goose, flying, fine feather cvg, wall mount, EX condition, 22, RB 5/02/86 225

Decoys by Unknown Artists

Many early carvers rarely signed their work, yet these early examples are often easily attributed to a specific artist through the study of certain characteristics such as tail carving, paint patterns, head positions, general size and materials used in their construction.

The following are photographs of some of the finest decoys by unidentified carvers that sold over the past four seasons. They are sorted first by species, then from the highest to the lowest price realized within those groupings.

Black Duck, sleeping, raised wing cvg/incised feather cvg on bk, G orig pnt, average wear, chip out of tail, otherwise EX, from Greenport LI, RWO 7/05/85, $5,500.00.

Black Duck, sleeping, old rpt shows flaking/wear, in-use neck rpr, from Stratford CT, 44/22, RB 5/02/86, $2,750.00.

Black Duck, cvd wings, EX feather pnt shows average wear, initials LFW cvd in bottom, 21, RB 7/07/87, $825.00.

Black Duck, natural cork body, orig pnt, average wear, from Long Island, RB 7/08/86, 200%, $500.00.

Black Duck, hollow, orig pnt, average flaking, well preserved, from New Jersey, RB 7/08/86, $475.00.

Bluebill pr, hollow, cvd eyes, orig pnt, minimal wear, both branded AH Cobb, sm under-bill chips, RB 2/01/85, $2,500.00.

Bluebill drake, preening, orig pnt, average wear, structurally G, from Virginia, RWO 11/06/85, 55%, $1,400.00.

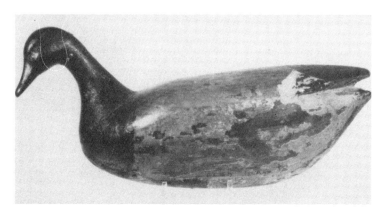

Brant, retains orig bill, very worn old pnt, from Cobb Island VA, RWO 7/05/85, $3,000.00.

Brant, EX orig pnt, minor wear, from Long Island, 39, RB 7/08/86, 140%, $1,000.00.

Canada Goose, head turned right & downward, EX orig pnt, average flaking/wear, tiny chip front of neck, from Hog Island, RB 7/08/86, $1,800.00.

Canada Goose, preening, hollow, fine old pnt, average wear, 88, RB 8/21/86, $1,300.00.

Canada Goose, flying, detailed feather cvg, M condition, RWO 11/06/85, $260.00.

Canada Goose, stick-up, much relief cvg, M condition, RWO 11/06/85, $250.00.

Canvasback drake, old working rpt, heavy flaking/wear, club label dated 1888-1893, 2 club brands, 21, RB 2/01/85, 220%, $1,100.00.

215

Coot, hollow, cvd wing tips, EX orig pnt, well preserved, from Nova Scotia, RB 8/21/86, 65%, $200.00.

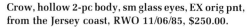

Crow, hollow 2-pc body, sm glass eyes, EX orig pnt, from the Jersey coast, RWO 11/06/85, $250.00.

Curlew, cvd 'V' tail, fine orig pnt, average wear, ls, 22/44, RB 5/02/86, $5,500.00.

Curlew, cvd eyes, orig pnt, moderate wear, rpl bill, tail chip, ls, from Cape Cod MA, RB 5/02/86, 22, $1,000.00.

Dove, pnt very cracked/crazed, tips of wings have been rpr/half of bill rpl, exceptional, early, from Long Island, RWO 7/05/85, $650.00.

Eider drake, inlet head, cvd w/mussel in open bill, G orig pnt, average wear, roughness on bill, from Bailey's Island ME, 22/44/45/46/47, RB 5/02/86, 165%, $50,000.00.

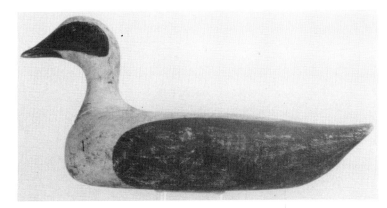

Eider drake, inlet head, orig pnt, average wear, hairline in neck, otherwise structurally EX, from Rockland ME, RWO 7/06/86, 235%, $1,650.00.

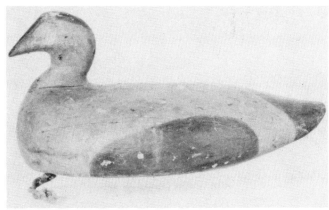

Eider drake, inlet head, EX bill cvg, working rpt, prof bill rstr, crack, age lines, oversize, J/G 9/19/87, 60%, $1,550.00.

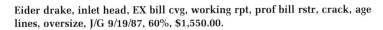

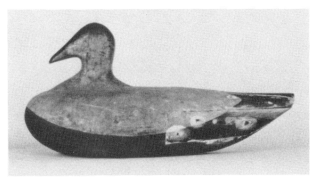

Eider, lg inlet neck, fine orig pnt, average flaking/wear, some age splitting, 39, RB 7/08/86, 175%, $700.00.

Goldeneye drake, well-detailed wing cvg, EX orig pnt, average wear, slight roughness to tail, ls, RB 8/21/86, $1,450.00.

Godwit, laminated wings, EX pnt pattern/patina, orig bill, orig pnt, minor wear, from southern New Jersey, RB 7/07/87, 60%, $750.00.

Greenwinged Teal hen, finely cvd wings, strong orig pnt w/only minor flaking, J/G 4/24/86, $2,475.00.

Gull, cvd wings, split tail, fine orig pnt, average wear, bold style, ls, from the south shore of Long Island, 3/76/90, RB 3/06/87, $32,500.00.

Gull, early stick-up, old working overpnt w/ some wear, tack eyes, wire legs, split tail, 2 age checks on body, tail/wing chips, oversize, 11, RWO 7/05/86, 170%, $6,000.00.

Heron, root-head, old pnt appears orig, moderate wear/flaking, several age splits in head/neck, 1800s, Long Island, RB 3/11/88, 216%, $1,300.00.

Labrador Duck, hollow, old pnt, average wear, structurally G, from Long Island, 76, RB 7/08/86, 150%, $3,700.00.

Mallard, stick-up, hollow, deeply cvd wings w/some feather detail, old pnt, average flaking/wear, slight age splitting, bill is rpr w/fishing twine, head is loose/slight neck split, early, Canadian, RB 3/11/88, 166%, $5,000.00.

Mallard hen, graceful lines, old rpt shows flaking/wear, structurally G, from the Illinois River area, 39, RB 7/08/86, 165%, $500.00.

Merganser pr, Redbreasted; inlet necks, cvd wings, drake's head in content postition; hen's head is downward w/open bill, fine orig pnt, average wear, slight age splits, otherwise EX, from Monhegan Island ME, 22/44/45/46, RB 5/02/85, 127%, $95,000.00.

Merganser hen, detailed bill cvg, raised cvd wings, orig pnt w/minor crazing, several pnt flakes, varnished, J/G 9/20/86, $22,500.00.

Merganser pr, hollow, cvd eyes, old pnt, average wear, structurally VG, Cape May NJ, ca 1890, RB 3/11/88, $6,250.00.

Merganser pr, Redbreasted; hollow, orig pnt, average wear, hen has neck split; drake's bill is old replacement, both have end-of-bill roughness, Cape May NJ, ca 1900, RB 3/11/88, 33%, $1,500.00.

Merganser pr, Redbreasted; inlet heads, drake has orig horsehair comb, old rpt, average wear, early, from Maine, RB 12/06/85, $750.00.

Old Squaw drake, head turned, fine orig pnt, minor wear, from Kettle Cove ME, 22/44/45, RB 5/02/86, 200%, $8,000.00.

Old Squaw drake, EX old dry orig pnt in stylish pattern, SB branded into bottom, structurally EX, sm, from Massachusetts, RWO 7/05/86, $3,750.00.

Pintail drake, 'Carriage House' type, head turned left, cvd wings, orig pnt, average wear, structurally G, RB 7/07/87, 133%, $2,400.00.

Pintail drake, turned head, cvd wings, hollow, fine orig pnt w/some overpnt, part of bill is rpl, 39/45, RB 7/08/86, $1,500.00.

Plover, Blackbellied; EX shoulder cvg, orig pnt, average wear, dated 1904 on bottom, thin check in breast, from New Jersey, RWO 2/13/87, $1,000.00.

Plover, Blackbellied; herringbone-type cvg allover body & head, orig pnt, average wear, slight chip top of head, rpl bill, from the Chas Hammond rig, ca 1850, Chatham MA, 22/44, RB 5/02/86, $1,200.00.

Plover, Golden; hollow, orig pnt, minor flaking/wear, from Cape Cod MA, 22/44, RB 5/02/86, 332%, $10,000.00.

Plover, Golden; hollowed out from the bottom, designed to turn in the wind, orig pnt, EX patina, structurally perfect, RWO 7/05/86, $2,750.00.

Plover, Golden; hollow, EX orig pnt, average wear, NM condition, from Cape Cod MA, 22/44, RB 5/02/86, 160%, $2,200.00.

Plover, Golden; EX orig pnt, average wear, few areas to bare wood, structurally EX, from Massachusetts, RWO 7/04/87, 66%, $600.00.

Plover, pull-string mechanism activates canvas-covered wings, orig pnt, average wear, RB 7/07/87, 40%, $600.00.

Redhead hen, sleeping, hollow, interior weight secured by copper nails is loose, old pnt taken down to some orig (mostly natural), slight rough area on bill, otherwise EX, Stratford CT, ca 1875, R/B 6/28/88, 43%, $3,000.00.

Redhead drake, hollow, old pnt appears orig, minor wear, structurally G, from the St Clair Flats area, RB 7/07/87, $550.00.

Ruddy Duck, worn old pnt, prof bill rstr, crack in bk of head, ca 1890, from Cecil Co MD, 69, J/G 9/19/87, $1,050.00.

Ruddy Duck, old working rpt, ms, from Churches Island, 33, J/G 9/19/87, $1,000.00.

Ruddy Duck, old pnt is worn/weathered, shot scars in head, chunk missing at base of neck, from Cedar Island, Back Bay NC, RWO 7/04/87, 70%, $525.00.

Swan, hollow, early, old orig dry pnt w/flaking & wear, age checks to body/neck, from Chesapeake Bay, 3/11/99, RWO 7/05/86, $14,500.00.

Ruddy Turnstone, EX orig pnt, minor flaking, rpl bill, from New Jersey, 22, RB 5/02/86, 225%, $4,100.00.

Swan, hollow 3-pc body, old pnt, considerable flaking/wear to bare wood overall, age checks on bk/under tail, from Talbot Co MD, 70, RWO 7/05/86, 65%, $6,500.00.

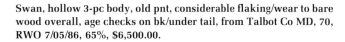

Swan, preening, hollow, EX form, orig pnt, minimal wear, sm tail chip, from New Jersey, RB 7/07/87, $900.00.

Swan, old rpt, average wear, chip at end of tail, 39, RB 7/08/86, 133%, $400.00.

Scoter, Surf; cvd eyes/wings, old pnt, average wear, ls, sm chip at end of bill, from Monhegan Island ME RB 7/08/86, 65%, $4,500.00.

Scoter, Surf; inlet head, orig pnt, most of which may be orig, branded DA Young, neck crack, chunk of wood missing on bottom, RWO 7/05/86, $1,500.00.

Scoter, Whitewinged; cvd wings, graceful head, old pnt appears orig, average wear, slight age splitting, from Monhegan Island ME, RB 7/07/86, 47%, $3,750.00.

Sandpiper, cvd/applied wings & tail, EX orig pnt, little wear, ls, rpl bill, wing chips, 22/44, RB 5/02/86, $1,800.00.

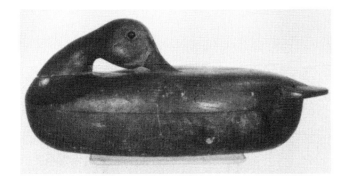

Widgeon drake, preening, nearly all pnt worn away, structurally VG, branded WBL Jr, from Connecticut, 8, RWO 7/05/86, 50%, $1,000.00.

Widgeon pr, raised wing tips/tail feathers, fine orig pnt, average wear, structurally G, from the Delaware River area, RB 8/21/86, $825.00.

Yellowlegs, running, cvd wings, brass tack eyes, EX orig pnt, unused, slight chip on tail, from the south shore area of Maine, RB 7/09/85, $5,000.00.

Yellowlegs, 2-pc hinged body, detachable head, RWO 7/05/85, $2,900.00.

Provenances and Related Material

1. From the Ted Mulliken collection
2. From the Joel Barber collection
3. From the William Mackey collection
4. From the hunting rig of Charles Birdsall
5. From the Norris Pratt collection
6. From the Shelbourne Museum collection
7. From the Earle Poggemoeller collection
8. From the Phillip DeNormandie collection
9. From the Richard Moeller collection
10. From the Frank Ash collection
11. From the Mort Hansen collection
12. From the Robert Uiklein collection
13. From the Malcolm Flemming collection
14. From the Quandy collection
15. From the gunning rig of A. W. Stein
16. From the Will Penningston collection
17. From the William Purnell collection
18. From the Thomas Marshall collection
19. From the George Thompson collection
20. From the Dr. Jack Conover collection
21. From the Carter Smith collection
22. From the Dr. George Ross Starr collection
23. From the Stanley Murphey collection
24. From the Dr. Cunningham collection (Brookline, MA)
25. From the Dr. Burke collection
26. From the John Hillman collection
27. From the Audubon collection
28. From the Roy Bull collection
29. From the Errol McBoyle collection; Mr. McBoyle was the owner of the Idaho - Maryland gold mine in Grace Valley, CA
30. From the rig of Alger Pike
31. From the Donald O'Brian collection
32. From the William Kross collection
33. From the James S. Lewis, Jr., collection
34. From the Somers Headly collection
35. From the Hal Evans collection
36. From the Peter Vale collection
37. From the Lloyd Johnson collection
38. From the Andy Williams collection
39. From the Corbin collection
40. From the Hollander collection
41. From the Henry Fleckenstein collection
42. From the Alan Haid collection
43. From the R. D. Congdon collection
44. Illustrated in *Decoys of the Atlantic Flyway* by George Ross Starr
45. Illustrated in *The Art of the Decoy* by Adele Earnest
46. Illustrated in *The Bird Decoy* by Paul A. Johnsgard
47. Illustrated in *Decoy Collector's Guide* by Paul A. Johnsgard
48. Illustrated in *New England Decoys* by Delph
49. Illustrated in *Southern Decoys* by H. A. Fleckenstein, Jr.
50. Illustrated in *New Jersey Decoys* by H. A. Fleckenstein, Jr.
51. From the rig of Andy Anderson
52. Retains US National Decoy Show label from 1970
53. Illustrated in *Decoys, A North American Survey* by Kangas
54. Illustrated in *The National Directory of Decoy Collectors, Book II* by Kangas
55. Shown on 1976 television program 'A Different Look at American Folk Art'
56. Shown in exhibition catalog for American Folk Art in Ohio Collections, 1976, Akron Art Institute

57. From the Frank C. Munson collection
58. From the Hanke rig; Mr. Hanke was a former owner of the Boston Red Sox
59. First Place in the Marsh Duck division of the 1965 National Decoy Contest, Davenport, IA
60. First Place in the 1970 US National Contest, Babylon, NY
61. Illustrated in *Encyclopedia of Collectibles, Time Life Books*
62. Illustrated in *Decoys of Lake Champlain* by Harrell
63. Illustrated in *National Directory of Decoy Collectors, Book I* by Kangas, 1978
64. Formerly owned by Orson D. Munn of South Hampton, LI; Mr. Munn was the editor and publisher of *Scientific America*
65. Illustrated in *Floating Sculpture* by Houster and Knight
66. Illustrated in *Duck Shooting Along the Atlantic Tidewater* by E. V. Connett
67. From the rig of Judge Glen Cameron
68. Illustrated in *Decoys of the Mississippi Flyway* by Haid
69. Illustrated in *Decoys of the Mid-Atlantic Region* by H. A. Fleckenstein, Jr.
70. Illustrated in *Chesapeake Bay Decoys* by R. H. Richardson
71. From the 'Famous Fifty' rig of Clarence Winters
72. From the rig of Walter L. Bush
73. From the rig of Lou Penneck
74. From the rig of Charles 'Shang' Wheeler
75. Illustrated in *The Outlaw Gunner* by Harry Walsh
76. Illustrated in *American Bird Decoys* by William Mackey
77. Illustrated in *Decoys at the Shelbourne Museum*
78. Illustrated in *Shore Bird Decoys* by Fleckenstein
79. Illustrated in *Wetland Heritage — The Louisiana Duck Decoy*
80. Illustrated in *Duck Shooting Along the Atlantic Tidewater* by E. V. Connett
81. Illustrated in *Working Decoys of the Jersey Coast and Delaware Valley* by Kenneth Gosner
82. Illustrated in *Decoy Series Portfolio* by Milt Wiler
83. From the rig of Jack Conover's grandfather, ca 1880
84. Illustrated in *The Judas Birds Les Trompeurs*
85. Inscribed 'Nathan Cobb / Cobb Is. / Virginia / 1870-80 / Used by Pres. Cleveland / at Cobb Island' (in Bill Mackey's hand)
86. Illustrated in *Mason Decoys* by Byron Cheever
87. From the hunting rig of Dr. John C. Phillips
88. Illustrated in *Decoys of Maritime Canada* by Dale and Gary Guyette
89. Illustrated in *Decoys and Decoy Carvers of Illinois* by Parmalee and Loomis
90. Illustrated in *American Decoys* by Quintina Colio
91. First Place winner PSWA Open, Feb. 8, 1975
92. Illustrated in *Shorebird Portfolio*
93. Illustrated in *American Factory Decoys* by Fleckenstein
94. Illustrated in *Floaters and Stickups* by George Reeger
95. Illustrated in *Shang* by Dixon Merkt
96. From the estate and duck club of Henry O. Havemeyer
97. From the C. F. Spear collection
98. From Keys Chadwick's garage
99. Illustrated in *Decoy Collector's Guide, 1966-67*
100. Used at Satchawine Gun Club, Henry, IL
101. Bears F. Winthrop brand
102. First Place winner in the Marsh Duck division, Duck Hunter's Tournament, Point Mouillee, MI, 1963
103. From the Robert Bell collection
104. From the Mallory Family collection
105. From the Ralph Lasbury collection
106. Purchased in 1930 from Hart by Walter J. Sugden
107. From a hunting rig used at Ragged Point, Dorchester County , MD, repainted in 1951 by the Ward Brothers
108. Illustrated in *Decoys Collectors Guide,* Winter 1953
109. A rare miniature; part of Wheeler's estate; acquired from his heirs; Wheeler is known to have made only three dozen miniatures
110. Drake is branded 'JTN' for John T. Nichols, St. Clair Flats Shooting Club member from 1901 to 1935; hen is branded 'BS Warren' for Benjamin S. Warren, St. Clair Flats Shooting Club member from 1914 to 1930
111. Part of Wheeler's estate and the Wheeler Decoy Collection, purchased by Remington Arms and donated to the C. T. Audubon Society, where it was housed in their Birdcraft Museum in Fairfield, CT
112. Branded 'JT McMillan,' used at St. Clair Flats Shooting Club, Walpole Island, Ontario

113. Illustrated in *Waterfowl Decoys of Michigan and the Lake St. Clair Region* by Clune Walsh and Lowell Jackson
114. Recently found in an old Ferrisburg, VT, hunting camp; uncirculated; several are the first of their type ever offered at public auction
115. Illustrated in *Gunner's Paradise* by Jane Townsend
116. From the J. Creighton Riepe, Jr., collection
117. From the same rig as pictured on Plate 94, *Art of the Decoy;* this bird is numbered '3'
118. Illustrated in *Martha's Vineyard Decoys* by Stanley Murphy
119. From the Larry Simpson collection; illustrated in *The Fish Decoy* by Kimball
120. Illustrated in *Wildlife Magazine,* Jan. 8, 1978
121. Ex-collection of Bobby Richardson; once used at Bishop's Head Club
122. Illustrated in *Wildlife Magazine,* Dec. 7, 1977
123. Signed by Conklin 'My Own Personal Rig, Gunning Stool, carved and painted in 1951,' signed at the Point Pleasant Decoy Show
124. Illustrated in *Wildlife Magazine,* Nov. 7, 1977
125. Illustrated in *Wildlife Magazine,* Nov. 8, 1978
126. Illustrated in *Wildlife Magazine,* Feb. 8, 1978
127. Featured in oil painting 'Knott's Island Decoys,' by Bob Timberlake; numbered print included in the lot
128. One of the oldest documented decoys known; stenciled 'GAS' for George Stanley, a member of the Winows Point Club in Port Clinton, OH, from 1857 to 1884
129. Sold in April 1987 auction; legs broken in shipment; now professionally restored and being sold by the shipping company
130. Inscribed 'Made for Malcolm McFarlane, Pintail Drake, by Ken Anger'
131. From the hunting rig of Louis H. Barkhausen, co-founder and 1939 president of Ducks Unlimited
132. From the estate of Dr. Charles Pike, Wellsley, MA; purchased during the 1920's
133. Wing and tail feathers are individually carved and inserted; artist has exhibited and won ribbons in many natural bird carving shows; this piece has been exhibited at the Peabody Museum in Salem, MA
134. Illustrated in *The Decoy Hunter,* Sept. and Oct. 1983, and *Decoy Collectors Guide,* Jan./Feb. 1964
135. Illustrated in *Decoy Collectors Guide,* 1984
136. From the Richard Park collection
137. Shown at the Peabody Museum at Salem, MA
138. From the rig of Bill McKenzie (Henry, IL)
139. Illustrated in Classic Waterfowl Display Catalog for the Midwest Decoy Collectors Show
140. Illustrated in the catalog of the Third Annual Mid-Atlantic Waterfowl Festival in Virginia Beach in 1978
141. Illustrated in *Arts Inquiry Magazine,* The Journal of Interdisciplinary Inquiry of the Arts, Bellingham, WA, 1984
142. Placed second in class, US National Decoy Show of 1981, Great South Bay Waterfowlers Association
143. Presented to Laura Mattoon in 1902 as she established Camp Kewonke near Wolfboro, NH; it was sold in 1985 by the former owner of the camp with the procedes going to NH Lakes Region Conservation Trust
144. Made at their Old Saybrook, CT, factory
145. Made at their Point Pleasant, NJ, factory
146. Made at their Quogue, Long Island, NY, factory
147. From the Princeton, IL, Fish and Game Club; Skinner rig
148. Deaccessioned by the Museums at Stony Brook, LI
149. From the rig of Bernard M. Baruch — so branded
150. Used at the Point Muille Shooting Club, ca 1880-1890
151. Made especially for Dr. Phillips
152. Bears rare original stamped mark: Made by A. Wilson, South Portland, ME
153. Illustrated in *Decoy Collectors Guide,* Jan.-March 1965
154. From the Priscilla and Spencer Smith rig (Hyannis Port, MA)
155. From the Gilbert Hinsdale rig (Metatoisett, MA)
156. From the Capt. J. Crumb rig
157. Pictured on page 125 of the first Mason book
158. Made in 1930 for Robert Weeks, member of the Princeton Fish and Game Club
159. Made in 1889 for Wm Gable, member of the Princeton Fish and Game Club
160. Inscribed 'The last of the group of my personal rig — 1984, M. J. McNair, P.B.S. broadcast'
161. Inscribed in a banner 'Open Water Shooting Stool'
162. From the same rig as the Crowell Plovers on the dust jackets of *American Bird Decoys* by Mackey and *New England Decoys* by Delph
163. Newberry was a member of the St. Clair Flats Shooting Co. from 1900 to 1914; he was a US Senator and the Secretary of the Navy under Teddy Roosevelt

164. Made for competition in the 1932 NY Sportsman's Show; show stamp is on the bottom
165. Inscribed 'Made for our personal friend, John Hunt, with compliments, Lem Ward, Steve Ward, 1968'
166. The hen has the first-place ribbon from the Greater Snow Goose Decoy Exhibit, Chincoteague, VA; the drake has the second-place ribbon from the same exhibit
167. Both have brass name tags for Dr. L. H. Champney, Quarryville, PA
168. From a rig carved for and used by the owners of the Morton Company; used on Thompson Lake
169. One of a rig of twelve ordered from the Wards in 1935 or 1936 by John Hopkins of Newark, DE; used briefly on the Appoquinimink River by him and his son
170. From the rig of Cal Thompson
171. Branded 'Chandler Roach,' a 19th-century Delaware River pilot
172. Believed to have been carved by Stephan Badlum of Dorchester, MA, (1805-1890); they were purchased in 1948 from his niece
173. Inscribed 'From Ted Mulliken's Wildfowler Decoys, Old Saybrook, CT, 1956, to John H. Thomas, Darien, CT'
174. From the Bishop's Head Gunning Club, Dorchester County, MD ; rigmate is shown on page 179 of Decoys of the Mid-Atlantic Region by Fleckenstein
175. Inscribed 'Shooting Stool, Made by Steve, painted by Lem, 1968, painted for our good friend and gentleman, Fred Bradshaw, by Lem'
176. From the Manning rig
177. Made ca 1930 for Stanley Kowalski for use at the Split Rick Gun Club, LaSalle, IL
178. Made for Fred Dering and Bob Tully; Dering was a reknown trapshooter; the two men were hunting partners at the Horican Marsh Club from 1880 to 1925
179. Branded 'Kennedy' for Reginold Kennedy, a member of the St. Clair Flats Shooting Co. from 1887 to 1892
180. J. L. Rhodes is written in bold script on the underside; Rhodes was a member of the St. Clair Flats Shooting Co. from 1877 to 1906
181. Branded 'G. S. Hendrie,' a member of the St. Clair Flats Shooting Co. from 1886 to 1919
182. From the collection of Richard Parks
183. Illustrated in *Decoy Hunter Magazine*, July/August 1982
184. The name Hoover (vacuum cleaner magnate) is painted on the underside; from the Toussaint Shooting Club, Ft. Clinton, OH (ca 1925)
185. Illustrated in *Decoys Collector's Guide*, 1963, 1964, 1965
186. From the rig of H. W. Cain
187. Ex-collection of Ellery H. Clark
188. From the rig of J. H. Carpenter
189. From the estate of Fred W. Noyes, Jr.
190. Purchased in 1917 from the Iver Johnson Sporting Goods store in Boston
191. From the Foote hunting rig
192. Ex-collection of Stuart Gregory
193. From the collection of William Humbracht
194. From the rig of Andy Anderson
195. From the rig of D. G. Elliot (a 19th-Century American sporting writer and hunting partner of George Burnell)
196. From the rig of Fred Hildebrand
197. Illustrated in *Factory Decoys*
198. From the rig of D. B. Day; branded DBD
199. From the Jolly rig
200. Both birds are inscribed 'Watie Hawk from Chas. B. Walker, 1938'
201. Bears tag reading 'Rare, the only Pintail hen made, Charles Walker, ca 1930'; from the Humbracht collection
202. Made for W. C. Peacock, used at the Peacock Lodge at Portage La Prairie, Manitoba
203. One of a rig of twelve made for and used at the Millionaires' Club, Horseshoe Lake, IL
204. Bears the brand of the Pequaw Hunt Club
205. Signed on the bottom 'Made and Painted by Steve Ward'
206. Illustrated in *L. T. Ward and Bros. ..., Wildfowl Counterfeiters* by Bryon Cheever
207. Signed on the bottom '1948 L. T. Ward, Bros., Lem — Steve, Crisfield, MD, Repaint by Lem Ward, 1977, for Somers Headley, with compliments'
208. 'Gibbs' stenciled on bottom, and 'B. M. Gibbs' impressed into the weight
209. From the rig of Luther Nottingham (Chesapeake, VA); bears his initials 'LLN'
210. From the collection of Ed Zern
211. Inscribed 'My first blue-ribbon bird, Ken Gleason, 1970'
212. Won best of species in professional class competition at the Ward Foundation World Championship in Salisbury, MD, in April 1979

213. Won first place in class at the Midwest Decoy Contest, second in class at the Pacific Flyway contest, 1979
214. Won best of show in Santa Ana, New York, and Michigan
215. Signed 'L. T. Ward — Bros., 1966, Lem Ward — Steve Ward'
216. Signed 'Lem T. Ward, Crisfield, MD, 1948; One of three, Lem Ward'
217. Made for the Cunningham family who gunned with Crowell and Dr. John Phillips of Beverly, MA
218. Made in 1952 and presented to Mr. Horace Green of Medwood, NY
219. As the story goes, Donald Voorhees ordered a rig of one dozen of the now-famous geese from Charles Schoenheider, Sr., of Peoria; learning of their price, he refused to pay and commissioned another maker to make a replacement rig of standing geese of which this bird is one of the best (From RWO 2/12/88)
220. From the estate of Latham Snell, early settler of Grand River, Easton Township, Ionia County, MI, ca 1848

Schroeder's Antiques Price Guide

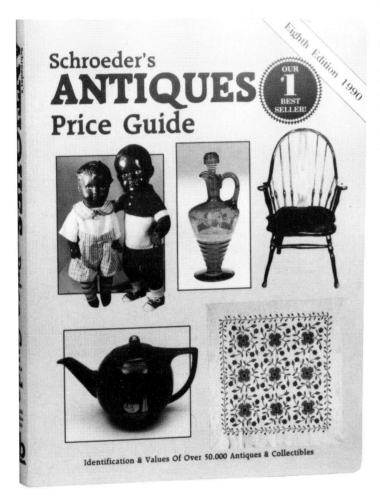

Schroeder's Antiques Price Guide has climbed its way to the top in a field already supplied with several well-established publications! The word is out, *Schroeder's Price Guide* is the best buy at any price. Over 500 categories are covered, with more than 50,000 listings. But it's not volume alone that makes Schroeder's the unique guide it is recognized to be. From ABC Plates to Zsolnay, if it merits the interest of today's collector, you'll find it in Schroeder's. Each subject is represented with histories and background information. In addition, hundreds of sharp original photos are used each year to illustrate not only the rare and the unusual, but the everyday "fun-type" collectibles as well -- not postage stamp pictures, but large close-up shots that show important details clearly.

Each edition is completely re-typeset from all new sources. We have not and will not simply change prices in each new edition. All new copy and all new illustrations make Schroeder's THE price guide on antiques and collectibles.

The writing and researching team behind this giant is proportionately large. It is backed by a staff of more than seventy of Collector Books' finest authors, as well as a board of advisors made up of well-known antique authorities and the country's top dealers, all specialists in their fields. Accuracy is their primary aim. Prices are gathered over the entire year previous to publication, from ads and personal contacts. Then each category is thoroughly checked to spot inconsistencies, listings that may not be entirely reflective of actual market dealings, and lines too vague to be of merit. Only the best of the lot remains for publication. You'll find *Schroeder's Antiques Price Guide* the one to buy for factual information and quality.

No dealer, collector or investor can afford not to own this book. It is available from your favorite bookseller or antiques dealer at the low price of $12.95. If you are unable to find this price guide in your area, it's available from Collector Books, P. O. Box 3009, Paducah, KY 42001 at $12.95 plus $2.00 for postage and handling.

8½ x 11, 608 Pages $12.95

cb

COLLECTOR BOOKS

A Division of Schroeder Publishing Co., Inc.